introduction to
advanced biology

introduction to
advanced biology

C J CLEGG

JOHN MURRAY

Titles in this series:
Introduction to Advanced Biology 0 7195 7671 7
Introduction to Advanced Chemistry 0 7195 8587 2
Introduction to Advanced Physics 0 7195 8588 0

Further Advanced Chemistry 0 7195 8608 9
Further Advanced Physics 0 7195 8609 7

The cover image shows a blood starfish *(Henricia sanguinolenta)*, found mainly in relatively exposed habitats around the British Isles. Its five arms have tube feet on their lower surface, used for locomotion and in feeding.

Feeding occurs through its central mouth by inverting the stomach onto the food, which consists of soft-bodied animals such as sponges and sea anemones. Shellfish such as mussels are also eaten; the starfish opens the shells with its tube feet.

© C J Clegg 2000

First published in 2000
by John Murray (Publishers) Ltd
50 Albemarle Street
London W1X 4BD

Illustrations by Oxford Designers and Illustrators
Layouts by Black Dog Design
Picture research by Marilyn Rawlings

Typeset in 10/12 pt Gill Sans by Wearset, Boldon, Tyne and Wear
Printed and bound in Great Britain by Butler and Tanner Ltd, Frome and London

A catalogue entry for this title is available from the British Library

ISBN 0 7195 7671 7

Contents

Introduction

Introduction to Advanced Biology is designed to meet the needs of all AS and A2 level Biology students following the new modular specifications. The matrix on page x summarises this coverage. In addition, this book should be valuable to those studying Advanced GNVQ Science, Scottish Higher Grade, the International Baccalaureate, and students of Human Biology at AS/A level.

The special features include the following.

- Topics start at the level required for a grade C at GCSE Science, and then build gradually so the student can achieve a good grade in all modules. Relevant extension text is present, distinctively boxed to differentiate it from core and development materials. The necessary physical science background is spelt out as issues arise, or is covered in Appendix 1.
- Chapters begin with Starting points, which summarise basic issues, and end with a comprehensive Summary.
- The text is written in straightforward language, uncluttered by unnecessary detail. Biology is generally recognised to have a demanding vocabulary, so terms are explained as they arise, and 'reminders' are given in the Glossary.
- Photographs, electron micrographs and full-colour illustrations are linked to support the relevant text, with extra annotations included to elaborate the context, function or application.
- Explanations of structure are linked to function and behaviour in living things, and the habitat and environment of organisms are identified where appropriate. Applications of biology in modern industries – biotechnology – pervades many chapters. Economic, environmental and ethical consequences of developments are highlighted as they arise.
- Processes of science (science methods) are implicit in the ways that issues are presented. Science methods are also experienced in individual investigations. Guidance in the selection and planning of investigations is given in Appendix 2. Data handling is discussed in Appendix 3.
- Self-assessment questions support research of interconnecting ideas, and comprehension. At the end of chapters, examination questions from the most recent past papers are given, especially selected to help you with the new examinations.
- Most chapters provide a Skills task/s, which develop the key skills of Communication, Information Technology and Application of number.

Author's acknowledgements

In creating the manuscript of *Introduction to Advanced Biology* I have taken advice on developments from well-informed biologists, and discussed issues of presentation in relation to learning problems that may arise for students at this level with teachers. In addition, many perceptive observations have been made by the team of Biology teachers who read the manuscript in whole or in part. All their contributions have been invaluable.

Dr Persephone Borrow (Edward Jenner Institute of Vaccine Research, Newbury)
Dr Robin Cook (The Marine Laboratory, Aberdeen)
Professor John Dodge (formerly Royal Holloway & Bedford New College, London)
Dr Margaret Frayne (formerly The James Allen Girls' School, Dulwich)
Dr Leslie Gartner (University of Maryland, Baltimore, USA)
Mr John Hickman (Northbrook Comprehensive School, Lewisham)
Ms Sarah Howes (St Francis Xavier College, London)
Dr Mike Jackson (IACR Long Ashton Research Station, University of Bristol)
Mr Paul Jackson (John Branston Comprehensive School, Witham, Essex)
Dr Richard Johnson (formerly Botany Department, University of Aberdeen)

Mrs Sandra Lewis & Mr Byron Lewis (St Aidan's Church of England High School, Harrogate)
Ms Katie Mackenzie Stuart (Science Publisher, John Murray (Publishers) Ltd)
Dr Gary Mantle MBE (Director, Wiltshire Wildlife Trust, Devizes)
Mr Norman Parker (formerly Millfield School, Street, Somerset)
Mrs Jean Scrase-Walsh (Key Skills Coordinator, Salisbury College)
Mrs Ilse Towler (Health & Safety Adviser, London Borough of Croydon)

Nevertheless, any remaining inaccuracies are my sole responsibility. I hope readers will write to point out any faults they find.

Sources of data and artwork have been duly acknowledged at the back of this book. If I have inadvertently overlooked any copyright and used materials that are the intellectual property of another, then I request that John Murray (Publishers) Ltd of 50 Albemarle Street, London, are contacted so that correction can be made.

Finalising the design and presentation of this book in the time available has been a specially demanding task for author, page designers and illustrators. I am indebted to my in-house team of Julie Jones, Helen Townson and Katie Mackenzie Stuart at John Murray (Publishers) Ltd, who enabled the process to run smoothly.

Dr Chris Clegg
Salisbury, Wilts
May 2000

Specification-matching matrix

Board	AQA (AEB) Biology A						AQA (NEAB) Biology B								Edexcel Biology										OCR Biology									WJEC			
Module*	**1** B/HB	**2** B	**3** HB	5 B/HB	6 B	7 HB	**1**	**2**	**3**	4	5	6P	6Q	6R	**1**	**2** B	**2** H	3	4	A	B	C	5 B	5 H	A	B	C1	D	E1	E2	E3	E4	E5	1	2	4	5
Chapter 1	✓						✓								✓										✓									✓			
Chapter 2		✓					✓								✓										✓									✓			
Chapter 3		✓	✓				✓								✓										✓									✓			
Chapter 4	✓	✓				✓	✓						✓		✓			✓							✓							✓		✓			
Chapter 5		✓	✓	✓				✓							✓								✓	✓		✓		✓		✓				✓			✓
Chapter 6		✓	✓	✓		✓		✓							✓								✓	✓		✓		✓		✓		✓			✓		
Chapter 7			✓		✓				✓												✓			✓									✓		✓		
Chapter 8		✓			✓	✓				✓		✓							✓							✓		✓								✓	
Chapter 9						✓				✓												✓	✓			✓											
Chapter 10		✓		✓	✓	✓								✓					✓			✓	✓			✓		✓	✓								
Chapter 11		✓				✓																✓														✓	✓
Chapter 12		✓		✓	✓	✓				✓		✓		✓		✓	✓		✓				✓	✓								✓	✓	✓			
Chapter 13		✓		✓	✓	✓		✓		✓		✓				✓	✓				✓			✓				✓									
Chapter 14					✓	✓				✓										✓						✓											
Chapter 15		✓				✓				✓			✓			✓	✓			✓	✓		✓			✓			✓								
Chapter 16		✓	✓	✓		✓				✓				✓		✓	✓						✓	✓	✓			✓	✓				✓			✓	✓
Chapter 17		✓	✓								✓	✓				✓	✓						✓	✓			✓	✓			✓	✓		✓	✓	✓	
Chapter 18		✓									✓	✓				✓	✓	✓					✓	✓			✓	✓				✓		✓	✓		
Chapter 19		✓				✓		✓						✓	✓				✓				✓	✓					✓	✓							✓
Chapter 20				✓						✓													✓	✓				✓		✓							✓
Chapter 21				✓						✓					✓		✓						✓	✓				✓		✓							✓

* Modules in **bold** make up the AS course. B Biology; H/HB Human Biology

I

WORKING CELLS

Cells, the building blocks

STARTING POINTS ● The cell is the **basic unit of life**. Living things are made of **cells**.
● Cells are too small to be seen with the naked eye. They must be viewed using a **microscope**.
● Plant and animal cells all have a **nucleus**, **cytoplasm** and **cell membrane** (**plasma membrane**).
● Many living things consist of a single cell (**unicellular organisms**). Others are built of many cells (**multicellular organisms**).
● In most multicellular organisms the cells are **adapted** to perform **specialised** functions.

Cells, the basic unit of living things

Living organisms are made of **cells**. The cell is the basic unit of structure and function in living matter; it is the smallest part of an organism that we can say is alive. Some organisms consist of a **single cell**, and are called 'unicellular'. Examples of **unicellular organisms** are the bacteria and many of the tiny plants and animals that drift just below the surface of seas and lakes, such as *Euglena* and *Chlorella* (see Figure 1.2). There are vast numbers of unicellular organisms in the living world, many with a very long evolutionary history. Other organisms are made of **many cells**, and are known as **multicellular organisms**. Examples of multicellular organisms are the mammals and the flowering plants.

Cell size

Most cells are extremely small, so small we need to use a microscope to investigate their structure. You will probably be familiar with a light microscope as a piece of laboratory equipment. You may have used one to view living plant and animal cells, such as those shown in Figure 1.1.

Since cells are so extremely small, we need appropriate units to measure them. The **metre** (symbol **m**) is the standard unit of length used in science (it is an internationally agreed unit, or **SI unit**), but it is far too large a unit to use for measuring cells. Look at Table 1.1: it shows how we use subdivisions of the metre to measure cells and their contents. They are listed in descending order of size. You will see that each subdivision is $\frac{1}{1000}$ of the unit above it. The smallest units are probably new to you; they may take some getting used to.

Table 1.1
Units of length used in microscopy.

1 metre (m)	= 1000 millimetres (mm)
1 mm	= 1000 micrometres (µm, or microns)
1 µm	= 1000 nanometres (nm)

1 How many cells of 100 µm diameter will fit side by side along a millimetre?

The dimensions of cells are expressed in the unit called a **micrometre** or **micron** (**µm**). A micron is one-thousandth (10^{-3}) of a millimetre. This gives us a clear idea about how small cells are when compared to the millimetre, which you can see on a standard ruler. Bacteria are typically 0.5–10 µm in size. Most plant and animal cells are in the size range 50–150 µm, or larger.

The structure of animal and plant cells

Figure 1.1
Plant and animal cells from multicellular organisms.

Figure 1.1 shows the size and structure of some typical plant and animal cells taken from multicellular organisms.

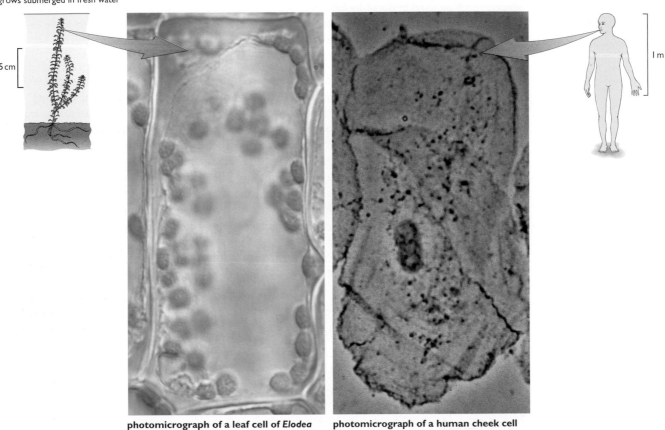

Canadian pondweed (*Elodea*) grows submerged in fresh water

5 cm

human

1 m

photomicrograph of a leaf cell of *Elodea* (×400)

photomicrograph of a human cheek cell (×800)

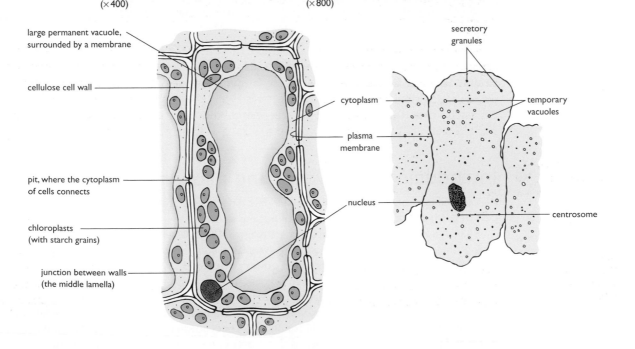

large permanent vacuole, surrounded by a membrane

cellulose cell wall

pit, where the cytoplasm of cells connects

chloroplasts (with starch grains)

junction between walls (the middle lamella)

cytoplasm

plasma membrane

nucleus

secretory granules

temporary vacuoles

centrosome

You can see from the labelled drawings in Figure 1.1 that plant and animal cells have at least three structures in common. These are their **cytoplasm** with its **nucleus**, and the surrounding cell surface membrane or **plasma membrane**.

Each of these components is the subject of a separate chapter in this book. The nucleus controls and directs the activities of the cell (Chapter 5, page 98). The cytoplasm is the site of all the chemical reactions of life (Chapter 4, page 75). Although the plasma membrane is too thin a structure to be seen in detail by light microscopy, it is a barrier that separates the contents of the cell from its surroundings or environment. The many substances that enter and leave cells have to cross the plasma membrane (Chapter 3, page 53).

There are some important **differences between plant and animal cells**:

- Plant cells have a tough, slightly elastic **wall of cellulose**. Animal cells do not have cell walls. The cellulose of cell walls is produced in the cytoplasm and is secreted. The wall-building processes are then completed outside the cell. You will find that the cell walls of plants makes the boundaries of cells easy to see when you examine plant tissues by microscopy.

  The presence of a cellulose wall allows plant cells to develop high internal pressure due to water uptake, without danger of the cell bursting. This is a major difference between plant and animal cells (Chapter 3). Tiny strands of cytoplasm called **plasmodesmata** pass through holes in the cellulose walls, called **pits**, and connect each plant cell to its neighbour.
- A **vacuole** is a fluid-filled space within the cytoplasm, surrounded by a single membrane. Plant cells frequently contain a large permanent vacuole. Some animal cells have small vacuoles, but these are mostly short-lived.
- Green plant cells also contain **chloroplasts**, tiny structures in the cytoplasm. These are not found in animal cells. The chloroplast is an example of an **organelle**, a unit of cell substructure. We will look in detail at several of the organelles later in this chapter. Chloroplasts are the sites where green plant cells manufacture food substances by a process known as **photosynthesis**.
- The **centrosome**, an organelle that lies close to the nucleus in animal cells, is not present in plants. This tiny organelle, which consists of two centrioles, is involved in nuclear division in animal cells (Chapter 5, page 102).

The key features of animal and plant cells are listed in Table 1.2.

Table 1.2
Plant and animal cells compared.

Plant cells	Animal cells
cytoplasm surrounded by plasma membrane and containing a nucleus	cytoplasm surrounded by plasma membrane and containing a nucleus
cellulose cell wall present	no cellulose cell wall
many cells contain chloroplasts, site of photosynthesis	no chloroplasts; animal cells cannot carry out photosynthesis
carbohydrates stored as starch often present	carbohydrates stored as glycogen often present
large, fluid-filled vacuole normally present	no large permanent vacuoles
no centriole	a centriole present outside the nucleus

Introducing eukaryotes and prokaryotes

All cells fall into one of two major classes. The difference between them lies in the basis of their **cell organisation**, including the type of nucleus present.

All plants, animals, fungi and protoctists (page 350) have cells with a large, obvious nucleus, lying in their cytoplasm. The surrounding cytoplasm contains many different membranous organelles. These types of cell are called **eukaryotic cells**.

On the other hand, bacteria contain no true nucleus and their cytoplasm does not have the organelles of eukaryotes. These are called **prokaryotic cells**.

We will return to this issue later, when we have studied the organelles in plant and animal cells in more detail. For the moment we will continue to concentrate on eukaryotic cells found in animals, plants and protoctists, but remembering this is only one type of fundamental cell organisation.

How cells make organisms

There are very many kinds of **unicellular organism**. These are structurally simple living things in the sense that they perform all the functions and activities of life within a single cell. The cell feeds, respires, excretes, is sensitive to internal and external conditions (and may respond to them), may move, and eventually divides or reproduces. Unicellular organisms are extremely diverse: good examples are the unicellular members of the plankton (Figure 1.2).

Figure 1.2
Unicellular organisms of the plankton of fresh waters.

Euglena viridis, a unicellular organism that is common in stagnant fresh water rich in ammonium salts and urea

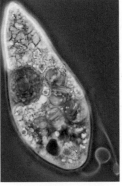

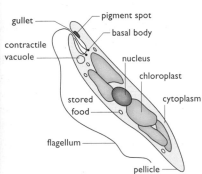

Chlorella vulgaris, a free-floating unicellular 'plant' common in fresh water (and sometimes found living in the inner cell layer of *Hydra*, page 358)

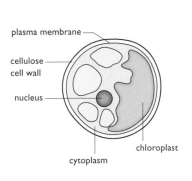

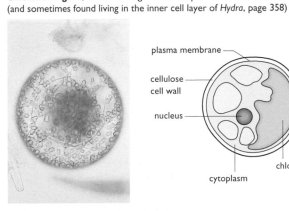

All other organisms are **multicellular organisms**. Multicellular organisms are an even more diverse group. For example, some multicellular organisms are little more than a **colony** of identical cells that appear to have remained together after division. One of the most simple examples is a mass of yeast (*Saccharomyces*) cells that have failed to divide (Figure 1.3).

Figure 1.3
Multicellular organisms that are colonies of similar cells.

scanning electron micrograph of yeast, budding

Yeast (*Saccharomyces*), an individual cell found in soil and in sugar solutions like nectar (page 413) sometimes buds faster than the cells are able to separate.

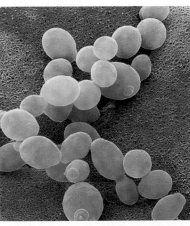

photomicrograph of *Spirogyra* filaments

Spirogyra, an unbranched filament of identical cells, occurs in freshwater ponds.

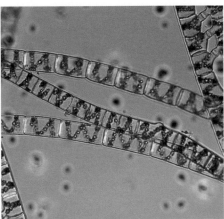

An organism that is always multicellular, but which appears structurally to be a collection of more or less identical cells that take up a particular shape, is the freshwater filamentous alga *Spirogyra*. In *Spirogyra* the first cell of a filament functions as an anchoring 'holdfast', but the bulk of *Spirogyra* in ponds often breaks away from its holdfast cell and floats at the surface of the water as a linear strand of cells.

Multicellular organisms with 'division of labour' between cells

The majority of multicellular organisms are like mammals and flowering plants in that they are made of cells, most of which are highly **specialised** to perform particular functions. Specialised cells are each efficient at carrying out their particular function, such as transport, or support, or protection. At the same time, specialised cells do not have the ability to do other things. We say the resulting differences between cells are due to **division of labour**.

It seems that in this type of specialisation, increased efficiency comes at a price. The specialised cells are now totally dependent on the activities of other cells. For example, the nerve cells of animals are adapted for carrying nerve impulses, but depend on blood cells for oxygen, and on heart muscle cells to pump the blood.

In a multicellular organism, cells specialised to carry out particular tasks are organised into tissues and organs. A **tissue** is a group of similar cells specialised to perform a particular function (such as muscle tissue of mammals or mesophyll cells of flowering plant leaves, Figure 1.4). An **organ** is a collection of different tissues that together perform a specialised function (for example, a leaf of a plant or the gut of a mammal, Figure 1.5).

Figure 1.4
Tissues of a leaf.

Two of the many tissues that make up a leaf are illustrated here. The structure of the pores is shown in Chapter 8, page 171, and that of the vascular tissue that delivers water and takes away sugar in Chapter 11, page 240.

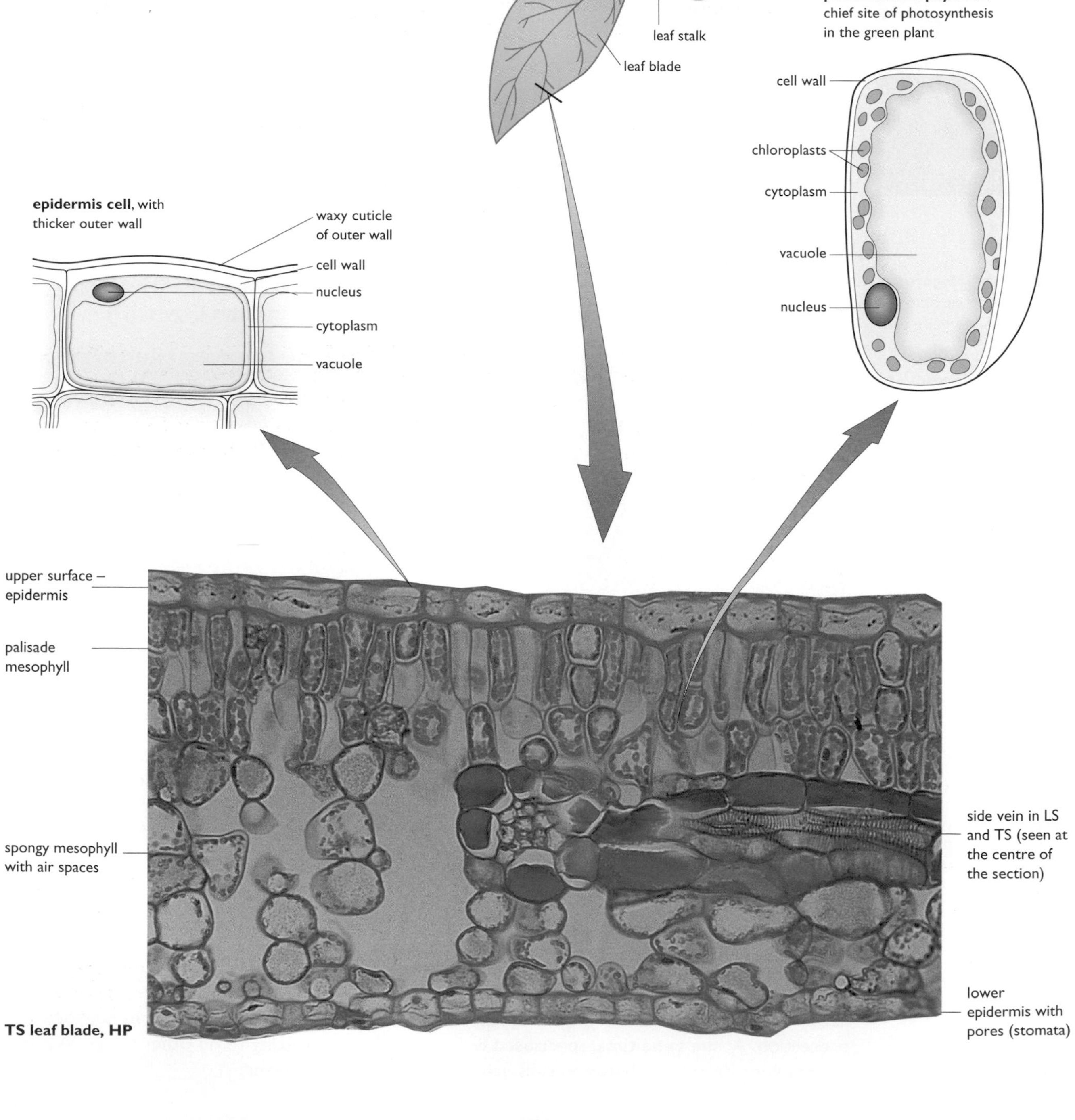

veins
stem
midrib
lateral bud
leaf base
leaf stalk
leaf blade

palisade mesophyll cell, chief site of photosynthesis in the green plant

cell wall
chloroplasts
cytoplasm
vacuole
nucleus

epidermis cell, with thicker outer wall

waxy cuticle of outer wall
cell wall
nucleus
cytoplasm
vacuole

upper surface – epidermis

palisade mesophyll

spongy mesophyll with air spaces

side vein in LS and TS (seen at the centre of the section)

lower epidermis with pores (stomata)

TS leaf blade, HP

Figure 1.5
Tissues of part of the mammal gut (the small intestine).

Two of the many tissues that make up the gut are illustrated here. The structure of the villi is shown in Chapter 7, page 157, and that of the capillaries that deliver oxygen and take away most of the products of digestion in Chapter 11, page 235.

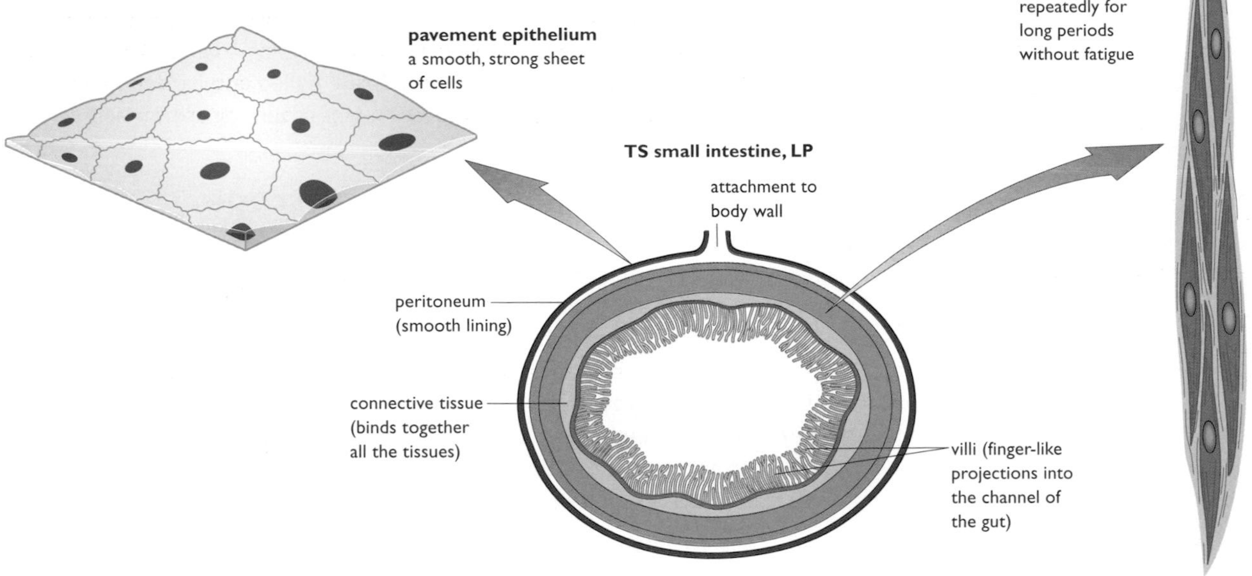

pavement epithelium
a smooth, strong sheet of cells

smooth muscle
(circular and longitudinal) can contract and relax repeatedly for long periods without fatigue

TS small intestine, LP

attachment to body wall

peritoneum (smooth lining)

connective tissue (binds together all the tissues)

villi (finger-like projections into the channel of the gut)

Microscopy

Light microscopy

Figure 1.6 shows a light microscope. In this instrument, known as a **compound microscope**, light rays are focused by the **condenser** on to a specimen on a microscope slide. Light transmitted through the specimen is then focused by two sets of lenses (hence the name 'compound' microscope, because a 'simple' microscope – a hand lens – has one lens). The **objective lens** forms an image (in the microscope tube) that is then further magnified by the **eyepiece lens**, producing a greatly enlarged image.

Figure 1.6
Using a compound microscope.

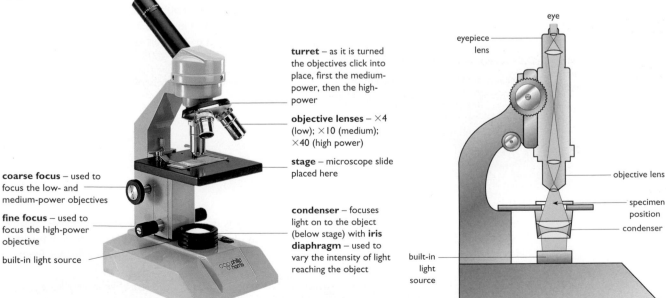

eyepiece lens

turret – as it is turned the objectives click into place, first the medium-power, then the high-power

objective lenses – ×4 (low); ×10 (medium); ×40 (high power)

stage – microscope slide placed here

coarse focus – used to focus the low- and medium-power objectives

fine focus – used to focus the high-power objective

built-in light source

condenser – focuses light on to the object (below stage) with **iris diaphragm** – used to vary the intensity of light reaching the object

eye

eyepiece lens

objective lens

specimen position

condenser

built-in light source

Biological material to be examined by light microscopy must be sufficiently transparent for light to pass through. When tissues and parts of organs are to be examined, thin sections are cut. Thin sections are largely colourless, so **stains** are used to colour the different structures present, increasing the contrast. When living material is observed a stain such as methylene blue may be used; methylene blue is a **'vital' dye** – a substance able to penetrate living cells without killing them. Living material is mounted in water or a suitable solution, forming a **temporary mount**.

Other stains normally require living material to be first 'fixed' (killed and hardened in as life-like a form as possible) before sectioning, staining and permanent mounting are carried out. **Permanent mounts** are stored and can be reused.

'Magnification' and 'resolution' of a microscope

Magnification is the number of times that an image is larger than the specimen. The magnification obtained with a compound microscope depends on which of the lenses you use. For example, if you use a ×10 eyepiece and a ×10 objective lens (medium power), the image is magnified ×100 (10 × 10). When you switch to the ×40 objective (high power) with the same eyepiece lens, then the magnification becomes ×400 (10 × 40). These are the most likely orders of magnification that you will use in your laboratory work.

Actually, there is **no limit to magnification**. For example, if a magnified image is photographed, then further enlargement can be made photographically. This is what may have happened with the photomicrographs in this book. Magnification is given by the formula:

$$\text{magnification} = \frac{\text{size of image}}{\text{size of specimen}}$$

Suppose that a plant cell of 150 μm diameter is photographed with the microscope and the image enlarged photographically. If a print is made showing the cell at 15 cm diameter (150 000 μm), the magnification is:

$$\frac{150\,000}{150} = 1000$$

If a further enlargement is made, to show the same cell at 30 cm diameter (300 000 μm), then the magnification is:

$$\frac{300\,000}{150} = 2000$$

2 What magnification is obtained with a ×6 eyepiece and a ×10 objective?

The image size has been doubled, *but the detail will be no greater*. You will not be able to see, for example, details of cell membrane structure, however much the image is enlarged (Figure 1.7). This is because the layers making up a cell membrane are too thin to be seen as separate structures.

Figure 1.7
Magnification with and without resolution.

chloroplast enlarged (×6000)

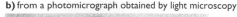

a) from a transmission electron micrograph

b) from a photomicrograph obtained by light microscopy

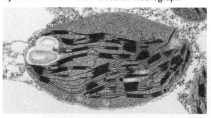
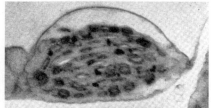

The **resolving power** (resolution) of the microscope is its ability to separate the images of small objects that are very close together. If two separate objects cannot be resolved they will be seen as one object. Merely enlarging them will not separate them. Resolution is quite different from magnification – and more important.

Resolution is determined by the wavelength of light. Light is composed of relatively long wavelengths, whereas shorter wavelengths give better resolution. For the light microscope, the resolving power is limited to about 0.2 μm. This means two objects less than 0.2 μm apart will be seen as one object.

Resolving cell ultrastructure

The nucleus is the largest organelle of a cell, and may be seen in outline with the light microscope. But the nucleus is not a typical organelle; few other organelles in the cytoplasm are large enough to be viewed by light microscopy, and none is large enough for internal details to be seen.

Electron microscopy

The **electron microscope** uses electrons to make a magnified image in much the same way as the optical microscope uses light. An electron beam has a much shorter wavelength, however, so its resolving power is much greater. For the electron microscope used with biological materials, the limit of resolution is about 5 nm (the size of the nanometre is given in Table 1.1, page 2).

Only the electron microscope can show the detailed structures of the cell organelles. This is why the electron microscope is used to resolve fine detail of the contents of cells, the organelles and cell membranes. These fine details make up the **cell ultrastructure**. Electron microscopy has played an enormously important part in establishing our detailed knowledge of cells.

In the electron microscope, the electron beam is generated by an electron gun. Focusing is by electromagnets, rather than glass lenses. We cannot see electrons, so the electron beam is focused on to a fluorescent screen for viewing, or on to a photographic plate for permanent recording (Figure 1.8).

3 How has the electron microscope increased our knowledge of cell structure?

Figure 1.8
Using the transmission electron microscope.

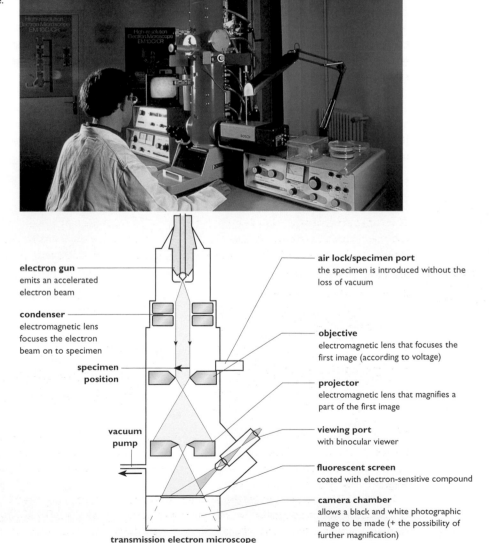

electron gun
emits an accelerated electron beam

condenser
electromagnetic lens focuses the electron beam on to specimen

specimen position

vacuum pump

air lock/specimen port
the specimen is introduced without the loss of vacuum

objective
electromagnetic lens that focuses the first image (according to voltage)

projector
electromagnetic lens that magnifies a part of the first image

viewing port
with binocular viewer

fluorescent screen
coated with electron-sensitive compound

camera chamber
allows a black and white photographic image to be made (+ the possibility of further magnification)

transmission electron microscope

● Extension   Limitation of the electron microscope

The electrons travel at very high speed but at very low energy, and this has practical consequences.

Electrons cannot penetrate materials as well as light does

Specimens must be extremely thin for the electron beam to penetrate them, and for some of the electrons to pass through. Biological specimens are sectioned by a special slicing machine, called a microtome. Then the membranes and any other tiny structures present must be stained with heavy metal ions (such as lead or osmium) to make them absorb electrons (we say they become 'electron-opaque'). These structures will stand out as dark areas in the image.

Air inside the microscope would deflect the electrons and destroy the beam

The interior of the microscope must be under a vacuum. Because of the vacuum, no living specimens can survive inside the electron microscope when it is in use. Water in cells would boil away in the vacuum. Consequently a specimen must have all the water removed (be dehydrated). This has to be carried out whilst keeping the specimen as 'life-like' in structure as is possible: this is a challenge, given that cells are 80–90% water. The dehydrated sections then have the electron-dense stains added. The images produced when these types of sections are observed by the electron microscope are called **transmission electron micrographs** (**TEMs**).

In an alternative method of preparation, biological material is instantly frozen solid in liquid nitrogen. In this method there is no opportunity for materials to change shape as all the water content is removed (dehydration). The solidified tissue is then broken up in a vacuum, and the exposed surfaces are allowed to lose some of their ice. The surface is said to be 'etched'. A carbon replica (a form of 'mask') of this exposed surface is made and coated with heavy metal to strengthen it. The mask is then examined in the electron microscope. The resulting electron micrograph is described as being produced by **freeze-etching**.

The examination of a cell nucleus by transmission electron microscopy and by freeze-etching is shown in Figure 1.9. Figure 1.10 shows the results obtained with an alternative technique, **scanning electron microscopy**. The picture we get of nucleus structure is consistent. We can have confidence that our views of cell structure obtained by electron microscopy are realistic.

Figure 1.9
Transmission electron micrographs from thin-sectioned and freeze-etched material.

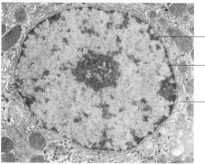
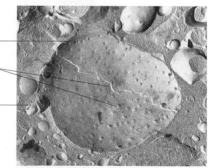

the nucleus of a liver cell

nuclear membrane (a double membrane)

nuclear membrane with pores

cytoplasm with mitochondria

observed as thin section

and replica of freeze-etched surface

Figure 1.10
An alternative form of electron microscopy.

In **scanning electron microscopy**, the surface of the whole specimen is scanned by a beam of electrons. The three-dimensional image is created from electrons reflected from the surface and also from electrons generated there ('secondary electrons'). Larger specimens can be viewed by scanning electron microscopy than by transmission electron microscopy, but the resolution is not as great.

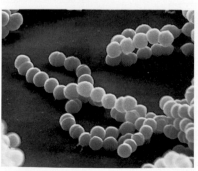
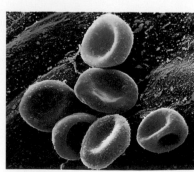

Streptococcus is a bacterium (and therefore a prokaryotic cell).

Red blood cells are eukaryotic cells.

There is a marked difference in size.

Streptococcus pyogenes (0.7 μm in diameter)

red blood cells (5.7 μm in diameter)

The ultrastructure of the cell

Today, the cell is seen as a 'bag' of organelles, such as the nucleus, mitochondria and (in green plant cells) chloroplasts, together with many others. Many of the organelles are made of membranes, but others are not. The fluid around the organelles is a watery solution of chemicals, called the **cytosol**. The chemicals in the cytosol are substances formed and used in the chemical reactions of life. All the reactions of life are known collectively as **metabolism**, and the chemicals are known as **metabolites**. Cytosol and organelles are contained within a special membrane, the **plasma membrane**. All the metabolites that move between the cytosol and the environment of the cell do so by crossing the plasma membrane.

Cytosol, organelles and the plasma membrane make up a cell – a unit of structure and function that is remarkably able to survive and replicate itself. The molecules that make up the cell contents are the subject of Chapter 2. The structure of the cell membrane, and the processes by which chemicals enter and leave cells, are dealt with in Chapter 3. How the chemical reactions of life are regulated is the subject of Chapter 4. The structure and function of the organelles are what we consider next.

Figure 1.11
The ultrastructure of eukaryotic animal and plant cells.

Our picture of the arrangement of organelles within the plasma membrane of the cell has been built up by the examination of very many TEMs. This detailed picture is represented diagrammatically in Figure 1.11. The green labels are those structures found only in plant cells; the red label is found only in animal cells.

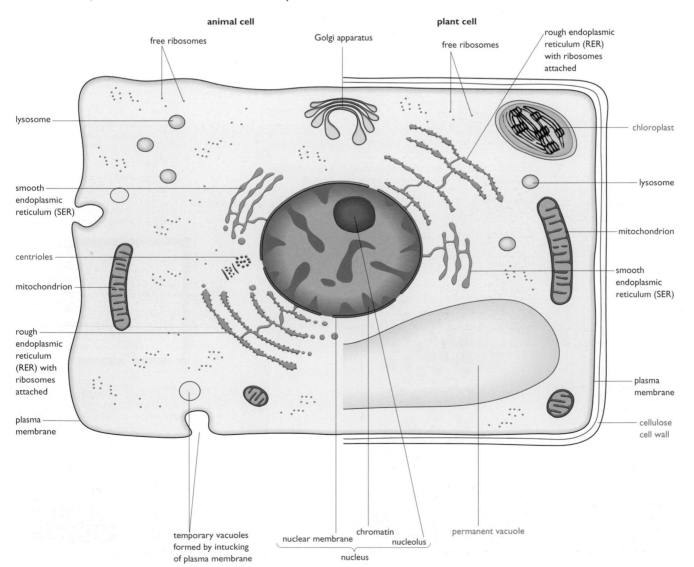

animal cell

free ribosomes

Golgi apparatus

plant cell

free ribosomes

rough endoplasmic reticulum (RER) with ribosomes attached

lysosome

chloroplast

smooth endoplasmic reticulum (SER)

lysosome

mitochondrion

centrioles

smooth endoplasmic reticulum (SER)

mitochondrion

rough endoplasmic reticulum (RER) with ribosomes attached

plasma membrane

plasma membrane

cellulose cell wall

temporary vacuoles formed by intucking of plasma membrane

nuclear membrane

chromatin

nucleolus

permanent vacuole

nucleus

Organelle structure and function

The electron microscope shows us the detailed structure of organelles. But just looking at their structure does not tell us about what the organelles do in the cell. This is where another analytical technique comes in.

By **cell fractionation**, organelles are extracted from cells and separated (Figure 1.12). Isolated organelles are then analysed for the reactions that go on in them, and for the enzymes they contain. In other words, their biochemical roles can be studied.

Figure 1.12
The steps to cell fractionation.

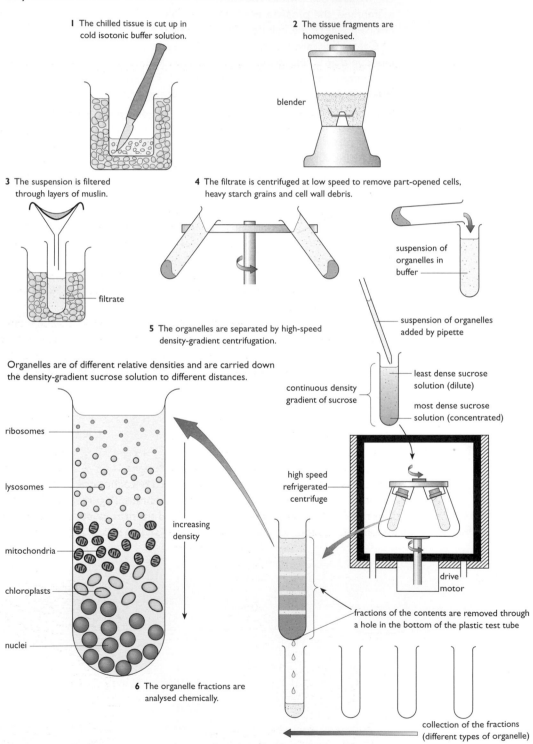

1 The chilled tissue is cut up in cold isotonic buffer solution.

2 The tissue fragments are homogenised.

blender

3 The suspension is filtered through layers of muslin.

filtrate

4 The filtrate is centrifuged at low speed to remove part-opened cells, heavy starch grains and cell wall debris.

suspension of organelles in buffer

suspension of organelles added by pipette

5 The organelles are separated by high-speed density-gradient centrifugation.

Organelles are of different relative densities and are carried down the density-gradient sucrose solution to different distances.

continuous density gradient of sucrose

least dense sucrose solution (dilute)

most dense sucrose solution (concentrated)

ribosomes

lysosomes

increasing density

high speed refrigerated centrifuge

mitochondria

chloroplasts

drive motor

fractions of the contents are removed through a hole in the bottom of the plastic test tube

nuclei

6 The organelle fractions are analysed chemically.

collection of the fractions (different types of organelle)

Organelles are delicate structures. Fractionation has to be carried out skilfully if most of the organelles are to be recovered intact and in a condition similar to that in the living cell. Two precautions are particularly important:

- Firstly, all the processes of fractionation are carried out at low temperature, just above freezing point. This prevents self-digestion (**autolysis**) by enzymes from the disrupted cells.
- Secondly, all solutions used are at the same concentration (for example, of sugars and ions) as the cell solution. This prevents damage to the organelles from sudden movements of water in or out of them, due to osmosis (page 63). Solutions at the same concentration are called **isotonic solutions**. The solutions used are also buffered (see Appendix, page 481) to maintain a constant pH.

We shall look at the structures and functions of each type of organelle in turn.

The nucleus

This is the largest organelle in the eukaryotic cell, typically 10–20 μm in diameter. The nucleus is surrounded by a double membrane, which contains many pores. These pores are tiny, about 100 nm in diameter, yet there are so many of them that they make up about one-third of the nucleus membrane's surface area. This suggests that communication between nucleus and cytoplasm is important. The appearance of the nucleus in an electron micrograph is shown in Figure 1.9 (page 10).

The nucleus contains the **chromosomes**, thread-like structures that become visible at the time the nucleus divides. At other times, the chromosomes are dispersed as a diffuse network, called **chromatin**. One or more **nucleoli** are present in the nucleus. A nucleolus is a tiny, rounded, darkly staining body, where ribosomes (see below) are synthesised. Chromatin, chromosomes and the nucleolus are visible only if stained with certain dyes. The everyday role of the nucleus in cell management, and its behaviour when the cell divides, are the subject of Chapter 5 (page 98).

Most cells contain one nucleus but there are interesting exceptions. For example, both the mature red cells of mammals (page 226) and the sieve tube element of the phloem of flowering plants (page 248) are without a nucleus. Each of the individual cylindrical fibres of voluntary muscle consists of a multinucleate sac (page 308). Fungal mycelia also contain multinucleate cytoplasm.

Mitochondria

Mitochondria usually appear in electron micrographs as rod-shaped or cylindrical organelles, although occasionally they have other shapes too. They are large compared with some other organelles, typically 0.5–1.5 μm wide and 3.0–10.0 μm long. Mitochondria are found in all cells, usually in very large numbers; cells that are metabolically very active, such as muscle fibres and hormone-secreting cells, contain thousands of mitochondria in their cytoplasm.

The mitochondrion also has a double membrane (Figure 1.13). The outer membrane is a smooth boundary, while the inner is infolded to form **cristae**. The interior of the mitochondrion contains an aqueous solution of metabolites and enzymes, called the **matrix**. The mitochondrion is the site of the aerobic stages of respiration.

Figure 1.13
The mitochondrion.

stereogram of a mitochondrion, cut open to show the inner membrane and cristae

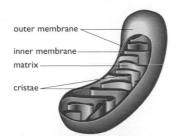

outer membrane
inner membrane
matrix
cristae

In the mitochondrion many of the enzymes of respiration are housed, and the 'energy currency' molecules adenosine triphosphate (ATP) are formed.

TEM of a thin section of a mitochondrion

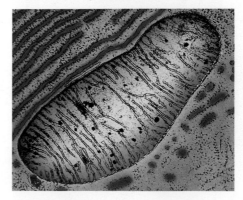

Figure 1.14
The ribosome highly magnified.

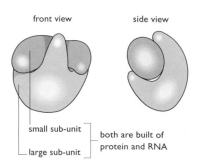

front view   side view

small sub-unit ⎤ both are built of
large sub-unit ⎦ protein and RNA

Ribosomes

Ribosomes are minute structures, approximately 25 nm in diameter (Figure 1.14). They are built of two subunits, and do not have membranes as part of their structures. They are constructed of protein and a nucleic acid known as ribonucleic acid (RNA). Many types of cell contain vast numbers of ribosomes. Ribosomes are the site of protein synthesis. Some of the cell's proteins are structural components. Most, however, are enzymes, the biological catalysts that make the reactions of metabolism possible (Chapter 4).

Endoplasmic reticulum

Endoplasmic reticulum (ER) consists of a network of folded membranes forming interconnected sheets, tubes or sacs. The structure originates from the outer membrane of the nucleus, to which it may remain attached. The cytoplasm of metabolically active cells is usually packed with endoplasmic reticulum. Two distinct types are recognised (Figure 1.15):

- **Rough endoplasmic reticulum** (**RER**) has ribosomes attached. Vesicles are formed from swellings at the margins that become pinched off. (A **vesicle** is a small, spherical organelle bounded by a single membrane, which is used to store and transport substances around the cell.) For example, RER is the site of synthesis of proteins such as the digestive enzymes. These are 'packaged' in the vesicles, and are discharged from the cell.
- **Smooth endoplasmic reticulum** (**SER**) has no ribosomes. SER is the site of synthesis of substances needed by cells. For example, SER is important in the manufacture of lipids. In the cytoplasm of voluntary muscle fibres, a special form of SER is the site of storage of calcium ions, which have an important role in the contraction of muscle fibres (Chapter 14, page 309).

Figure 1.15
Endoplasmic reticulum, rough (RER) and smooth (SER).

SER and RER in cytoplasm, showing origin from outer membrane of nucleus

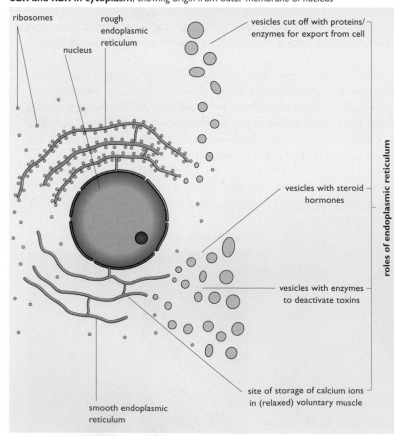

ribosomes

rough endoplasmic reticulum

nucleus

vesicles cut off with proteins/enzymes for export from cell

vesicles with steroid hormones

vesicles with enzymes to deactivate toxins

site of storage of calcium ions in (relaxed) voluntary muscle

smooth endoplasmic reticulum

roles of endoplasmic reticulum

TEM of RER

TEM of SER

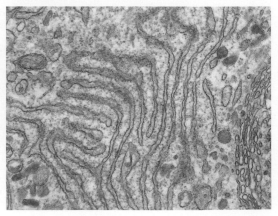

Golgi apparatus

The Golgi apparatus (Figure 1.16) consists of a stack-like collection of flattened membranous sacs. One side of the stack of membranes is formed by the fusion of membranes of vesicles from ER. At the opposite side of the stack, vesicles are formed from swellings at the margins that become pinched off.

The Golgi apparatus is present in all cells, but it is specially prominent in metabolically active cells such as secretory cells. It is the site of synthesis of certain chemicals, including hormones, enzymes and polysaccharide macromolecules, which are then packaged into vesicles. In animal cells these vesicles may form lysosomes (see below). Those in plant cells may contain polysaccharides for cell wall formation.

Figure 1.16
The Golgi apparatus.

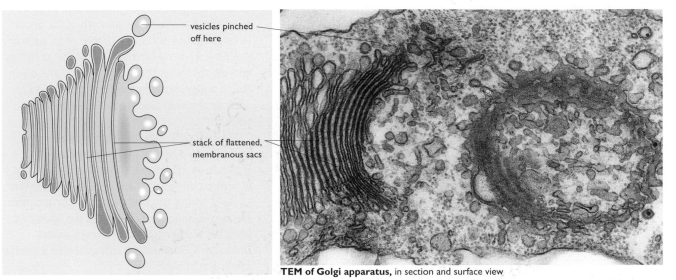

TEM of Golgi apparatus, in section and surface view

Lysosomes

Lysosomes are small spherical vesicles bound by a single membrane. They contain a concentrated mixture of hydrolytic (meaning 'digestive') enzymes, which are produced either in the Golgi apparatus or by the ER.

Lysosomes are involved in the breakdown of the contents of imported food vacuoles. An example might be a harmful bacterium that has invaded the body and been engulfed by one of the body's defence cells. It is then broken down, and the products of digestion escape into the liquid of the cytoplasm (Figure 1.17). Lysosomes also fuse with and digest any broken-down organelles in the cytoplasm. When an organism dies, the hydrolytic enzymes in the lysosomes of the cells escape into the cytoplasm and cause self-digestion (autolysis).

Figure 1.17
Lysosomes.

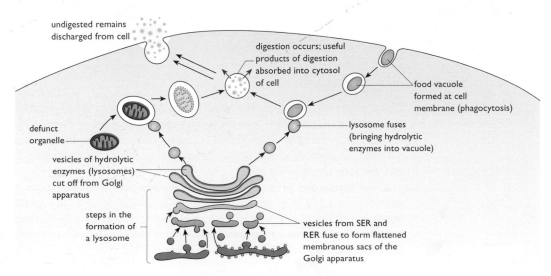

Microtubules

Microtubules are straight, unbranched hollow cylinders, only 25 nm wide. They are common in the cytoplasm of eukaryotic cells. These tubes are made of a globular protein called tubulin, and are built up and broken down as needed by cells. Microtubules are involved in movements of cell components within the cytoplasm, acting to guide and direct organelles. The spindle fibres that appear during nuclear division are microtubules, and they are responsible for the movement of chromosomes to the poles of the spindle. Microtubules also form the centrioles of the centrosome, and rings of microtubules make up the bodies of cilia and flagella.

Figure 1.18
Cilia and flagella, structure and movement.

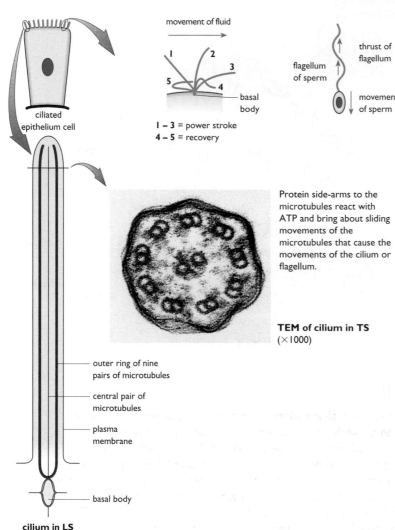

movement of fluid

1 – 3 = power stroke
4 – 5 = recovery

basal body

flagellum of sperm

thrust of flagellum

movement of sperm

ciliated epithelium cell

Protein side-arms to the microtubules react with ATP and bring about sliding movements of the microtubules that cause the movements of the cilium or flagellum.

TEM of cilium in TS
(×1000)

outer ring of nine pairs of microtubules

central pair of microtubules

plasma membrane

basal body

cilium in LS

Cilia and flagella

Cilia and flagella are organelles that project from the surface of certain cells. Cilia occur in large numbers on some large cells, such as the ciliated lining (epithelium) of the air tubes serving the lungs (bronchi). Flagella are often found singly, typically on small, motile cells, such as a sperm. Sometimes they occur in pairs.

Structurally, cilia and flagella are almost identical, and both can move. Their movement may cause a motile cell such as a sperm to move, or may cause the movement of fluid across the cell surfaces – for example, the movement of mucus along the bronchial lining. In a unicellular animal such as the protozoan *Paramecium*, cilia generate a special feeding current.

Structurally, both cilia and flagella consist of nine pairs of microtubules arranged in an outer ring, surrounding a single central pair, all enclosed in an extension of the plasma membrane (Figure 1.18). These microtubules are connected to a **basal body**, just below the body surface. All along the microtubules are 'side-arms', also made of protein. These side-structures contain enzymes that release energy from adenosine triphosphate (ATP), the energy currency of cells, and they appear to work in a similar way to the 'sliding filament' action of actin and myosin in muscle myofibrils (page 310).

Chloroplasts

Chloroplasts are members of a larger group of organelles called **plastids**. Plastids are found in many plant cells but never in animals. The other members of the plastid family are **leucoplasts** (colourless plastids) in which starch is stored, and **chromoplasts** (coloured plastids), which contain non-photosynthetic pigments such as carotene. Chromoplasts are found in flower petals and the root tissue of carrots.

Chloroplasts are large organelles, typically biconvex in shape, about 4–10 μm long and 2–3 μm wide (Figure 1.19). In green plants, most chloroplasts occur in the mesophyll cells of leaves, but they are also found in the cells of the outer parts of non-woody (herbaceous) stems. A mesophyll cell may be packed with 50 or more chloroplasts. Photosynthesis takes place in chloroplasts, especially in the leaves of green plants.

The chloroplast has a double membrane. The outer layer of the membrane is a continuous boundary, but the inner layer becomes intucked to form a system of branching membranes called lamellae or **thylakoids**. In the interior of the chloroplast the thylakoids are arranged in a large number of flattened circular piles called **grana** (*singular* **granum**), which look a little like stacks of coins. It is here that the photosynthetic pigments are found. Between the grana, the branching membranes are very loosely arranged in an aqueous matrix that may contain small starch grains. This part of the chloroplast is called the **stroma**.

Figure 1.19
The structure of the chloroplast.

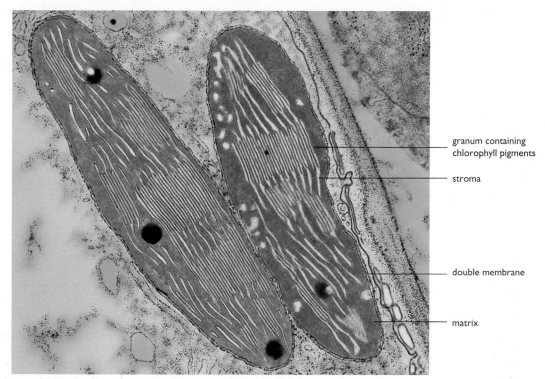

granum containing chlorophyll pigments

stroma

double membrane

matrix

TEM of a thin section of a chloroplast

The plant cell wall

Only plant cells have cell walls. The wall is entirely outside the cell, surrounding the cell membrane. The wall is not an organelle, but it is produced by the actions of organelles. Plant cell walls are primarily constructed from cellulose, an extremely strong material (page 31). When a growing plant cell divides, a cell wall is laid down across the old cell, dividing the contents (Figure 1.20). We can follow the steps to wall formation, by observing a series of electron micrographs taken of dividing plant cells. Between cell walls is a gel-like layer of calcium pectate, called the **middle lamella**. In wall formation, this is the first layer to be deposited. Endoplasmic reticulum trapped across the middle lamella often persists and forms cytoplasmic connections between the two new cells (the plasmodesmata mentioned on page 4).

On to this middle lamella the **primary cell wall** layers of cellulose are laid down. Many more layers of cellulose are normally added, forming the **secondary cell wall**. In the secondary wall cellulose fibres are found running in different directions. You can see an electron micrograph of cellulose fibres laid in different directions in Figure 2.9 (page 31). In some plant cells the secondary layers of cellulose become very thick indeed. In addition, a complex chemical called **lignin** may also be laid down in the wall. Lignin hardens and further strengthens the wall. Lignified walls are seen in the water-conducting element (xylem vessels, page 245) and in fibres (sclerenchyma, page 317). Another substance added to walls is seen in Figure 1.4, which shows how the outermost wall of the epidermal cells of stems and leaves may become coated with **wax**. This is a highly water-repellent layer which gives additional protection to the plant surface. In the endodermis of roots, **suberin** is deposited on the lateral walls (Figure 11.25, page 244).

Figure 1.20
The formation of a new plant cell wall.

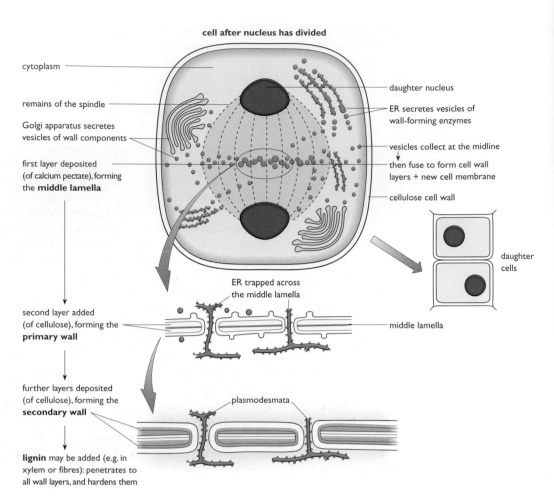

cell after nucleus has divided

cytoplasm

remains of the spindle

Golgi apparatus secretes vesicles of wall components

first layer deposited (of calcium pectate), forming the **middle lamella**

daughter nucleus

ER secretes vesicles of wall-forming enzymes

vesicles collect at the midline

then fuse to form cell wall layers + new cell membrane

cellulose cell wall

daughter cells

second layer added (of cellulose), forming the **primary wall**

ER trapped across the middle lamella

middle lamella

further layers deposited (of cellulose), forming the **secondary wall**

plasmodesmata

lignin may be added (e.g. in xylem or fibres): penetrates to all wall layers, and hardens them

The life history of a cell

Multicellular organisms begin life as a single cell. This grows and divides, forming very many cells, which eventually make up the adult organism. So cells arise by division of existing cells. The time between one cell division and the next is known as the **cell cycle**.

During growth and development, some cells continue to divide repeatedly. But most of the cells of a multicellular organism like a human grow, enlarge and become highly **specialised for a particular function**. Many specialised cells are then unable to divide again, such as mammalian nerve cells, red blood cells and plant strengthening fibres. Other specialised cells may divide again but only during particular seasons (for example, bark-forming cells of a tree trunk), or if a special need arises such as when they are damaged, as is the case with mammalian liver cells.

A few cells are able to continue to divide and do so frequently throughout the life of the organism. Examples include the cells of the outer layers of mammalian skin, blood-forming cells in the bone marrow and the cells of the growing points of flowering plants.

The outcomes of these different types of 'life history' are shown in Figure 1.21.

Figure 1.21
The life history of a cell.

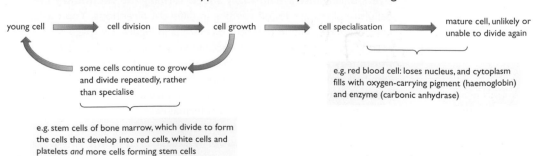

young cell → cell division → cell growth → cell specialisation → mature cell, unlikely or unable to divide again

some cells continue to grow and divide repeatedly, rather than specialise

e.g. red blood cell: loses nucleus, and cytoplasm fills with oxygen-carrying pigment (haemoglobin) and enzyme (carbonic anhydrase)

e.g. stem cells of bone marrow, which divide to form the cells that develop into red cells, white cells and platelets *and* more cells forming stem cells

Division of the nucleus: an introduction

When a cell divides, the nucleus divides first. The nucleus contains the chromosomes of the cell, and the chromosomes contain the 'blue-print' (coded instructions) for the organisation and activities of cells and for the whole organism. Chromosomes are involved both in the continuous control of cell activity and in reproduction, carrying instructions from one generation to the next.

Only when a cell divides is it possible to see the chromosomes. At this time the chromosomes present in the nucleus can be counted. The number of chromosomes in the cells varies from one species to another (but the cells of any one organism of the same species all have the same number of chromosomes). For example, all the cells of a buttercup have four chromosomes, and human cells have 46.

Every time the nucleus divides in growth and development the daughter cells formed have identical numbers of chromosomes to those of the parent cell from which they have formed. In fact, this is essential in growth and development: otherwise, different parts of our body might start working to different blue-prints. The result would be chaos! Division of the nucleus in which the daughter cells have identical numbers of chromosomes is called **mitosis**. The structure of chromosomes and the way mitosis works are explained in Chapter 5.

There is also a different type of nuclear division, which happens only in sex cells. In sexual reproduction two sex cells (called **gametes**) fuse: this is **fertilisation**. The resulting cell is called the **zygote**, and it will grow and develop into a new individual. Because two nuclei fuse at fertilisation, the chromosome number is doubled at that time. For example, human gametes have just 23 chromosomes each; when the male and female gametes fuse, the full component of 46 chromosomes is restored in the zygote.

Figure 1.22
Mitosis and meiosis, the significant differences.

The disaster of the chromosome number being doubled every time sexual reproduction occurs (that is, in every generation) is overcome by another type of division that halves the chromosome number. This **reductive division** normally occurs when the sex cells are formed. The reductive division is given the name **meiosis**. The differences between mitosis and meiosis are summarised in Figure 1.22.

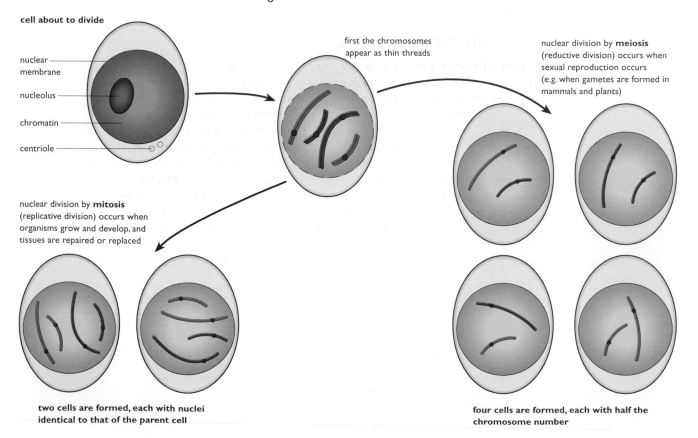

cell about to divide

nuclear membrane
nucleolus
chromatin
centriole

first the chromosomes appear as thin threads

nuclear division by **meiosis** (reductive division) occurs when sexual reproduction occurs (e.g. when gametes are formed in mammals and plants)

nuclear division by **mitosis** (replicative division) occurs when organisms grow and develop, and tissues are repaired or replaced

two cells are formed, each with nuclei identical to that of the parent cell

four cells are formed, each with half the chromosome number

In summary: the cell theory

The cell, the basic unit of life, exhibits all the characteristics of living things. This means it feeds (it requires nutrients), respires (it releases energy from nutrients), excretes (it disposes of waste substances from its life processes), is responsive and sensitive, moves about or causes movement, grows and develops and is able to reproduce itself.

The theory that living things consist of cells is known as the '**cell theory**'. The cell theory is now accepted by all biologists. It really covers four ideas about cells, and these are listed in Table 1.3.

Table 1.3
Points to the cell theory.

cells are the **building blocks** of structure in living things
cells are derived from other cells by **division**
cells contain a **blue-print** (information) for their growth, development and behaviour
cells are the site of all the chemical reactions of life (**metabolism**)

Prokaryotic and eukaryotic cells

Animals and plants are only two of the Kingdoms of living things. Biologists recognise at least five Kingdoms in the living world (Chapter 16, page 347). More importantly, the five Kingdoms are divided into **two fundamental groupings** according to the type of nucleus the cells of their members have. We call the two groupings the prokaryotes and eukaryotes.

The **eukaryotes** are animals, plants, fungi and protoctists. The cells of the eukaryotes contain a 'good' nucleus (which is what 'eukaryote' means). Several individual chromosomes are found within the nucleus, which is a relatively large spherical sac, bound by a nuclear membrane.

The **prokaryotes** are bacteria and cyanobacteria (photosynthetic bacteria). The cells of the prokaryotes have no true nucleus, but contain a single, circular chromosome in the cytoplasm.

Another key difference between the cells of the prokaryotes and eukaryotes is their size. Prokaryote cells are exceedingly small – about the size of the individual organelles found in the cells of eukaryotes, such as mitochondria and chloroplasts.

Prokaryotic cell structure

Bacteria and other prokaryotes have a fundamentally different structure from that of cells of eukaryotes. The organelles of eukaryotic cells, which this chapter has introduced, have no parallels in prokaryotes like the bacteria. The most elaborate structures in the cytoplasm of prokaryotes are ribosomes, which are functionally similar to those of eukaryotes but smaller. Also present in some bacteria are modest intuckings of the cell membrane, forming simple membrane systems to which particular enzymes or pigments may be attached.

All these features are illustrated in Figure 1.23. The differences between prokaryotic and eukaryotic organisation are compared in Table 1.4.

Table 1.4
Prokaryotic and eukaryotic cells compared.

4 Distinguish between the following pairs of terms:
- cell wall and plasma membrane
- chromatin and chromosome
- nucleus and nucleolus
- prokaryote and eukaryote
- plant cell and animal cell
- mitosis and meiosis
- gamete and zygote
- centriole and chloroplast.

Prokaryotes, e.g. bacteria, cyanobacteria	**Eukaryotes**, e.g. mammals, green plants, fungi
cells are extremely small, typically about 5–10 μm	cells are larger, typically 50–150 μm
nucleus absent; circular DNA helix in the cytoplasm, DNA not supported by histone protein	nucleus has distinct nuclear membrane (with pores), with chromosomes of linear DNA helix supported by histone protein
cell wall present (not of cellulose)	cell wall present in plants and fungi
few organelles; membranous structures absent or very simple	many organelles bounded by double membrane (e.g. chloroplast, mitochondria, nucleus) or single membrane (e.g. Golgi apparatus, lysosome, vacuole, endoplasmic reticulum)
proteins synthesised in small ribosomes	proteins synthesised in large ribosomes
some cells have simple flagella without microtubules, 20 nm in diameter	some cells have cilia or flagella with 9+2 arrangement of microtubules, 200 nm in diameter
some can fix atmospheric nitrogen gas for use in the production of amino acids for protein synthesis (page 372)	none can metabolise atmospheric nitrogen gas, but instead require nitrogen already combined in molecules in order to make proteins from amino acids (page 112)

Figure 1.23
The structure of a bacterium.
The diagram is drawn in two separated halves: the left half shows structures found in all bacterial cells; the right half shows structures that are present in some bacteria only.

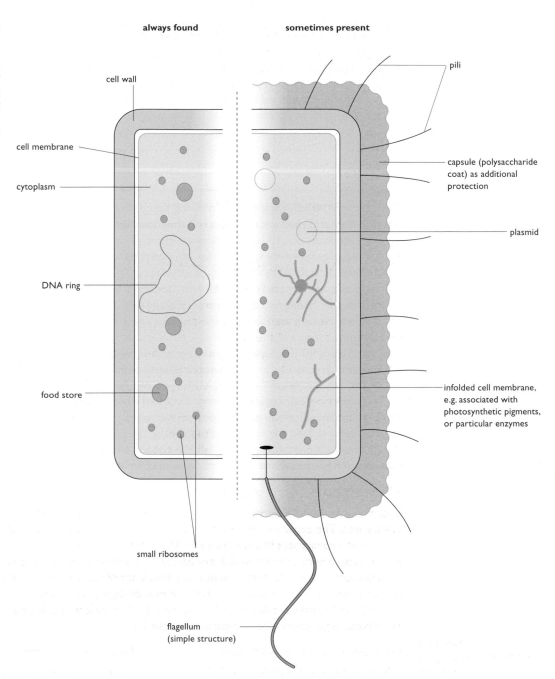

always found   sometimes present

cell wall

cell membrane

cytoplasm

DNA ring

food store

small ribosomes

flagellum
(simple structure)

pili

capsule (polysaccharide coat) as additional protection

plasmid

infolded cell membrane, e.g. associated with photosynthetic pigments, or particular enzymes

● Extension   A possible origin for mitochondria and chloroplasts

Both mitochondria and chloroplasts contain a ring of deoxyribonucleic acid (DNA) double helix, just like that contained in a bacterial cell. They also contain small ribosomes like those of prokaryotes. These features have caused some evolutionary biologists to suggest that these organelles may be descendants of free-living prokaryotic organisms that came to inhabit larger cells. It seems a fanciful idea, but not an impossible one.

Present-day prokaryotes are similar to fossil prokaryotes, some of which are 3500 million years old. By comparison, the earliest eukaryote cells date back only 1000 million years. Thus as eukaryotes evolved, they must have been surrounded by prokaryotes that were long-established organisms. It is possible that, in the evolution of the eukaryotic cell, prokaryotic cells (which at one stage were taken up into food vacuoles for digestion) came to survive as organelles instead. If so, they will have become integrated into the biochemistry of their 'host' cell, with time.

● **Skills task**   Prepare a poster presentation on the structure and function of **one cell organelle**.
Obtain information from your textbook, from library sources such as a CD-ROM on cell structure, and from a scientific paper (for example, a recent edition of *Biological Sciences Review*).

Before you produce your poster, look at posters, advertisements and public notices displayed in your school, college and library and in the press to help you decide what is visually effective.

Your diagram can be copied from disc or page, but reproduce it large enough, and devise your own labels to explain what the structures do in a way your fellow students can understand.

SUMMARY
- Cells are the **building blocks** of living things. They are derived from other cells by **division**, and they are the site of all the **chemical reactions in life** (metabolism). A cell is the smallest unit of organisation we can say is alive.
- Cells are **extremely small**. They are measured in units of a thousandth of a millimetre (micron, µm), and are viewed by microscopy.
- Plant and animal cells have **common features**, including the nucleus, cytoplasm and cell membrane. The distinctive features of plant cells are a cellulose cell wall, the presence of large permanent vacuoles and the possible presence of chloroplasts, the site of photosynthesis.
- Many **unicellular organisms** exist, but cells have also become combined together in their evolutionary history to make **multicellular organisms**. The simplest multicellular organisms are little more than a collection of cells that have divided but not separated.
- Most multicellular organisms show a marked **division of labour** between cells. These specialised cells are organised into tissues and organs. Some, though not all, specialised cells tend to lose the ability to divide and grow.
- The instructions or 'blue-print' for the control of growth and development of a cell exists in the **chromosomes**. Chromosomes become visible at the time of cell division, provided they are stained. At other times the nuclear contents are dispersed as a granular chromatin.
- When the cell divides the nucleus divides first. For **growth and development**, the nuclear division produces daughter nuclei that contain **identical chromosomes**. This 'replicative' division of a nucleus is called **mitosis**.
- In **sexual reproduction** two sex cells fuse (**fertilisation**) and the contents of their nuclei also fuse. Associated with sexual reproduction, **the chromosome number must be halved**. This type of nuclear division, a 'reductive' division, is called **meiosis**.
- The simplest cellular organisation is that of bacteria. Here there is no true nucleus. These unicellular organisms are called **prokaryotes**. They are much smaller than the cells of plants and animals.
- The cells of plants, animals and fungi are large and they have a true nucleus. Their cytoplasm contains many organelles, some about the size of bacteria. These living things are called **eukaryotes**.
- The cytoplasm of the eukaryotic cell contains more than half a dozen different types of **organelles**, suspended in an aquatic solution of metabolites (called the **cytosol**) surrounded by the cell membrane.
- Organelles are mostly too small to be seen by the light microscope, but the electron microscope has the necessary resolving power. Our knowledge of the structure of organelles comes largely from the interpretation of **electron micrographs**.
- The **biochemical roles of the organelles** are investigated by disrupting cells and isolating the organelles for further investigation. The procedures have to be carried out at low temperatures to minimise autolysis, and the extracting media have to be isotonic with the cytosol to prevent osmotic damage. A buffer is used to keep the pH constant.
- The organelles are mostly **membrane-bound structures** (nucleus, mitochondria, chloroplasts, etc.) with specific roles in metabolism.

Examination questions

1 Cell organelles can be separated by centrifuging a cell extract in a sucrose density gradient. The organelles settle at the level in the sucrose solution which has the same density as their own.

Some animal cells were broken open and the cell extract centrifuged in a sucrose density gradient. Three distinct fractions were obtained, **A**, **B** and **C**, as shown in the diagram.

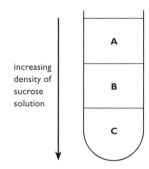

increasing density of sucrose solution

One fraction contained nuclei, one contained ribosomes and a third contained mitochondria.

Complete a table by identifying the organelle in each fraction and describing **one** function of each organelle. (4)

AQA(NEAB), A level, Paper 1, Sections A & B, June 1999

2 The diagram shows a bacterium.

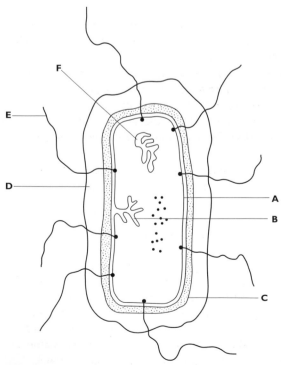

Identify the structures labelled **A** to **F** and give **one** function of each. (6)

AQA(NEAB), AS/A level, Module BY06, Mar 1999

3 a An electron microscope has a much greater resolving power than an optical microscope.
   i Explain the meaning of the term *resolving power*. (1)
   ii Explain the reason for this difference in resolving power. (1)

The diagram represents the structure of an animal cell as it would appear when seen with an electron microscope.

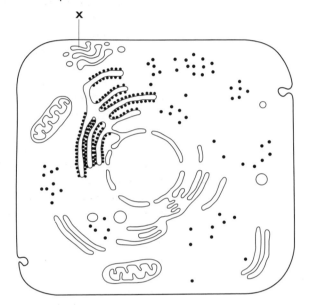

b Name **one** structure:
   i that is present in this cell but would **not** be in a bacterial cell; (1)
   ii that is **not** present in this cell but may be present in a bacterial cell. (1)
c Describe **one** function of the organelle labelled **X**. (1)

AQA(AEB), AS/A level, Module 1, June 1999

4 a Complete each row in the table, which compares a prokaryotic and a eukaryotic cell, with a tick if the statement is correct or a cross if it is incorrect.

	Prokaryotic cell	Eukaryotic cell
contains ribosomes attached to the endoplasmic reticulum		
genetic material consists of linear chromosomes		
diameter of the cell is 1 µm		

(2)

continued

b A student was asked to describe the structure of two organelles which were present on an electron micrograph. From the descriptions below, identify the organelles and, in each case, name the internal structures underlined.

i This organelle was disc shaped and had an outer envelope of two membranes. Within it was a series of further membranes which crossed the organelle like railway tracks. At intervals the membranes appeared to repeatedly double back on themselves to form <u>stack-like structures</u>. In the spaces between the membranes was a granular material. (2)

ii This organelle had a round shape and had an outer envelope of two membranes, which was perforated in places. Within it were <u>thin strands</u> which did not appear to have the width or organisation of membranes. One large round structure was visible internally. (2)

AQA(NEAB), AS/A level, Module BY01, June 1999

5 a The table shows some features of cells. Complete the table with ticks to show those features which are present in an epithelial cell from the small intestine and those features which may be present in a prokaryotic cell.

Feature	Epithelial cell from small intestine	Prokaryotic cell
Golgi apparatus		
mitochondrion		
nuclear envelope		
plasmid		
ribosome		

(2)

b i Explain why it is possible to see the detailed structure of a prokaryotic cell with an electron microscope but not with a light microscope. (2)

ii Care must be taken in interpreting electron micrographs. Some features visible in an electron micrograph may not be present in the living cell. Explain why. (1)

AQA(AEB), A level, 0642/1, June 1999

6 The table below gives descriptions of organelles found in eukaryotic cells. Complete the table by writing the name of each organelle in the spaces provided.

Description	Name of organelle
usually rod-shaped, 1 μm wide and up to 7 μm long; have a double membrane; the inner membrane is folded to form cristae	
rounded organelle approximately 25 nm in diameter; consists of RNA and protein	
disc-shaped structure, about 1 μm wide and up to 5 μm long; contains a system of thylakoids	
hollow, cylindrical structure; consists of nine triplets of microtubules	
contains the genetic material of a cell; surrounded by a double membrane	

(5)

London, AS/A level, Module B/HB1, June 1999

2 Biological molecules

STARTING POINTS ● Appendix 1, '**Background chemistry for biologists**' (page 474), may be useful to read when studying this chapter, especially if you are not fully familiar with elements, atoms, molecules and compounds, and with the ways atoms form molecules.
● The element **carbon** has a branch of chemistry to itself, known as **organic chemistry**. Compounds built from carbon are called **organic compounds**.
● A vast number of organic compounds make up living things, but most of them fall into one of **four groups of compounds**, each with distinctive structures and properties. They are **carbohydrates**, **lipids** (such as fats and oils), **protein** and **nucleic acids**.
● Most cells are at least 80% water by mass. The properties of **water** are discussed in Chapter 3, along with those of the **mineral salts**.

Introducing carbon and its compounds

Many different chemical elements make up the Earth – the soil and rocks, water, the atmosphere and living things. Only 16 of these elements are essential for life, and just four of them, **carbon**, **hydrogen**, **oxygen** and **nitrogen**, make up 95% of all living matter.

Compounds built from carbon are called **organic compounds**. Carbon is not a common element of the Earth's crust. It is quite rare compared with silicon and aluminium, for example. But in living things carbon is the second most abundant element by mass, after oxygen. In fact, organic compounds make up the largest number of molecules found in living things. Fortunately, most of the huge number of carbon compounds in cells fall into one of four groups of chemicals: the **carbohydrates**, **lipids**, **proteins** and **nucleic acids**.

Carbohydrates

Carbohydrates are the largest group of organic compounds found in living things. They include sugars, starch, glycogen and cellulose. Carbohydrates contain only three elements: carbon, hydrogen and oxygen, with hydrogen and oxygen present in the ratio 2 : 1 (as they are in water, H_2O). In fact, we represent carbohydrates by the **general formula $C_x(H_2O)_y$**.

We start by looking at the simplest carbohydrates.

Monosaccharides, the simple sugars

Monosaccharides are carbohydrates with relatively small molecules. They are soluble in water and they taste sweet. In biology, **glucose** is an especially important monosaccharide. All green leaves manufacture glucose using light energy, our bodies transport glucose in the blood, all cells use glucose in respiration, and in cells and organisms it is the building block for larger molecules including cellulose and many others.

The structure of glucose

Glucose has a chemical or **molecular formula** of $C_6H_{12}O_6$. This indicates the component atoms and their numbers in the molecule: glucose is a six-carbon sugar, or **hexose**. But the molecular formula does not tell us the structure of the molecule.

The structure of glucose can be written down on paper as a straight line, but the molecule cannot exist in this form. Instead it is folded, taking a ring or cyclic form (Figure 2.1).

The carbon atoms of an organic molecule may be numbered when the structural formula is written down. This allows us to identify which atoms are affected when the molecule reacts and changes shape. For example, when the glucose ring closes up, the oxygen on carbon-5 attaches itself to carbon-1. The glucose ring contains five carbon atoms and an oxygen atom, and is called a **pyranose ring**. As Figure 2.1 shows, the pyranose ring exists in two forms, called an α-form and a β-form, depending on whether a —H atom was trapped 'up' (α-form) or 'down' (β-form) when the ring closed.

Figure 2.1
Glucose as a straight chain and in two ring forms. In solution, glucose molecules constantly change between straight chain and ring structures.

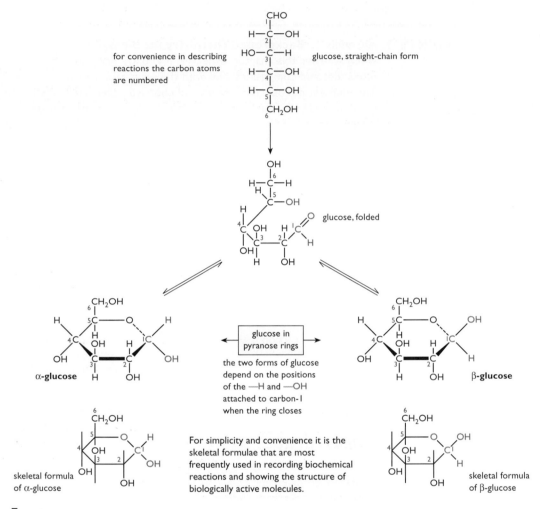

Fructose

Fructose is another hexose sugar found in cells. It has a ring structure that is different from that of glucose. Fructose forms into a ring with four carbon atoms and an oxygen atom, called a **furanose ring** (Figure 2.2). Fructose is by far the sweetest common sugar, and is used in the food industry in the manufacture of sweets and various kinds of confectionery.

Figure 2.2
Fructose.

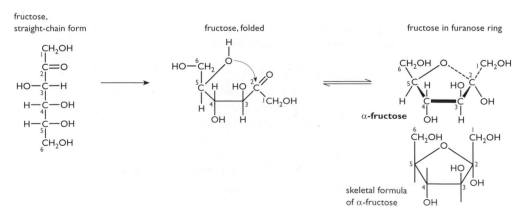

Functional groups of sugars

The huge number of organic compounds fit into a relatively small number of 'families' of compounds. The families are identified by the part of their molecule that is the **functional group**. The atoms of the functional group and their arrangement gives the organic compound its characteristic chemical properties. The chemical structures of some important functional groups are shown in Figure 2.3. The rest of the organic molecule, referred to as the **R-group**, has little or no effect on the chemical properties of the functional group. The R-group does, however, influence the physical properties of the molecule, such as whether a compound is a solid or liquid (its melting point), and at what temperature a liquid becomes vapour (its boiling point).

All monosaccharides contain one of two functional groups. Some, like glucose, are **aldehydes** and are called aldo-sugars or **aldoses**. Others, like fructose, are **ketones** and are called keto-sugars or **ketoses**.

Figure 2.3
Some functional groups of sugars.

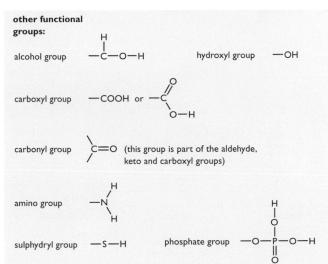

Aldoses and ketoses are **reducing sugars**. When a reducing sugar is heated with an alkaline solution of copper(II) sulphate (a blue solution, called Benedict's solution), the aldehyde or ketone group reduces Cu^{2+} ions to Cu^+ ions, forming a brick-red precipitate of copper(I) oxide. In the process, the aldehyde or ketone group is oxidised to a carboxyl group (—COOH).

This reaction is used to test for reducing sugars, and is known as **Benedict's test**. If no reducing sugar is present the solution remains blue. The colour change observed depends on the concentration of reducing sugar. The greater the concentration the more precipitate is formed and the greater the colour change, from blue → green → yellow → brown → red (Figure 2.4).

Figure 2.4
The test for reducing sugars.

5 cm³ of Benedict's solution (blue) was added to 10 cm³ of solution to be tested → test tubes were placed in a boiling water bath for 5 minutes → tubes were transferred to a rack and the colours compared

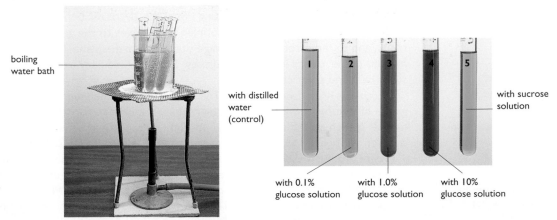

Other monosaccharides of importance in cells

Glucose and fructose are both hexose sugars. Several other sugars are produced by cells and used in their chemical reactions. They include three-carbon sugars (**trioses**, the early products in photosynthesis) and five-carbon sugars (**pentoses**, important components of nucleic acids) (Table 2.1).

Table 2.1
The monosaccharides important in cell biochemistry.

Length of carbon chain	Name of sugar	Molecular formula	Formula	Roles
3C = triose	glyceraldehyde	$C_3H_6O_3$	(structure: H–C=O, H–C–OH, CH_2OH)	intermediate in respiration and photosynthesis
5C = pentoses	ribose	$C_5H_{10}O_5$	(structure: H–C=O, H–C–OH, H–C–OH, H–C–OH, CH_2OH; ring form with CH_2OH, OH, HO, OH)	in RNA, ATP and hydrogen acceptors NAD and NADP
	deoxyribose	$C_5H_{10}O_4$	(structure: H–C=O, H–C–H, H–C–OH, H–C–OH, CH_2OH; ring form with CH_2OH, OH, HO)	in DNA
6C = hexoses	glucose	$C_6H_{12}O_6$	see Figure 2.1	product of photosynthesis, energy source in respiration, building block (monomer) for starch, glycogen and cellulose
	fructose	$C_6H_{12}O_6$	see Figure 2.2	energy source in respiration, component of sucrose

Disaccharides

Disaccharides are carbohydrates made of two monosaccharides combined together. For example, **sucrose** is formed when a molecule of α-glucose combines with a molecule of fructose. A reaction in which a molecule of water is removed when two molecules combine is called a **condensation reaction**. When monosaccharides combine in this way the bond formed is called a **glycosidic bond** – a strong, covalent bond. In the reverse process, disaccharides can be 'digested' into monosaccharides by a **hydrolysis reaction**. This reaction involves adding a molecule of water (*hydro-*) and splitting (*-lysis*) the glycosidic bond (Figure 2.5).

Sucrose is the sugar that is transported from leaves to the growing points of plant stems and roots, and to the carbohydrate storage sites all over the plant. This is also the 'sugar' most humans prefer to use in foods and drinks. The sugar industry extracts and purifies sucrose from sugar beet and sugar cane.

Sucrose is *not* a reducing sugar. This is because the aldehyde group of glucose and the ketone group of fructose (which are reducing groups) are used to form the glycosidic bond in sucrose; neither is then available to reduce copper(II) to copper(I) in a Benedict's test. So Benedict's solution will remain blue when heated with sucrose (see Figure 2.4).

There are many different disaccharides formed, depending on which monosaccharides are involved, and whether they are in their α or β condition (see Figure 2.1). Two other disaccharides that are common in cells are maltose and lactose. **Maltose** (α-glucose + glucose) is a product of starch hydrolysis. The extraction of maltose from germinating barley (as malt extract) is an important industry. Malt is used in brewing and in food manufacture. **Lactose** (β-galactose + glucose) is the sugar found in the milk of mammals.

1 What is meant by:
  a a non-reducing sugar?
  b a glycosidic link?

Figure 2.5
Disaccharides, and the
monosaccharides that
form them.

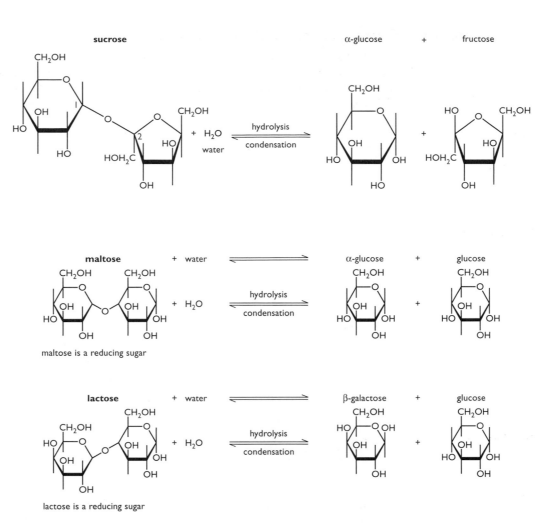

Polysaccharides

A polysaccharide is built from many monosaccharides linked by glycosidic bonds. *Poly* means many, and in fact thousands of 'saccharide' (sugar) units make up a polysaccharide. So a polysaccharide is a giant molecule, a **macromolecule**. Normally each polysaccharide contains only one type of **monomer**. A chemist calls this structure a **polymer** because it is constructed from a huge number of *identical* monomers.

Some polysaccharides function as stores of energy; glycogen and starch are examples. Other polysaccharides, such as chitin and cellulose, have a structural role.

Starch

Starch is a mixture of two polysaccharides, both of which are polymers of α-glucose. The **amylose** molecule is an unbranched chain, whereas **amylopectin** has branches at points along its chain. The bonds between glucose in starch bring the molecules together so that a helix forms. The whole starch molecule is stabilised by countless hydrogen bonds (page 54) between parts of the component glucose molecules.

Starch is the major storage carbohydrate of most plants. It is laid down as compact grains in leucoplasts (page 16). Starch is an important energy source in the diet of many animals, too. It is useful because its molecules are both compact and insoluble, but are readily hydrolysed to form sugar when required. We sometimes see 'soluble starch' as an ingredient of manufactured foods. Here the starch molecules have been broken down into short lengths, making them more easily dissolved.

We test for starch by adding iodine in potassium iodide solution. Iodine molecules fit neatly into the centre of the starch helix, creating a blue–black colour (Figure 2.6).

Figure 2.6
Starch.

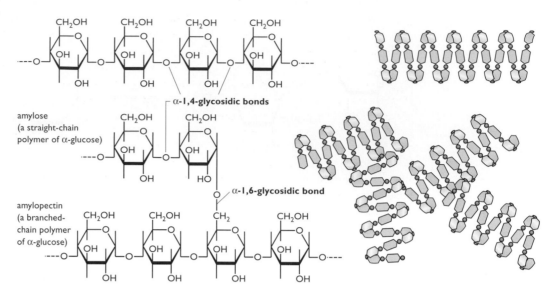

α-1,4-glycosidic bonds

amylose
(a straight-chain
polymer of α-glucose)

α-1,6-glycosidic bond

amylopectin
(a branched-
chain polymer
of α-glucose)

test for starch with iodine in potassium iodide solution, the blue–black colour comes from a starch/iodine complex

a) on a potato tuber cut surface

b) on starch solutions of a range of concentrations

starch chain

iodine molecules

Figure 2.7
Glycogen granules
in liver cells.

mitochondria   glycogen granules

TEM of a liver cell (×7000)

Glycogen

Glycogen is a polymer of α-glucose. It is chemically very similar to amylopectin, although the glycogen molecule is more highly branched. Granules of glycogen can be seen in liver cells and muscle fibres using the electron microscope (Figure 2.7), but they occur throughout the human body except in the brain cells (where there are virtually no energy reserves). During strenuous exercise we draw on our glycogen reserves first. Only when these are exhausted does the body start to metabolise stored fat.

Cellulose

In cellulose, the links between the glucose molecules give the characteristic straight, unbranched cellulose chain. Each cellulose molecule forms many hydrogen bonds (page 54) with the surrounding cellulose molecules, forming an extremely strong structure: insoluble, tough and durable and slightly elastic (Figure 2.8). In cell walls the cellulose fibres are laid down in layers running in different directions, adding further strength to the walls (Figure 2.9). The chemical test for cellulose is that it gives a purple colour with Schultz's solution.

Cellulose is the major component of the cell walls of green plants, and by far the most abundant carbohydrate. In the environment, it makes up more than 50% of all organic carbon (the gas carbon dioxide, CO_2, and the mineral calcium carbonate, $CaCO_3$, are examples of 'inorganic' carbon). In addition to plant cell walls, it forms part of the debris of plants in and on the soil. Cellulose fibres extracted from plants are used as cotton, and are manufactured into paper, rayon fibres for clothes manufacture, nitrocellulose for explosives, cellulose acetate for films and cellophane for packaging.

> **2** What are the functions of
> **a** starch, and
> **b** cellulose
> in a green plant?

Figure 2.8
The chemistry of cellulose.

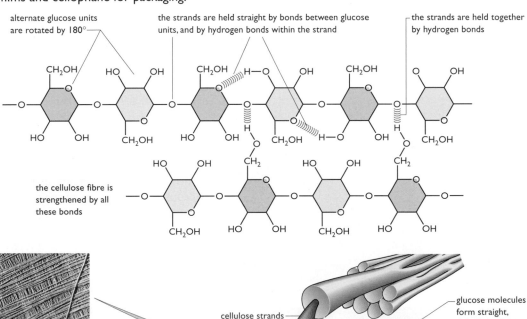

alternate glucose units are rotated by 180°

the strands are held straight by bonds between glucose units, and by hydrogen bonds within the strand

the strands are held together by hydrogen bonds

the cellulose fibre is strengthened by all these bonds

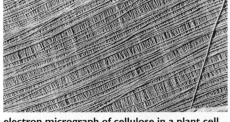

electron micrograph of cellulose in a plant cell wall (×1500)

Figure 2.9
The structure of cellulose.

fibres of cellulose laid down at different angles

cellulose strands packed together

glucose molecules form straight, unbranched chains

> **3** Starch is a powdery material, cellulose is a strong, fibrous substance, yet both are made of glucose. What features of the cellulose molecule account for its strength?

Chitin is chemically related to cellulose, but the monomers from which this polymer is built are glucosamine units (glucose in which one —OH is replaced by —$NHCOCH_3$). Chitin molecules are also long, straight chains, very similar to those of cellulose. Chitin is the second most abundant carbohydrate. Just as cellulose is important to plants, so chitin is found in the Animal Kingdom, mainly in the external skeleton of insects and other arthropods (page 361).

Other sugar compounds

In addition to cellulose, plant cell walls contain small quantities of substances called pectins and hemicelluloses. These are mixtures of polysaccharides formed from other sugars and from organic acids derived from sugars. These 'acids' occur as their calcium salts, forming calcium pectate. We can think of pectins and hemicelluloses as the 'glues' that hold the cellulose of plant cell walls together. At the junction between the walls these substances appear as a layer called the **middle lamella** (see page 17). Pectins and hemicelluloses also pass between the cellulose fibres, adding to the strength of the cell wall. The pectins are important 'setting agents' in jam-making.

Lipids

Lipids are a diverse group of substances, quite hard to define. They contain the elements carbon, hydrogen and oxygen, as do carbohydrates, but in lipids the proportion of oxygen is much less. Lipids are insoluble in water, and they generally behave as 'water-hating' molecules. They are said to be **hydrophobic**. They can, however, be dissolved in organic solvents such as alcohol (ethanol), propanone and ether.

Lipids occur in living things as animal **fats** and plant **oils**, **waxes** of plants and animals, **phospholipids** of cell membranes, and **steroids**, from which many growth and sex hormones are produced.

Figure 2.10
Fats and oils.

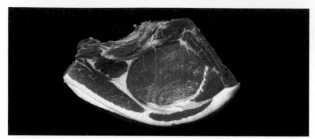
meat joint with fat layers around the blocks of muscle fibres

olive oil

nuts and seeds rich in oils, e.g. maize, sunflower

oils and fats leave a translucent stain on paper or fabric

Fats and oils

Fats and oils (Figure 2.10) are compounds called **triglycerides** (strictly, triacylglycerols). They are formed by reactions in which water is removed (i.e. a condensation reaction) between **fatty acids** (full name, monocarboxylic acids) and an alcohol called **glycerol** (Figure 2.11). Three fatty acids combine with one glycerol to form a triglyceride. This is quite a large molecule, though smaller than those of macromolecules like glycogen and starch. It is only because of their hydrophobic properties that triglyceride molecules clump together (aggregate) into huge globules that makes them *appear* to be macromolecules.

The fatty acids combined in fats and oils have long hydrocarbon 'tails', typically containing about 16–18 carbon atoms, though there may be anything between 14 and 22. The hydrophobic properties of triglycerides are due to these hydrocarbon tails.

Fatty acids are acids because their functional group (—COOH) tends to ionise (slightly) to produce hydrogen ions, which is the property of an acid (page 481):

$$-COOH \rightleftharpoons -COO^- + H^+$$

The —COOH functional groups of three organic acids react with the three —COH functional groups of glycerol to form a triglyceride (Figure 2.11). The bonds formed are known as **ester bonds**.

Fats and oils are both formed in this way, and they have the same chemical structure. The only chemical difference between them is that at about 20 °C (room temperature) **oils are liquids** and **fats are solid**.

oil forms a layer on water, but when shaken together, forms an **emulsion** (milky in appearance) which may take a while to disperse

Saturated and unsaturated triglycerides

Fats and oils that are **saturated** have no **double bonds** (—C=C—, page 479) between the carbon atoms in their hydrocarbon tails, whereas unsaturated fats and oils have one or more. Fats containing several double bonds are called **polyunsaturated**. Fats with unsaturated fatty acids melt at a lower temperature than those with saturated fatty acids, because their unsaturated hydrocarbon tails do not pack so closely together. You can see why in Figure 2.12.

This difference between saturated and polyunsaturated fats is important in the manufacture of margarine/butter spreads, since polyunsaturates perform better 'from the fridge'. There is controversy about the value of polyunsaturates in the human diet. What seems clear is that it is better to eat less rather than more fat in our diet.

Figure 2.11
The formation of triglyceride.

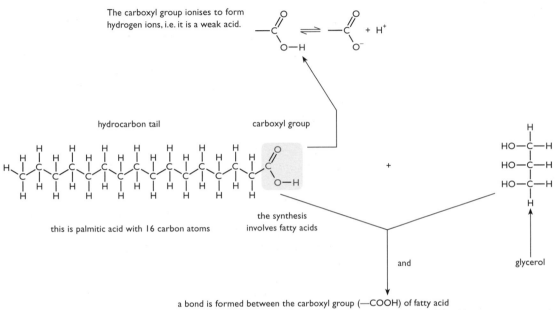

Figure 2.12
Saturated and unsaturated fatty acids, and the triglycerides they form.

palmitic acid, $C_{15}H_{31}COOH$, a saturated fatty acid

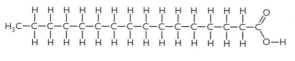

space-filling model

skeletal formula

oleic acid, $C_{17}H_{33}COOH$, an unsaturated fatty acid

space-filling model

skeletal formula

(the double bond causes a kink in the hydrocarbon 'tail')

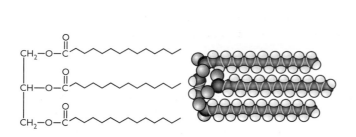

tristearin, m.p. 72 °C

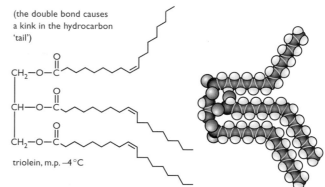

triolein, m.p. −4 °C

The roles of fats and oils in living things

Energy source and metabolic water source

When triglycerides are oxidised in respiration, a lot of energy is released and used to make ATP (page 48). Mass for mass, fats and oils release more than twice as much energy when they are respired as carbohydrates do. This is because fats are more reduced than carbohydrates. More of the oxygen in the respiration of fats comes from the atmosphere, whereas in the oxidation of carbohydrate, more oxygen is present in the carbohydrate molecule itself. Fat therefore forms a concentrated, insoluble energy store.

Fat layers are typical of animals that endure long unfavourable seasons, in which they survive by using up concentrated reserves of food stored in their bodies. Oils are a major energy store in many seeds and fruits. Certain fruits and seeds are used commercially as sources of edible oils for humans. Examples include maize, olives and sunflower.

Complete oxidation of fats and oils produces a large amount of water, far more than when the same mass of carbohydrate is respired. Desert animals like the camel and the desert rat (page 269) retain much of this 'metabolic water' within their bodies, helping them to survive when there is no liquid water for drinking. The development of the embryo of birds and reptiles, whilst in their shells, also benefits from metabolic water formed by the oxidation of the stored fat in their egg's yolk.

Subcutaneous fat as a buoyancy aid

Fat is stored in animals as **adipose tissue** (Figure 2.13), typically under the skin, where it is known as **subcutaneous fat**. Aquatic, diving mammals have so much, it is identified as blubber. This gives buoyancy to the body (because fat is not as dense as muscle or bone). If fat reserves like these have a restricted blood supply and (as is commonly the case) the heat of the body is not especially distributed to the fat under the skin, then the subcutaneous fat also functions as a heat insulation layer.

Figure 2.13
Adipose tissue.

cells with fat deposit —

capillary —

Waterproofing of hair and feathers

Oily secretions of the sebaceous glands, which are found in the skin of mammals, act as a water-repellent. They prevent fur and hair from becoming waterlogged when wet. Birds have a preen gland that fulfils the same function for feathers.

Electrical insulation

Myelin lipid in the membranes of Schwann cells, which form the sheaths around the axons of neurones (page 277), electrically isolates the cell plasma membrane. This makes it possible for the nerve impulse to pass down the axon.

Phospholipids

4 Sketch a phospholipid molecule in outline, and label
a the hydrophilic part, and
b the hydrophobic part.

A phospholipid has a very similar chemical structure to triglyceride, except that one of the fatty acid groups is replaced by a phosphate group (Figure 2.14). The phosphate group is ionised, having a negative charge, so water molecules are attracted to this part of the molecule. So phospholipids combine the hydrophobic properties of the hydrocarbon chain with the water-loving (**hydrophilic** properties) of the phosphate group. We return to this point when looking at the structure of cell membranes (Chapter 3).

Figure 2.14
Phospholipids.

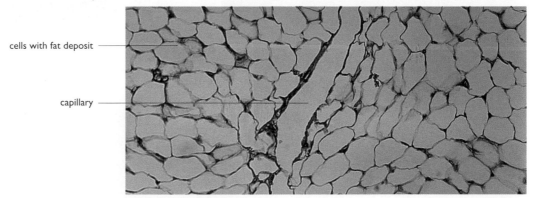

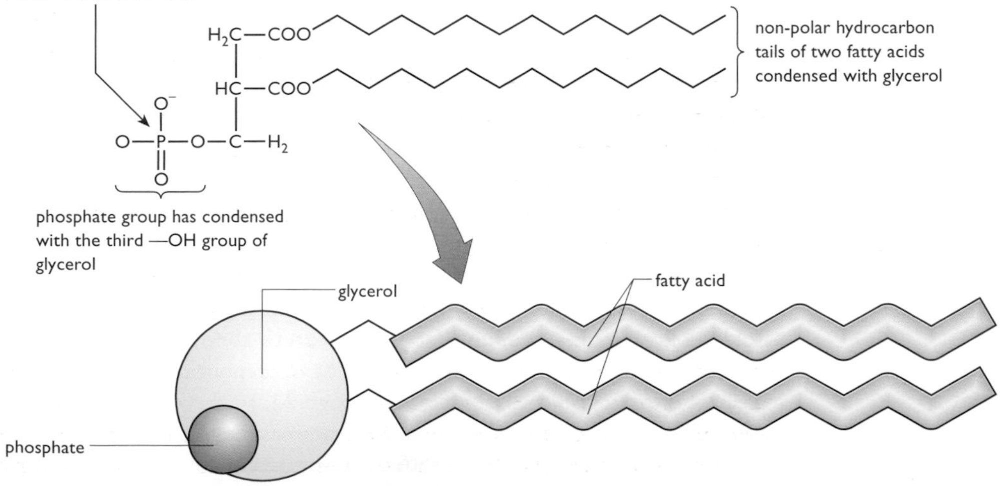

phosphate group ionised under conditions in cells

H_2C—COO⁻   non-polar hydrocarbon tails of two fatty acids condensed with glycerol

HC—COO⁻

O⁻
|
O—P—O—C—H_2
‖
O

phosphate group has condensed with the third —OH group of glycerol

glycerol

fatty acid

phosphate

Waxes

Waxes are esters formed from a fatty acid and a complex alcohol (in place of glycerol). They are produced by plants and form the waxy cuticle that protects the plant stem and leaf surfaces from loss of water by evaporation. The same role is fulfilled by the wax secreted by insects on the outer surface of their cuticle. Bees use wax in the honeycomb cells they build for rearing their larvae and storing honey (Figure 2.15).

Figure 2.15
Wax in use in organisms.

leaf epidermal cells covered by wax

insect cuticle covered by wax

bee's wax comb

Steroids

If you compare the structure of a steroid (like the one shown in Figure 2.16) with that of a triglyceride (Figure 2.11), you can see just how structurally diverse the lipids are. The 'skeleton' of a steroid is a set of complex rings of carbon atoms. The bulk of the molecule is hydrophobic, but the polar —OH group is hydrophilic. Steroids occur in both plants and animals, and one widespread form is the substance **cholesterol**.

Figure 2.16
The steroid cholesterol.

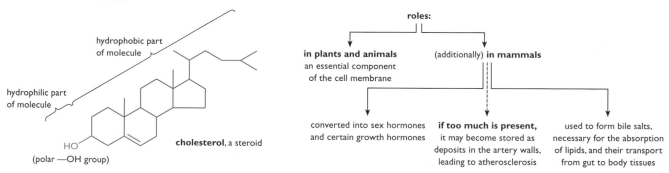

Cholesterol is an essential component of the cell membrane of plants and animals. In mammals, the sex hormones progesterone, oestrogen and testosterone, and also growth hormones, are all produced from it. Bile salts (involved in lipid transport from the intestine to the tissues, in the blood) are also synthesised from cholesterol. Consequently, cholesterol is essential for normal, healthy metabolism.

Cholesterol is made in cells and tissues, as required. In mammals, cholesterol is obtained from the diet, and also made, mostly in the liver. Diets high in fats, and especially fats containing saturated fatty acids (i.e. animal fats), may lead to abnormally high blood-cholesterol levels. Excess blood cholesterol may lead to the development of harmful deposits in artery walls, causing a disease called atherosclerosis (page 323).

Because it is insoluble (like all lipids), mammals have to transport cholesterol in the blood plasma combined with soluble proteins. The combination is called **lipoprotein**. In this form, lipids are carried to sites where they are metabolised or stored.

Proteins

Proteins make up about two-thirds of the total dry mass of a cell. They differ from carbohydrates and lipids in that they contain the element nitrogen, and usually the element sulphur, as well as carbon, hydrogen and oxygen. Most proteins are huge molecules, formed from amino acids combined in a long chain. Typically several hundred or even thousands of amino acid molecules are combined together to make a protein.

Once the chain is constructed, a protein takes up a specific shape. The shape of a protein is closely related to the functions it performs. We will return to this aspect of protein structure after we have examined the properties of individual amino acids, and again, in Chapter 4, on enzymes.

Amino acids, the building blocks of proteins

As the name implies, amino acids carry two functional groups: a basic **amino group** ($-NH_2$) and an acidic **carboxyl group** ($-COOH$). In the naturally occurring amino acids, both functional groups are attached to the same carbon atom (Figure 2.17). Since the carboxyl group is acidic:

$$-COOH \rightleftharpoons -COO^- + H^+$$

and the amino group is basic:

$$-NH_2 + H^+ \rightleftharpoons -NH_3^+$$

an amino acid is both an acid and a base. It is said to be **amphoteric**.

The rest of the molecule, the side-chain or R-part, is very variable. Figure 2.18 shows a selection of the 20 amino acids that make up cell proteins, together with their chemical formulae. Whilst amino acids have the same basic structure, they are all rather different in character. This is because they carry different R-groups. For example, some amino acids have additional carboxyl groups (the **acidic** amino acids), and others have additional amino groups (the **basic** amino acids). There are other differences too, as you can see.

Figure 2.17
The structure of amino acids.

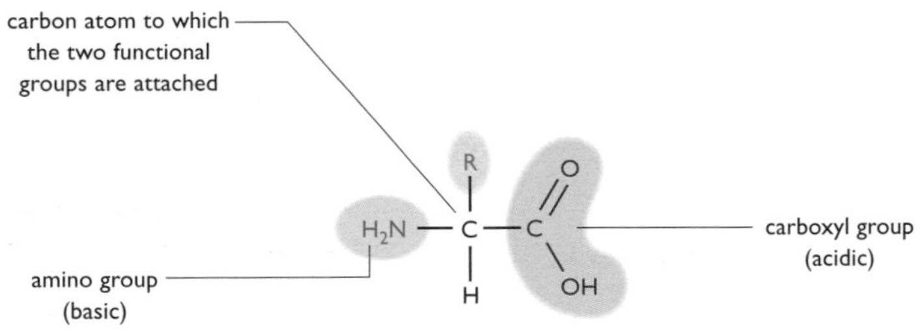

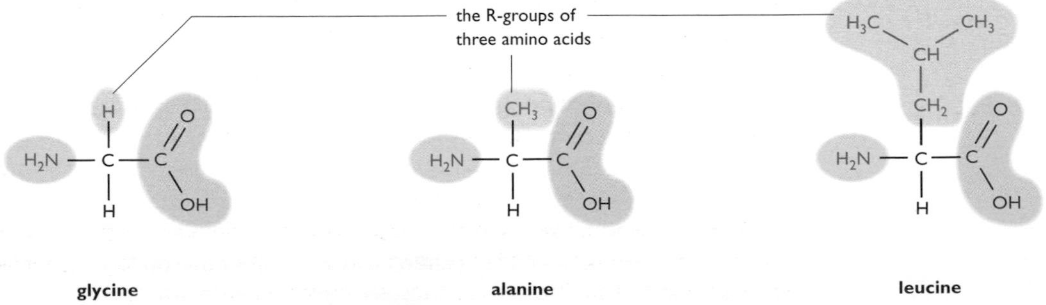

Bringing amino acids together in different combinations produces proteins with very different properties. This helps explain how the range of proteins in organisms are able to fulfil the very different biological functions they have.

Figure 2.18
Some of the 20 amino acids used in protein synthesis. These formulae show how diverse the R-groups are. (The amino acids are in their ionised forms that occur at pH 7.0.)

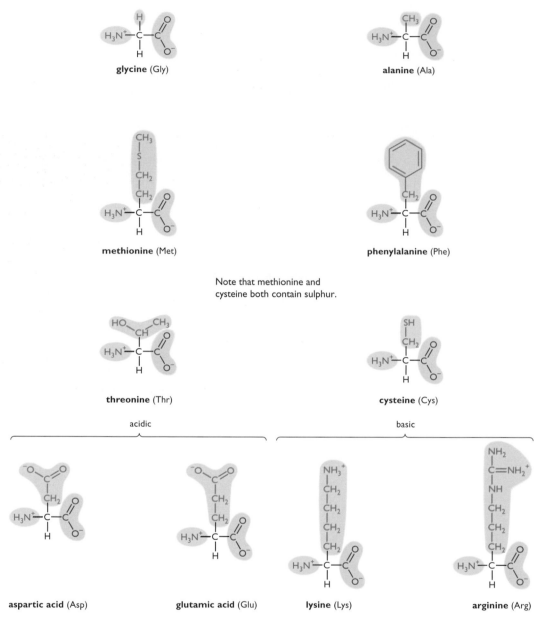

glycine (Gly)

alanine (Ala)

methionine (Met)

phenylalanine (Phe)

Note that methionine and cysteine both contain sulphur.

threonine (Thr)

cysteine (Cys)

acidic

basic

aspartic acid (Asp)

glutamic acid (Glu)

lysine (Lys)

arginine (Arg)

Peptide linkages

Two amino acids can react together with the loss of water to form a dipeptide. The amino group of one amino acid reacts with the carboxyl group of the other, forming a **peptide bond** (—CONH—, Figure 2.19). Long strings of amino acids linked by peptide bonds are called **polypeptides**. A peptide or protein chain is assembled by adding on one amino acid at a time.

The terms 'polypeptide' and 'protein' can be used interchangeably, but when a polypeptide is about 50 amino acid molecules long it is generally agreed to be have become a protein.

The **biuret test** is used as an indicator of the presence of protein because it gives a purple colour in the presence of peptide linkages. To a solution thought to contain protein, an equal quantity of sodium hydroxide solution is added and mixed. Then a few drops of 0.5% copper(II) sulphate are introduced with gentle mixing. A distinctive purple colour develops without heating (Figure 2.20).

Figure 2.19
Peptide bond formation.

Amino acids combine together, the amino group of one with the carboxyl group of the other:

For example, glycine and alanine can react like this:

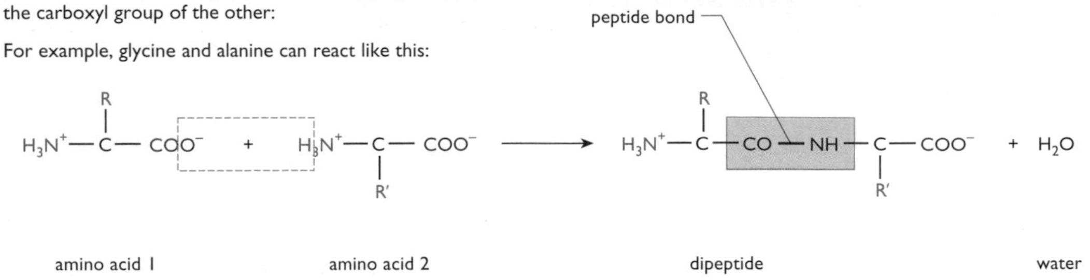

$$H_3N^+ - \overset{R}{\underset{}{C}} - COO^- \quad + \quad H_3N^+ - \overset{}{\underset{R'}{C}} - COO^- \quad \longrightarrow \quad H_3N^+ - \overset{R}{\underset{}{C}} - \boxed{CO - NH} - \overset{}{\underset{R'}{C}} - COO^- \quad + \quad H_2O$$

peptide bond

amino acid 1   amino acid 2   dipeptide   water

But if the amino group of glycine reacts with the carboxyl group of alanine, a different dipeptide, alanyl-glycine, is formed.

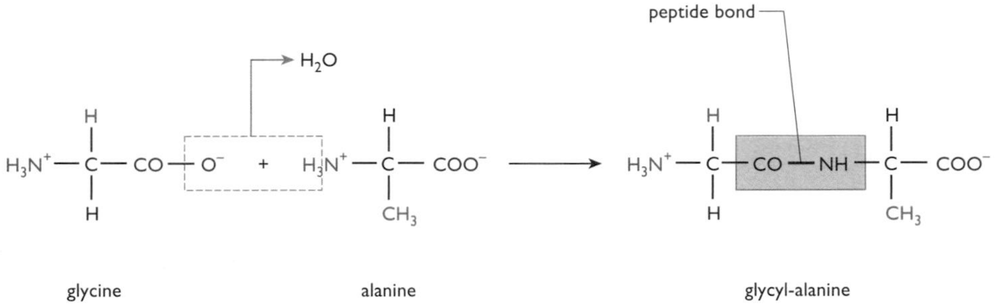

$$H_3N^+ - \overset{H}{\underset{H}{C}} - CO - O^- \quad + \quad H_3N^+ - \overset{H}{\underset{CH_3}{C}} - COO^- \quad \longrightarrow \quad H_3N^+ - \overset{H}{\underset{H}{C}} - \boxed{CO - NH} - \overset{H}{\underset{CH_3}{C}} - COO^-$$

→ H_2O

peptide bond

glycine   alanine   glycyl-alanine

Three amino acids combine together to form a tripeptide:

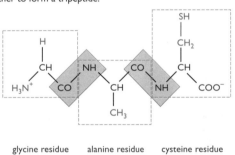

glycine residue   alanine residue   cysteine residue

Figure 2.20
The biuret test for protein.

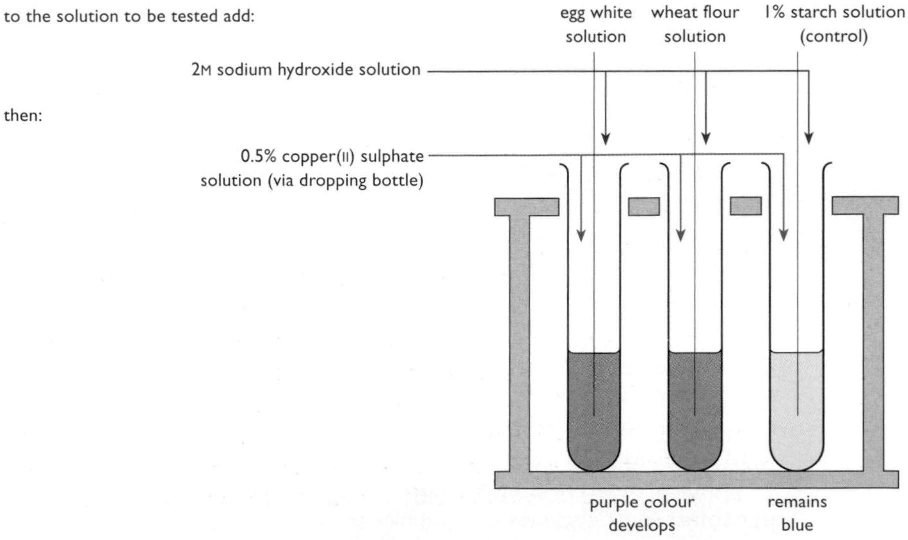

to the solution to be tested add:

2M sodium hydroxide solution

then:

0.5% copper(II) sulphate solution (via dropping bottle)

egg white solution   wheat flour solution   1% starch solution (control)

purple colour develops   remains blue

The structure of proteins

The **primary structure** of a protein is the arrangement of the long chain of amino acids in its molecule. Proteins differ in the variety, number and order of their constituent amino acids. In the living cell, the sequence of amino acids in the polypeptide chain is controlled by the coded instructions stored in the DNA of the chromosomes in the nucleus (Chapter 5). Just changing one amino acid in the sequence of a protein may alter its properties completely. This sort of 'mistake' or mutation does happen (page 116).

The **secondary structure** of a protein develops when parts of the polypeptide chain take up a particular shape, immediately after formation at the ribosome. Parts of the chain become folded or twisted, or both, in various ways. The most common shapes are formed either by coiling to produce an **α-helix** or by folding into **β-sheets** (Figure 2.21). These shapes are permanent, held in place by hydrogen bonds (page 54).

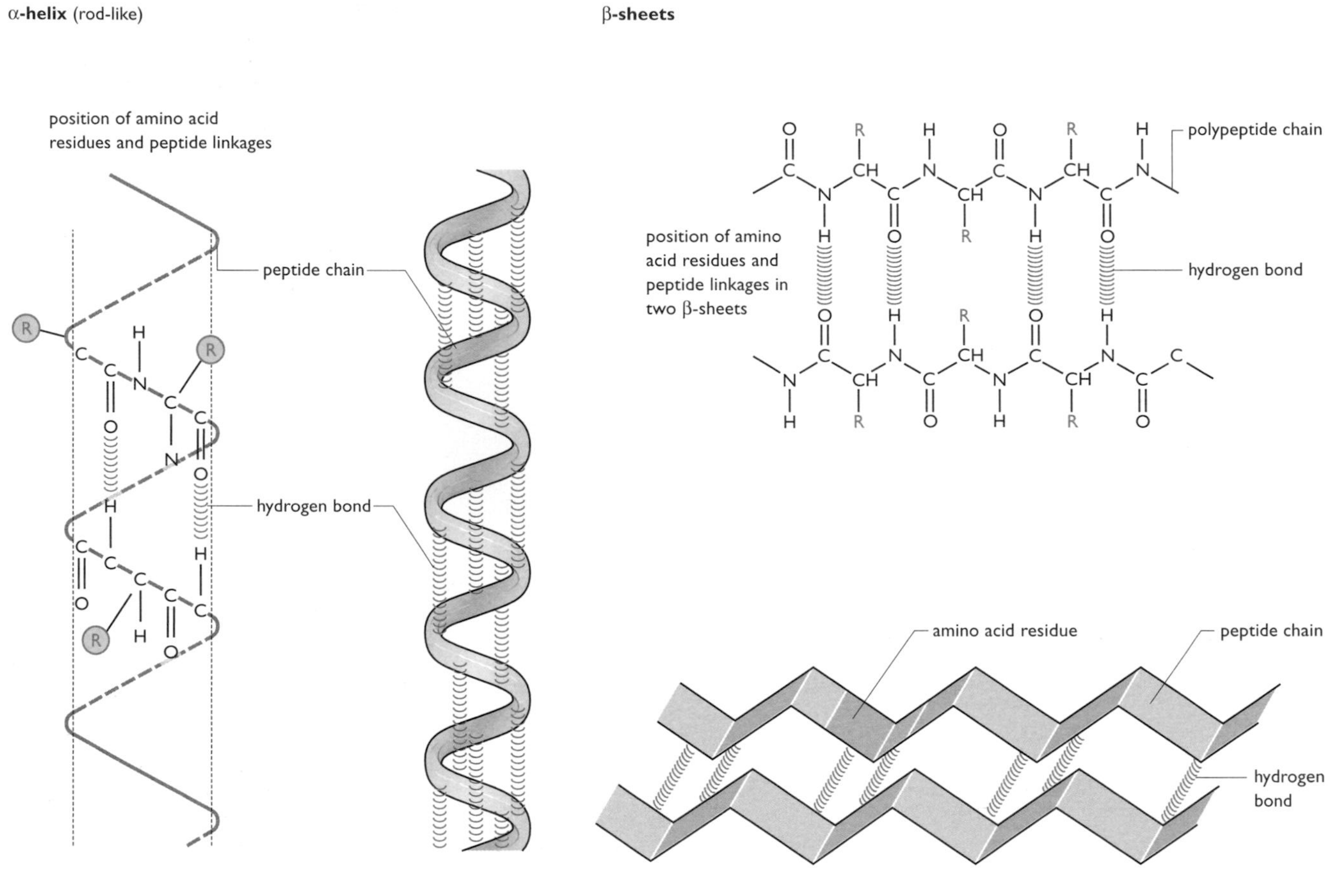

Figure 2.21
The secondary structure of proteins.

α-helix (rod-like)

β-sheets

The **tertiary structure** of a protein is the precise, compact structure, unique to that protein, that arises when the molecule is further folded and held in a particular complex shape. This shape is made permanent by four different types of bonding, established between adjacent parts of the chain (Figure 2.22). The primary, secondary and tertiary structures of the protein called lysozyme are shown in Figure 2.23.

Some proteins take up a tertiary structure in the form of a long, much-coiled chain. These are called **fibrous proteins**. Examples of fibrous proteins are **fibrin**, a blood protein involved in the clotting mechanism, **collagen**, a component of bone and tendons, and **keratin**, found in hair, horn and nails.

Other proteins take up a tertiary structure that is more spherical, and are called **globular proteins**. Most enzymes are globular proteins (Chapter 4).

The **quaternary structure of protein** arises when two or more proteins become held together, forming a complex, biologically active molecule. An example is haemoglobin, which consists of four polypeptide chains held around a non-protein haem group, which contains an atom of iron (Chapter 11).

Figure 2.22
Crosslinking within a polypeptide.

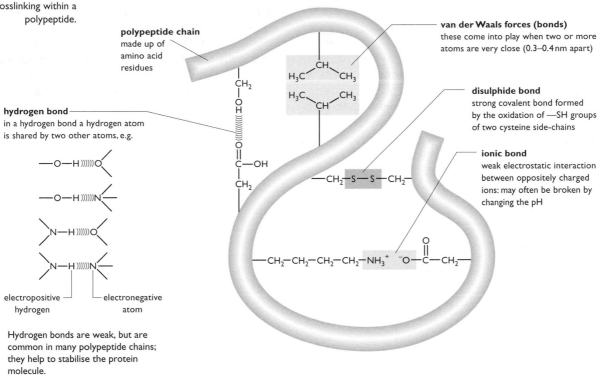

polypeptide chain
made up of amino acid residues

hydrogen bond
in a hydrogen bond a hydrogen atom is shared by two other atoms, e.g.

electropositive hydrogen — — electronegative atom

Hydrogen bonds are weak, but are common in many polypeptide chains; they help to stabilise the protein molecule.

van der Waals forces (bonds)
these come into play when two or more atoms are very close (0.3–0.4 nm apart)

disulphide bond
strong covalent bond formed by the oxidation of —SH groups of two cysteine side-chains

ionic bond
weak electrostatic interaction between oppositely charged ions: may often be broken by changing the pH

Figure 2.23
Lysozyme: primary, secondary and tertiary structure.

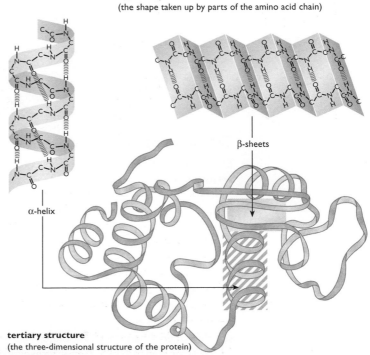

primary structure
(the sequence of amino acids)

secondary structure
(the shape taken up by parts of the amino acid chain)

β-sheets

α-helix

tertiary structure
(the three-dimensional structure of the protein)

Amino acids and proteins as 'buffers'

In solution, amino acids ionise; both the amino group and the carboxyl group do this. We have already noted that the carboxyl group can produce H^+ ions and so it acts as an acid:

$$-COOH \rightleftharpoons -COO^- + H^+$$

The amino group can remove H^+ ions from solution, so it acts as a base:

$$-NH_2 + H^+ \rightleftharpoons -NH_3^+$$

In neutral solution both the amino group and the carboxyl groups are ionised. In an acid solution (low pH) the amino acid picks up H^+ ions and becomes positively charged. In an alkaline solution (high pH) the amino acid donates H^+ to the solvent and becomes negatively charged (Figure 2.24). Consequently, amino acids tend to stabilise the pH of a solution, because they remove excess H^+ or excess OH^- ions, forming water. They are acting as **buffers** (page 481).

This buffering capacity is retained when amino acids are built up into proteins. This is because of the presence of additional amino groups and carboxyl groups of the basic and acidic amino acid residues of the protein. So proteins (and amino acids) play an important part as buffers in cells and organisms. The pH of blood is partly buffered by blood proteins, for example.

Figure 2.24
Amino acids in solution.

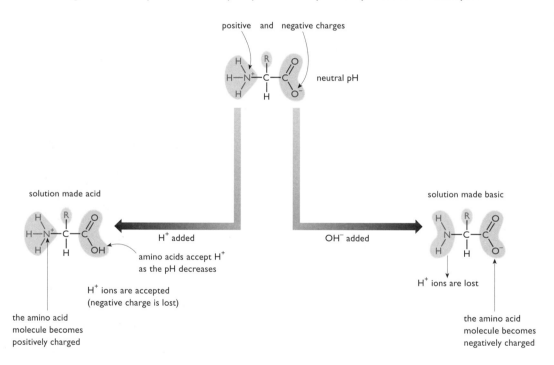

Denaturation of protein

Denaturation of a protein is the loss of the three-dimensional structure. It happens when the relatively weak bonds that maintain the three-dimensional shape of the protein molecule are changed. This may be caused by exposure to high temperature, heavy metal ions and some organic solvents, but is also triggered by very low pH (extreme acidity) or very high pH (extreme alkalinity) and by certain other chemicals.

Many of the properties and uses of proteins within cells and organisms depend on their particular shape. When the shape of a protein changes, the protein may cease to be useful. The biochemistry of cells and organisms is extremely sensitive to conditions that alter proteins in this way.

When high temperature and heavy metal ions cause denaturation the changes are irreversible. A denatured protein generally forms long, disorganised strands, which are insoluble in water. We see this when a hen's egg is cooked. The translucent egg 'white' is a globular protein, albumen, which when denatured becomes irreversibly opaque and insoluble.

● **Extension**   Electrophoresis

Electrophoresis is the laboratory technique most frequently used to separate charged particles in mixtures. For example it is used to separate amino acids from cell extracts or from hydrolysed protein. It is also used to separate proteins and peptide fragments (and also DNA fragments, see page 111). The separation process is carried out on inert supporting material, often polyacrylamide gel (PAG), to which a potential difference is applied (Figure 2.25). Charged particles move in the electric field: the greater the charge, the greater the rate of movement. Additionally, the PAG acts as a molecular sieve, slowing larger particles and allowing smaller particles to move through the tiny pores of the gel more quickly. Therefore in electrophoresis, separation depends on both charge and particle size, and the process is extremely efficient. Tiny quantities, as low as 10 mg, can be separated and the components located and identified.

Figure 2.25
Separation of amino acids and polypeptide fragments by charge and size by electrophoresis.

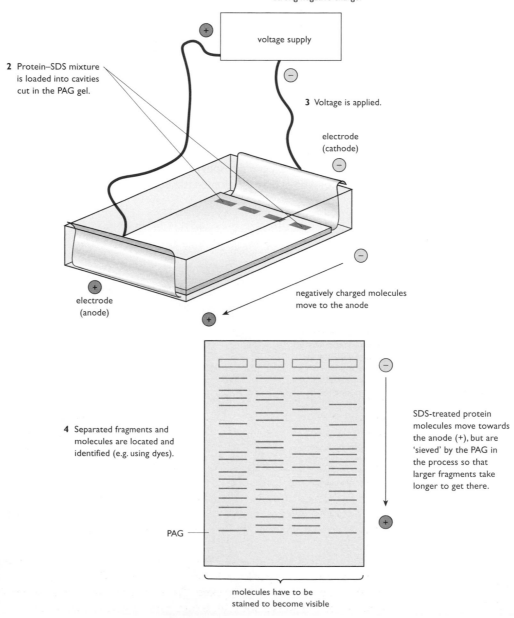

1 Protein is treated with a detergent called SDS. The effect is to unwind the protein and attach SDS molecules to the peptide bonds. This also leaves many negatively charged groups of SDS exposed. As a result the protein/peptide fragments have a strong negative charge.

voltage supply

2 Protein–SDS mixture is loaded into cavities cut in the PAG gel.

3 Voltage is applied.

electrode (cathode)

negatively charged molecules move to the anode

electrode (anode)

4 Separated fragments and molecules are located and identified (e.g. using dyes).

SDS-treated protein molecules move towards the anode (+), but are 'sieved' by the PAG in the process so that larger fragments take longer to get there.

PAG

molecules have to be stained to become visible

Roles of proteins

Many proteins have a **structural role**, such as those in membranes around the cell and in cell organelles. Another example is the fibrous protein collagen, which forms part of the structure of hair, tendon, bones and teeth. Very many cell proteins are **enzymes**, some free-floating in the liquid part of the cytoplasm (the cytosol). Others are built into membranes. Certain membrane proteins are **pumps** that transport molecules across membranes. Other proteins are **carrier molecules**, involved in bulk transport of essential resources, or acting as **pH buffers** in the blood. A major group are the **antibodies**, involved in combating disease and invasion by bacteria. Some **hormones** are also proteins.

● **Extension**   Collagen

Collagen is a fibrous protein, and the most abundant structural protein found in animals. Skin is largely composed of collagen; it forms a mat in the deeper layers. Collagen is a major component of bones, teeth and tendons. Chemically, collagen consists of three polypeptide chains, each about 1000 amino acid residues long, wound together as a triple helix – a unique arrangement in proteins. Under the microscope, a collagen fibril looks like a twisted rope.

The primary structure of collagen has glycine (the smallest amino acid) at every third point in the chain. In fact, the collagen polypeptide has a repeating sequence of 'glycine–X–Y, where X and Y are often the amino acids proline and hydroxyproline. The m–R parts of the molecules of these amino acids are ring structures. Rings prevent collagen from folding or forming pleated sheets (its secondary structure), and force it to take up the triple helix shape.

Collagen is an insoluble protein. It is assembled by cells as procollagen, a soluble molecule that is built up to make collagen. Outside the cell, covalent crosslinks form between the polypeptide chains as they are assembled as collagen fibrils. Collagen then binds with other components, enormously increasing its strength. For example, in healthy bone it binds with a mineral, a form of calcium phosphate. People unable to produce normal-functioning collagen (an inherited condition) may develop brittle bone disease (Figure 2.26).

Figure 2.26
Collagen.

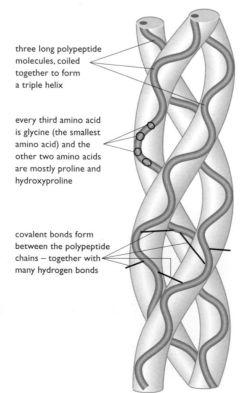

three long polypeptide molecules, coiled together to form a triple helix

every third amino acid is glycine (the smallest amino acid) and the other two amino acids are mostly proline and hydroxyproline

covalent bonds form between the polypeptide chains – together with many hydrogen bonds

Patients with brittle bone disease may suffer multiple fractures of their bones.

The disease arises because the patient's collagen does not form links to the mineral component of bone.

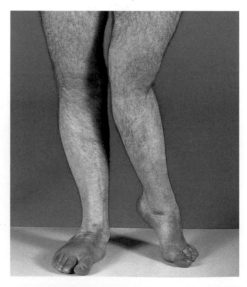

5 What tests would you use to identify
a collagen, and
b cellulose?
What positive result would each give?

Nucleic acids

Nucleic acids are the **information molecules of cells** throughout the living world. This is because the code containing the information in nucleic acids, known as the **genetic code**, is a universal one. That means that it makes sense in all organisms. It is not specific to any one organism or even to larger groups like mammals, or bacteria, alone.

There are two types of nucleic acid: **deoxyribonucleic acid** (**DNA**), and **ribonucleic acid** (**RNA**). These molecules have roles in the day-to-day control of cells and organisms, and in the transmission of the genetic code from generation to generation. The roles of DNA and RNA are discussed in Chapters 5 and 6. Here we look at the structures of their molecules.

Nucleotides

Nucleic acids are built up from repeating units called **nucleotides**. A nucleotide consists of three substances combined together (Figure 2.27):

- a **nitrogenous base**, either cytosine (C), guanine (G), adenine (A), thymine (T) or uracil (U)
- a **pentose sugar**, either ribose or deoxyribose
- **phosphoric acid**.

Figure 2.27 The components of nucleotides.

the components:

phosphoric acid

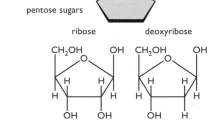

pentose sugars

condensation to form a nucleotide:

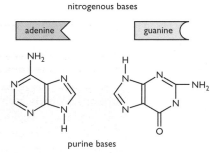

shown diagrammatically as:

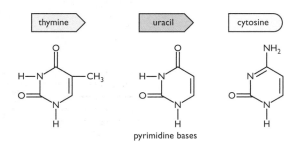

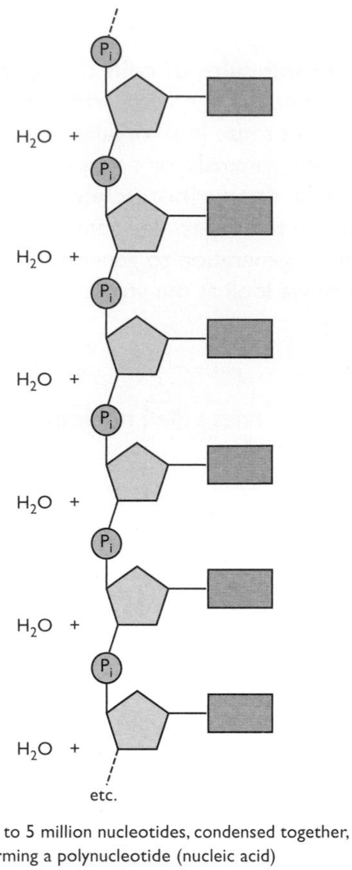

Figure 2.28
How nucleotides make up nucleic acid.

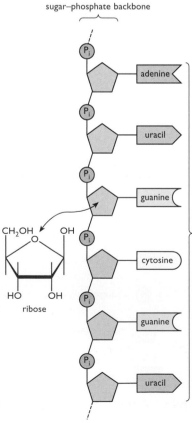

up to 5 million nucleotides, condensed together, forming a polynucleotide (nucleic acid)

Figure 2.29
RNA structure.

sugar–phosphate backbone

ribose

single strand of polynucleotide with ribose sugar and nitrogenous bases: adenine, uracil, guanine and cytosine

Nucleotides become condensed together to form huge molecules – the nucleic acids, also known as **polynucleotides**. A nucleic acid or polynucleotide is a very long, thread-like macromolecule. Alternating sugar and phosphate groups form the 'backbone' to the polynucleotide, with a nitrogenous base attached to each sugar along the strand (Figure 2.28).

The differences between RNA and DNA

RNA molecules are much shorter than those of DNA. In fact, RNAs tend to be from one hundred up to thousands of nucleotides long, depending on the particular role they have. In all RNA molecules the nucleotides contain **ribose**. The bases in RNA are cytosine, guanine, adenine and uracil, but never thymine. RNA is always a single strand (Figure 2.29).

In the 'information business' of cells there are **three functional types of RNA**, known as messenger RNA (mRNA), transfer RNA (tRNA), and ribosomal RNA. All three use information from the nucleus in the construction of proteins by the ribosomes in the cytoplasm.

DNA molecules occur in the chromosomes and form very long strands indeed, containing around several million nucleotides. In all DNA molecules the nucleotides contain **deoxyribose**. The bases in DNA are cytosine, guanine, adenine and thymine, but never uracil.

The DNA molecule consists of **two polynucleotide strands**, paired together, and held by hydrogen bonds (page 54). The two strands take the shape of a double helix (Figure 2.30). The pairing of bases is between adenine and thymine, and between cytosine and guanine, because these are the only combinations of bases that will fit together within the helix. This pairing, known as **complementary base pairing**, is the key to the way information is held in nucleic acids, and the form in which it is transferred to RNA (mRNA) to be used in the cytoplasm.

Table 2.2 summarises the differences between RNA and DNA.

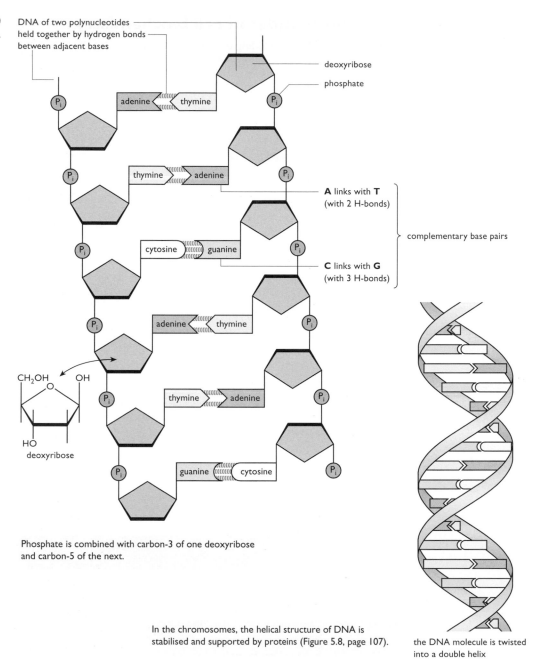

Figure 2.30
DNA structure.

DNA of two polynucleotides
held together by hydrogen bonds
between adjacent bases

deoxyribose

phosphate

adenine — thymine

thymine — adenine

A links with **T**
(with 2 H-bonds)

cytosine — guanine

complementary base pairs

C links with **G**
(with 3 H-bonds)

adenine — thymine

CH₂OH   OH
O
HO
deoxyribose

thymine — adenine

guanine — cytosine

Phosphate is combined with carbon-3 of one deoxyribose
and carbon-5 of the next.

In the chromosomes, the helical structure of DNA is
stabilised and supported by proteins (Figure 5.8, page 107).

the DNA molecule is twisted
into a double helix

Table 2.2
The differences between
DNA and RNA.

DNA	RNA
very long strands, several million nucleotides long	relatively short strands, 100–1000 nucleotides long
contains deoxyribose	contains ribose
contains bases C, G, A and T (not U)	contains C, G, A and U (not T)
consists of two polynucleotide strands of complementary base pairs:	consists of a single strand, and in three functional forms: • messenger RNA
C with G, and A with T	• transfer RNA
and held by H-bonds in the form of a double helix	• ribosomal RNA

Roles of nucleic acids

The ways DNA and RNA function in cells and organisms have been briefly mentioned here. They
are discussed fully in Chapter 5.

Other nucleotides in cell biochemistry

In addition to being the building blocks of the nucleic acids, certain nucleotides (and molecules made from nucleotides) are important in the metabolism of cells.

Adenosine triphosphate (ATP)

ATP consists of adenine combined with a pentose sugar (ribose), which in turn is combined with a string of three phosphate groups (Figure 2.31). When the ATP molecule reacts, one (or less frequently two) of these groups can be lost. Adenosine diphosphate (ADP) and inorganic phosphate (P_i) are formed as a result.

Figure 2.31
The structure and role of ATP.

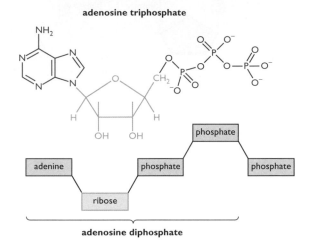

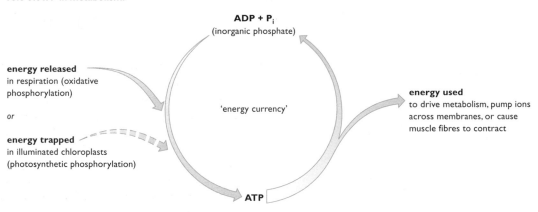

ATP is a reservoir of stored chemical energy, and is involved in most energy-requiring reactions. It acts in this way in every living organism. This is why ATP is often called the 'energy currency' of cells (page 194).

ATP is made continuously, more or less as it is required, and used almost immediately. ATP is formed in respiration and in photosynthesis, but only a small amount is held in cells (in store, so to speak).

NAD and NADP

NAD (nicotinamide adenine dinucleotide) consists of two nucleotides combined with two phosphate groups. In one of the combined nucleotides, the organic base is replaced by a substance called nicotinamide. Nicotinamide is derived from a vitamin (page 147) of the B complex, called nicotinic acid.

Figure 2.32
The structure and
role of NAD.

NAD is a 'carrier' of hydrogen ions
and electrons in respiration

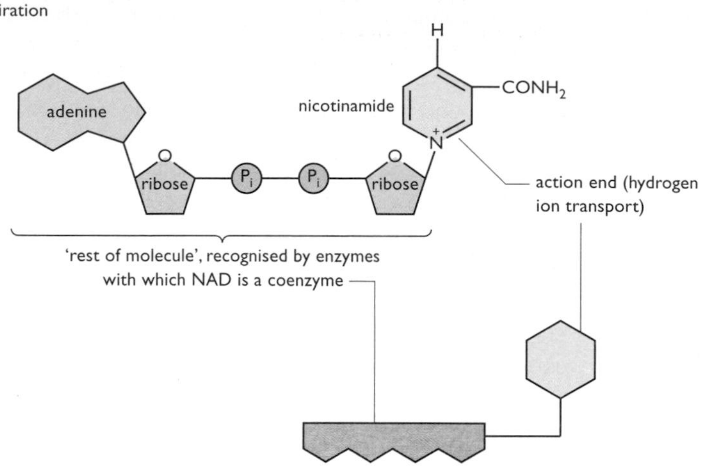

adenine

nicotinamide

H

CONH$_2$

ribose — P$_i$ — P$_i$ — ribose

N$^+$

action end (hydrogen
ion transport)

'rest of molecule', recognised by enzymes
with which NAD is a coenzyme

mode of action:
summary:

$$NAD^+ + 2H^+ + 2e^- \rightleftharpoons NADH + H^+$$

changes at 'action end':

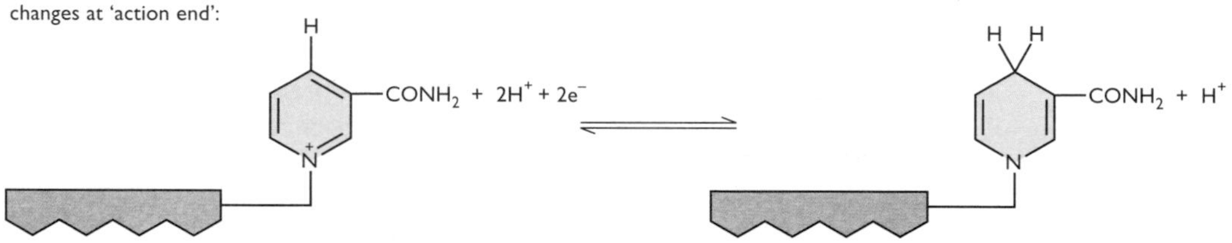

H

CONH$_2$ + 2H$^+$ + 2e$^-$

N$^+$

$\rightleftharpoons$

H H

CONH$_2$ + H$^+$

N

6 Distinguish between the following:

• organic and inorganic compounds
• primary and secondary structure of a protein
• functional group and R-part of molecule
• condensation and hydrolysis reactions
• cellulose and starch
• monosaccharide and disaccharide
• amino group and carboxyl group
• reducing and non-reducing sugars
• aldehyde and ketone
• fats and oils
• saturated and unsaturated fatty acids
• polypeptides and proteins
• phospholipids and steroids
• hydrophobic and hydrophilic
• NAD and ATP.

Nicotinamide is a ring molecule that accepts hydrogen ions and electrons. When it accepts them it is said to be **reduced** (page 196). Reduced NAD can pass hydrogen ions and electrons on to other acceptor molecules quite easily: when it does so it becomes oxidised back to NAD again (Figure 2.32). The transport of hydrogen ions and electrons like this is an important part of respiration. NAD is one of the substances called **coenzymes**. It works with different enzymes of respiration. It also takes part in other processes in cells.

A second substance, **NADP** (nicotinamide adenine dinucleotide phosphate), which contains an additional phosphate group, has a similar role in photosynthesis.

Skills task

Choose one macromolecule to be found in cells, and research its composition, structure and roles.

Obtain information from your textbook, from library sources such as a CD-ROM or from a scientific paper (for example, a recent edition of *Biological Sciences Review*).

Prepare a handout on one side of A4 paper in which you report on the structure and function of the macromolecule by means of an image of the molecule. Include annotations on its chemical composition and structure, presented in your own words. Add your conclusions about the roles of the macromolecule as concise 'bullet points', relating your molecule to living organisms.

SUMMARY

- Organic compounds contain the elements **carbon** and **hydrogen**, usually with oxygen and other elements. Carbon atoms form strong **covalent bonds** (sharing electrons between atoms) with other carbon atoms and with atoms of other elements, forming a huge range of compounds. Many of the organic compounds of life fall into one of four groups of compounds: **carbohydrates**, **lipids**, **proteins** and **nucleic acids**.

- **Carbohydrates** contain carbon, hydrogen and oxygen only, and have the general formula $C_x(H_2O)_y$. They consist of the **sugars** (monosaccharides and disaccharides) and macromolecules built from sugars (**polysaccharides**).

- **Monosaccharides** include the three-carbon sugars (**trioses**) formed in photosynthesis and respiration, five-carbon sugars (**pentoses**) found in nucleic acids, and the six-carbon sugars (**hexoses**), which include glucose, fructose and galactose. Hexoses all have the same molecular formula ($C_6H_{12}O_6$) but different arrangements of the atoms (different structural formulae). Pentoses and hexoses exist as ring molecules, and react in this form with other molecules.

- Two hexose monosaccharides can combine together with the removal of water (a **condensation reaction**) to form **disaccharide** sugars, held together by **glycosidic bonds**. Disaccharides include **sucrose** (glucose and fructose), **maltose** (two glucose units) and **lactose** (galactose and glucose).

- Monosaccharides and many disaccharides are **reducing sugars**. When heated with alkaline copper(II) sulphate (Benedict's solution, blue) they produce reduced copper(I) oxide as a **brick-red precipitate**. The sugar is oxidised to a sugar acid. Sucrose is not a reducing sugar.

- Most **polysaccharides** are built from glucose units condensed together, and are true **polymers** (made up of identical building blocks). They may be **food stores** (starch, glycogen) or **structural components** of organisms (cellulose, chitin).

- **Lipids** contain the elements carbon, hydrogen and oxygen, with a low proportion of oxygen. They are insoluble in water, but otherwise their properties and structure vary widely.

- **Fats** are solids at room temperature. **Oils** are liquids. They are formed by condensation reactions between the hydroxyl groups of glycerol and three fatty acids. These form a **triglyceride**, with ester bonds. The fatty acids may be **saturated** or **unsaturated** (unsaturated fatty acids contain double bonds between carbon atoms in the hydrocarbon tails). Fats and oils are effectively **energy stores**.

- In **phospholipids**, one of the hydroxyl groups of glycerol reacts with phosphoric acid. The product has a hydrocarbon 'tail' (**hydrophobic**) and an ionised phosphate group (**hydrophilic**). Phospholipids form **bilayers** on water. Together with proteins, phospholipids make up the membranes of cells.

- **Waxes** are monoglycerides of complex alcohols. They are used in **waterproofing** plant and animal structures.

- **Steroid** molecules contain complex rings of carbon atoms. The bulk of a steroid molecule is hydrophobic, but it also has a polar part (hydrophilic). **Cholesterol** is an example. It is a component of the cell membranes of plants and animals. In mammals cholesterol is metabolised into hormones and bile salts.

- **Proteins** contain nitrogen and some sulphur, in addition to carbon, hydrogen and oxygen. The building blocks of proteins are **amino acids**, and many hundreds or even thousands of amino acid residues go to make up a typical protein. Amino acid molecules have a basic **amino group** (—NH₂) and an acidic **carboxyl group** (—COOH) attached to a carbon atom, to which the rest of the molecule (—R) is also attached.

- Many amino acids are known, but only about 20 go to make the proteins of living things. Amino acids combine by forming **peptide bonds** between the carboxyl group of one molecule and the amino group of another, to form a polypeptide chain.

- The properties of polypeptides and protein are determined by the amino acids they are built from and the sequence of the amino acids in the molecule. The sequence of amino acids is the **primary structure of the protein**, and is indirectly controlled by the DNA of the nucleus.

continued

● The shape of the protein molecule determines its properties. Part of a polypeptide chain forms into a helix and part into sheets (the **secondary structure** of a protein). The whole chain is held in position by bonds between parts folded together, forming the **tertiary structure** of a protein. Separate polypeptide chains combine, sometimes with other substances, to form the **quaternary structure**.

● Some proteins have a structural role. These are **fibrous proteins**; they include the collagen of skin, bone and tendon. Many proteins are enzymes, antibodies or hormones, and these are **globular proteins**.

● There are two forms of nucleic acid, **DNA** and **RNA**. Nucleic acid consists of **five-carbon sugar** and **phosphate**, which alternate in a long backbone. To each sugar is also attached a **nitrogenous base**. Sugar, phosphate and an organic base form a **nucleotide**, so a length of nucleic acid is a **polynucleotide**. The bases are often referred to by their initials **C** and **G**, **A** and **T** (or **U**).

● DNA and RNA differ in the five-carbon sugar they contain, in the bases they contain and in their roles in cells. DNA exists as a **double strand** in the form of a helix. RNA is single-stranded. DNA occurs in the nucleus, and RNA in the nucleus and cytoplasm.

● In the DNA double strand, complementary base pairing occurs between adenine and thymine, and between cytosine and guanine. The sequence of bases in DNA is the form in which information is stored in the molecule.

● Other nucleotides have key roles in metabolism, including **ATP** (as energy currency) and **NAD/NADP** (hydrogen ion transport).

Examination questions

1 a The diagrams show fatty acid molecules in saturated and unsaturated triglycerides.

saturated   unsaturated

Complete the diagrams to show the difference between a saturated fatty acid and an unsaturated fatty acid. (2)

b In the human gut, a triglyceride may be converted to glycerol and fatty acids by hydrolysis.
i Explain what is meant by *hydrolysis*. (1)
ii Describe the part played by bile in the hydrolysis of triglycerides. (2)

AQA(AEB), A level, 0642/1, June 1999

2 The figure shows the molecular structure of α glucose.

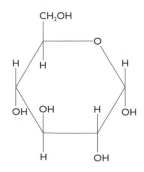

a i Show how α glucose molecules are joined to form the long chains found in starch. (2)
ii Name the bond formed in **a i**. (1)

Cellulose is also formed from long chains of glucose molecules.

b Explain how cellulose differs from starch
i in structure; (3)
ii in function. (2)
c Describe how you would test an unknown sample of food for the presence of a non-reducing sugar. (3)

OCR (Cambridge), A level, 9264/3, Nov 1999

3 The table below refers to **two** organic molecules.

If the statement is correct for the molecule, place a tick (✓) in the appropriate box. If it is incorrect, place a cross (✗) in the appropriate box. (5)

Statement	Triglyceride	Glycogen
contains only carbon, hydrogen and oxygen		
glycosidic bonds present		
soluble in water		
provides storage of energy		
occurs in flowering plants and animals		

London, AS/A level, Module B/HB1, June 1998

4 a The diagram shows the formula of a molecule of an organic compound.

$$H_2N-\underset{\underset{H}{|}}{\overset{\overset{CH_3}{|}}{C}}-COOH$$

  i To which group of organic compounds does this molecule belong?
  ii Give **one** way in which this molecule differs from other compounds in the group. (2)

b The table shows some of the organic compounds found in a bacterial cell.

Compound	Percentage of total dry mass	Number of different types of molecule
protein	55.0	1050
RNA	20.5	463
DNA	3.1	1
lipid	9.1	4
glycogen	2.5	1

  i Glycogen and protein are both polymers. Explain why there can only be one type of glycogen molecule, but there can be many types of protein molecule. (2)
  ii Explain why there are many types of RNA found in this cell. (2)

  AQA(NEAB), A level, Paper 1/Sections A & B, June 1999

5 A diagram of the molecular structure of part of a glycoprotein found at the cell surface membrane is shown below.

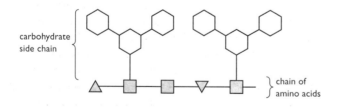

  a State how the following are linked in a glycoprotein:
  i adjacent amino acids (1)
  ii adjacent molecules of the sugar in the carbohydrate side chain. (1)
  b State **two** functions of glycoproteins in cell surface membranes. (2)
  c Explain why cell surface membranes are described as having a *fluid mosaic* structure. (4)

  UCLES, AS/A level, 4801, June 1998

6 The diagram below shows the structure of part of a molecule of deoxyribonucleic acid (DNA).

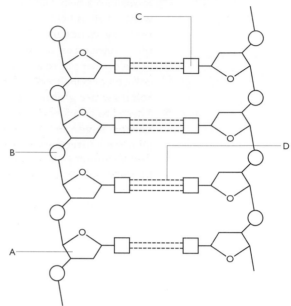

  a Name the parts labelled A, B, C and D. (4)
  b **i** On the diagram, draw a ring around **one** nucleotide. (1)
  ii What type of chemical reaction is involved in the formation of a molecule of DNA from nucleotides? (1)

  London, AS/A level, Module B/HB1, June 1996

7 a Show how the two glucose molecules in the diagram below may join together. (2)

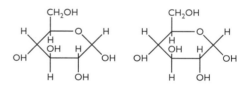

  b Explain **two** ways in which the properties of a cellulose molecule make it suitable for its role in the structure of plant cell walls. (2)

  NEAB, AS/A level, Module BY01, Mar 1998

8 a The diagram shows an amino acid molecule.

$$H_2N-\underset{\underset{H}{|}}{\overset{\overset{R}{|}}{C}}-COOH$$

  Draw a diagram of two amino acids linked together. (2)
  b Name the type of reaction by which amino acids are linked together. (1)

  NEAB, A level, Paper 1/Sections A & B, June 1996

3 Traffic across cell membranes

STARTING POINTS ● Cells are contained by the cell membrane (**plasma membrane**). The membrane forms a barrier across which all substances entering and leaving the cell must pass.
● **Organic molecules**, e.g. sugars, fatty acids and amino acids, and **inorganic molecules**, e.g. water, carbon dioxide and ions of essential minerals, pass in and out of cells in the course of respiration, nutrition and excretion, and other processes of metabolism.
● The chemistry of the organic molecules of life is introduced in Chapter 2. The properties of **water** and the **minerals** are also important to the story of transport across membranes, and are discussed here.
● '**Background chemistry for biologists**' in Appendix 1 (page 474) may be useful to read when studying this chapter, especially if you are not familiar with the ways atoms form molecules and ions.

What passes?

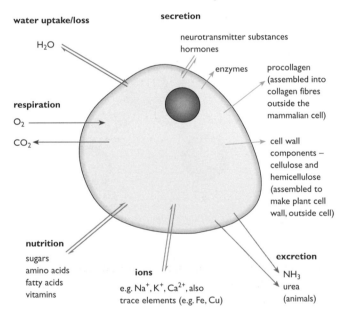

water uptake/loss

H_2O

secretion

neurotransmitter substances
hormones

enzymes

procollagen (assembled into collagen fibres outside the mammalian cell)

respiration

O_2

CO_2

cell wall components – cellulose and hemicellulose (assembled to make plant cell wall, outside cell)

nutrition
sugars
amino acids
fatty acids
vitamins

ions
e.g. Na^+, K^+, Ca^{2+}, also trace elements (e.g. Fe, Cu)

excretion
NH_3
urea
(animals)

Figure 3.1
Movement of substances across the cell membrane.

Traffic in molecules across the plasma membrane is continuous and very heavy. Into and out of cells pass **water**, **respiratory gases** (oxygen and carbon dioxide), **nutrients**, **essential ions** and **excretory products**. Cells may secrete substances such as **hormones** and **enzymes**, and they may receive **growth substances** and **hormones**. Plant cells secrete the chemicals that make up their walls through their cell membranes, and the wall is assembled and maintained outside the membrane. Certain mammalian cells secrete **structural proteins**, such as collagen, in a form that can be assembled outside the cells. In addition, the membrane at the cell surface is where the cell is identified by surrounding cells and organisms. For example, protein **receptor sites** are recognised by hormones and neurotransmitter substances (from nerve cells), as well as other chemicals sent from other cells. Figure 3.1 is a summary of this membrane traffic.

The structure of the plasma membranes and the mechanisms by which substances cross them are explored in this chapter. First, we look at the water molecule and its properties important to life, and at the mineral ions required by cells. Remember, water is the universal solvent and all an organism's transport and cell chemistry is water-based.

The water molecule

Water makes up about 80% of the cell contents; it is the environment for the chemical reactions of life. All in all we often take water for granted, yet its molecular structure and properties are unusual (Figure 3.2). Two hydrogen atoms are combined with an oxygen atom by sharing of electrons (covalent bonding, page 476). The three atoms form a triangle, not a straight line. Within the molecule the oxygen nucleus draws electrons (negatively charged) away from the hydrogen nuclei (positively charged). So overall the water molecule is electrically neutral, but there is a net negative charge on the oxygen atom and a net positive charge on both the hydrogen atoms. A molecule carrying such an unequal distribution of electrical charge is called a **polar molecule**.

Figure 3.2
The water molecule and its hydrogen bonds.

one oxygen atom combines with two hydrogen atoms by sharing electrons (covalent bond)

↓

in the water molecule the oxygen nucleus draws electrons (negatively charged) away from the hydrogen nucleus (positively charged)

↓

the water molecule carries an **unequal distribution of electrical charge**, even though overall it is electrically neutral

↓

polar water molecule

↓

there is electrostatic attraction between the positively charged region of one water molecule and the negatively charged region of a neighbouring one, giving rise to weak bonds called **hydrogen bonds**

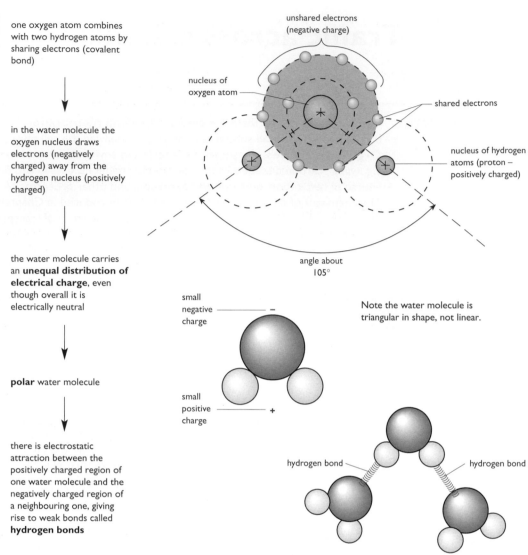

unshared electrons (negative charge)

nucleus of oxygen atom

shared electrons

nucleus of hydrogen atoms (proton – positively charged)

angle about 105°

small negative charge –

small positive charge +

Note the water molecule is triangular in shape, not linear.

hydrogen bond   hydrogen bond

Hydrogen bonding in water

The positively charged hydrogen atoms of one water molecule are attracted to the negatively charged oxygen atoms of nearby water molecules by forces called **hydrogen bonds**. We have already seen that hydrogen bonds also occur in certain organic molecules, including proteins (Figure 2.21, page 40), the DNA double helix (Figure 2.30, page 47) and cellulose (Figure 2.8, page 31).

Hydrogen bonds are weaker than covalent bonds. But they are strong enough to hold water molecules together. Because of their hydrogen bonds, water molecules are attracted to charged particles or charged surfaces. In fact, hydrogen bonds largely account for the unique properties of water. We will examine these properties next.

Water is a liquid

Water has a relative molecular mass of only 18, yet it is a liquid at room temperature. This is surprising; it contrasts with most other small molecules, which are usually gases. Examples include methane (CH_4), with a relative molecular mass of 16, ammonia (NH_3), 17, and carbon dioxide (CO_2), 44. But none of these other molecules contain hydrogen bonds.

In gases, molecules are widely spaced and free to move about independently. In liquids, molecules are closer together. In water, hydrogen bonds pull the molecules very close to each other, which is why water is a liquid at the temperatures and pressures that exist over much of the Earth's surface. So we have the liquid medium for life.

Heat energy and the temperature of water

A lot of heat energy is required to raise the temperature of water. This is because much energy is needed to break the hydrogen bonds that restrict the movements of water molecules. This property of water is known as its **specific heat capacity**. The specific heat capacity of water is the highest of any known substance. Consequently, aquatic environments like streams and rivers, ponds, lakes and seas are all very slow to change temperature when the surrounding air temperature changes. Aquatic environments have more stable temperatures than terrestrial (land) environments do.

Another consequence is that cells and the bodies of organisms do not change temperature readily. Bulky organisms particularly tend to have a stable body temperature in the face of a fluctuating surrounding temperature, whether in extremes of heat or cold.

Evaporation and heat loss

The hydrogen bonds between water molecules make it difficult for them to be separated and vaporised (i.e. evaporated). This means that much energy is needed to turn liquid water into water vapour (a gas). This amount of energy is known as the **latent heat of vaporisation**, and for water it is very high. Consequently, the evaporation of water in sweat on the skin, or in transpiration from green leaves, causes marked cooling because the escaping molecules take a lot of energy with them. You experience this when you stand in a draught after a shower. And since a great deal of heat is lost with the evaporation of a small amount of water, cooling by evaporation of water is economical on water too.

Heat energy and freezing

The amount of heat energy needed to melt ice is very high, and the amount of heat that must be removed from water to turn it to ice is also great. This amount of heat energy is known as the **latent heat of fusion**. Again, it is very high for water. This means that both the contents of cells and the water in the environment are slow to freeze when it is very cold.

The density of ice

Most liquids contract on cooling, reaching their **maximum density** at their freezing point. Water is unusual in reaching its maximum density at 4 °C. So as water freezes, the ice formed is less dense than the cold water around it. The ice floats on top (Figure 3.3). The floating layer of ice insulates the water below. This is why the bulk of ponds, lakes or the sea rarely freeze solid. Aquatic life can generally survive a freeze-up.

Figure 3.3 Ice forms on the surface of water.

Because ice freezes from below, it is difficult to judge its depth. It can therefore be very dangerous to walk on!

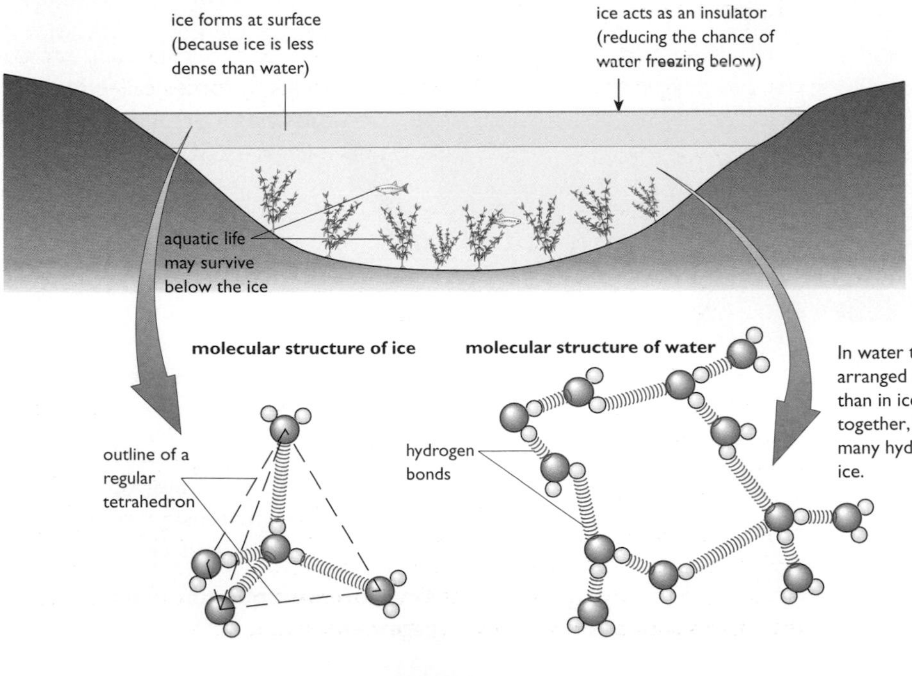

The angle between the covalent bonds in the water molecule is very close to the angles of a perfect tetrahedron. In ice the molecules form a regular tetrahedral arrangement, and are spaced more widely apart than they are in liquid water.

In water the molecules are arranged more irregularly than in ice and are closer together, but with almost as many hydrogen bonds as in ice.

Figure 3.4
A pond skater (*Gerris* species) moving over a water surface. The photograph shows the interference patterns created by the water's surface tension.

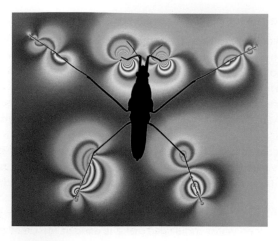

Water molecules at surfaces

The outermost molecules of water form hydrogen bonds with water molecules below them. This gives a very high **surface tension** to water – higher than that of any other liquid except mercury. Surface tension is exploited by insects that 'surface skate' (Figure 3.4). The insect's waxy cuticle prevents wetting of its body, and the mass of the insect is not great enough to break through the surface.

Viscosity

Below the surface, water molecules slide past each other very easily. We say that water has a low **viscosity**. As a result, water flows readily through narrow capillaries.

Adherence and tension resistance

Figure 3.5
Water is drawn up a tree trunk.

Water adheres strongly to most surfaces and can be drawn up into long columns through narrow tubes like the xylem vessels of plant stems, without the water column breaking (Figure 3.5). Compared with other liquids, water has extremely strong **adhesive and cohesive properties** that prevent the column breaking under tension.

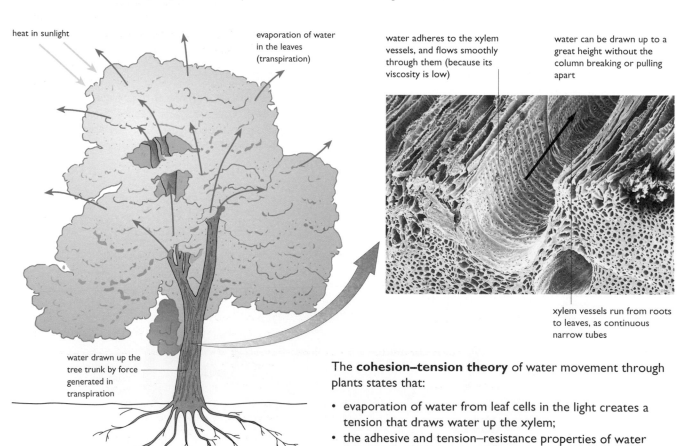

heat in sunlight

evaporation of water in the leaves (transpiration)

water adheres to the xylem vessels, and flows smoothly through them (because its viscosity is low)

water can be drawn up to a great height without the column breaking or pulling apart

xylem vessels run from roots to leaves, as continuous narrow tubes

water drawn up the tree trunk by force generated in transpiration

water taken from soil by root cells

The **cohesion–tension theory** of water movement through plants states that:

* evaporation of water from leaf cells in the light creates a tension that draws water up the xylem;
* the adhesive and tension–resistance properties of water maintain a continuous column of water throughout the plant.

The movement of water in plants is discussed in Chapter 11, page 244.

Ionic compounds like NaCl dissolve in water,

$$NaCl \rightleftharpoons Na^+ + Cl^-$$

with a shell of orientated water molecules around each ion:

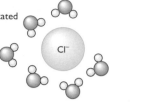

Sugars and alcohols dissolve due to hydrogen bonding between polar groups in their molecules (e.g. —OH) and the polar water molecules:

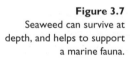

Figure 3.6
Water as solvent.

I In an aqueous solution of glucose, which component is the solvent and which is the solute?

Figure 3.7
Seaweed can survive at depth, and helps to support a marine fauna.

Water as a solvent

Water is a powerful solvent for polar substances. These include ionic substances like sodium chloride (Na^+ and Cl^-, page 477), and also organic molecules with ionised groups (such as the carboxyl group —COO^-, and amino group —NH_3^+, page 37). These cations (negatively charged ions) and anions (positively charged ions) become surrounded by a shell of orientated water molecules (Figure 3.6). Soluble organic molecules like sugars dissolve in water due to the formation of hydrogen bonds between the water molecules and the slightly charged hydroxyl (—OH) groups in these organic molecules.

Once dissolved, the molecules of a substance (now referred to as the **solute** dissolved in the **solvent** – water) are free to move around. This makes them more reactive chemically than when they form part of an undissolved solid. At the same time, non-polar substances are repelled by water, as in the case of oil on the surface of water. Non-polar substances are hydrophobic (water-hating).

Water is transparent

Because light penetrates water, aquatic photosynthetic plants can live at some depth. These plants support aquatic food chains, and therefore animal life (Figure 3.7). Light aids sight in aquatic animals.

A summary of the life-giving properties of water is given in Table 3.1.

Table 3.1
Water and life, a summary.

Property	Benefit to life
a liquid at room temperature, water dissolves more substances than any other common liquid	liquid medium for living things and for the chemistry of life
much heat energy needed to raise the temperature of water	aquatic environment slow to change temperature; bulky organisms have stable temperatures
evaporation of water requires a great deal of heat	evaporation causes marked cooling; much heat is lost by evaporation of a small quantity of water
much heat has to be removed before water freezes	cell contents and water in aquatic environments are slow to freeze in cold weather
ice is at maximum density at 4 °C	ice forms on the surface of water, insulating the water below, and allowing much aquatic life to survive freezing
surface water molecules orientate with hydrogen bonds formed inwards	certain animals exploit surface tension to move over water surfaces
water molecules slide past each other easily	water flows easily through narrow capillaries (low viscosity)
water molecules adhere to surfaces	water adheres to walls of xylem vessels as it is drawn up the stem to the leaves, from the roots
water column does not easily break or pull apart under tension	water can be lifted by forces applied at the top, and so can be drawn up xylem vessel of tree trunk by force generated in transpiration from leaves
water is transparent	aquatic plants can photosynthesise at some depth in water

Mineral elements

'Minerals' are inorganic elements, some of which are needed by organisms. In some minerals such as sodium chloride, **ionic bonding** occurs. In ionic bonding one or more electrons are transferred completely from one atom to another, to produce a stable arrangement of electrons. Ionic bonding transforms reactive atoms into stable ions. Ionic bonding in sodium chloride is shown in Figure A3 (page 477). Ionic bonding and the formation of ions contrast with covalent bonding, which is shown in water (see Figure 3.2) and methane (see Figure A2, page 477).

Essential minerals

Living things need a wide range of inorganic ions, but only a handful of them in relatively large quantities. These are known as the **major mineral elements**. Some are in the form of **cations**, like calcium (Ca^{2+}), iron (Fe^{2+} and Fe^{3+}) and magnesium (Mg^{2+}). Others are needed in the form of **anions**, like phosphate ($H_2PO_4^-$), nitrate (NO_3^-) and sulphate (SO_4^{2-}).

Table 3.2
The principal mineral elements required by organisms.

Element	Form obtained by plants	Sources for animals	Functions
Major minerals:			
nitrogen (N)	nitrate and ammonium ions	lean meat, fish, beans	synthesis of proteins from amino acids; synthesis of many other important compounds, e.g. chlorophyll, coenzymes
phosphorus (P)	phosphate ions	milk, eggs, cheese, peanuts	synthesis of nucleic acids, ATP and phospholipids; built into bone
sulphur (S)	sulphate ions	proteins in meat, fish and milk	synthesis of proteins, e.g. keratin; in other compounds, e.g. coenzyme A
calcium (Ca)	calcium ions	milk, cheese, bread, watercress	middle lamella formation between plant cells; constituent of bone; used in muscle contraction, impulse transmission across synapse, blood clotting
magnesium (Mg)	magnesium ions	green vegetables	part of the chlorophyll molecule; cofactor of many enzymes
potassium (K)	potassium ions	vegetables, coffee	involved with Na^+ in membrane function; nerve impulse transport; stomatal opening
sodium (Na)	sodium ions	salted foods	involved with potassium in membrane function and impulse transport
chlorine (Cl)	chloride ions	salted foods	osmotic relations of cells; production of HCl acid in stomach
Micronutrients:			
iron (Fe)	iron compounds	meat, eggs, vegetables	part of haem group in haemoglobin and myoglobin; electron-transport molecules, e.g. cytochromes; involved in chlorophyll synthesis
manganese (Mn)	manganese compounds	vegetables	component of specific enzymes; involved in bone development
copper (Cu)	copper compounds	meat, bread, cereals	activates specific enzymes; haemoglobin formation; melanin production; electron-transport molecules of photosynthesis
cobalt (Co)	cobalt compounds	meat, milk, eggs	as vitamin B_{12}; in cell division, e.g. red cell formation
zinc (Zn)	zinc compounds	meat, milk, cheese, bread	component of specific enzymes, e.g. alcohol dehydrogenase, carbonic anhydrase (enhances CO_2 transport in blood plasma)
molybdenum (Mo)	molybdenum compounds	[not needed]	component of enzymes of amino acid synthesis, and of enzyme of nitrogen fixation in *Rhizobium* (bacterium)
boron (B)	boron compounds	[not needed]	required in cell division processes in plants
fluorine (F)	[not needed]	milk, locally in water supply	component of bones and teeth (enamel)
iodine (I)	[not needed]	sea foods, salt	constituent of thyroxine (hormone controlling basal metabolic rate)

The roles of major mineral elements may be as components of the **structure** of essential substances. These include calcium in bones and as a part of plant cell walls, phosphates in nucleic acid and ATP, and nitrogen and sulphur in amino acids, peptides and proteins. Iron forms a part of haemoglobin, and magnesium of chlorophyll. Some major elements also play a part in the **activities** of cells. For example, potassium, sodium and chloride ions are involved in the transmission of nerve impulses. Calcium ions have an essential role in the transmission of impulses at the synapse, and in the contraction of muscles.

Many other inorganic elements are required in tiny amounts only. These are referred to as trace elements or **micronutrients**. Examples include ions of metals like copper (Cu^{2+}) and zinc (Zn^{2+}), and ions of non-metals like iodide (I^-) and molybdate (MoO_4^{2-}).

Many micronutrients act as **cofactors** in the catalytic activity of certain enzymes (page 73). The essential inorganic elements and their main uses are reviewed in Table 3.2.

The structure of the plasma membrane

Cell membranes are made almost entirely of protein and lipid, together with a small and variable amount of carbohydrate. How are these components assembled into the plasma membrane?

The lipid of membranes is **phospholipid**. The chemical structure of phospholipid is shown in Figure 2.14 (page 35). Look at its structure again now. This molecule has a 'head' composed of a glycerol group to which is attached an ionised phosphate group. This gives this part of the phospholipid molecule **hydrophilic properties** (water-loving). For example, hydrogen bonds readily form between the phosphate head and water molecules. Also attached to the glycerol are two long, fatty acid residues, composed of hydrocarbon chains. These hydrocarbon 'tails' have **hydrophobic properties** (water-hating). A small quantity of phospholipid in contact with water will float with the hydrocarbon tails exposed above the water, forming a monolayer of phospholipid (Figure 3.8). If more phospholipid is added, the molecules arrange themselves as a bilayer, with the hydrocarbon tails facing together. This latter arrangement is the situation in the plasma membrane, for the basis of the plasma membrane is a **lipid bilayer** (Figure 3.9).

The proteins of cell membranes are globular proteins. They are buried in and across the lipid bilayer, and most protrude above the surfaces. These proteins include enzymes, receptors and antigens.

The carbohydrate molecules are relatively short-chain polysaccharides. Some are attached to the proteins (glycoproteins) and some to the lipids (glycolipids). Glycoproteins and glycolipids are only found on the outer surface of the cell membrane.

This membrane is described as a **fluid mosaic** (Figure 3.10): 'fluid' because the whole structure (lipids and proteins) is on the move, and 'mosaic' because the proteins are scattered about in this pattern. This is the currently accepted view of the structure of the cell membrane.

The composition of the **glycocalyx** (this is the name given to the glycoproteins and glycolipids of the fluid mosaic membrane) varies from one cell type to another. The glycocalyx probably has several different functions in the working membrane, and these variations may reflect these differences. The functions of the glycocalyx may be summarised as follows:

- cell–cell recognition (the components functioning as antigens, for example)
- as receptor sites for chemical signals, such as hormone messengers
- assisting in the binding together of cells to form tissues.

> **2** What is the difference between a lipid bilayer and the 'double membrane' of many organelles?

Figure 3.8
Phospholipid molecules.

a phospholipid molecule has a **hydrophobic tail** – which repels water – and a **hydrophilic head** – which attracts water

in contact with water forming a monolayer

mixing with water to form a bilayer

Phospholipid molecules in contact with water form a **monolayer**, with the heads dissolved in the water and the tails sticking outwards.

When mixed with water, phospholipid molecules arrange themselves into a **bilayer**, in which the hydrophobic tails are attracted to each other.

Figure 3.9
Cell membrane structure:
evidence from the electron
microscope.

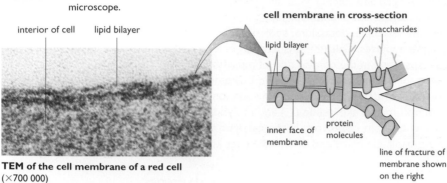

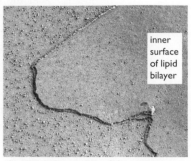

electron micrograph of the cell
membrane (freeze-etched)

TEM of the cell membrane of a red cell
(×700 000)

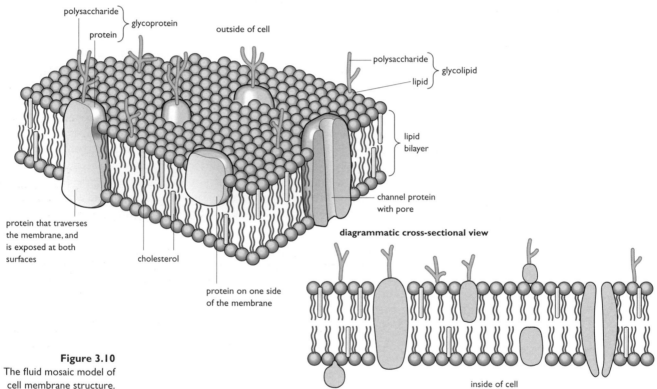

Figure 3.10
The fluid mosaic model of
cell membrane structure.

Movement across membranes

The plasma membrane is the boundary to the cytoplasm, but it is not inert. It is a genuine organelle, and is very active in the regulation of transport of molecules.

All living cells are immediately surrounded by water, whether plant or animal cells, or unicellular organisms. For example, although flowering plant cells are contained within a cellulose cell wall, the spaces within this wall (about 50% of the wall volume) are filled with a very dilute solution of ions and other substances (**tissue fluid**). This solution bathes the cell membrane, too. In mammals the outermost layer of the body consists of dead cells, but below this dead skin are living cells. Living cells are all bathed in tissue fluid.

So all transport of substances into and out of cells occurs in solution. For example, although the oxygen we breathe is a gas, it dissolves in a surface film of water before it passes into the blood capillaries of the lungs. Once in solution, substances may enter cells by various mechanisms. These are summarised in Figure 3.11. They are considered in the following sections.

Figure 3.11
Mechanisms of movement
across membranes.

All three mechanisms can cause movement in either direction – *and* simultaneously!

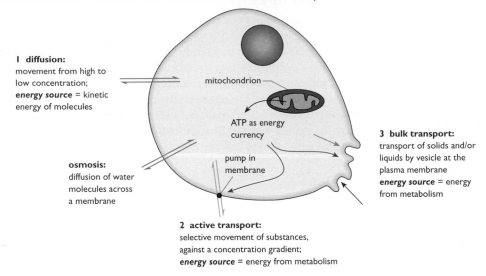

1 diffusion:
movement from high to
low concentration;
energy source = kinetic
energy of molecules

mitochondrion

ATP as energy
currency

3 bulk transport:
transport of solids and/or
liquids by vesicle at the
plasma membrane
energy source = energy
from metabolism

osmosis:
diffusion of water
molecules across
a membrane

pump in
membrane

2 active transport:
selective movement of substances,
against a concentration gradient;
energy source = energy from metabolism

Movement by diffusion

The atoms, molecules and ions of liquids and gases are in continuous random motion. These movements result in the even distribution of the components of gas mixtures and, given time, of ions in solution. For example, we can take a small sample of a solution and analyse it to find the concentration of dissolved substances in the *whole* solution. Similarly, every breath we take has in it the same proportions of oxygen, nitrogen and carbon dioxide as the atmosphere as a whole.

Where there is a difference in concentration between parts of a gas or a liquid, random movements carry particles (atoms, molecules or ions) from a region of high concentration to one of lower concentration. As a result, the particles become evenly dispersed. We call this transport and mixing of particles **diffusion**. We say that the energy for diffusion comes from the **kinetic energy** of the particles. 'Kinetic' means that a particle has this energy because it is in continuous motion.

Diffusion in a liquid can be illustrated by adding a crystal of a coloured mineral to distilled water (Figure 3.12). Even without stirring, the ions become evenly distributed throughout the water. The process takes time, of course, especially as the solid has first to be dissolved.

Figure 3.12
Diffusion in a liquid
demonstrated.

1 A crystal of potassium permanganate (potassium manganate(VII), $KMnO_4$) is placed in distilled water.

2 As the ions dissolve, random movements disperse them throughout the water.

3 The ions become evenly distributed. Random movements continue, but there is now no net movement in any particular direction.

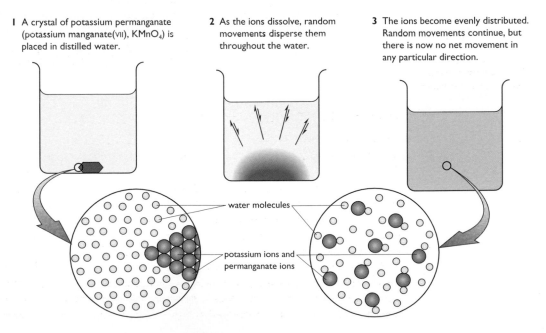

water molecules

potassium ions and
permanganate ions

Diffusion in cells

Diffusion occurs across the cell membrane where the membrane is fully **permeable** to the solute (that is, the solute can cross it without any difficulty), or where the pores in the membrane are large enough for a solute to pass through (Figure 3.13). For example, the lipid bilayer of the plasma membrane is permeable to non-polar substances like steroids and glycerol, and also to gases like oxygen and carbon dioxide in solution. All these diffuse via this route. Water diffuses across the plasma membrane too, but passes via the protein-lined pores of the membrane (Figure 3.16, page 64). It can also diffuse via tiny spaces between the phospholipid molecules, especially where the fluid mosaic membrane is rich in phospholipids with unsaturated hydrocarbon tails (Figure 2.14, page 35). This is because in these regions the membrane is especially leaky.

Figure 3.13
Diffusion across a cell membrane.

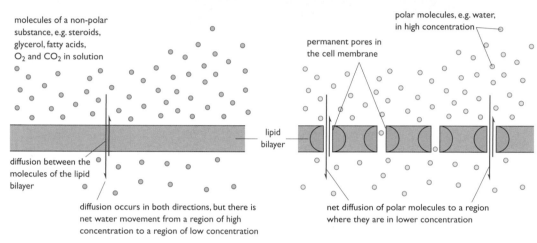

Facilitated diffusion

In facilitated diffusion, substances that might otherwise not diffuse across the membrane at all are enabled to do so by the action of a particular molecule in the membrane. This is a large molecule that forms itself into a pore of a size large enough to allow a particular substance to diffuse through it. The pore forms in the presence of that substance, and it closes when the substance is no longer present (Figure 3.14). The pore-forming substance is most likely to be a globular protein. In facilitated diffusion the energy comes from the kinetic energy of the molecules involved, as is the case in all forms of diffusion. Energy from metabolism is not required.

Important examples of facilitated diffusion include the movement of ADP into mitochondria and the exit of ATP from mitochondria (Chapter 8). Others include the movements of K^+ and Na^+ ions in the establishment of a resting potential before an impulse may be transmitted along a nerve fibre (page 277).

Figure 3.14
Facilitated diffusion.

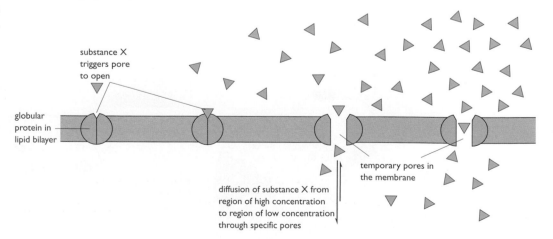

Osmosis, a special case of diffusion

Osmosis is the diffusion of water molecules across a membrane that is partially permeable. Since water makes up 70–90% of living cells, and cell membranes are partially permeable membranes, osmosis is very important in biology.

Firstly, *why does osmosis happen?*

Dissolved substances attract a 'cloud' of polar water molecules around them. The 'cloud' is held by weak chemical bonds, including hydrogen bonds. Consequently, these water molecules cannot move freely. Organic substances like sugars, amino acids, polypeptides and proteins, as well as inorganic ions like Na^+, K^+, Cl^- and NO_3^-, all have this effect on the water molecules around them.

The stronger the solution (that is, the more solute it contains per volume of water), the larger is the number of water molecules that are slowed up and held. So, in a very concentrated solution, very many more of the water molecules have restricted movements than in a dilute solution. On the other hand, in pure water *all* the water molecules are free to move about randomly, and do so.

When a solution is separated from water (or from a more dilute solution) by a membrane permeable to water molecules, those water molecules on the move tend to diffuse. Dissolved particles and their 'cloud' of water molecules move very much less. So there is a net flow of water from pure water (or a weaker solution) across the membrane into a more concentrated solution. The membrane is said to be **partially permeable**.

Osmosis is a special case of diffusion, and can be defined as the net movement of water (the solvent) from a solution of high concentration of water molecules to a region of lower concentration of water molecules, across a partially permeable membrane (Figure 3.15).

Figure 3.15 Osmosis.

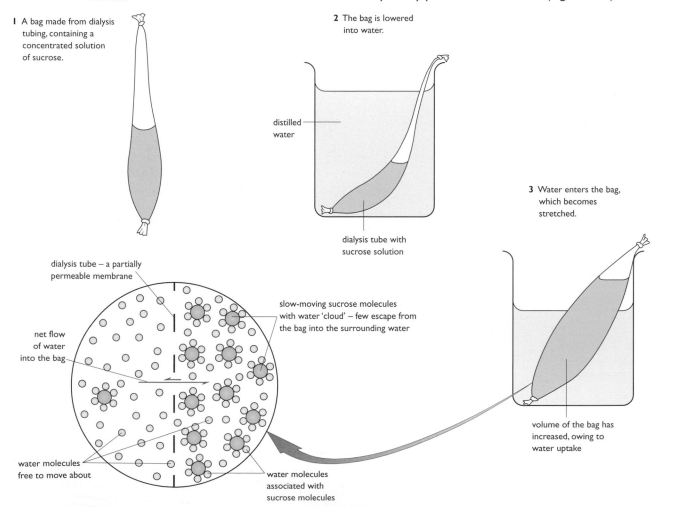

1 A bag made from dialysis tubing, containing a concentrated solution of sucrose.

2 The bag is lowered into water.

distilled water

dialysis tube with sucrose solution

3 Water enters the bag, which becomes stretched.

volume of the bag has increased, owing to water uptake

dialysis tube – a partially permeable membrane

net flow of water into the bag

slow-moving sucrose molecules with water 'cloud' – few escape from the bag into the surrounding water

water molecules free to move about

water molecules associated with sucrose molecules

3 Jam is made of equal weights of fruit and sucrose. What happens to a fungal spore that germinates after landing on jam?

Theoretically, the lipid bilayer of the plasma membrane is impermeable to water molecules, because they are polar. Yet water does enter and leave cells by osmosis (Figure 3.16). Water molecules are very small, however, and it is likely that tiny spaces open between the giant molecules of the lipid bilayer – which, you remember, are constantly moving about. In addition, quite small, protein-lined pores exist in the cell membrane and are permanently open. These spaces and the pores allow unrestricted water movement at all times.

We will look at the factors that affect osmosis.

Figure 3.16
How polar water molecules cross the lipid bilayer.

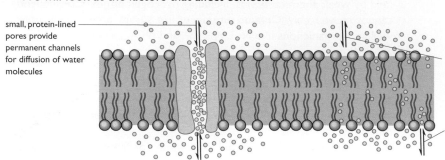

small, protein-lined pores provide permanent channels for diffusion of water molecules

molecules of the lipid bilayer are always on the move, producing tiny (short-lived) pores that are large enough for water molecules to pass through

Solute potential

We have seen that it is the presence of dissolved molecules in a solution that causes osmosis. The effect of the amount of dissolved solute present is known as the **solute potential** of the solution. It is given the symbol ψ_s. (Solute potential was previously referred to as osmotic pressure or osmotic potential, but these terms have now been abandoned.)

Using a simple osmometer as shown in Figure 3.17, we can demonstrate the solute potential of a solution. Once the osmometer is lowered into the beaker of water, very many more water molecules stream across the membrane into the solution and few move in the opposite direction. The solution is diluted by the inflow of water, and the level rises up the attached tube. Osmometers of this sort could be used to compare solute potentials of solutions with different concentrations.

Figure 3.17
An osmometer to demonstrate solute potential.

Pressure potential

The other factor to influence osmosis is mechanical pressure acting on the solution. This factor is given the name of **pressure potential** and is represented by the symbol ψ_p. (Pressure potential was previously referred to as turgor pressure, but this term has now been abandoned.) If a pressure greater than atmospheric pressure is applied to a solution, then this is an example of a pressure potential being created in a solution.

Pressure potentials of solutions or pure water are usually positive; that is, an external pressure is applied to the water/solution, literally pushing on it. But in the water-conducting tubes (xylem vessels) of the stems of plants in the sunlight, a water column is drawn up the stem by the leaves. This is because water is lost from the leaves by evaporation (Figure 3.5, page 56). Under these conditions the water column is under tension, and the pressure potential is negative.

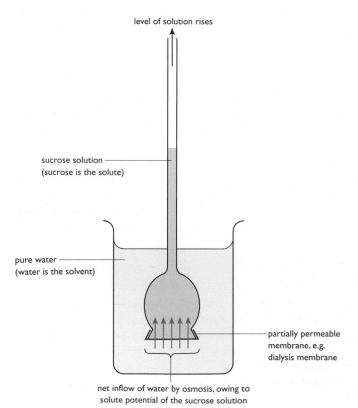

level of solution rises

sucrose solution (sucrose is the solute)

pure water (water is the solvent)

partially permeable membrane, e.g. dialysis membrane

net inflow of water by osmosis, owing to solute potential of the sucrose solution

In Figure 3.18, a short length of dialysis tube has been set up to show how the pressure potential of a sucrose solution can be large enough to stop the osmotic uptake of water altogether.

Figure 3.18
Pressure potential at work.

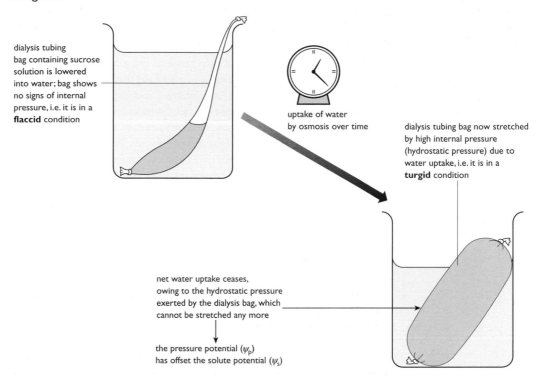

dialysis tubing bag containing sucrose solution is lowered into water; bag shows no signs of internal pressure, i.e. it is in a **flaccid** condition

uptake of water by osmosis over time

dialysis tubing bag now stretched by high internal pressure (hydrostatic pressure) due to water uptake, i.e. it is in a **turgid** condition

net water uptake ceases, owing to the hydrostatic pressure exerted by the dialysis bag, which cannot be stretched any more

the pressure potential (ψ_p) has offset the solute potential (ψ_s)

Water potential = solute potential + pressure potential

The concept of 'water potential' allows the effects of the two factors acting on water in a system (such as a dialysis tubing 'bag' or a living cell) to be brought together in a single equation:

$$\text{water potential} = \text{solute potential} + \text{pressure potential}$$
$$\psi = \psi_s + \psi_p$$

The **water potential** of a solution is the name we give to this tendency of water molecules to enter or leave the solution by osmosis. 'Water potential' is really a measure of the free kinetic energy of the water molecules, and the Greek letter *psi* (symbol ψ) is used to represent the water potential.

Pure water obviously has the highest water potential. By definition, this is set at zero. We have also seen that once a solute is dissolved in water, the water molecules are immediately *less* likely to diffuse (they are less mobile). So the effect of dissolving a solute in water is to *lower* its water potential, making it *more negative*. Consequently solutions at atmospheric pressure have a *negative value* of water potential, and the more concentrated the solution the *more negative* is its water potential. For example, a solution containing:

3.42 g of sucrose in 100 cm³ has a water potential of −270 kPa, and
34.2 g of sucrose in 100 cm³ has a water potential of −3510 kPa.

Do negative values like these give you problems? Not really, perhaps. You use them frequently in daily life. Imagine an international weather forecast that reports that the temperature in Siberia has changed from −10 °C to −25 °C. You immediately know this means it's turned much colder there. In other words, −25 °C is a much lower temperature than −10 °C, even though 25 is a larger number than 10.

In the same way −3510 kPa is a smaller water potential than −270 kPa, although 3510 is a larger number than 270.

4 When a concentrated solution of glucose is separated from a dilute solution of glucose by a partially permeable membrane:
a which solution has a higher water potential?
b which solution has a higher concentration of water molecules?
c which solution will show a net gain of water molecules?

Osmosis in plants

First consider osmosis in a single plant cell, with its cellulose cell wall (Figure 3.19). Whether the net direction of water movement is into or out of a plant cell depends upon whether the water potential of the cell solution is more or less negative than that of the external solution.

When the water potential of the external solution is **less negative** (that is, little or no dissolved solutes), there is a net flow of water into the cell. The cell solution becomes diluted. The cytoplasm is expanded by water uptake, and may come to press hard against the cell wall. If this happens the cell is described as **turgid**. The pressure potential that develops (due to the stretching of the wall) offsets the solute potential of the cell solution, and further net uptake of water stops. Incidentally, the cell wall has protected the delicate cell contents from damage due to osmosis.

When the water potential of the external solution is **more negative** (that is, much dissolved solutes), there is a net flow of water out of the cell. The cell solution becomes more concentrated. As the volume of cell solution decreases, the cytoplasm pulls away from parts of the cell wall (contact with the cell wall is maintained at points where there are cytoplasmic connections with neighbouring cells). The cells are said to be **plasmolysed** (from cyto*plasm* + *lysis* = splitting).

Figure 3.19
A plant cell in changing external solutions.

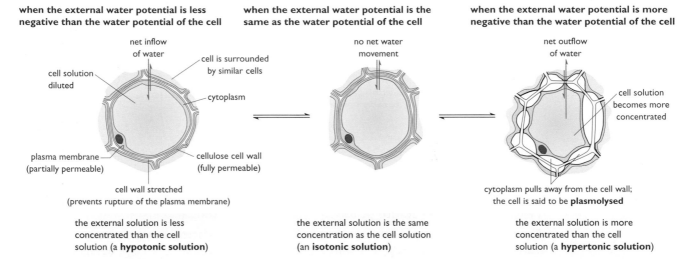

when the external water potential is less negative than the water potential of the cell

net inflow of water
cell solution diluted
cell is surrounded by similar cells
cytoplasm
plasma membrane (partially permeable)
cellulose cell wall (fully permeable)
cell wall stretched (prevents rupture of the plasma membrane)

the external solution is less concentrated than the cell solution (a **hypotonic solution**)

when the external water potential is the same as the water potential of the cell

no net water movement

the external solution is the same concentration as the cell solution (an **isotonic solution**)

when the external water potential is more negative than the water potential of the cell

net outflow of water
cell solution becomes more concentrated
cytoplasm pulls away from the cell wall; the cell is said to be **plasmolysed**

the external solution is more concentrated than the cell solution (a **hypertonic solution**)

Figure 3.20
Plasmolysed plant cells.

In the cells of the epidermis of the leaf stalk of rhubarb (*Rheum rhaponticum*) the solutions in the vacuoles are coloured. They can be seen under the microscope without staining. → When they are placed in a solution of water potential greater than that of the cell solution, plasmolysis of the cells can be observed by microscopy.

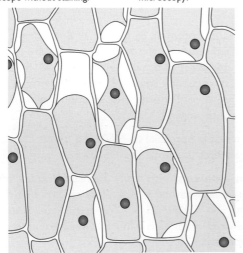

An external solution that causes plasmolysis in 50% of the cells (incipient plasmolysis) has the same water potential as that of the cells.

Plasmolysis is most easily observed in cells that have a coloured solution in their vacuoles. It can be seen in beetroot tissue or the epidermis of rhubarb leaf stalks (Figure 3.20). In the plasmolysed cell the wall exerts no pressure at all (pressure potential = 0). As a plasmolysed cell starts to take up water the contents enlarge. At the point where the cytoplasm starts to push against the wall, a slight pressure potential is produced (Figure 3.21). As water uptake continues, the pressure potential eventually becomes large enough to reduce the cell's water potential to zero. Water uptake stops.

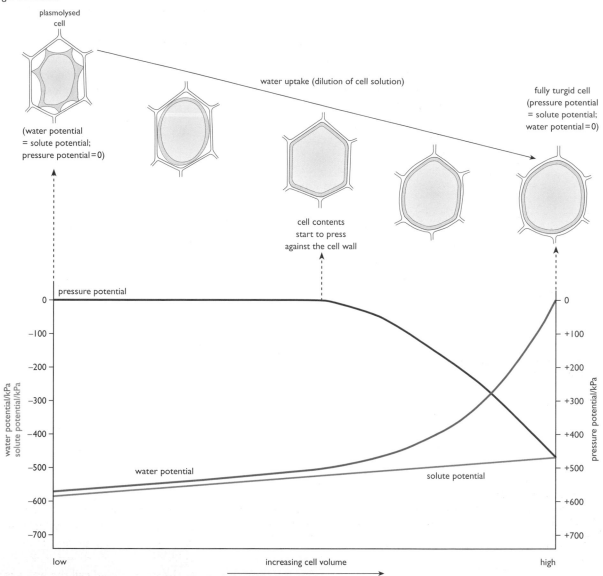

Figure 3.21
Changing water potential of a plant cell, from flaccid to turgid condition.

plasmolysed cell

water uptake (dilution of cell solution)

fully turgid cell
(pressure potential
= solute potential;
water potential = 0)

(water potential
= solute potential;
pressure potential = 0)

cell contents
start to press
against the cell wall

pressure potential

water potential/kPa
solute potential/kPa

pressure potential/kPa

water potential

solute potential

low   increasing cell volume   high

well-watered potted plant with turgid cells

water loss continues; many cells of the leaves and stem become plasmolysed; flaccid cells provide no support

Plasmolysis and wilting

The cytoplasm of plant cells is largely undamaged by a period of plasmolysis. The cells promptly recover when water becomes available. In non-woody plants (they are called **herbaceous plants**, to tell them apart from trees and shrubs), a state of turgor is the normal condition. The turgidity of all the cells plays a key part in support of the plant body. If a herbaceous plant becomes short of water for a while, it wilts. A wilted plant will die if it does not receive water (Figure 3.22).

Figure 3.22
Wilting of an herbaceous plant.

Osmosis in animals

An animal cell lacks the protection of a cellulose wall. Compared with a plant cell, it is far more easily damaged by changes in the external solution. If a typical animal cell is placed in pure water, it will quite quickly disintegrate from the pressure potential generated. Figure 3.23 shows what happens to an animal cell (a red blood cell) when the external solution has a water potential that is either less negative or more negative than the cell solution.

In most animals these problems are avoided because the osmotic concentrations of body fluids (blood plasma and tissue fluid) are very precisely regulated. The same water potential is maintained both inside and outside the body cells. This process is a part of **osmoregulation** (Chapter 12, page 263).

Figure 3.23
A red cell in changing external solutions.

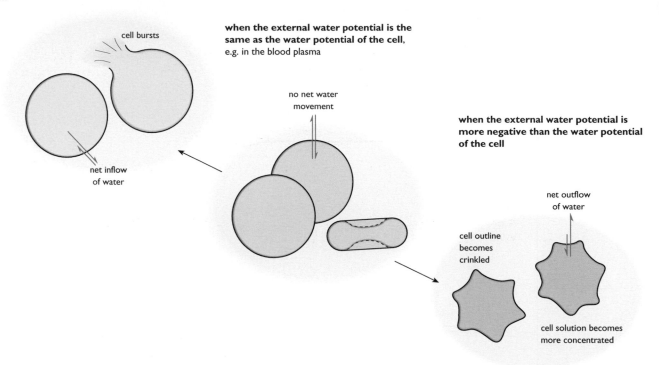

when the external water potential is less negative than the water potential of the cell

cell bursts

net inflow of water

when the external water potential is the same as the water potential of the cell, e.g. in the blood plasma

no net water movement

when the external water potential is more negative than the water potential of the cell

net outflow of water

cell outline becomes crinkled

cell solution becomes more concentrated

Figure 3.24
Amoeba, the role of the contractile vacuole.

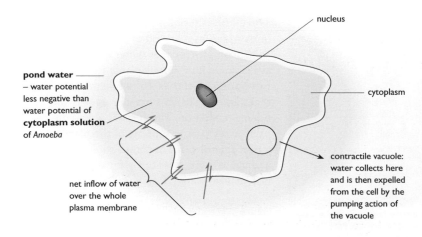

nucleus

cytoplasm

pond water – water potential less negative than water potential of **cytoplasm solution** of *Amoeba*

net inflow of water over the whole plasma membrane

contractile vacuole: water collects here and is then expelled from the cell by the pumping action of the vacuole

Aquatic unicellular animals

Many unicellular animals live in water, and survive even though their surroundings normally have a water potential that is much less negative than the cell solution. All the time, water is flowing into these animals by osmosis. They are in constant danger that their plasma membrane will burst because of the rising pressure inside it.

One example of such an animal is the protozoan *Amoeba*. In fact, the cytoplasm of amoebae contains a tiny water pump, known as a **contractile vacuole**. This works continuously to pump out the excess water. How important the contractile vacuole is to the organism is fatally demonstrated if the cytoplasm is temporarily anaesthetised. The *Amoeba* quickly disintegrates (Figure 3.24).

● **Extension**   Calculating the water potential of cells

You can tackle the following calculations using the formula:

water potential = solute potential + pressure potential
$$\psi \quad = \quad \psi_s \quad + \quad \psi_p$$

Case one

Plant tissue has been immersed in water overnight. Cells in the tissue are found to have a solution potential (ψ_s) of -600 kPa.
Can their water pressure potential be calculated?

Answer:
Yes! Plant tissue that has stood in water overnight will be fully turgid.
(So much so, it will be brittle to handle and snap easily if bent.)
Turgid cells have a water potential (ψ) of 0.

$\psi = \psi_s + \psi_p$,
$0 = -600$ kPa $+ ?$
Therefore $\psi_p = +600$ kPa

Here the cell will have a pressure potential (ψ_p) of $+600$ kPa

Case two

A plasmolysed plant cell is found to have a solute potential (ψ_s) of -750 kPa.
What is the water potential (ψ) of this cell?

Answer:
Since the cell is plasmolysed, its pressure potential (ψ_p) $= 0$.
From the equation $\psi = \psi_s + \psi_p$, $\psi = -750$ kPa.

Case three

Two adjacent animal cells, M and N, are part of a compact tissue. They have:

	cell M	cell N
solute potential (ψ_s)	-580 kPa	-640 kPa
pressure potential (ψ_p)	$+410$ kPa	$+420$ kPa

Will net water flow be from cell M to cell N?

Answer:
First work out the water potential of each cell.

M: $\psi = -580 + 410$ **N:** $\psi = -640 + 420$
$\psi = -170$ kPa $\psi = -220$ kPa

Net water flow will be from cell M to cell N, because water flows
from a less negative to a more negative water potential.

Movement by active transport

In active transport metabolic energy produced by the cell, held as ATP, is used to drive the transport of molecules and ions across cell membranes. There are marked differences between active transport and movement by diffusion.

1 **Active transport occurs against a concentration gradient**, that is, from a region of low to a region of higher concentration. The cytosol of a cell normally holds some reserves of molecules valuable in metabolism, like nitrate ions in plant cells, or calcium ions in muscle fibres. The reserves of useful molecules and ions do not escape; the cell membrane retains them inside the cell. Yet when more of the useful molecules or ions become available for uptake, they are actively absorbed into the cells. This happens even though the concentration outside is lower than inside.

2 **Active uptake is highly selective**. For example, in a situation where potassium chloride (K^+ and Cl^- ions) is available to an animal cell, K^+ ions are more likely to be absorbed, since they are needed by the cell. Where sodium nitrate (Na^+ and NO_3^- ions) is available to a plant cell, it is likely that more of the NO_3^- ions are absorbed than the Na^+, since this too reflects the needs of these cells.

3 **Active transport involves special molecules of the membrane called 'pumps'**. The pump molecule picks up particular molecules and transports them to the other side of the membrane, where they are then released. The pump molecules are globular proteins that span the lipid bilayer. Movement by these pump molecules requires reaction with ATP; this reaction supplies metabolic energy to the process. Most membrane pumps are specific to particular molecules, and this is how selective transport is brought about. If the pump molecule for a particular substance is not present, the substance will not be transported.

Figure 3.25
Active transport of a single substance.

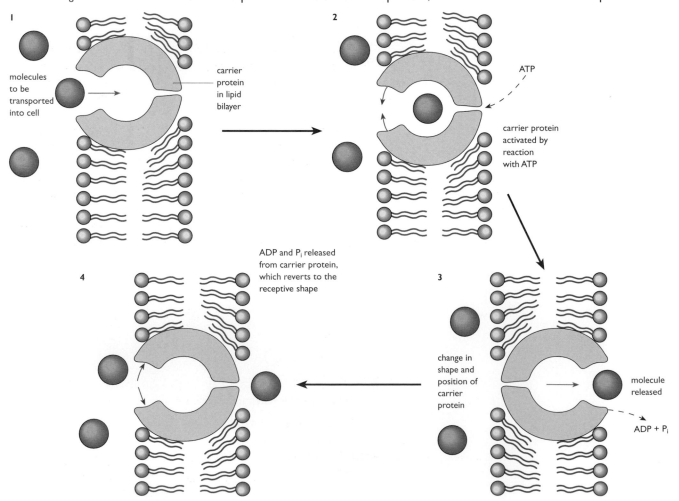

1 molecules to be transported into cell

carrier protein in lipid bilayer

2 ATP

carrier protein activated by reaction with ATP

ADP and P_i released from carrier protein, which reverts to the receptive shape

4

3 change in shape and position of carrier protein

molecule released

ADP + P_i

5 Nitrate ions may be taken up from a soil solution into root cells where the concentration of NO_3^- is already higher than in the soil. What does this tell you about the mechanism of absorption?

Active transport is a feature of most living cells. We meet examples of active transport in the gut where absorption occurs (Chapter 7), in the active uptake of ions by plant roots (Chapter 8), in the kidney tubules where urine is formed (Chapter 12) and in nerve fibres where an impulse is propagated.

Pumps are of different types. Some transport a particular molecule or ion in one direction (Figure 3.25), while others transport two substances (like Na^+ and K^+) in opposite directions (Figure 3.26). Occasionally, two substances are transported in the same direction, for example, Na^+ and glucose (Figure 7.17, page 158).

Figure 3.26
The sodium/potassium ion pump.

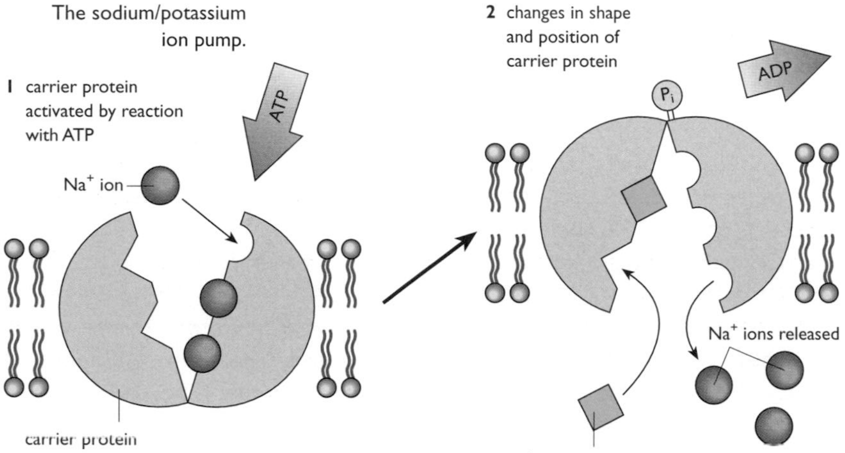

1 carrier protein activated by reaction with ATP

ATP

Na^+ ion

carrier protein in lipid bilayer

2 changes in shape and position of carrier protein

P_i

ADP

Na^+ ions released

K^+ ions loaded

3

K^+ ions released

P_i

Movement by bulk transport

6 Distinguish between the following pairs:

- proteins and lipids in cell membranes
- passive diffusion and facilitated diffusion
- solute potential and pressure potential
- hypotonic and hypertonic solutions
- turgid and flaccid cells
- endocytosis and exocytosis.

Bulk transport occurs by movements of **vesicles** (tiny membrane-bound sacs of matter, either solids or liquids) across the plasma membrane. The flexibility of the fluid mosaic membrane makes this activity possible, and energy from metabolism (ATP) is required. The process is known as **cytosis**. When substances are being imported into cells in this way, the process is referred to as **endocytosis** (Figure 3.27).

In the human body there is a huge force of **phagocytic** cells. (**Phagocytosis** means 'cell eating'.) These are called the **macrophages**. They mop up the remains of damaged or dying cells and dispose of them. The debris first sticks to the plasma membrane of the macrophage. The macrophage then surrounds it and encloses it in a vacuole within its own cytoplasm. For example we break down about 3×10^{11} red cells every day! All these are ingested and disposed of by the macrophages (page 261).

Bulk transport of fluids is referred to as **pinocytosis**. Bulk movements of lipids between cells and the surrounding tissue may occur in this way – after digestion of food, for example.

Figure 3.27
Transport by cytosis.

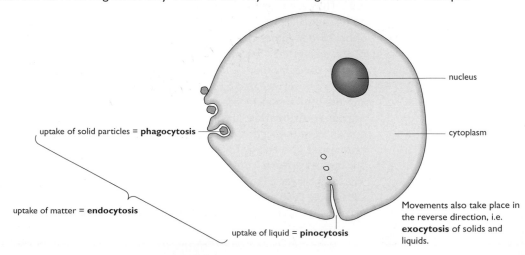

uptake of solid particles = **phagocytosis**

uptake of matter = **endocytosis**

uptake of liquid = **pinocytosis**

nucleus

cytoplasm

Movements also take place in the reverse direction, i.e. **exocytosis** of solids and liquids.

··

● **Skills task** Students were provided with cubes of slightly alkaline gelatin of different dimensions, containing an acid–alkali indicator that is red in alkalis but yellow in acids. The cubes were placed in dilute acid solution and observed carefully. The time taken for the colour in the gelatin to change from red to yellow throughout the gelatin was accurately measured with a stopclock. The colour change is due to the acid diffusing into the gelatin. The data from the experiment is given in the following table.

Dimensions/mm	Surface area/mm^2	Volume/mm^3	Time for colour change/minutes
$10 \times 10 \times 10$	600	1000	12
$5 \times 5 \times 5$	150	125	4.5
$4 \times 4 \times 4$	96	64	4.2
$2.5 \times 2.5 \times 2.5$	37.5	15.6	4.0

1 For each of the five blocks, calculate the ratio of surface area to volume.
2 Plot a graph of the surface area/volume ratio (horizontal or **x-axis**) against the time taken for the colour change (vertical or **y-axis**). Label your axes carefully.
3 Why does the colour change more quickly in some blocks than in others?

···

SUMMARY

● The **plasma membrane** surrounds and contains the cell contents. There is a continuous **movement of molecules** across the plasma membrane. Everything that is needed by cells, or is disposed of by them, moves across the membrane.

● The **water** molecule is electrically neutral. Because of its shape, however, it carries an unequal distribution of charge (oxygen with a negative charge, hydrogen with a positive charge). That is, it is a **polar** molecule. Consequently, water forms **hydrogen bonds** with other water molecules. These hydrogen bonds are responsible for the unusual properties of water.

● The inorganic elements needed by organisms (the **minerals**) are substances like potassium nitrate (KNO_3) that show **ionic bonding** and exist as stable, charged **ions** (K^+ and NO_3^-). Ionic bonding contrasts with **covalent bonding**, typical of carbon (and nitrogen and oxygen) atoms, in which electrons are shared between atoms.

● Mineral ions required in relatively large quantities, the **major mineral elements**, include calcium ions and phosphate ions. They may be components of cell structures, or they may play a major part in cell activities. Other mineral ions, the **micronutrients**, are required in trace amounts. They include copper ions and zinc ions, and they function as cofactors in the activities of particular enzymes.

● The **plasma membrane** is largely lipid and protein, with a small amount of carbohydrate. The lipids are phospholipids; their molecules have a hydrophilic 'head' and a hydrophobic 'tail'. They are organised into a **bilayer**, with the heads on the outsides. The protein components are globular proteins, and these are arranged in and across the lipid bilayer. Short carbohydrate chains are attached to some of the proteins and lipids on the outside of the membrane. The membrane is a **fluid mosaic**, as the components move about relative to each other.

● All cells are surrounded by an aqueous solution, and exchange of molecules between cells and their environment occurs in solution. There are **three mechanisms of transport across membranes**. In **diffusion** (and osmosis, a special case of diffusion), the energy comes from the kinetic energy of matter. In **active transport** (i.e. pumping) and in **bulk transport**, the energy for movement comes from metabolism.

● Substances **diffuse** from a region of high concentration to a region of low concentration. The lipid bilayer of the cell membrane acts as a barrier, at least to polar substances. Polar substances such as water diffuse through tiny pores. Some molecules react with membrane proteins to open a specific channel (**facilitated diffusion**).

continued

- Solute molecules in solution are surrounded by water molecules held by hydrogen bonds. In a concentrated solution, few water molecules are free to move. Therefore free water molecules in pure water or a dilute solution (water in high concentration) can diffuse through a partially permeable membrane (like the cell membrane) into a more concentrated solution (free water molecules in low concentration). This is known as **osmosis**.
- **Active transport** is a **selective** process, in which ions and organic substances move **against a concentration gradient**. The process requires energy from metabolism (ATP), and involves highly specific protein molecules in the membrane that act as **pumps**.
- **Bulk transport** is the movement of the contents of **vesicles** (membrane-bound sacs of solid or liquid) across the plasma membrane. The flexibility of the membrane makes this movement possible, but energy from metabolism (ATP) is required.

● Examination questions

I Below is a drawing of a unicellular organism found in that part of rivers where the sea invades at high tide. The organism possesses a contractile vacuole to expel excess water when necessary.

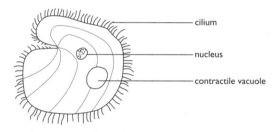

- cilium
- nucleus
- contractile vacuole

a State what determines the uptake of water across the cell surface membrane of this organism. (2)

This organism was placed in water of varying salt concentrations. The number of expulsions from the contractile vacuole was measured per hour. The results are shown below.

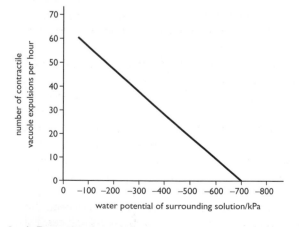

b i Describe the relationship between the activity of the contractile vacuole of this organism and the water potential of the surrounding solution. (2)
ii Explain the relationship that you have described. (4)

The structure of the cell surface membrane is important for the uptake of water and ions in the organism.
c i Describe **how** water passes through cell surface membranes. (3)
ii Describe the process by which ions can be taken up to establish an internal concentration higher than that of the surrounding solution. (4)

Mitochondria are essential for the maintenance of water balance in this organism.
d Suggest why this is so. (2)

UCLES, AS/A level, 4801, June 1998

2 The diagram below shows a plant cell, immersed in a sucrose solution. The pressure potential (ψ_p) of the cell and the solute potential (ψ_s) of the cell and of the sucrose solution are shown in the diagram.

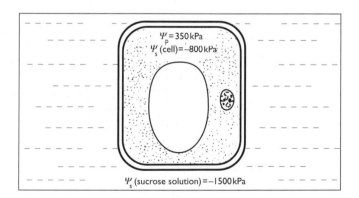

$\Psi_p = 350\,kPa$
$\Psi_s\,(cell) = -800\,kPa$

$\Psi_s\,(sucrose\ solution) = -1500\,kPa$

a Calculate the water potential of this cell (ψ_{cell}). Show your working. (2)
b State whether water will move into or out of the cell. Explain your answer. (2)
c State the water potential of this cell at the point of incipient plasmolysis. Assume that changes in ψ_s (cell) are negligible. (1)

London, AS/A level, Module B2, June 1998

3 The water potential of a plant cell (ψ_{cell}) can be calculated using the following equation:

$$\psi_{cell} = \psi_s + \psi_p$$

  where ψ_s = solute potential
  and ψ_p = pressure potential

a A plant cell was immersed in pure water until it was fully turgid. It was then placed in a concentrated solution until it was plasmolysed.

  The table below shows some of the values of the potentials in the cell at equilibrium under these different conditions.

  Complete the table by writing the missing values in the empty rows. (4)

Condition of cell	Potential/kPa		
	ψ_{cell}	ψ_s	ψ_p
fully turgid			+300
plasmolysed		−500	

b The diagram below shows a fully turgid plant cell.

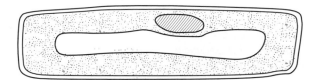

  Draw a diagram to show the same cell when it is plasmolysed. Label only the cell surface membrane. (3)

  London, AS/A level, Module B2, Jan 1997

4 Minerals are important to both autotrophic and heterotrophic organisms.
  a State **one** important function of magnesium in a plant. (1)
  b State **one** important function of iodine in the body of a vertebrate. (1)
  c State **two** important functions of calcium in an animal. (2)
  d Iron is required to form similar molecules common to both animals (in respiration) and plants (in the 'light-dependent' Z scheme reactions of photosynthesis). Name the type of molecule containing iron common to these reactions. (1)

  OCR (Oxford), A level, 6910, Mar 1999

5 The diagram represents part of an animal cell which has been put in distilled water.

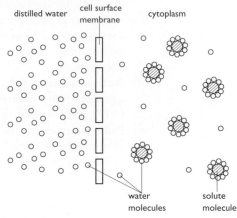

a Use the diagram to:
  i explain why the water potential of the distilled water is higher than the water potential of the cytoplasm of the cell; (2)
  ii describe the property of the cell surface membrane which allows osmosis to take place. (1)
b Osmosis has been described as a special case of diffusion. Describe **two** ways in which you would expect the movement of water into a cell by osmosis to be similar to the diffusion of oxygen into a cell. (2)

  AQA(AEB), AS/A level, Module 1, June 1999

6 The diagram shows the fluid mosaic model of cell membrane structure.

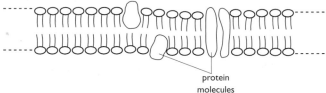

protein
molecules

a Suggest why this model is known as *fluid mosaic*. (2)
b Give **two** functions of the protein molecules in the cell membrane. (2)
c Explain how hydrophobic areas in the membrane are important to its function. (2)
d i The diagram shows the water potentials (Ψ) of three cells in contact with one another.
  Use arrows to show the net direction of water movement between **all three** cells.

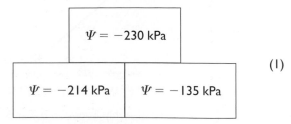

(1)

  ii If solute were added to a cell what effect would this have on the water potential within that cell? (1)

  AQA(NEAB), AS/A level, Module BY01, Mar 1999

Enzymes, in metabolism and for industry

STARTING POINTS ● Although cells are extremely small, their **cytoplasm** is the site of all the chemical reactions of life.
● Enzymes are **biological catalysts** that make possible chemical changes under the conditions in cells.
● Enzymes are **globular proteins**. They occur in solution in the cytosol and in organelles, and are built into membranes of organelles and the plasma membrane.
● **ATP** is the universal '**energy currency**' of cells. ATP is a reactant in most energy-requiring reactions.

What is metabolism?

Metabolism is the name for all the chemical reactions occurring in living organisms. Literally many thousands of metabolic reactions are constantly taking place. The substances involved in these reactions of life are collectively called **metabolites**. Many of these metabolites are made in organisms. Others are imported from the environment: they include food substances taken in, water, and the gases carbon dioxide and oxygen.

Most chemical reactions do not happen spontaneously. In a laboratory or an industrial process, a sequence of reactions is often made to occur by creating conditions of high concentration, high temperature, high pressure and/or an extreme of pH. Without these drastic conditions, very little product would be formed.

This chapter is about the remarkable way thousands of reactions of metabolism occur in the cells of organisms. The reactions go on simultaneously, at extremely low concentrations, at normal temperatures and under the very mild (almost neutral) aqueous conditions found in cells.

First, we need to look into metabolism in more detail.

Metabolic reactions are classified into just two types, according to whether they involve the build-up or breakdown of organic molecules (Figure 4.1).

In **anabolic reactions**, larger molecules are built up from smaller molecules. Examples of anabolism are the synthesis of proteins from amino acids, and the synthesis of polysaccharides from simple sugars.

In **catabolic reactions**, larger molecules are broken down into smaller ones. Examples of catabolism are the digestion of complex foods and the breakdown of sugar in respiration.

Overall:

$$\text{metabolism} = \text{anabolism} + \text{catabolism}$$

Metabolism and energy

Every molecule contains a quantity of **stored energy** equal to the quantity of energy needed to synthesise it originally. Chemical energy exists in the structural arrangement of the molecule, rather than in the chemical bonds.

When glucose is oxidised to carbon dioxide and water in aerobic respiration, energy is released (Chapter 9). This energy is no longer in store but is on the move; it is **active energy**. Actually, only part of the stored energy in a molecule is available. This energy is known as **free energy**, and it can be used to do work. Reactions that release free energy are known as **exergonic reactions**. The oxidation of glucose is an example of an exergonic reaction (Figure 4.2).

On the other hand, reactions that require energy are called **endergonic reactions**. The synthesis of a protein from amino acids is an example of an endergonic reaction.

Figure 4.1
Metabolism, an overview.

synthesis of complex molecules used in growth and development and in metabolic processes, e.g. proteins, polysaccharides, lipids, hormones, growth factors, haemoglobin, chlorophyll

↑

anabolism: energy-requiring reactions, i.e. **endergonic reactions**

sugars, amino acids, fatty acids, i.e. smaller organic molecules

nutrients →

catabolism energy-releasing reactions, i.e. **exergonic reactions**

↓

release of simple substances, e.g. small inorganic molecules, CO_2, H_2O, mineral ions

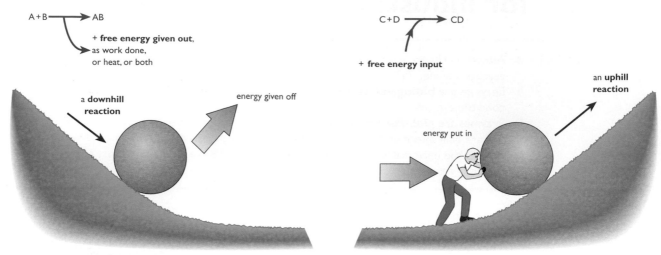

In an **exergonic reaction** the products have less stored energy than the reactants.

A + B ⟶ AB

+ **free energy given out**, as work done, or heat, or both

a **downhill reaction**

energy given off

In an **endergonic reaction** energy has to be put in, because the products have more stored energy than the reactants.

C + D ⟶ CD

+ **free energy input**

an **uphill reaction**

energy put in

Figure 4.2
Exergonic and endergonic reactions.

The many endergonic reactions of metabolism are made possible by being coupled to exergonic reactions. Coupling occurs through **ATP**, which biologists often call the **energy currency** molecule (Figure 2.31, page 48). Molecules of ATP work in metabolism by acting as common intermediates, linking energy-requiring and energy-yielding reactions. Most metabolic processes involve ATP, directly or indirectly.

Metabolism and enzymes

For two molecules to react, they must collide with each other. The molecules must collide in the right way and at the right speed. If the alignment at collision is not correct, the molecules bounce apart. If the alignments happen to be correct but the collision speed is wrong and the impact too gentle, there will be insufficient energy for the rearrangements of electrons and the making of a new bond. Only if the molecules are lined up and collide with the correct energies do they react (Figure 4.3).

The 'right' conditions are so rare that we may say that the reaction doesn't happen to any significant extent normally. Only if we introduce extreme conditions, such as very high temperatures (faster molecular movements), or very high pressure, or extreme acidity or alkalinity, does the reaction happen.

On the other hand, if an **enzyme** exists for this particular reaction, then it can make the molecules react at great speed. Enzymes are amazing molecules in this respect.

Enzymes are biological catalysts

All the reactions of metabolites are catalysed by enzymes, almost all of which are proteins. Without enzymes, not one of the chemical activities of cells would be possible under the conditions in cells. As it is, the reactions of metabolism happen at astonishing speeds, but in an orderly manner. As a result, the products that the organism requires become available, exactly when it needs them. Sometimes reactions happen even though the reacting molecules are quite few and far between.

Some enzymes are released from cells, such as the digestive enzymes. Enzymes like these that are parcelled up and secreted, and 'work' externally, are called **extracellular enzymes**. Most enzymes, however, remain within cells and work there. These are the **intracellular enzymes**. They are found inside organelles, in the membranes of organelles, in the cytosol and in the plasma membrane. What properties of enzymes enable them to bring about metabolism of the organism, in this controlled and regulated way?

Figure 4.3
Can a reaction occur
without an enzyme?

1 The reaction: hydrolysis of sucrose to form glucose and fructose

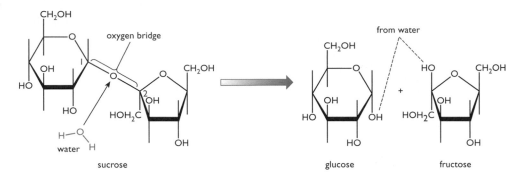

2 Random collision possibilities:
when sucrose and water collide at the wrong angle

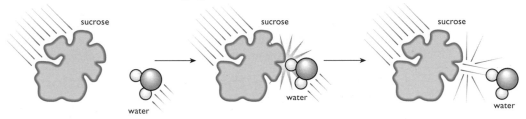

when sucrose and water collide at the wrong speed

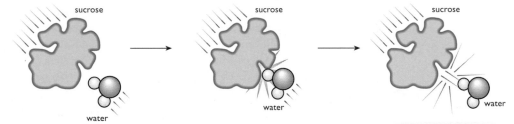

for the reaction to occur, sucrose and water must collide in
just the right way – glucose and fructose are formed

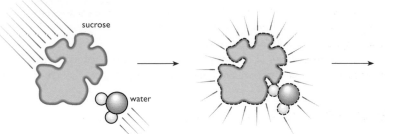

These events are what
happens at most random
collisions.

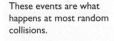

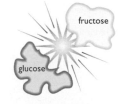

Under normal conditions
this happens so very
infrequently it is an
insignificant event.

3 In the presence of one molecule of the enzyme sucrase (invertase),
approximately 3.0×10^4 molecules of sucrose are hydrolysed each
minute!

Enzymes as catalysts

By 'catalyst', we mean a substance that speeds up a chemical reaction. In a reaction catalysed by
an enzyme the starting substance is called the **substrate**, and what it is converted to is the
product. For example, in the reaction in Figure 4.3 above sucrose is the substrate, the enzyme is
sucrase, and the products are glucose and fructose.

Catalysts have a long history in chemistry and industry, although these have been inorganic catalysts rather than proteins. So the general properties of catalysts are well known.

- Catalysts are **effective in small amounts**. The **turnover number** of a catalyst is the number of molecules of substrate 'processed' by one catalyst molecule in a minute. Inorganic catalysts, such as those used in industry, have turnover numbers between 100 and 3 000 000. Enzymes have much larger turnover numbers. For example, a single molecule of carbonic anhydrase in a red blood cell catalyses 3.6×10^7 molecules of CO_2 to HCO_3^- in a minute, which allows the efficient transport of carbon dioxide in the blood.
- Catalysts are **unchanged at the end of the reaction**, even though they are chemically involved in the reaction. Consequently, a catalyst can be used over and over again without undergoing permanent chemical change.
- Catalysts **speed up the rate at which equilibrium position is reached**. In a reversible reaction:

$$A + B \rightleftharpoons C + D$$

A and B react to form C and D. This is a reversible reaction, as shown by the sign $\rightleftharpoons$. As soon as C and D start to accumulate some will react to form A and B. The reversible reaction reaches an equilibrium point when the rate of the forward reaction equals the rate of the reverse reaction. Most enzyme-catalysed reactions are reversible: the presence of the enzyme for this reaction means the equilibrium position is reached quickly.

Enzymes lower the energy of activation

As molecules react they form unstable, high-energy intermediates, but only momentarily. We say they are in a **transition state**, because the products are formed immediately. The products have a lower energy than that of the substrate molecules. The minimum amount of energy needed to raise substrate molecules to their transition state is called the **activation energy**. This is the energy barrier that has to be overcome before the reaction can happen. Enzymes work by lowering the amount of energy required to activate the reacting molecules.

For another 'model' of what is going on, think of a boulder (*substrate*) perched on a slope, prevented from rolling down by a small hump (*activation energy*) in front of it (Figure 4.4). The boulder can be pushed over the hump, or the hump can be dug away (= *lowering the activation energy*). Either allows the boulder to roll, and it shatters at a lower level (*products*).

Figure 4.4
Activation energy.

'boulder on hillside' model of activation energy

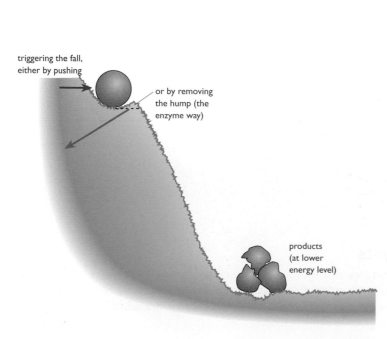

triggering the fall, either by pushing

or by removing the hump (the enzyme way)

products (at lower energy level)

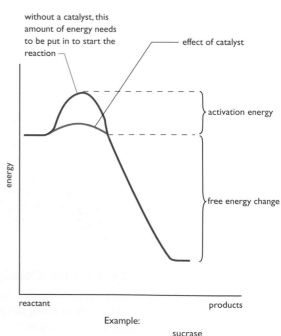

without a catalyst, this amount of energy needs to be put in to start the reaction

effect of catalyst

activation energy

energy

free energy change

reactant

products

Example:

sucrase
sucrose + water ⟶ glucose + fructose

Enzyme–substrate complex

Enzymes work by binding to their substrate molecule at a specially formed pocket in the enzyme. This binding point is called the **active site**. The idea that enzyme and substrate bind in this way is called the 'lock and key' hypothesis of enzyme action. As the enzyme (**E**) and substrate (**S**) form a complex (**ES**), the substrate is raised in energy to a transition state, and then breaks down to products (**Pr**) plus unchanged enzyme (Figure 4.5):

$$E + S \rightleftharpoons ES \rightleftharpoons Pr + E$$

All the metabolites in cells are substrate molecules for at least one enzyme. Most enzymes are large molecules, and most substrate molecules are quite small by comparison. Even when the substrate molecules are very large, such as the polysaccharides, only one bond in the substrate is in contact with the enzyme's active site. The active site takes up a relatively small part of the total volume of the enzyme molecule.

1 What is meant by 'active site'?

Figure 4.5
The enzyme–substrate complex and the active site.

The sequence of steps to an enzyme-catalysed reaction:

enzyme + substrate ⟶ E–S complex ⟶ product + enzyme available for reuse
[substrate raised to transition state]

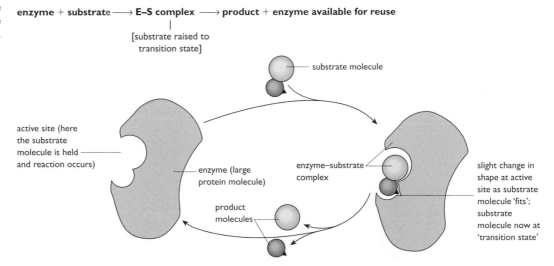

active site (here the substrate molecule is held and reaction occurs)

substrate molecule

enzyme (large protein molecule)

enzyme–substrate complex

product molecules

slight change in shape at active site as substrate molecule 'fits'; substrate molecule now at 'transition state'

Example:

ATP + glucose ⟶ ADP + glucose-6-phosphate
hexokinase

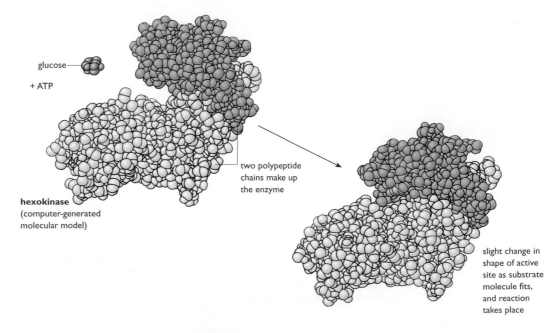

glucose
+ ATP

two polypeptide chains make up the enzyme

hexokinase
(computer-generated molecular model)

slight change in shape of active site as substrate molecule fits, and reaction takes place

Enzymes with a non-protein component

Enzymes are made of protein, but not many enzymes consist of protein only (Figure 4.6). An example of a **protein-only enzyme** is lysozyme, found in tears and saliva. Lysozyme digests the wall components of bacteria, causing the wall to break down (lysis). It is one of the smaller enzymes, consisting of a single polypeptide chain of 129 amino acid residues.

Most enzymes are **conjugated proteins**, meaning they have an important non-protein part attached to the protein. This non-protein part is essential to enzyme function. It often forms part of the active site.

The non-protein component may be permanently (or almost permanently) attached. If so, it is known as a **prosthetic group**. An example is the zinc ion in carboxypeptidase. This enzyme catalyses the hydrolysis of a peptide bond in a short-chain peptide, freeing a terminal amino acid (Figure 7.9, page 150). The zinc ion is tightly bound within the enzyme and remains attached.

Alternatively, the non-protein component may be readily detached in order to work with other enzymes in additional reactions. In these cases the non-protein component is known as a **coenzyme**. A good example is the dinucleotide NAD (pages 48–9), which is involved in the transport of hydrogen ions in respiration. In animals, most of the coenzymes are derived from food components called vitamins. NAD is obtained from a substance called niacin, which is a vitamin of the B complex.

Figure 4.6
Protein-only and conjugated protein enzymes.

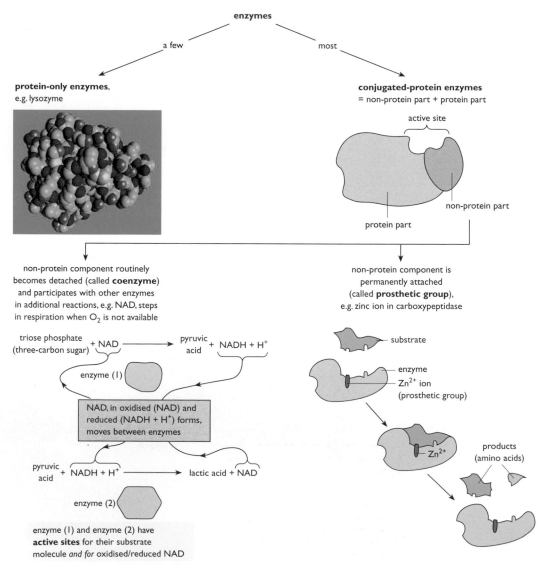

Enzyme specificity

Enzymes are highly **specific** in their action. Each enzyme catalyses either a single chemical reaction or a group of closely related reactions. This makes them different from most inorganic catalysts. They are specific because of the way they bind with their substrate at the active site, which is a pocket or crevice in the protein. At the active site, the arrangement of a few amino acid molecules in the protein (enzyme) matches certain groupings on the substrate molecule, enabling the enzyme–substrate complex to form (Figure 4.7). As it forms, it seems a slight change of shape is induced in the enzyme molecule (**induced fit hypothesis**). It is this change of shape that is important in raising the substrate molecule to the transition state in which it is able to react.

Meanwhile, other amino acid molecules of the active site bring about the breaking of particular bonds in the substrate molecule at the point where it is temporarily held by the enzyme. The reason why each enzyme is specific is that different enzymes have different arrangements of amino acids in their active sites.

Figure 4.7
Enzyme specificity and the active site.

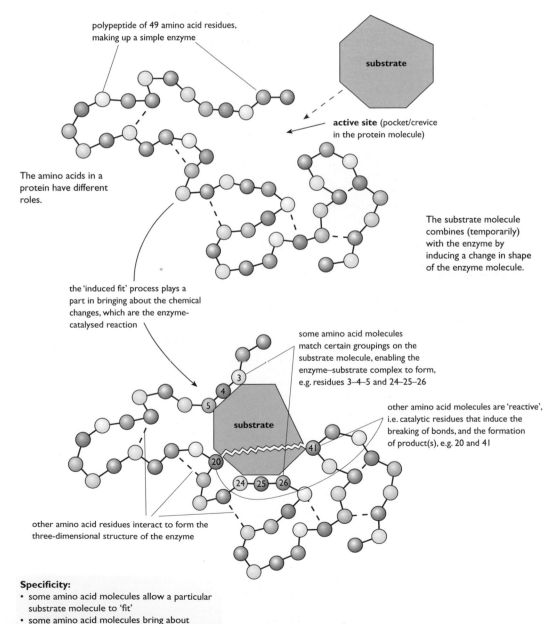

polypeptide of 49 amino acid residues, making up a simple enzyme

substrate

active site (pocket/crevice in the protein molecule)

The amino acids in a protein have different roles.

The substrate molecule combines (temporarily) with the enzyme by inducing a change in shape of the enzyme molecule.

the 'induced fit' process plays a part in bringing about the chemical changes, which are the enzyme-catalysed reaction

some amino acid molecules match certain groupings on the substrate molecule, enabling the enzyme–substrate complex to form, e.g. residues 3–4–5 and 24–25–26

other amino acid molecules are 'reactive', i.e. catalytic residues that induce the breaking of bonds, and the formation of product(s), e.g. 20 and 41

substrate

other amino acid residues interact to form the three-dimensional structure of the enzyme

Specificity:
• some amino acid molecules allow a particular substrate molecule to 'fit'
• some amino acid molecules bring about particular chemical changes.

Studying enzyme-catalysed reactions

Enzyme-catalysed reactions are fast reactions. We know this from the very large numbers of substrate molecules converted to products by a molecule of enzyme in one minute. The enzyme **catalase** catalyses the breakdown of hydrogen peroxide to water and oxygen. It is a good example to use in studying the rate of enzyme-catalysed reactions.

$$2H_2O_2 \xrightarrow{\text{catalase}} 2H_2O + O_2$$

Catalase occurs very widely in the cells of living things. It functions as a protective mechanism for the delicate biochemical machinery of cells. This is because hydrogen peroxide is a common by-product of some of the reactions of metabolism. At the same time it is a highly toxic substance (a very powerful oxidising agent, page 483). Catalase inactivates hydrogen peroxide as soon as it forms, before it can damage the cell.

You can demonstrate the presence of catalase in fresh liver tissue by dropping a small piece of the tissue into dilute hydrogen peroxide solution. Compare the result obtained with that from a similar piece of liver that has been boiled in water (high temperature denatures and destroys enzymes, including catalase) (Figure 4.8). If you do not wish to use animal tissues, then you can use potato, or soaked and crushed dried peas, instead.

Figure 4.8
Liver tissue in dilute hydrogen peroxide solution, a demonstration.

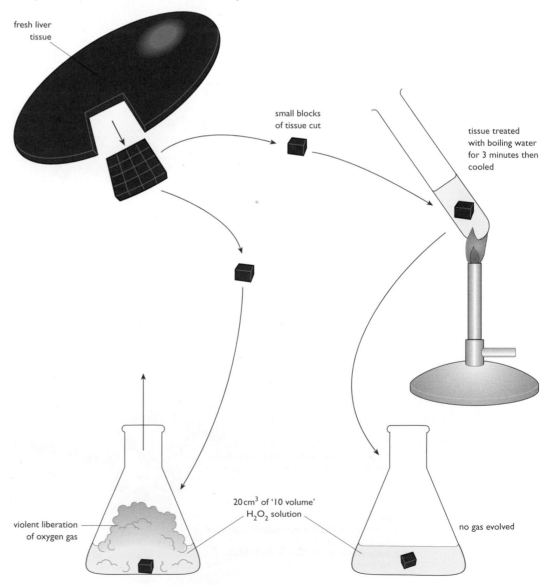

fresh liver tissue

small blocks of tissue cut

tissue treated with boiling water for 3 minutes then cooled

violent liberation of oxygen gas

$20\,cm^3$ of '10 volume' H_2O_2 solution

no gas evolved

Measuring the rate of reaction

In practical terms, the rate of an enzyme-catalysed reaction is taken as the amount of substrate that has disappeared from a reaction mixture, or the amount of product that has accumulated, in a period of time. For example, when working with catalase it is convenient to measure the rate at which the product (oxygen) accumulates. In the experiment described in Figure 4.9, the volume of oxygen that has accumulated at half-minute intervals is recorded on the graph.

We find that, over a period of time, the initial rate of reaction is not maintained but falls off quite sharply. This is typical of enzyme actions *studied outside the cell*. There are several possible reasons for the fall-off, but usually it is because the concentration of the substrate in the reaction mixture has fallen. Consequently, it is the **initial rate of reaction** that is measured. This is the slope of the tangent to the curve in the initial stage of reaction. Figure 4.9 shows how this is calculated.

Figure 4.9
Measuring the rate of reaction, using catalase.

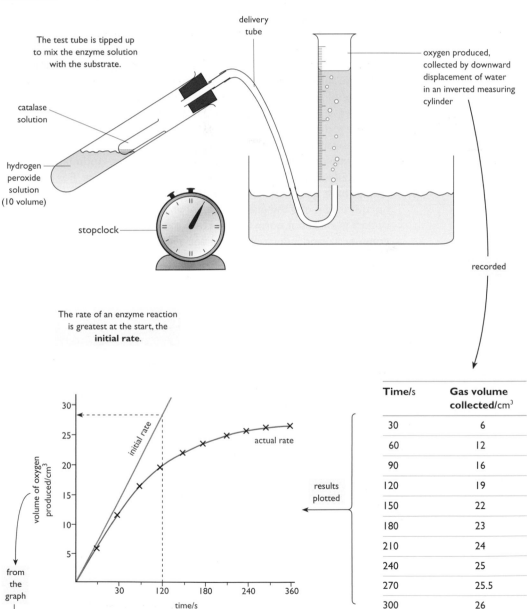

Time/s	Gas volume collected/cm^3
30	6
60	12
90	16
120	19
150	22
180	23
210	24
240	25
270	25.5
300	26

If the initial rate of O_2 production continued for 120 s, then 28 cm^3 of O_2 would be produced.

Therefore the initial rate = 28/120 $cm^3 s^{-1}$

= 0.23 $cm^3 s^{-1}$

Factors that change the rate of reaction of enzymes

Enzymes are sensitive to environmental conditions. Many factors affect enzymes and therefore alter the rate of the reaction being catalysed. Investigations of these factors, including temperature, pH and (in particular) substrate concentration have helped us to understand how enzymes work.

Temperature

As temperature is increased molecules have increased active energy, and reactions between them go faster. In *chemical reactions*, for every 10 °C rise in temperature the rate of the reaction approximately doubles. We can speak of the **temperature coefficient** (Q_{10}) of a chemical reaction:

$$Q_{10} = \frac{\text{rate of reaction at } (x + 10\,°C)}{\text{rate of reaction at } x\,°C}$$

$$\approx 2 \text{ (for most chemical reactions)}$$

In *enzyme-catalysed reactions* the effect of temperature is more complex. As the temperature rises, the substrate and the enzyme molecules move more rapidly and are more likely to collide. The rate of reaction rises. Proteins are denatured by heat, however, and the rate of denaturation increases at higher temperatures. Heat denaturation is an irreversible change in the enzyme, because it destroys the active site. So as the temperature rises the amount of active enzyme progressively decreases, and the rate falls (Figure 4.10). As a result of these two effects of heat on enzyme-catalysed reactions, there is an apparent 'optimum temperature' for an enzyme.

Not all enzymes have the same optimum temperature. For example, the bacteria in hot springs have enzymes with optima of 80–100 °C or even higher. The enzymes of seaweeds of northern seas and the plants of the tundra have optima closer to 0 °C. Human enzymes have optima at or about normal body temperature. This feature of enzymes is often exploited in the commercial and industrial uses of enzymes (page 90).

Figure 4.10
Temperature and the rate of an enzyme-catalysed reaction.

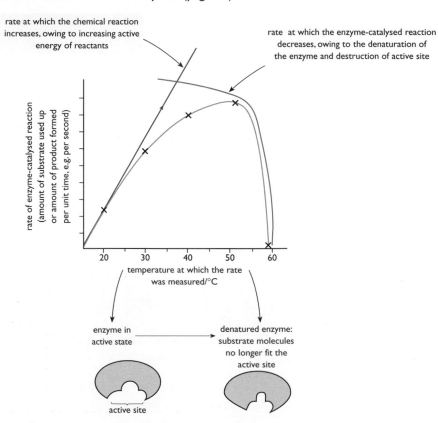

pH

A change in pH can have a dramatic effect on the rate of an enzyme-catalysed reaction. This is because the secondary and tertiary structure of a protein (and therefore the shape of the active site) is maintained by various bonds (Figure 2.22, page 41). A change in pH alters ionic charges on some groups. As a result, the shape of the protein and therefore of the active site may change (Figure 4.11). But the effects of pH on the active site are, by and large, reversible. When the pH reverts to the optimum for the enzyme, the active site reappears.

Figure 4.11
The effect of pH on enzyme shape and activity.

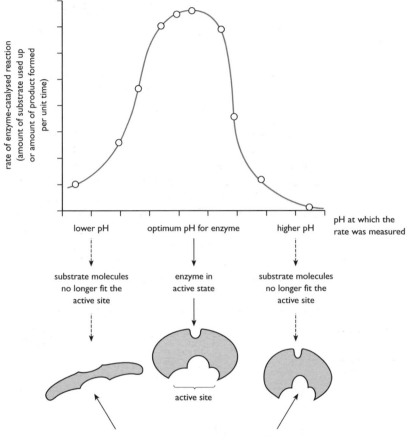

secondary/tertiary structure of protein changes when a change of pH alters the ionic charge on —COO⁻ (acidic) and —NH₃⁺ (basic) groups in the peptide chain, so the shape of the active site is lost

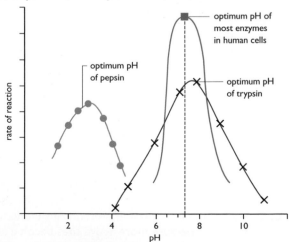

Substrate concentration

The effect of different concentrations of substrate on the rate of an enzyme-catalysed reaction can be shown using catalase and hydrogen peroxide, in the apparatus illustrated in Figure 4.9. The experiment is repeated at different concentrations of substrate, but keeping the amount of enzyme the same. The initial rate of reaction is plotted in each case. The graph of these results shows a curve of two phases. At lower concentrations the rate increases in direct proportion to the substrate concentration. But at higher substrate concentration the rate of reaction becomes constant (Figure 4.12).

The result confirms the theory that an enzyme works by forming a short-lived enzyme–substrate complex. At low substrate concentration, all molecules can find an active site without delay. The rate of reaction is set by how much substrate is present. At high substrate concentration there is more substrate than enzyme, and substrate molecules have to 'queue up' to join an active site. Increase in substrate concentration does not change the rate of reaction.

2 When all the active sites of an enzyme are occupied, what is the effect on the rate of reaction of increasing the concentration of substrate?

Figure 4.12
The effect of substrate concentration.

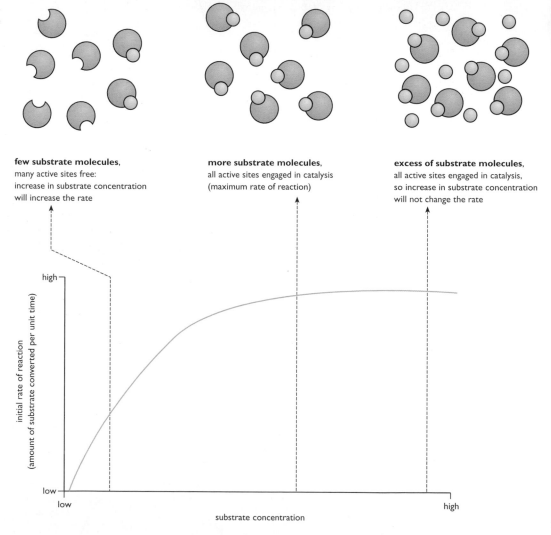

few substrate molecules, many active sites free: increase in substrate concentration will increase the rate

more substrate molecules, all active sites engaged in catalysis (maximum rate of reaction)

excess of substrate molecules, all active sites engaged in catalysis, so increase in substrate concentration will not change the rate

initial rate of reaction (amount of substrate converted per unit time)

high

low

substrate concentration

low

high

Enzyme concentration

If there are plenty of substrate molecules in a reaction mixture, then the more enzyme that is present the faster the reaction will be. This is the situation in a cell, where enzyme reactions occur with only a little enzyme present. Any increase in enzyme production will speed up the reaction, simply because more active sites become available.

Inhibitors of enzymes

Certain substances present in cells (and some that enter from the environment) may react with an enzyme, altering the rate of its reaction. These substances are known as **inhibitors**, since their effects are generally to lower the rate of reaction. Studies of the effects of inhibitors has helped our understanding of:

- the chemistry of the active site of enzymes
- the natural regulation of metabolism, and the pathways that operate
- the ways certain commercial pesticides and some drugs work by inhibiting specific enzymes and preventing particular reactions.

Inhibitors react with enzymes in different ways. Some bind irreversibly to an enzyme and destroy its catalytic properties completely. These substances are usually very poisonous to cells because they close down some part of metabolism. Many pesticides work to deadly effect by irreversible inhibition of enzymes. Ideally their effects are specific to enzymes in the target organisms, as in the action of malathion on insects.

Other inhibitors bind less tightly to enzymes and are known as **reversible inhibitors** (Figure 4.13). These too have important effects.

For example, molecules that resemble the substrate in shape may compete with it to occupy the active site. They are known as **competitive inhibitors**. The enzyme that catalyses the reaction between carbon dioxide and the 'acceptor molecule' in photosynthesis, known as ribulose bisphosphate carboxylase (page 181), is competitively inhibited by oxygen in the chloroplasts.

Because these inhibitors are not acted on by the enzyme and turned into 'products' as normal substrate molecules are, they tend to remain attached. If the concentration of the substrate molecule is raised to a sufficiently high level, however, the inhibitor molecules are progressively displaced from the active sites.

Alternatively, an inhibitor may be unlike the substrate molecule, yet still combine with the enzyme. In these cases, the attachment occurs at some other part of the enzyme, probably quite close to the active site. Here the inhibitor may partly block access to the active site by substrate molecules, or it may cause the active site to change shape and thus become unable to accept the substrate. These are called **non-competitive inhibitors**, since they do not compete for the active site. So adding excess substrate does not overcome their inhibiting effects. For example, cyanide ions combine with cytochrome oxidase but not at the active site. Cytochrome oxidase, a respiratory enzyme present in all cells, is a component in a sequence of enzymes and carriers that oxidise the hydrogens removed from a respiratory substrate such as glucose, forming water. Reaction with cyanide disrupts the sequence, with rapidly fatal results to the cell.

3 What is meant by
a a competitive inhibitor,
b a non-competitive inhibitor?

Figure 4.13
Competitive and non-competitive inhibitors, the principles.

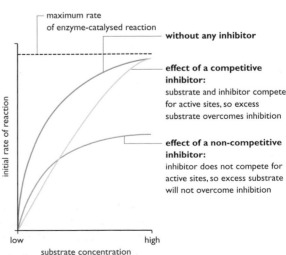

Extension Enzymes and the control of metabolism

The metabolic pathways of cells and tissues are many, and they often interconnect. We have seen that the reactions of metabolism are made possible by the presence of specific enzymes. In addition, the enzyme machinery of a cell plays a part in the **control** of the pathways of metabolism. How do enzymes achieve this?

- The **specificity of enzymes** means that a reaction happens only in the presence of a specific enzyme. If the enzyme is not present, the reaction cannot happen at all.
- Because **enzymes are effective in very small amounts**, the production of a specific enzyme leads to immediate reactions and the formation of products.
- Where enzymes compete for the same substrate molecule the **amount of each enzyme present** and how readily each forms its **enzyme–substrate complex** decides the extent to which pathways operate (Figure 4.14).
- Many enzymes are always present in cells, but some enzymes are produced **only in the presence of the substrate**. This is a case of the substrate molecule triggering the machinery by which the enzyme is produced.

4 Why are several enzymes involved in a metabolic pathway?

Figure 4.14
Some metabolic pathways and the roles of enzymes.

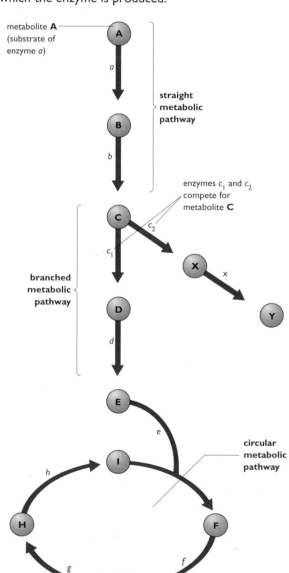

metabolite **A** (substrate of enzyme *a*)

straight metabolic pathway

enzymes c_1 and c_2 compete for metabolite **C**

branched metabolic pathway

How much of metabolite **C** is converted to **X** or to **D** depends on the relative amounts of enzymes c_1 and c_2, and how readily each forms its enzyme–substrate complex.

circular metabolic pathway

- Many metabolic pathways are switched on or off by a process known as **allosteric inhibition**. Allosteric enzymes have two sites. One is the active site of the enzyme and the other is an additional site where another substance can 'lock in'. Once it is locked in, the whole enzyme is altered.

    In **allosteric *inhibition***, the arrival of the additional binding substance **inactivates** the active site.

    In **allosteric *stimulation***, the active site is **activated** by the arrival of the additional binding substance.

    Allosteric inhibition provides a method by which individual enzymes may be switched on or off. This allows the metabolism as a whole to be regulated and adjusted. An example is **end-product inhibition**. Here the final product inhibits the enzyme that catalyses the first step in the pathway. So as the product molecules accumulate, the steps in their production are switched off; but if the product molecules are used up in subsequent metabolic reactions, production starts up again.

Figure 4.15
End-product and allosteric inhibition of metabolism.

Allosteric means 'having two shapes'.

Allosteric enzymes have two shapes, one active and the other inactive.

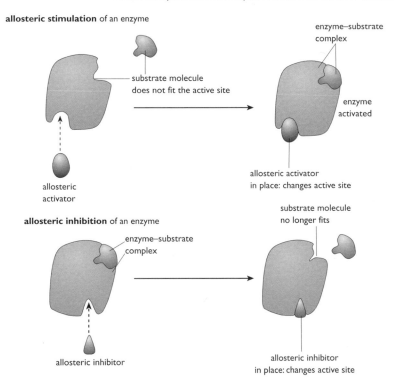

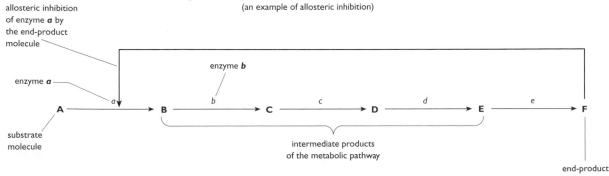

This is an example of the regulation of a metabolic pathway by **negative feedback**.

● **Extension**

Naming enzymes

Many enzymes have a name derived from the name of their substrate, with the ending *-ase* added. For example, lactase hydrolyses lactose, and amylase hydrolyses amylose.

Other enzymes have been given less informative names. Examples include many of the enzymes of digestion, such as pepsin, trypsin and rennin.

Systematic naming of enzymes is based on an agreed classification of enzymes (given below), and on the name of the substrate of the reaction catalysed. These names are long and detailed. They are used by enzymologists, but they have not caught on in everyday usage. The classification of enzymes based upon the reactions catalysed divides them into six major groups (Table 4.1).

Table 4.1
Classification of enzymes by type of reaction.

Enzyme	Reaction catalysed
Oxidoreductases	These enzymes catalyse biological oxidation and reduction by the transfer of hydrogen, oxygen or electrons from one molecule to another. Example: $$lactic\ acid + NAD \xrightarrow{\ lactic\ dehydrogenase\ } pyruvic\ acid + NADH + H^+$$
Transferases	These enzymes catalyse the transfer of a chemical group from one substrate to another. Example: $$\underset{\text{(amino acid)}}{glutamic\ acid} + \underset{\text{(organic acid)}}{pyruvic\ acid} \xrightarrow{\ aminotransferase\ } \underset{\text{(organic acid)}}{\alpha\text{-ketoglutaric acid}} + \underset{\text{(amino acid)}}{alanine}$$
Hydrolases	These enzymes catalyse the formation of two products from a larger substrate molecule by a hydrolysis reaction. Example: $$sucrose + H_2O \xrightarrow{\ sucrase\ } glucose + fructose$$
Lyases	These enzymes catalyse the non-hydrolytic removal (or addition) of parts of a substrate molecule. Example: $$pyruvic\ acid \xrightarrow{\ pyruvate\ decarboxylase\ } ethanol + CO_2$$
Isomerases	These enzymes catalyse the internal rearrangement of molecules. Example: $$glucose\text{-}1\text{-}phosphate \xrightarrow{\ phosphoglucomutase\ } glucose\text{-}6\text{-}phosphate$$
Ligases	These enzymes catalyse the joining together of two molecules with the simultaneous hydrolysis of ATP. Example: $$amino\ acid + specific\ tRNA + ATP \xrightarrow{\ synthetase\ } amino\ acid\text{–}tRNA\ complex + ADP + Pi$$

● Industrial uses of enzymes

In industrial production processes, inorganic catalysts are frequently used. Iron, for example, is used in the production of ammonia from nitrogen and hydrogen in the Haber process. Some enzymes (biological catalysts) also have a long tradition of industrial use. For example, in leather tanning, hides have for centuries been softened and hair removed using proteases naturally present in faeces. In brewing, enzymes present in barley grains at germination are used to convert the starch stored in the grain to sugars and the proteins to amino acids. These sugars and amino acids are then used by yeast for growth and alcohol production. In cheese manufacture, the proteins in milk are coagulated (made insoluble), using the stomach enzyme rennet (rennin, page 151) of young mammals, obtained from veal calves.

Today there are many new developments in the use of enzymes as industrial catalysts, forming a part of the current revolution in biotechnology. **Biotechnology** is defined as the industrial and commercial applications of biology, particularly of microorganisms, enzymology and genetic engineering (page 121). The use of enzymes in industrial processes is known as **enzyme technology**.

5 What is a catalyst? Give two differences between inorganic catalysts and enzymes.

Advantages of enzymes as industrial catalysts

Enzymes are produced by living cells. Many, however, can be separated from cells and continue to function outside the cell, in test tubes or industrial reactor vessels (known as *in vitro* conditions). Enzymes have advantages over inorganic catalysts in industrial processes, particularly because:

- they are highly specific, usually catalysing change in one particular compound or only one type of bond
- they are efficient, in that a tiny quantity of enzyme catalyses the production of a huge quantity of products
- they work at normal temperatures and pressures, and so need much less input of energy than most chemical catalysts require.

Sources of industrial enzymes

Useful enzymes are obtained from both plant and animal sources. For example, enzymes for use in the medical treatment of thromboses are extracted from pineapple juice and from mammalian pancreas tissue. But most enzymes are obtained from microorganisms, mainly bacteria and fungi. The values of using microorganisms as the source of enzymes are:

- they are grown economically in bulk fermenters (Figure 4.16), often using relatively low-grade nutrients
- they have high growth rates and contain a larger proportion of enzymes in relation to their body mass than most animal or plant sources do
- their growth is not limited by season or climate, as it is in many animal or plant sources
- they occur naturally in a wide range of habitats, sometimes under extreme environmental conditions, and consequently some contain enzymes adapted to function efficiently under abnormal or extreme conditions – of temperature and pH, for example
- they may be manipulated genetically relatively easily (gene technology, page 120) to receive genes from other organisms. For example, a human gene for insulin production has been introduced into a strain of the bacterium *Escherichia coli*.

Figure 4.16
The industrial production of enzymes.

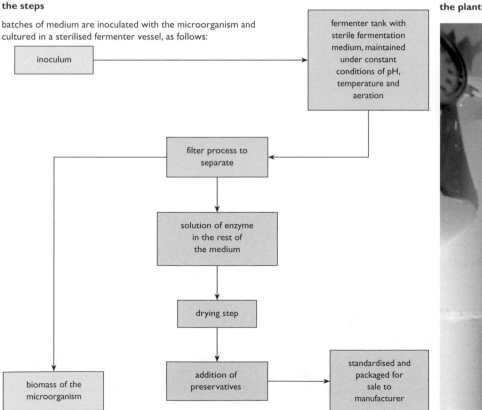

Whole-cell and cell-free preparations of enzymes

Initially, biological catalysts were used in industrial processes in the form of **whole-cell preparations**. These preparations were cultures of particular microorganisms, usually some species of bacteria. This is not necessarily efficient, because much of the nutrients provided may become built up into the microorganisms themselves, rather than into the product molecules. Sometimes unwanted by-products are produced, too. The conditions for growth of the microorganisms do not necessarily favour maximum production of the desired product, either. Microorganisms and by-products have to be separated from the product, eventually, at some cost to the manufacturer.

Cell-free preparations of enzymes have tended to replace the use of whole cells. This happens especially where the enzymes are secreted by the microorganism into the medium, and so are easily isolated for use. Whole-cell preparations are, however, still used where the enzyme is unstable outside the cells in which it is produced. Also where it is difficult to extract an enzyme from the cell source, or where a whole series of enzymes is involved in interconnected reactions, whole-cell preparations are used.

Immobilised enzymes

One disadvantage of isolated enzymes as industrial catalysts is that they cannot be used over and over again. Also, the enzyme may need to be removed from the product, and this may be expensive.

An alternative arrangement is the use of **immobilised enzymes**. Immobilised enzymes are held in granules, or attached to fibres, then packed into a column through which a supply of the reactants is continuously passed, to form the product (Figure 4.17).

The advantages of using an immobilised enzyme in industrial productions are:

- it allows the enzyme preparation to be reused
- the product is obtained enzyme-free
- the enzyme may be much more stable and long-lasting, since it is protected by the inert matrix.

Figure 4.17
Methods for the immobilisation of enzymes.

1 **Entrapment** of enzyme molecules between fibres: the enzyme is not chemically attached, but access of reactant molecules may be restricted.

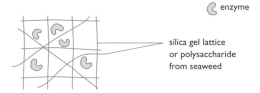

enzyme

silica gel lattice or polysaccharide from seaweed

2 **Covalent bonding** of enzyme to matrix, which prevents enzyme molecules from being leached away; some enzyme molecules may be denatured by the bonding process.

matrix of a polymer such as cellulose or collagen

3 **Entrapment** of enzyme molecules in permeable microcapsules; the enzyme is held securely, but the reactant and product molecules must be small enough to pass through the pores.

capsule wall

4 **Direct crosslinking** of enzyme molecules by covalent bonding with bridging molecules; reactants and product molecules have easy access, but some enzyme may be denatured.

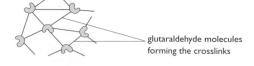

glutaraldehyde molecules forming the crosslinks

5 **Adsorption** of enzyme on to a surface, where it is held by weak electrostatic forces; there is no denaturation, but the enzyme may be dislodged or other molecules may also be adsorbed, in either case reducing the efficiency of the enzyme.

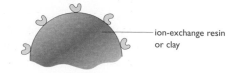

ion-exchange resin or clay

Examples of developments in the applications of enzymes

Biological detergents

Most of the enzymes for 'biological' washing powders come from bacteria adapted to live in hot springs (at or above 45 °C). Their enzymes are not denatured at these temperatures and can therefore be used in washing programmes carried out at moderate temperatures. Washing powder enzymes must also be able to function at alkaline pH, usually in the presence of an excess of phosphate ions, which are present in most detergents.

A 'biological' detergent washing powder often contains the following enzymes:

Figure 4.18
SEM of 'biological' washing powder granules.

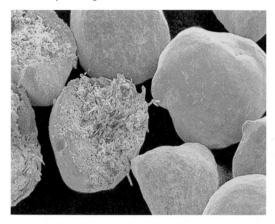

- a **protease** to degrade proteins present in blood, grass and egg stains
- an **amylase** to remove starch stains
- a **cellulase** which digests free cellulose microfibrils from damaged cotton fibres, returning the fabric to a generally softer, brighter appearance
- a **lipase** to digest fat, oil and grease stains.

'Biological' washing powder enzymes can produce an irritating dust that may trigger reactions in the lungs and the exposed skin of some people to prolonged contact. To avoid this, washing powder contents are often contained in capsules that only release their contents in water (Figure 4.18).

Medical treatment of thromboses

Thromboses are the blood clots that sometimes build up in damaged blood vessels as a product of atherosclerosis (page 323). These clots are in danger of being dislodged at any moment, and may be carried around in the blood circulation until they come to block a smaller artery. If cardiac muscle is blocked the result may be a heart attack; if a brain artery, a stroke.

Figure 4.19
Glucose is found in the urine of people with diabetes (page 261). Measuring glucose in urine using Clinistix™.

Blood clots may be digested away by the use of enzyme preparations. The basis of the clot is fibres of fibrin (insoluble protein) in which blood cells are trapped. So the enzymes used in this treatment are proteases (obtained from a range of sources), which dissolve the fibrin.

the principles

$$\text{glucose} + \text{oxygen} \xrightarrow{\text{glucose oxidase}} \text{gluconic acid} + H_2O_2$$

$$\underset{\substack{\text{reduced}\\\text{chromogen}\\\text{(colourless)}}}{DH_2 + H_2O_2} \xrightarrow{\text{peroxidase}} 2H_2O + \underset{\substack{\text{chromogen}\\\text{(coloured)}}}{D}$$

the process

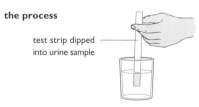

test strip dipped into urine sample

If glucose is present, the colour produced indicates the amount.

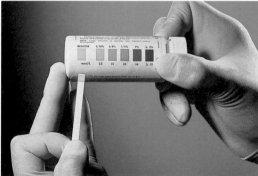

Analytical uses of isolated enzymes

An example of the use of enzymes in the analysis of small quantities of biochemicals are the Clinistix™ used to measure glucose in urine samples. These test strips contain two enzymes, glucose oxidase and peroxidase, and a colourless hydrogen donor compound called chromogen. The strip is dipped into the urine sample. If glucose is present, it is oxidised to gluconic acid and hydrogen peroxide. The second enzyme catalyses the reduction of hydrogen peroxide and the oxidation of chromogen. The products are water and the oxidised dye, which is coloured. The more glucose present in the urine, the more coloured dye is formed. The colour of the test strip is then compared with a printed scale to indicate the amount of glucose in the urine (Figure 4.19).

Fruit juice production

Millions of tonnes of fruit are converted to juice annually; it is a huge and growing market. During the manufacture of fruit juice the cells of the fruits have to be broken down before the bulk of the juice can be extracted. Plant cell walls are built of cellulose, strengthened by hemicelluloses and other substances, and they are extremely tough. If very high temperatures are used to break down fruit tissues to release the juice, it is difficult to maintain the colour and aroma of the fruit in the juice obtained. Instead, as well as crushing the fruits to release the juice, enzyme preparations containing cellulases and hemicellulases are added. These cause the wall materials to break up and most of the liquid of the plant cells in the fruit is released. Enzymatic juice extraction increases the yield by about 20%.

The use of enzymes is illustrated in a laboratory experiment in Figure 4.20. In industry the principle is the same, but the ratio of enzyme to fruit pulp is much lower; less than 150 cm³ of enzyme preparation is added per tonne of apples.

Figure 4.20
Enzymatic juice extraction from apples.

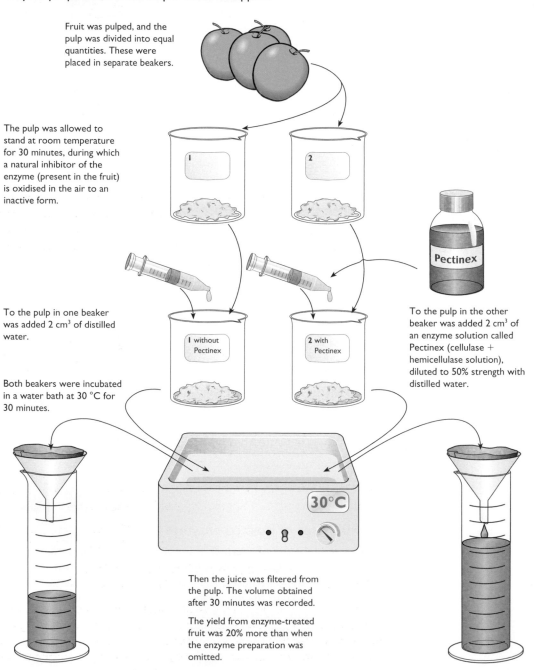

Fruit was pulped, and the pulp was divided into equal quantities. These were placed in separate beakers.

The pulp was allowed to stand at room temperature for 30 minutes, during which a natural inhibitor of the enzyme (present in the fruit) is oxidised in the air to an inactive form.

To the pulp in one beaker was added 2 cm³ of distilled water.

To the pulp in the other beaker was added 2 cm³ of an enzyme solution called Pectinex (cellulase + hemicellulase solution), diluted to 50% strength with distilled water.

Both beakers were incubated in a water bath at 30 °C for 30 minutes.

30°C

Then the juice was filtered from the pulp. The volume obtained after 30 minutes was recorded.

The yield from enzyme-treated fruit was 20% more than when the enzyme preparation was omitted.

1 without Pectinex

2 with Pectinex

Pectinex

94

Lactose-free milk

People unable to produce lactase in their pancreatic juice (page 151) fail to digest milk sugar (lactose) in their small intestine. As a result, bacteria in the large intestine feed on the lactose there, producing fatty acids and methane. The result is diarrhoea and flatulence. The patient is advised to avoid ordinary milk and to drink lactose-free milk. Lactose-free milk can be produced by passing milk through a column containing immobilised lactase, which hydrolyses the lactose to glucose and galactose (Figure 4.21). The enzyme is obtained from bacteria and enclosed in capsules.

Figure 4.21
Production of lactose-free milk.

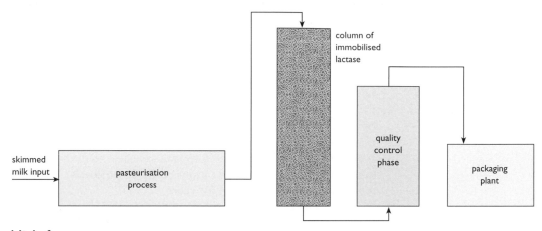

6 Distinguish between the following pairs:

- anabolic reactions and catabolic reactions
- endergonic reactions and exergonic reactions
- intermediates and inhibitors
- ADP and ATP
- inorganic catalysts and biological catalysts
- substrates and products
- active site and activation energy
- coenzyme and prosthetic group
- carboxyl group and amino group
- allosteric activator and allosteric inhibitor.

High-fructose syrup

A sweetener that is widely used in food and drinks is high-fructose corn syrup (HFCS). It is manufactured from starch in corn fruits (maize). The grains are milled to a starch slurry and the enzyme amylase is added. This produces a glucose syrup, which is then decolorised and concentrated. Finally, this syrup is passed down a column of immobilised glucose isomerase enzyme: this converts much of the glucose to fructose. Fructose has the same energy content as glucose, yet it is far sweeter than glucose (or sucrose) – much less is needed. So HFCS is used to sweeten foods without adding too many 'calories' (Figure 4.22).

ingredients: corn syrup, rye flour, fruit 24%

Figure 4.22
Corn syrup as an ingredient of manufactured food.

● **Skills task** In an investigation of oxygen production from hydrogen peroxide solution by the enzyme catalase (see Figure 4.9), the following results were obtained:

Time of readings/s:	0	20	40	60	80	100	120
Volume of O$_2$ produced/cm^3:	0	43	66	78	82	91	92

1 Plot a graph to show oxygen production against time.
2 From your graph, find the *initial rate* of the reaction.

To do this, draw a straight line that continues at the same angle as at the very beginning of the curve on your graph. Continue this line until it crosses a vertical line at '20 s'. Read off the volume of oxygen that would be produced if the initial rate had been maintained for 20 seconds. Express the initial rate as volume of oxygen produced per second (or per minute).

SUMMARY
● **Metabolism** is the sum of all the chemical reactions of life. It consists of **anabolic reactions** (the build-up of complex molecules from smaller ones, e.g. protein synthesis) and **catabolic reactions** (the breakdown of complex molecules, e.g. oxidation of sugar in respiration).

● Chemical **energy** exists in the structure of molecules – the quantity of energy needed to synthesise them initially. Some of this energy is available (known as **free energy**), and can be used to do work in chemical reactions. **Endergonic reactions** require an input of free energy, but **exergonic reactions** release free energy.

● **ATP** is an energy currency molecule by which the free energy from exergonic reactions is made available to drive endergonic reactions.

● All reactions of metabolism are made possible by **enzymes**. Enzymes are biological catalysts, most made of protein. An enzyme is **highly specific**, normally catalysing only one type of reaction for one type of substrate.

● Enzymes work by forming a temporary complex with a substrate molecule at a special part of the enzyme surface, called the **active site** ('**lock and key' hypothesis**). Enzymes work by lowering the **activation energy** needed for a reaction to occur.

● A slight change in shape of the substrate molecule to fit the active site helps raise the molecule to a transition state ('**induced fit' hypothesis**), from which the products may form. The enzyme is released for reuse.

● The rate of an enzyme-catalysed reaction is found by measuring the disappearance of the substrate or the accumulation of the product in unit time. Since the reaction rate falls with time, the **initial rate of reaction** is used to study the reaction.

● The **factors that affect the rate of an enzyme-catalysed reaction** include pH and temperature (through their effects on protein structure), and also the concentration of the substrate. When molecules of substances recognised as inhibitors are in contact with enzyme molecules, the rate of a reaction may be lowered in characteristic ways.

● # Examination questions

I A student carried out an investigation to find the effect of temperature on the activity of the enzyme amylase and plotted the graph shown.

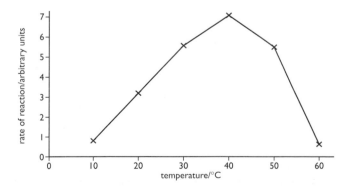

a Explain the results obtained
  i between 10 °C and 20 °C
  ii above 50 °C. (5)
b The student concluded that the optimum temperature for amylase activity was 40 °C. Why may this conclusion not be valid? (1)
  NEAB, AS/A level, Module BY01, Mar 1998

2 a i Describe the structure of a triglyceride molecule. (3)

  ii Describe a test that identifies the presence of lipids. (2)

Biological washing powders make use of enzymes such as lipases and proteases to help in removing stains. The manufacturers of these powders recommend a washing temperature of 40 °C.
b Explain:
  i how biological washing powders help to remove protein stains from clothing (4)
  ii the effect on the protease of increasing the washing temperature from 30 °C to 40 °C. (3)
c Suggest why research into bacteria which live in hot springs has been significant in the development of biological washing powders. (2)
  UCLES, AS/A level, 4801, Mar 1998

3 The diagram shows the sequence of bases in a short length of mRNA.

A U G G C C U C G A U A A C G G C C A C C A U G

a **i** What is the maximum number of amino acids in the polypeptide for which this piece of mRNA could code? (1)

  ii How many different types of tRNA molecule would be used to produce a polypeptide from this piece of mRNA? (1)

  iii Give the DNA sequence which would be complementary to the first five bases in this piece of mRNA. (1)

b Name the process by which mRNA is formed in the nucleus. (1)

c Give **two** ways in which the structure of a molecule of tRNA differs from the structure of a molecule of mRNA. (2)

AQA(NEAB), AS/A level, Module BY02, Mar 1999

4 Read through the following passage about enzymes, then write on the dotted lines the most appropriate word or words to complete the passage.

Enzymes are globular proteins which act as biological catalysts. An individual enzyme will usually catalyse a single type of chemical reaction between particular substrates. This property of enzymes, which is referred to as ...., is due to the presence in the enzyme molecule of a region called the .... which temporarily binds to the substrate.

If the shape of the enzyme molecule is altered, as occurs when it is denatured by ...., the catalytic activity is lost.

Binding with .... instead of the substrate can also slow down the rate of reaction. Enzymes which catalyse similar reactions are grouped under common names. For example, enzymes which catalyse the transfer of electrons between different substrates are known as .... (5)

London, AS/A level, Module B/HB1, June 1999

5 Lactose intolerance in humans is the inability to hydrolyse lactose due to the lack of the enzyme lactase in the alimentary canal. The condition is inherited. The fungus, *Aspergillus oryzae*, is now used to produce lactase on an industrial scale. The enzyme is extracted, purified and immobilised and then used to catalyse the hydrolysis of lactose in milk into simple sugars that can be metabolised by lactose-intolerant people.

a **i** Describe how the immobilised lactase might be used to catalyse the hydrolysis of lactose in milk in a school laboratory. (3)

  ii Suggest how the lactase enzyme might be immobilised. (2)

b **i** List **three** advantages of using immobilised enzymes. (3)

  ii State **three** advantages of using purified enzymes in an industrial process in preference to whole cells. (3)

  iii Suggest **one** reason why it may be necessary in some processes to use whole cells rather than an isolated enzyme. (1)

c Lactase-treated milk is sweeter than untreated milk. Suggest why this might be an advantage in the manufacture of flavoured milk drinks. (1)
The figure shows the structure of lactose.

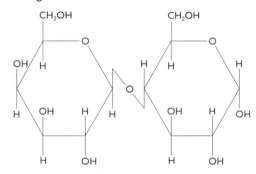

d Describe the hydrolysis of lactose, naming the bond which is broken and one of the products formed. (4)

OCR (Cambridge), A level, 4806, Mar 1999

6 Insulin is a protein. It is made in the cells of the pancreas from a larger molecule called pro-insulin. An enzyme breaks the pro-insulin into insulin and a short polypeptide. This is shown in the diagram.

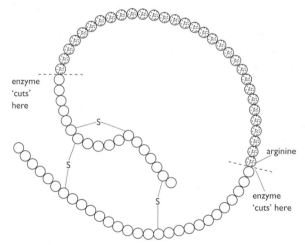

a Name the type of monomer which forms insulin. (1)

b Describe the result you would expect if the enzyme were tested with biuret reagent. (1)

c If the amino acid arginine is replaced by glycine in a molecule of pro-insulin, insulin will not be produced. Explain why the enzyme will no longer break down pro-insulin. (3)

AQA(NEAB), AS/A level, Module BY01, June 1999

5 The nucleus: in division and in control

STARTING POINTS
- The **nucleus** is the largest organelle in the cytoplasm of a cell. It is visible using light microscopy.
- When cells divide the **nucleus divides first**, and each daughter cell receives a nucleus.
- The nucleus **controls and directs the activities of the cell** throughout life.
- The nucleus contains the **hereditary material** that is passed from generation to generation during reproduction.

The nucleus in the life cycle of the cell

Cell growth and cell division are more or less continuous processes in living things. In suitable conditions a unicellular organism will soon divide; the daughter cells grow to full size, and then divide again. Multicellular organisms begin life as a single-celled zygote produced at fertilisation. The zygote grows and divides repeatedly to form the new organism. Growth and cell division continue throughout life as old or damaged cells are replaced.

Before any cell divides, the nucleus divides first. The cytoplasm then divides around the nuclei to form daughter cells. In fact the nucleus is the organising centre of a cell, and has a double function. Firstly, it controls all the activities of the cell throughout life. Secondly, it is the location within the cell of the hereditary material that is passed from generation to generation during reproduction.

Both these functions depend on 'information'. The information in the nucleus is contained within the **chromosomes**. It is the chromosomes that:

- control cell activities
- are copied from cell to cell when cells divide
- are passed into new individuals when sex cells fuse together in sexual reproduction.

The nucleus, its chromosomes and genes

The nucleus is the largest organelle in the cell. It is large enough to be seen by light microscopy. Electron microscopy has shown that the contents of a nucleus are bound by a **double membrane** (page 10). The nuclear membrane is not a continuous sheet but has a large number of tiny holes or **pores**, through which there is communication between nucleus and cytoplasm. The pores are highly significant in the day-to-day management of the cell. We will return to the role of these pores later.

The chromosomes lie inside the nucleus. At the time a nucleus divides they become compact, much-coiled structures. When in this condition they can be made visible by staining with certain dyes. At all other times they are very long, loosely coiled thin threads, which give the stained nucleus a granular appearance. The granules are called **chromatin**.

The nucleus holds information on its chromosomes in the form of a nucleic acid called **deoxyribonucleic acid (DNA)**. DNA is a huge molecule, made up of two paired strands in the form of a double helix (Figure 2.30, page 47). A DNA molecule runs the full length of each chromosome. The chemistry and activities of DNA will be considered later in this chapter.

Each chromosome is effectively a line of **genes**. We can define 'gene' in different ways. For example, a gene is:

- a specific region of a chromosome that can determine the development of a specific characteristic of an organism
- a specific length of the DNA double helix, hundreds or (more often) thousands of base pairs long, that codes for a protein
- a unit of inheritance.

A particular gene always occurs on the same chromosome in the same position. The position of a gene is called its **locus** (*plural* loci). As we will see in a later chapter, each gene may have two or more forms, called **alleles**. The word 'allele' just means 'alternative form'.

Introducing chromosomes

There are four characteristic features of chromosomes.

The number of chromosomes is fixed for any species

The number of chromosomes in the cells of different species varies, but in any one species the number of chromosomes per cell remains the same. For example, mouse cells have 40 chromosomes, onion cells have 16, human cells have 46 and meadow buttercup cells have 14. These are the **chromosome numbers** for these species.

Chromosomes occur in pairs

Chromosome numbers are always even. The reason is that chromosomes occur in pairs, called **homologous pairs**. 'Homologous' means 'similar in structure'. One chromosome of each homologous pair was inherited from one parent, and the second from the other. So, for example, of the 46 human chromosomes, 23 came originally from each parent.

You can see this from the photomicrographs in Figure 5.1. Here, human chromosomes are shown at a stage of nuclear division, and also cut out from a photograph and arranged in descending order of size. Homologous pairs are traditionally numbered in this way in order to be able to identify them.

Figure 5.1
Chromosomes as homologous pairs, as seen during nuclear division.

human chromosomes of a male (seen at the equator of the spindle during nuclear division)

chromosomes arranged as homologous pairs in descending order of size

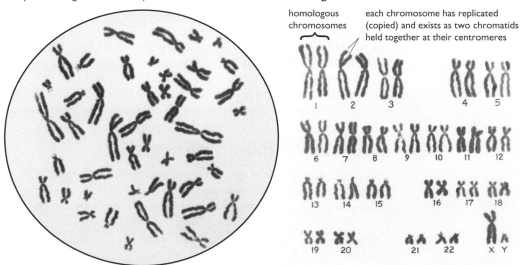

homologous chromosomes

each chromosome has replicated (copied) and exists as two chromatids held together at their centromeres

The shape of a chromosome is characteristic

Chromosomes are long thin structures of a particular fixed length. Somewhere along the length of the chromosome there is a narrow region called the **centromere**. Centromeres may occur anywhere along the chromosome, but they are always in the same position on any given chromosome. The position of the centromere, as well as the length of a chromosome, is how chromosomes are identified in photographs.

Chromosomes copy themselves

Between nuclear divisions, whilst the chromosomes cannot be seen, each chromosome makes a copy of itself. It is said to **replicate**. The two identical structures formed are called **chromatids**. The chromatids remain attached by their centromeres until they are separated during nuclear division (Figure 5.2). Of course, when chromosomes copy themselves the critical event is the copying of the DNA double helix that runs the length of the chromosome. This happens in a particular way, as we shall see shortly.

I Why do chromosomes occur in cells in homologous pairs?

Figure 5.2
One chromosome
as two chromatids.

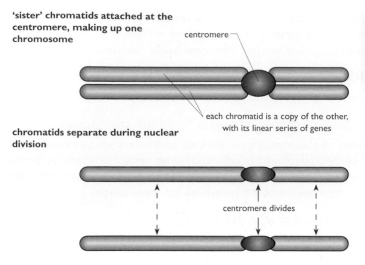

'sister' chromatids attached at the
centromere, making up one
chromosome

centromere

each chromatid is a copy of the other,
with its linear series of genes

Each chromosome (and each chromatid)
is made up of a chain (a linear series) of
genes, from several hundred to some
thousands in all depending on the
chromosome. (The individual genes are
too small to be seen.)

chromatids separate during nuclear
division

centromere divides

The chromosomes in nuclear division

Divisions of the nucleus are very precise processes, ensuring the correct distribution of
chromosomes between the daughter cells. There are two types of nuclear division, known as
mitosis and meiosis.

In **mitosis**, the daughter cells produced have the same number of chromosomes as the
parent cell. Usually there are two of each type: this is known as the **diploid** (**2n**) state. Mitosis is
the nuclear division that occurs when the cells grow, when old cells are replaced, and when an
organism reproduces asexually.

In **meiosis**, the daughter cells contain half the number of chromosomes of the parent cell.
That is, one chromosome of each type is present in the nuclei formed; this is known as the
haploid (**n**) state. Meiosis is the nuclear division that occurs during sexual reproduction,
normally when the gametes are formed.

Whichever division takes place, it is normally followed by division of the cytoplasm to form
separate cells. Division of the cytoplasm of the cell is called **cytokinesis**.

Mitosis: cell division for growth

The cycle of growth and division of a cell is called the **cell cycle**. The cell cycle has three main
stages: **interphase**, **division of the nucleus** and **cell division** (Figure 5.3). Interphase is always
the longest part of the cell cycle, but its length is extremely variable. In cells of the growing point
of a young stem or of a developing human embryo, interphase may last about 24 hours or less. In
mature cells that seldom divide it lasts for a very long time, sometimes indefinitely. Some cells,
once they have differentiated, never divide again and the nucleus remains at interphase
permanently until death of the cell. The range of cell cycles is illustrated in Figure 1.21 (page 18).

What happens to the nucleus in interphase? At first glance the nucleus appears to be 'resting',
for the chromosomes are no longer visible. But this is not the case. Throughout interphase the
chromosomes are actively synthesising proteins. From the chromosomes copies of the
information of particular genes (or groups of genes) are taken for use in the cytoplasm. In the
organelles of the cytoplasm called **ribosomes** (page 14), proteins are assembled from amino
acids, in sequences dictated by the information from the gene. Early during interphase, new
organelles are synthesised in the cytoplasm. Later, the chromosomes are copied or replicated as
chromatids. Finally there is an accumulation of energy stores before the nucleus divides again.

The process of mitosis

In mitosis the chromosomes, present as the chromatids that were formed during interphase, are
separated and accurately and precisely distributed to two daughter nuclei. Mitosis is usually
described as a process in four phases, but this is only for convenience. Mitosis is one continuous
process with no breaks between the phases.

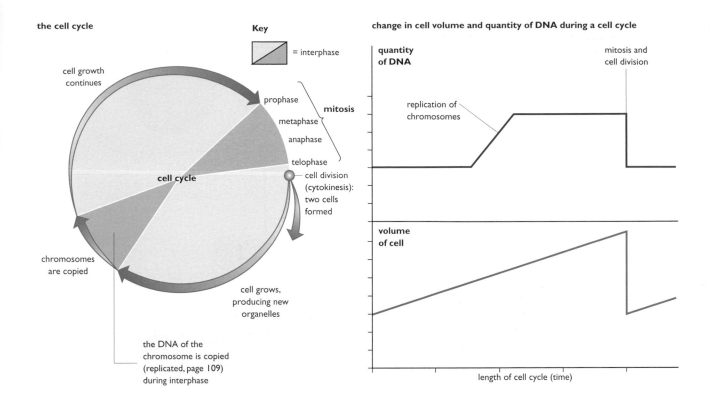

Figure 5.3
The stages of the cell cycle.

In **prophase** the chromosomes become visible as long thin threads. They increasingly shorten and thicken by a process of coiling. Only at the end of prophase can it be seen that each consists of two chromatids held together at the centromere. At the same time, the nucleolus gradually disappears and the nuclear membrane breaks down.

In **metaphase** in animal cells, the centrioles move to opposite ends of the cell. Microtubules of the cytoplasm start to form into a **spindle**, radiating out from the centrioles (Figure 5.4). Microtubules attach to the centromeres of each pair of chromatids, and these are arranged at the equator of the spindle. (In plant cells, a spindle of exactly the same structure is formed, but it is without centrioles.)

In **anaphase** the centromeres divide, the spindle fibres shorten and the chromatids are pulled by their centromeres to opposite poles. Once separated, the chromatids are referred to as chromosomes.

In **telophase** a nuclear membrane re-forms around both groups of chromosomes at opposite ends of the cell. The chromosomes 'decondense' by uncoiling, becoming chromatin again. The nucleolus re-forms in each nucleus. Interphase follows.

Division of the cytoplasm (cytokinesis) follows telophase. During division, cell organelles like mitochondria and chloroplasts become distributed evenly between the cells. Animal cells divide by intucking of the plasma membrane at the equator of the spindle, 'pinching' the cytoplasm in half (Figure 5.4). In plant cells, the Golgi apparatus forms vesicles of new cell wall materials. These collect along the line of the equator of the spindle and lay down a cell wall between the two cells (Figure 1.20, page 18).

The significance of mitosis

- Daughter cells produced by mitosis have sets of chromosomes that are identical to each other, and to those of the parent cell from which they were formed. In growth and development it is important that all cells carry the same information as the existing cells.
- Similarly, when damaged or worn-out cells are repaired, they are exact copies of what they replace.
- Mitotic cell division is also the basis of all forms of asexual reproduction, in which the offspring produced are identical to the parent.

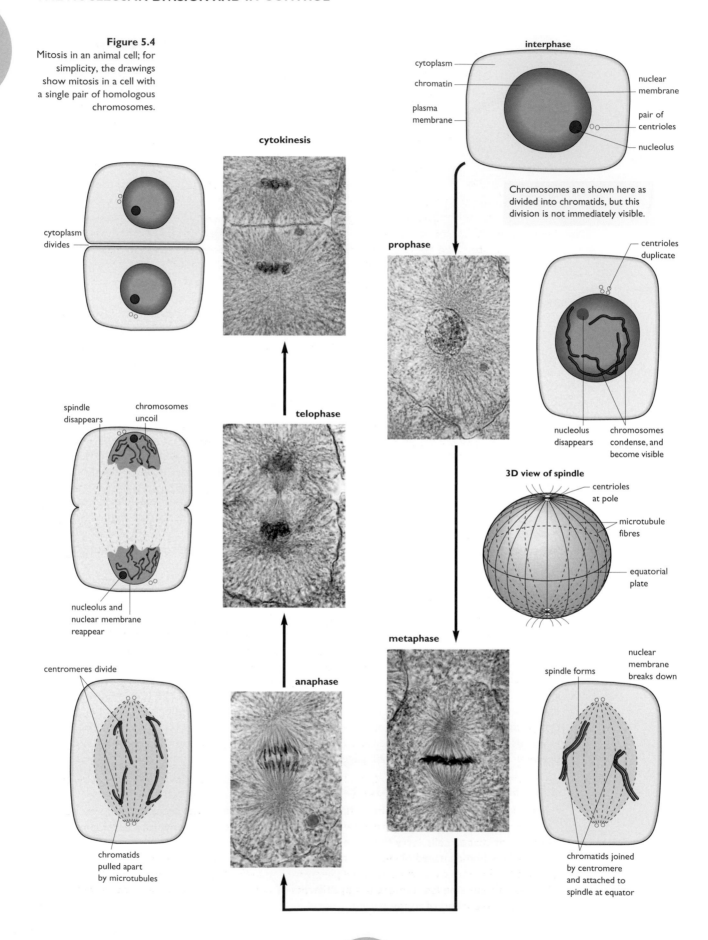

Figure 5.4
Mitosis in an animal cell; for simplicity, the drawings show mitosis in a cell with a single pair of homologous chromosomes.

interphase

cytoplasm
chromatin
plasma membrane
nuclear membrane
pair of centrioles
nucleolus

Chromosomes are shown here as divided into chromatids, but this division is not immediately visible.

cytokinesis

cytoplasm divides

prophase

centrioles duplicate

nucleolus disappears

chromosomes condense, and become visible

telophase

spindle disappears

chromosomes uncoil

nucleolus and nuclear membrane reappear

3D view of spindle

centrioles at pole

microtubule fibres

equatorial plate

anaphase

centromeres divide

chromatids pulled apart by microtubules

metaphase

nuclear membrane breaks down

spindle forms

chromatids joined by centromere and attached to spindle at equator

● **Extension** Cancer = uncontrolled cell division

There are very many different forms of cancer, affecting different tissues of the body. Cancer is not thought of as a single disease. In all cancers, however, cells divide by mitosis repeatedly, without control or regulation. An irregular mass of cells, called a tumour, is formed. Sometimes tumour cells break away and are carried to other parts of the body, forming a secondary tumour. Unchecked, cancerous cells ultimately take over the body, leading to malfunction and death.

Cancer is caused by damage to DNA. 'Mistakes' of different types build up in the DNA in the body cells. Mistakes accumulate over time; this is why most cancers arise in older people. Different types of 'mistake' are possible, which is why cancer is not one single disease. For example, some mistakes occur in the genes that control cell division, and these mistakes may lead to cancer. Another possible cause is damage to the gene that codes for the protein, known as **p53**, that stops the copying of damaged DNA. This p53 protein and the gene that codes for it have been called 'the guardians of the genome'. The p53 protein works by halting the copying of the faulty DNA; other enzymes may then repair and correct the fault. When this happens, cancer is avoided.

Damage to DNA has many potential causes, including the effects of ionising radiation (such as X-rays, gamma-rays and others), certain chemicals (such as components of the tar in tobacco smoke) and some virus infections. Another set of factors is inherited, in that the members of some families are more likely than others to suffer from certain cancers.

● # Meiosis: the reductive division

Meiosis is a part of the life cycle of every organism that reproduces sexually. In meiosis four daughter cells are produced, each with half the number of chromosomes of the parent cell. Halving of the chromosome number is essential, since when two gametes fuse at fertilisation the number is doubled.

How does meiosis work? Meiosis involves two divisions of the nucleus, known as meiosis I and meiosis II, both of which *superficially* resemble mitosis. As in mitosis, chromosomes replicate to form chromatids during interphase. Then, early in meiosis I, homologous chromosomes pair up. By the end of meiosis I, the homologous chromosomes have separated again, but the chromatids they consist of do not separate until meiosis II. Thus, meiosis consists of *two* nuclear divisions but only *one* replication of the chromosomes.

The process of meiosis

The steps to meiosis are summarised in Figure 5.5. This shows that in the interphase that precedes meiosis the chromosomes are replicated as chromatids, but between meiosis I and II there is no further interphase (so no replication of the chromosomes *during* meiosis).

As meiosis begins, the chromosomes become visible as they shorten and thicken by coiling. At the same time, homologous chromosomes pair up. (Remember, in a diploid cell each chromosome has a partner that is the same length and shape and with the same linear sequence of genes.) When the homologous chromosomes have paired up closely, each pair is called a **bivalent**. Members of the bivalent continue to shorten and thicken.

During the coiling and shortening process within the bivalent, the chromatids frequently break. Broken ends rejoin more or less immediately, but often the chromatids swap pieces between each other. The point of join between two chromatids is called a **chiasma**. The event is known as a **crossing over**, because lengths of genes have been exchanged between chromatids. Then, when members of the bivalents start to repel each other and separate, the bivalents are (initially) held together by one or more chiasmata. This temporarily gives an unusual shape to the bivalent.

Next, the spindle forms. Members of the bivalents become attached by their centromeres to the microtubule fibres at the equatorial plate of the spindle. The spindle fibres pull the homologous chromosomes apart to opposite poles, but the individual chromatids remain attached by their centromeres.

Figure 5.5
Meiosis in an animal cell;
for simplicity, the drawings
show meiosis in a cell with
a single pair of homologous
chromosomes.

MEIOSIS I

prophase I (early)
During interphase the
chromosomes replicate into
chromatids held together by
a centromere (the
chromatids are not visible).
Now the chromosomes
condense (shorten and
thicken) and become visible.

prophase I (late)
Homologous chromosomes
repel each other.
Chromosomes can now be
seen to consist of
chromatids. Sites where
chromatids have broken and
rejoined, causing crossing
over, are visible as chiasmata.

anaphase I
Homologous chromosomes
separate. Whole
chromosomes are pulled
towards opposite poles of
the spindle, centromere first
(dragging along the
chromatids).

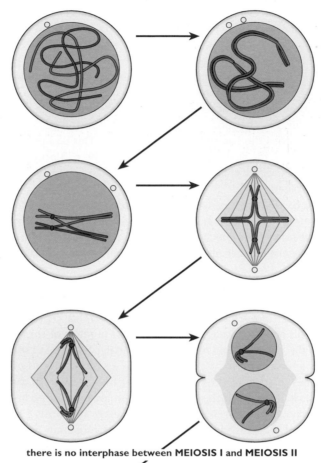

prophase I (mid)
Homologous chromosomes
pair up (becoming
bivalents) as they continue
to shorten and thicken.
Centrioles duplicate.

metaphase I
Nuclear membrane breaks
down. Spindle forms.
Bivalents line up at the
equator, attached by
centromeres.

telophase I
Nuclear membrane re-forms
around the daughter nuclei.
The chromosome number
has been halved. The
chromosomes start to
decondense.

there is no interphase between MEIOSIS I and MEIOSIS II

MEIOSIS II

prophase II
The chromosomes condense
and the centrioles duplicate.

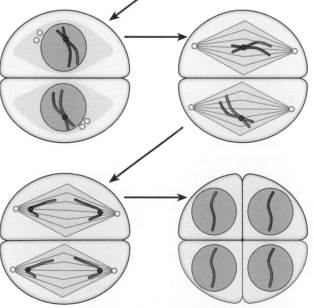

metaphase II
The nuclear membrane
breaks down and the spindle
forms. The chromosomes
attach by their centromeres
to spindle fibres at the
equator of the spindle.

anaphase II
The chromatids separate at
their centromeres and are
pulled to opposite poles of
the spindle.

telophase II
The chromatids (now called
chromosomes) decondense.
The nuclear membrane
re-forms. The cells divide.

**The parent cell contained two chromosomes, whereas the
four cells formed each contain a single chromosome.**

Meiosis I ends with two cells each containing a single set of chromosomes, each made of two chromatids. These cells do not go into interphase, but rather continue smoothly into meiosis II. This takes place at right angles to meiosis I, but is exactly like mitosis. Centromeres of the chromosomes divide and individual chromatids move to opposite poles. Now there are four cells, each with half the chromosome number of the original parent cell.

Meiosis and genetic variation

The four haploid cells produced by meiosis differ genetically from each other for two main reasons.

- There is **independent assortment** of maternal and paternal homologous chromosomes. The bivalents line up at the equator of the spindle in meiosis I in an entirely random order. Which chromosome of a given pair goes to which pole is unaffected by (independent of) the behaviour of the chromosomes in other pairs. This is illustrated in Figure 5.6, in a parent (diploid) cell with four chromosomes.

- There is **crossing over** of segments of individual maternal and paternal homologous chromosomes. This results in new combinations of genes on the chromosomes of the haploid cells produced. This is illustrated in Figure 5.7.

2 What are the essential differences between mitosis and meiosis?

Figure 5.6
Genetic variation due to independent assortment.

Independent assortment is illustrated in a parent cell with two pairs of homologous chromosomes (four bivalents).

(The more bivalents there are, the more variation is possible. In humans, for example, there are 23 pairs of chromosomes.)

At metaphase I, the bivalents move to the equator of the spindle. Then, when homologous chromosomes separate at anaphase I they move to the nearest pole. This may occur

leading, in meiosis II, to the following alternative combinations of individual chromosomes in the four haploid cells:

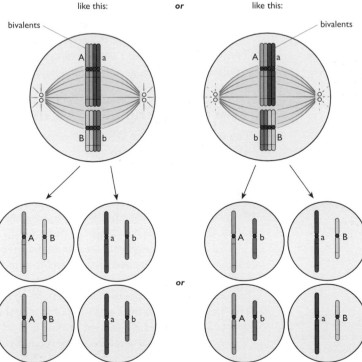

105

Figure 5.7
Genetic variation due
to crossing over.

The effects of chiasmata on genetic variation are illustrated in one pair of homologous chromosomes.
Typically, two or three chiasmata form between the chromatids of a bivalent in prophase I.

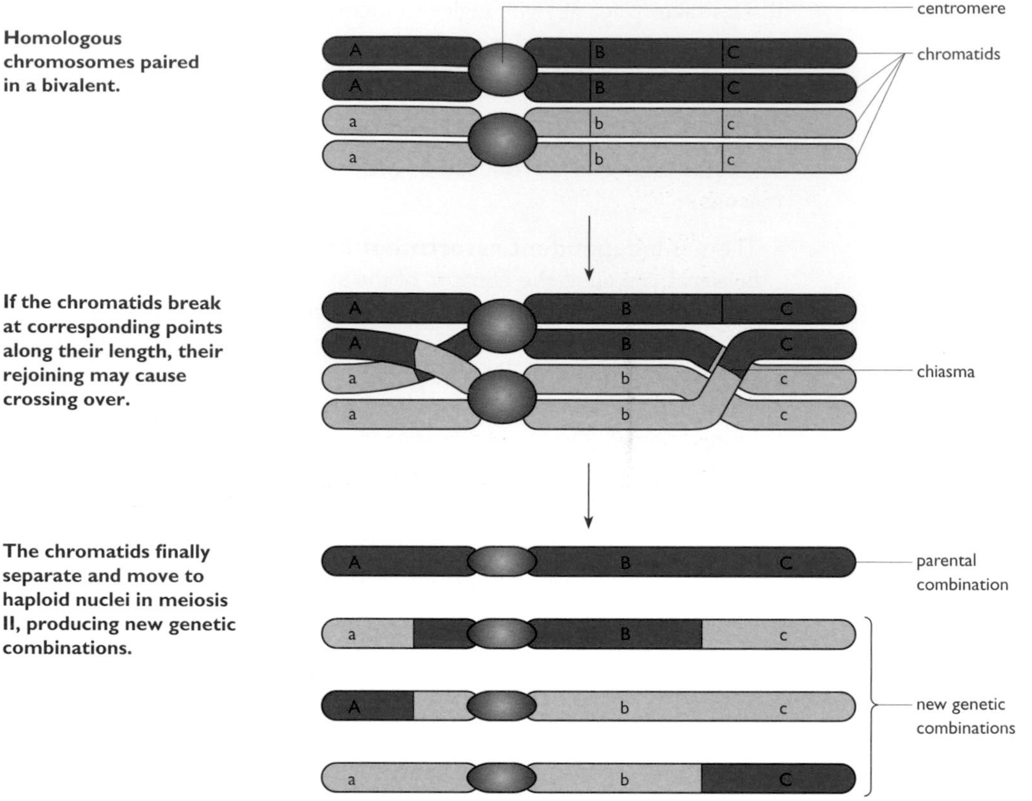

**Homologous
chromosomes paired
in a bivalent.**

centromere
chromatids

**If the chromatids break
at corresponding points
along their length, their
rejoining may cause
crossing over.**

chiasma

**The chromatids finally
separate and move to
haploid nuclei in meiosis
II, producing new genetic
combinations.**

parental
combination

new genetic
combinations

DNA, the genetic material

More than 50% of a chromosome consists of protein. No wonder people once speculated that
the protein of the chromosomes would prove to be the 'information substance' of the cell.
Another reason for this belief in protein was that it seemed to have more chemical 'variety'
within its structure than nucleic acid does.

We now know that DNA holds the information that codes for the sequence of amino acids
from which the proteins of the cell cytoplasm are built. Most of these proteins are enzymes that
regulate metabolism, growth and development. In this way, DNA controls and directs
metabolism.

The packaging of DNA in chromosomes

The total length of the DNA of the human chromosomes is over 2 m, shared out between the
46 chromosomes. Each chromosome contains one very long DNA molecule. Of course,
chromosomes are of different lengths (Figure 5.1), but we can estimate that a typical
chromosome 5 μm long will contain a DNA molecule approximately 5 cm long. That is, about
50 000 μm of DNA is packed into 5 μm of chromosome! Today we know that, whilst some of
the proteins of the chromosome are enzymes involved in the copying and repair reactions of
DNA, the bulk of chromosome protein simply supports and packages the DNA.

One sort of packaging protein is called **histone**. This is a basic (positively charged) protein
containing a high concentration of amino acid molecules with additional base groups ($-NH_2$),
such as lysine and arginine. These histones occur clumped together, and provide support to
lengths of the DNA double helix that are wrapped around them, looking like beads on a thread.
The 'bead thread' is itself coiled up, forming the chromatin fibre. The chromatin fibre is again
coiled, and the coils are looped around a 'scaffold' protein fibre, made of a non-histone protein.
This whole structure is folded ('supercoiled') into the much-condensed metaphase chromosome
(Figure 5.8).

3 What are the different
roles of proteins found
in chromosomes?

Figure 5.8
The packaging of DNA in a chromosome.

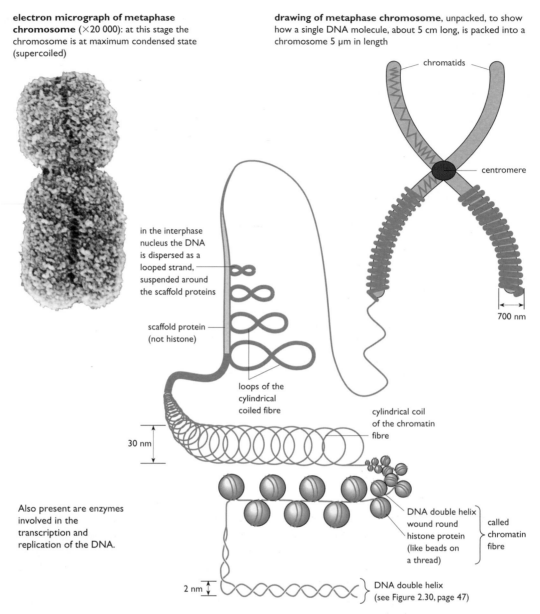

electron micrograph of metaphase chromosome (×20 000): at this stage the chromosome is at maximum condensed state (supercoiled)

drawing of metaphase chromosome, unpacked, to show how a single DNA molecule, about 5 cm long, is packed into a chromosome 5 μm in length

chromatids

centromere

700 nm

in the interphase nucleus the DNA is dispersed as a looped strand, suspended around the scaffold proteins

scaffold protein (not histone)

loops of the cylindrical coiled fibre

cylindrical coil of the chromatin fibre

30 nm

Also present are enzymes involved in the transcription and replication of the DNA.

DNA double helix wound round histone protein (like beads on a thread) } called chromatin fibre

2 nm

DNA double helix (see Figure 2.30, page 47)

● **Extension** Evidence for DNA as the 'information' molecule of the cell

That DNA is the genetic 'information' was confirmed by an experiment with a bacteriophage virus (a virus that parasitises a bacterium). Viruses consist of a protein coat surrounding a nucleic acid core. Once a virus has gained entry to a host cell it takes over the cell's metabolism, switching it to the production of new viruses. Eventually, the remains of the host cell break down (*lysis*) and the virus particle escapes, usually to repeat the infection with new host cells. The life cycle of a bacteriophage ('phage), which is a virus with a complex 'head' and 'tail' structure, is shown in Figure 5.9.

The bacteriophage (known as T_2) that attacks *E. coli* was used in an experiment to answer the question of whether 'genetic information' lies in the protein (coat) or the DNA (core) (Figure 5.10). Two batches of the bacteriophage were produced, one with radioactive phosphorus (^{32}P) built into the DNA core (the DNA was 'labelled') and one with radioactive sulphur (^{35}S) built into the protein coat (the protein was 'labelled'). Now sulphur occurs in protein, but there is no sulphur in DNA. Likewise, phosphorus occurs in DNA, but there is no phosphorus in protein. Thus these radioactive labels were specific.

continued

Two identical cultures of *E. coli* were infected, one with the ^{32}P-labelled virus and one with the ^{35}S-labelled virus. The cultures were incubated, and then the viruses were recovered. Only from the culture infected with virus labelled with ^{32}P were radioactively labelled viruses obtained. The ^{35}S label did not enter the host cell at all. This experiment demonstrated that it is the DNA part of the virus which enters the host cell and carries the genetic information for the production of new viruses.

Figure 5.9
The life cycle of a bacteriophage.

TEM of bacteriophage infecting a bacterium

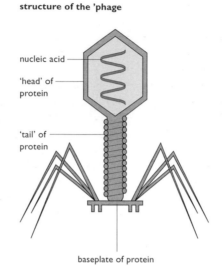

structure of the 'phage

nucleic acid

'head' of protein

'tail' of protein

baseplate of protein

steps to replication of the 'phage

1 The 'phage attaches to the bacterial wall and then injects the virus DNA.

2 Virus DNA takes over the host's synthesis machinery.

3 New viruses are assembled and then escape to repeat the infection cycle.

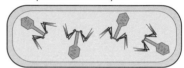

Figure 5.10
The Hershey–Chase experiment.

Is it the **protein coat** or the **DNA** of a bacteriophage that enters the host cell and takes over the cell's machinery, so causing new viruses to be produced?

The question was answered using:

1 'phage labelled with radioactive sulphur (^{35}S): sulphur is a component of protein *but not of DNA*

and

2 'phage labelled with radioactive phosphorus (^{32}P): phosphorus is a component of DNA *but not of protein*

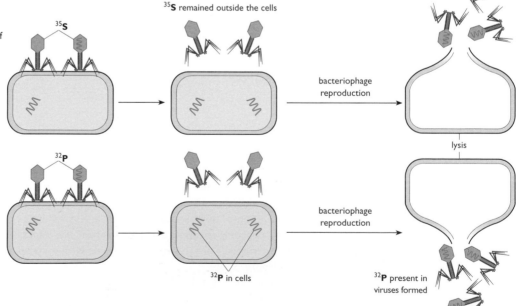

^{35}S remained outside the cells

^{35}S

bacteriophage reproduction

lysis

^{32}P

^{32}P in cells

bacteriophage reproduction

^{32}P present in viruses formed

Only the DNA part of the virus got into the host cell (and radioactively labelled DNA was present in the new viruses formed).
    It was the virus DNA that controlled the formation of new viruses in the host, so they concluded that **DNA carries the genetic message**.

Replication: how DNA copies itself

In order that a copy of each chromosome can pass into the daughter cells at cell division, the DNA of the chromosomes must first be duplicated, or **replicated**. As the DNA carries the genetic message, replication must be extremely accurate. Interestingly, replication is quite separate from cell division. Replication of DNA takes place in the interphase nucleus, well before the events of nuclear division (Figure 5.3, page 101).

Strands of the DNA double helix are built up individually by adding on free nucleotides. (The structure of a nucleotide is shown in Figure 2.27, page 45.) Before individual nucleotides can be condensed together in the correct sequence, the DNA double helix has to unwind, and the hydrogen bonds holding the strands together must be broken. This allows the two strands of the helix to separate. Enzymes are involved in these steps and an enzyme holds the strands apart whilst replication proceeds.

In replication, both strands act as templates. New nucleotides with the appropriate complementary bases line up opposite the bases of the exposed strands (A is always paired with T, and C with G – a process called **base pairing**). Hydrogen bonds then form between complementary bases, holding the nucleotides in place – see Figure 2.30, page 47. Finally the sugar and phosphate groups of adjacent nucleotides of the new strand condense together. (This reaction is catalysed by an enzyme called **DNA polymerase**.) Then each pair of the double strand winds up into a double helix. One strand of each new double helix comes from the parent chromosome and one is a newly synthesised strand. This arrangement is known as **semi-conservative replication**, because half the original molecule is conserved.

DNA polymerase also has a role in 'proof reading' the new strands. Any 'mistakes' that start to happen (for example, the wrong bases attempting to pair up) are immediately corrected. Each new DNA double helix is exactly like the original.

This process of DNA replication is summarised in Figure 5.11.

Figure 5.11
DNA replication.

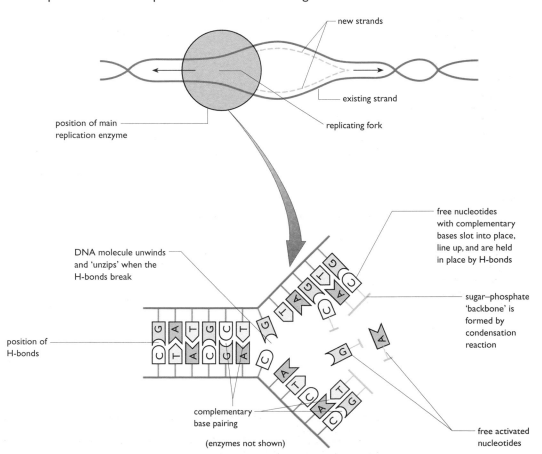

new strands

existing strand

replicating fork

position of main
replication enzyme

free nucleotides
with complementary
bases slot into place,
line up, and are held
in place by H-bonds

DNA molecule unwinds
and 'unzips' when the
H-bonds break

sugar–phosphate
'backbone' is
formed by
condensation
reaction

position of
H-bonds

complementary
base pairing

(enzymes not shown)

free activated
nucleotides

● **Extension**   ## The evidence for DNA replication

Experimental evidence that DNA is replicated semi-conservatively, and not by some other mechanism, came from a growing culture of the bacterium *E. coli* in a medium (food source) where the available nitrogen contained only the heavy nitrogen isotope ^{15}N. Consequently, the DNA of the bacterium became entirely 'heavy'.

These bacteria were then transferred to a medium of the normal (light) isotope, ^{14}N. New DNA manufactured by the cells now contained ^{14}N. The changes in concentration of ^{15}N and ^{14}N in the DNA of succeeding generations were measured. The bacterial cell divisions in the culture were naturally synchronised; every 60 minutes or so they all divided again. The DNA was extracted from samples of the bacteria from each generation and the DNAs in each sample were separated. This was done by placing the sample on top of a salt solution of increasing density, in a centrifuge tube. On being centrifuged, the different DNA molecules were carried down to the level where the salt solution was of the same density. Thus DNA with 'heavy' nitrogen ended up nearer the base of the tubes, whereas DNA with 'light' nitrogen stayed near the top of the tubes. Figure 5.12 shows the results that were obtained.

Figure 5.12
DNA replication is semi-conservative (the Meselson and Stahl experiment).

In this experiment the DNA of the bacterium *E. coli* was labelled with 'heavy' nitrogen (^{15}N), by growing it for several generations in a medium where the only nitrogen was 'heavy'.

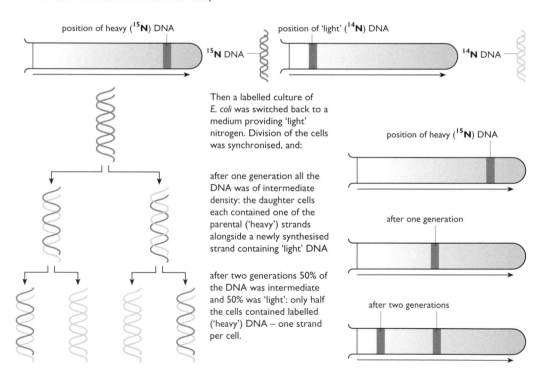

When DNA from labelled cells was extracted and centrifuged in a density gradient of different salt solutions, all the DNA was found to be 'heavy'.

In contrast, the DNA extracted from cells of the original culture (before treatment with ^{15}N) was 'light'.

position of heavy (^{15}N) DNA   position of 'light' (^{14}N) DNA ^{15}N DNA ^{14}N DNA

Then a labelled culture of *E. coli* was switched back to a medium providing 'light' nitrogen. Division of the cells was synchronised, and:

after one generation all the DNA was of intermediate density: the daughter cells each contained one of the parental ('heavy') strands alongside a newly synthesised strand containing 'light' DNA

after two generations 50% of the DNA was intermediate and 50% was 'light': only half the cells contained labelled ('heavy') DNA – one strand per cell.

position of heavy (^{15}N) DNA

after one generation

after two generations

DNA in protein synthesis

The genetic code

In effect, the role of DNA is to instruct the cell to make specific proteins. The huge length of the DNA molecule in a chromosome codes for a very large number of proteins. Within this extremely long molecule, the relatively short length of DNA that codes for a single protein is called a **gene**. Proteins are very variable in size: therefore, so are genes. A very few genes are as short as 75–100 nucleotides long. Most are at least a thousand nucleotides in length, and some are longer still.

4 The sequence of bases in a sample of mRNA was found to be:

GGU, AAU, CCU, UUU, GUU, ACU, CAU, UGU

a What sequence of amino acids does this code for?
b What was the sequence of bases in the coding strand of DNA from which this mRNA was transcribed?

Most proteins contain several hundred amino acids condensed together in a linear series. Only 20 or so amino acids are used in protein synthesis; all cell proteins are built from these. The unique properties of each protein lie in:

- which amino acids are involved in its construction
- the sequence in which these amino acids are joined.

The DNA code is in the form of a sequence of the four bases: cytosine (C), guanine (G), adenine (A) and thymine (T). This sequence dictates the order in which specific amino acids are to be assembled and combined together. The code lies in the sequence in one of the strands, the reference or **coding strand**. The other strand is complementary to the reference strand. The coding strand is always read in the same direction (Figure 5.13).

The code is a three-letter or **triplet code**, meaning that each sequence of three of the four bases stands for one of the 20 amino acids, and is called a **codon**. With a four-letter alphabet (C, G, A, T) there are 64 possible different triplet combinations ($4 \times 4 \times 4$). In other words, the genetic code has many more codons than there are amino acids. In fact most amino acids are coded by two or three similar codons. Also, some of the codons represent the 'punctuations' of the code; for example, there are 'start' and 'stop' triplets (Figure 5.14).

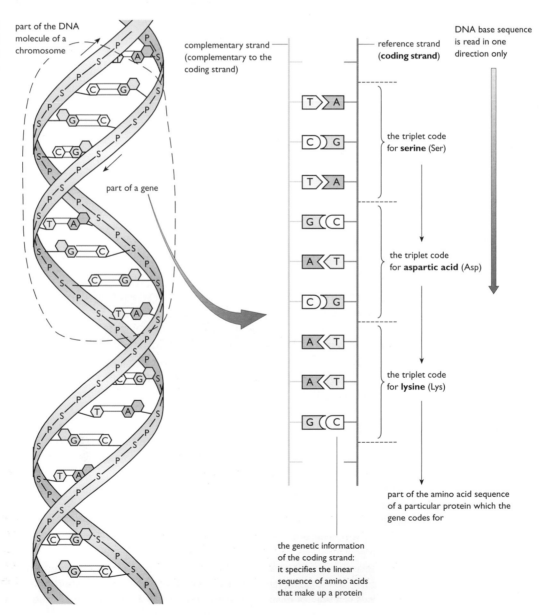

Figure 5.13 Part of a gene and how its DNA codes for amino acids.

Figure 5.14
The genetic code – a
universal code.

The genetic code is universal. A codon codes for the same amino acid in all organisms and in the viruses.

The 20 amino acids used in protein synthesis

Amino acids	Abbreviations
alanine	Ala
arginine	Arg
asparagine	Asn
aspartic acid	Asp
cysteine	Cys
glutamine	Gln
glutamic acid	Glu
glycine	Gly
histidine	His
isoleucine	Ile
leucine	Leu
lysine	Lys
methionine	Met
phenylalanine	Phe
proline	Pro
serine	Ser
threonine	Thr
tryptophan	Trp
tyrosine	Tyr
valine	Val

The genetic code in circular form
The codons are those of the complementary strand and of messenger RNA (where uracil, U, replaces thymine, T).

Read the code from the centre of the circle outwards along a radius. For example, serine is coded by UCU, UCC, UCA or UCG, or by AGU or AGC.

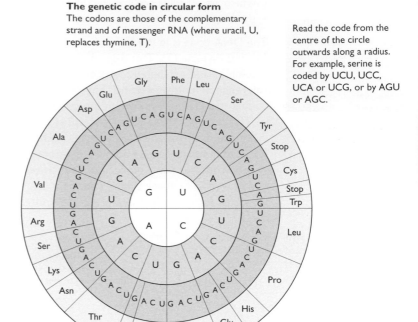

In addition, some codons stand for **stop**, signalling the end of a peptide/protein chain.

The steps to protein synthesis

There are three major steps in the process by which the information of the gene is used to determine how the protein molecule is constructed.

Stage one occurs in the nucleus, where a complementary copy of the code is made by the building of a molecule of **messenger RNA (mRNA)**. This process is called **transcription** (Figure 5.15), and the enzyme controlling it is RNA polymerase. One strand of the DNA, the coding strand, is used as the template. Once the mRNA strand is formed it leaves the nucleus through pores in the nuclear membrane and passes to ribosomes in the cytoplasm. This is where the information can be 'read' and is used.

In *Stage two* the amino acids are **activated** for protein synthesis by combining with short lengths of a different sort of RNA, called **transfer RNA (tRNA)**. This activation occurs in the cytoplasm. It is the tRNA that translates a three-base sequence into an amino acid sequence (Figure 5.16).

All the tRNAs have a clover-leaf shape, but there is a different tRNA for each of the 20 amino acids that go to make up proteins. At one end of each tRNA molecule is a site where a particular amino acid can be joined. At the other end, there is a sequence of three bases called an **anticodon**. This anticodon is complementary to the codon of mRNA that codes for the specific amino acid.

The amino acid is attached to its tRNA by an enzyme. These enzymes are specific to the particular amino acids (and types of tRNA) to be used in protein synthesis. The specificity of the enzymes is a way of ensuring the correct amino acids are used in the right sequence.

Figure 5.15

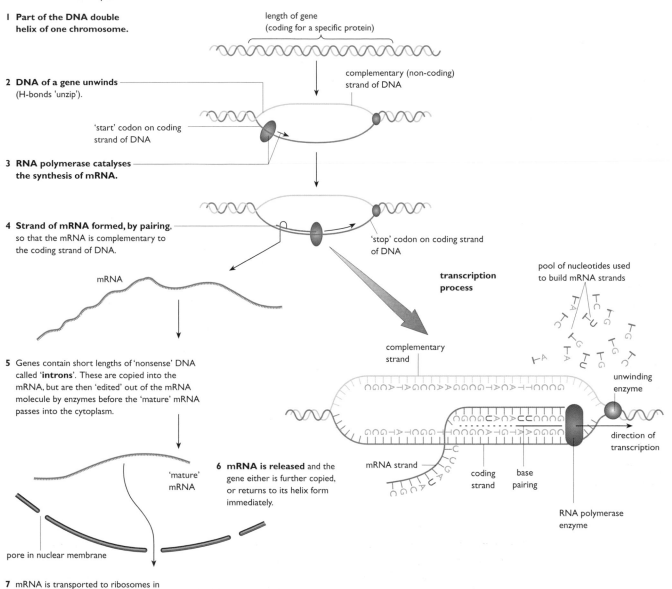

1 **Part of the DNA double helix of one chromosome.**

length of gene
(coding for a specific protein)

2 **DNA of a gene unwinds** (H-bonds 'unzip').

complementary (non-coding) strand of DNA

'start' codon on coding strand of DNA

3 **RNA polymerase catalyses the synthesis of mRNA.**

4 **Strand of mRNA formed, by pairing,** so that the mRNA is complementary to the coding strand of DNA.

'stop' codon on coding strand of DNA

mRNA

transcription process

pool of nucleotides used to build mRNA strands

5 Genes contain short lengths of 'nonsense' DNA called '**introns**'. These are copied into the mRNA, but are then 'edited' out of the mRNA molecule by enzymes before the 'mature' mRNA passes into the cytoplasm.

complementary strand

unwinding enzyme

direction of transcription

'mature' mRNA

6 **mRNA is released** and the gene either is further copied, or returns to its helix form immediately.

mRNA strand

coding strand

base pairing

RNA polymerase enzyme

pore in nuclear membrane

7 mRNA is transported to ribosomes in the cytoplasm.

Figure 5.16
Amino acid activation.

Each amino acid is linked to a specific transfer RNA (tRNA) before it can be used in protein synthesis. This is the process of amino acid activation. It takes place in the cytoplasm.

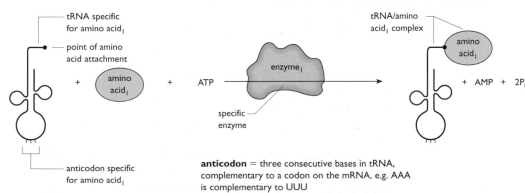

tRNA specific for amino acid$_1$

point of amino acid attachment

amino acid$_1$

+   +   ATP

enzyme$_1$

specific enzyme

tRNA/amino acid$_1$ complex

amino acid$_1$

+ AMP + 2P$_i$

anticodon specific for amino acid$_1$

anticodon = three consecutive bases in tRNA, complementary to a codon on the mRNA, e.g. AAA is complementary to UUU

In *Stage three* a protein chain is assembled, one amino acid residue at a time. This process is called **translation** (Figure 5.17). Tiny organelles called ribosomes (page 14) move along the mRNA 'reading' the codons from the start codon. In the ribosome, complementary anticodons of the amino acid–tRNA slot into place and are temporarily held in position by hydrogen bonds. Whilst being held there, the amino acids of neighbouring amino acid–tRNAs are joined by peptide bonds. This frees the first tRNA, which moves back into the cytoplasm for reuse. The ribosome then moves on to the next mRNA codon. The process continues until the ribosome meets a 'stop' codon.

Figure 5.17 Translation.

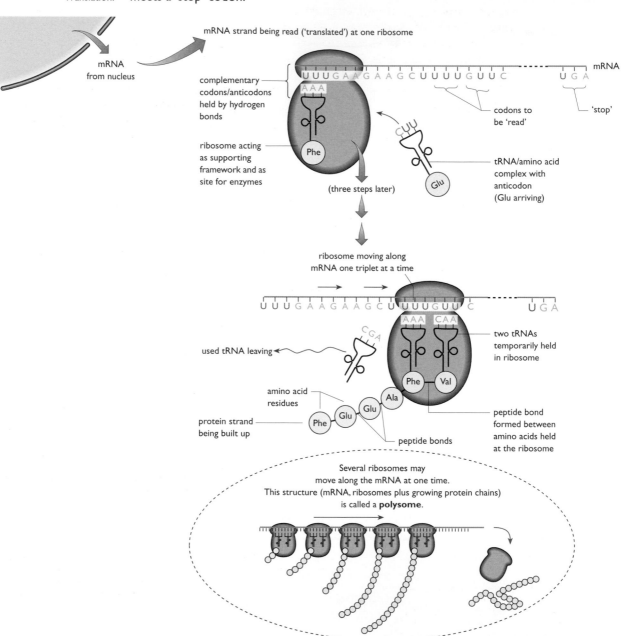

The central dogma

We have seen that DNA can copy itself (replication), and that copies of RNA are made and pass to the ribosomes in the cytoplasm during protein synthesis. This apparently one-way flow of information has been named the **central dogma of molecular biology**. This is to draw attention to the direction in which information travels – from the nucleus to the cytoplasm, and never the other way round.

DNA can change

A gene is a sequence of nucleotide pairs that codes for a sequence of amino acids. Normally, the sequence of nucleotides in DNA is maintained without changing, but change *can* happen at any base pair of any gene. Very occasionally, it does. If so, we say a **gene mutation** has occurred. A mutation is an unpredictable change in the genetic make-up of a cell.

At certain points in the cell cycle, and under particular external conditions mutations are more likely. One such point is when the DNA molecule is replicating. We have seen that the enzyme machinery that brings about the building of a complementary DNA strand also 'proof reads' and corrects most errors. Even so, mutations can and do occur spontaneously during this step. Certain chemicals may also cause change to the DNA sequence of bases. So do some forms of radiation, such as X-rays. Factors that increase the chances of a mutation are called **mutagens**.

Now that we have knowledge of the structure of DNA and of the way it codes for protein synthesis, it is possible to change the structure of a gene selectively, and to move genes between organisms. This activity is called **genetic engineering**. Genetic engineers deliberately carry out changes to DNA (see Chapter 6).

Figure 5.18
Sickle cell anaemia; an example of a gene mutation.

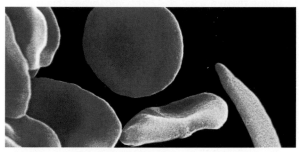

sickled red cells in the blood of a patient

Sickle cell anaemia is a genetically transmitted disease of the blood caused by an abnormal form of haemoglobin. Red cells with 'sickle' haemoglobin do not carry oxygen and can cause blockage of arterioles. Normally, sickle cell anaemia confers a disadvantage, but the malarial parasite (page 332) is unable to complete its life cycle in red cells with haemoglobin S, so the gene for sickle cell is selected for in regions of the world where malaria occurs.

Each **red cell** contains about 280 million molecules of haemoglobin. **Haemoglobin** consists of two α-haemoglobin and two β-haemoglobin sub-units that interlock to form a compact molecule. The **mutation** that produces sickle cell haemoglobin (haemoglobin S) is in the gene for β-haemoglobin.

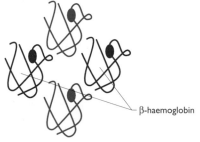

β-haemoglobin

normal	mutant
A = T	A = T
G ≡ C	G ≡ C
C ≡ G	C ≡ G
T = A	→ G ≡ C
T = A	T = A
A = T	A = T

sickle cell mutation involves a **substitution** of a base pair in part of the DNA strand coding for the β-haemoglobin. Valine is substituted for glutamic acid, so, the difference is due to a single amino acid residue

NORMAL = Valine – Histidine – Leucine – Threonine – Proline – Glutamic acid – Glutamic acid
VALINE = Valine – Histidine – Leucine – Threonine – Proline – Valine – Glutamic acid

The distribution of haemoglobin S is virtually the same as that of malaria.

Plasmodium (malarial parasite, a protozoan) cannot complete its life cycle in red cells with haemoglobin S, so, people with sickle cell trait are protected. Where malaria is endemic, e.g. Africa, the mutant gene is advantageous, and is selected for. That is, many of the people who contract malaria die of the diease (particularly children), so fewer of the alleles for normal haemoglobin are carried into the next generation.

a) **distribution of sickle cell gene in the population**

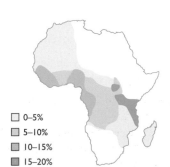

☐ 0–5%
☐ 5–10%
☐ 10–15%
■ 15–20%

b) **distribution of malaria** caused by *Plasmodium falciparum* or *P. vivax* (the forms of malaria that are most frequently fatal, especially in childhood)

Mutations

Mutations that change the sequence of bases in the DNA of a gene are called **gene mutations**. For example, a gene mutation is responsible for the condition known as **sickle cell anaemia** (Figure 5.18). Haemoglobin, the oxygen-transporting pigment of red cells, is made of four protein groups that interlock to form a compact molecule. Two of the haemoglobin molecules are α-haemoglobin and two are β-haemoglobin (Figure 11.14, page 237). The gene that codes for the amino acid sequence of β-haemoglobin occurs on chromosome 11. It is prone to a mutation in which one base pair (T–A) is substituted by another (C–G) at a point in the gene where the amino acid glutamic acid is coded for. The triplet CTC is changed to CAC, and this mutation causes valine to appear at that point instead. The molecules with this unusual haemoglobin tend to clump together and form long fibres that distort the red cells into sickle shapes. In this condition they cannot transport oxygen, and the cells may block smaller blood vessels.

Chromosome mutations are another form of mutation in which there is a change in the number or the sequence of genes. This can happen in various ways. Additional sets of chromosomes sometimes occur. For example, the cultivated potato has twice as many chromosomes as the smaller, wild potato (**polyploidy**, page 446). Alternatively, there may be an alteration to part of the chromosome set. For example, people with Down's syndrome have an extra chromosome 21 (three instead of two), giving them a total of 47 chromosomes (Figure 5.19). This mutation causes congenital heart defects, defects in the eyes, mental retardation and immune system deficiencies.

Figure 5.19
Down's syndrome, an example of a chromosome mutation.

An extra chromosome causes Down's syndrome. The extra one comes from a meiosis error. The two chromatids of chromosome 21 fail to separate, and both go into the daughter cell that forms the secondary oocyte.

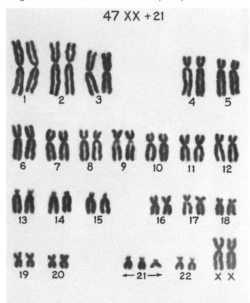

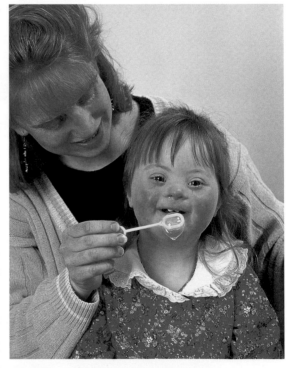

6 Distinguish between the following pairs:

- nuclear division and cell division
- chromatid and chromosome
- diploid and haploid
- nucleolus and nuclear membrane
- crossing over and chiasma
- DNA and RNA.

Alternatively, the breakages that occur in meiosis sometimes result in changes in the gene sequences of individual chromosomes. For example:

- part of a chromosome may be broken off and lost (= **deletion**)
- part of a chromosome becomes repeated (= **duplication**)
- part of a chromosome may break off and rejoin the other way around (= **inversion**)
- part of a chromosome may even rejoin another chromosome (= **translocation**).

A loss of genes via a chromosome mutation is usually fatal, but gain of genes is not necessarily harmful. New combinations of genes on chromosomes can sometimes be advantageous, too.

● **Skills task**   The tip of a plant root or stem contains cells that are actively dividing by mitosis (see Figure 11.19, page 240). Stages of mitosis may be observed in these cells. For example, the extreme tip of roots of the onion (*Allium* sp.) can be cut off, squashed below a microscope slide cover slip, and stained with aceto-orcein, a nucleic acid stain.

When these preparations are examined microscopically, the nucleus at interphase and chromosomes of cells at various stages of mitosis appear stained reddish-purple; the cytoplasm remains colourless. It is possible to count the number of cells showing chromosomes at the four stages of mitosis.

A team of five students carried out successful onion root tip squashes. They observed and recorded the number of nuclei at each stage of mitosis in 100 dividing cells. Their results were as follows:

Stage of mitosis	Student				
	1	2	3	4	5
prophase	64	70	75	68	73
metaphase	13	10	7	11	9
anaphase	5	5	2	8	5
telophase	18	15	16	13	13

1 Work out the mean percentage of dividing cells at each stage of mitosis. Present your results as a pie chart.
2 Assume that the process of mitosis took about 60 minutes to complete in the root tips used in the experiment. What do these results suggest to you about the process of mitosis in *Allium*?

SUMMARY

- The **nucleus** is the organising centre of the cell and has a double function. It controls the activities of the cell throughout life, and it is the location of the hereditary material that is passed from generation to generation in reproduction.
- **Chromosomes** occur in the nucleus but are only visible at times of nuclear division, and then only when stained. The number of chromosomes per nucleus is fixed for any species. Chromosomes occur in pairs and have a characteristic shape. When the nucleus divides the chromosomes divide first.
- **Mitosis** is the **replicative nuclear division** in which, after cell division, the nucleus present in each of two daughter cells has exactly the same number of chromosomes as the parent cell had. Mitosis is associated with cell divisions of growth and asexual reproduction.
- **Meiosis** is the **reductive nuclear division** in which, after cell division, the nucleus present in each of the four daughter cells has half the chromosome number of the parent cell. Meiosis is associated with sexual reproduction and the production of gametes.
- **DNA of chromosomes** carries the genetic message. DNA is a very large molecule in the form of a double helix. It occurs in the chromosome in a highly coiled state, supported by a protein framework. A specific length of the DNA double helix that codes for a particular protein is called a **gene**. A gene may be thousands of base pairs long.
- **Replication of DNA** of the chromosomes takes place in the interphase of the cell cycle when the chromosomes are less coiled, well before the nucleus divides. In replication the double strand separates, and each strand acts as a template for the building of a complementary strand.
- The **genetic code** is a sequence of the four bases present in DNA: adenine (A), thymine (T), guanine (G) and cytosine (C). The code is a three-letter (triplet) code, in that three of the four bases form a **codon**, and code for a particular amino acid.

continued

- There are **three stages to protein synthesis**. A copy of the gene is made in the form of a single strand of **messenger RNA** (mRNA), in the stage called **transcription**. The mRNA passes out into the cytoplasm. In the cytoplasm **amino acid activation** occurs, in which each of the 20 amino acids is attached to a specific **transfer RNA** (tRNA) molecule. Finally **new protein is assembled** when the information of the tRNA is **translated** ('read') in a ribosome. The tRNA–amino acids are assembled in the order given in the code and peptide bonds formed between the amino acids.
- **Genetic engineering** involves the identification and isolation of useful genes, and their transfer into unrelated organisms (mostly, but not exclusively, microorganisms) by artificial means. The outcomes are new varieties of organisms.
- **Mutations** are unpredictable changes in the genetic make-up of a cell, involving either the sequence of particular bases at one location (gene mutation) or changes to whole chromosomes (chromosome mutation).

● Examination questions

1 The table below refers to the first and second divisions of meiosis.

If the statement is correct, place a tick (✓) in the appropriate row and if the statement is incorrect, place a cross (✗) in the appropriate row. (5)

Statement	First division of meiosis	Second division of meiosis
pairing of homologous chromosomes occurs		
chromosomes consist of pairs of chromatids during prophase		
chiasmata are formed		
chromatids are separated		
independent assortment of chromosomes occurs		

London, AS/A level, Module B/HBI, Jan 1998

2 Read through the following passage on the cell cycle and mitosis, then write on the dotted lines the most appropriate word or words to complete the passage.

In the cell cycle, replication of DNA takes place during .... At the beginning of prophase the chromosomes become visible and can be seen to consist of two .... joined at the .... The .... and nuclear membrane disappear and a spindle develops in the cell.
The chromosomes become attached to the spindle at the equator during .... At anaphase one copy of each chromosome is pulled towards each .... of the spindle. The final phase, called telophase, involves the formation of two new nuclei. In plant cells the two daughter cells are separated by the formation of a .... (7)

London, AS/A level, Module B/HBI, Jan 1997

3 One of the processes in gene technology involves the synthesis of DNA using messenger RNA (mRNA) as a template. This is shown in the diagram below.

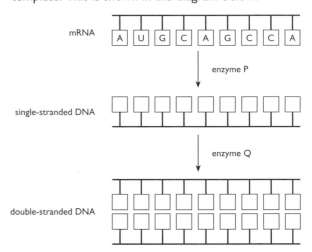

a Name enzyme P. (1)
b On the diagram above, write the sequence of bases which would be present in the single-stranded DNA. (2)
c Name enzyme Q. (1)
d The double-stranded DNA can be inserted into a bacterial cell, which will then synthesise a protein which is coded for by this DNA.

Name **one** protein which is produced in this way on an industrial scale. (1)

London, AS/A level, Module B/HB1, Jan 1998

4 The drawings **A**–**E** show stages of mitosis in an animal cell.

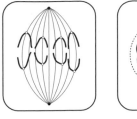  

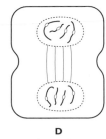 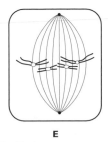

a Which of the drawings **A**–**E** shows
  i anaphase;
  ii telophase;
  iii metaphase? (3)
b Give **two** processes which occur during interphase and which are necessary for nuclear division to take place. (2)

AQA(NEAB), A level, Paper 1/Sections A & B, June 1999

5 There are two forms of nitrogen. ^{15}N is a heavier isotope than the normal isotope ^{14}N. In an investigation, a culture of the bacterium *Escherichia coli* was obtained in which all the nitrogen in the DNA was of the ^{15}N form. The bacteria were transferred to a medium containing only the normal isotope, ^{14}N, and allowed to divide once. A sample of this first generation was removed. The DNA was then extracted and spun in a high-speed centrifuge. This was done again with samples of the second and third generations.

The diagram shows the results of this investigation.
a Which part of a DNA nucleotide contains nitrogen? (1)

b Complete the diagram to show the positions of the DNA from generations 2 and 3.

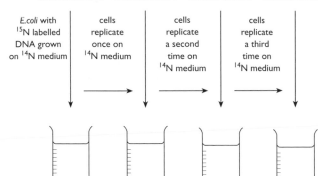

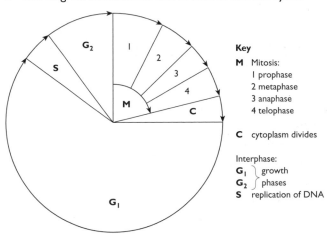

(2)

AQA(NEAB), A level, Paper 1/Sections A & B, June 1999

6 The diagram summarises the events of the cell cycle.

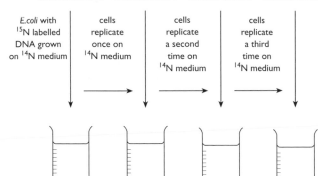

Key

M Mitosis:
  1 prophase
  2 metaphase
  3 anaphase
  4 telophase

C cytoplasm divides

Interphase:
G₁ } growth
G₂ } phases
S replication of DNA

a Shade the diagram to show where the spindle fibres would be shortening. (1)
b i During the **G₁** phase, the ratio of nucleus diameter to cell diameter decreases. Explain why. (1)
  ii How do the events of the **G₂** phase prepare the cell for mitosis? (1)
c Describe how the arrangement of chromosomes during metaphase of mitosis differs from the arrangement of chromosomes during metaphase of the first division of meiosis. (1)

AQA(AEB), A level, 0642/1, June 1999

6 Gene technology

STARTING POINTS ● The plants and animals we use as food or for transport and leisure pursuits, and all garden flowers, have been bred from wild species by **artificial selection**, carried out over very many years.
● The production of new varieties or organisms by any means is a form of **genetic modification**.
● Today genetic modification is also carried out by **genetic engineering**. In genetic engineering, genes are transferred from one organism to another (often unrelated) organism by artificial means.
● The products are new varieties of organisms, mostly (but not exclusively) of microorganisms.
● The genetic engineer applies novel techniques to naturally occurring organisms and their enzymes.
● Genetic engineering offers great practical benefits in biotechnology, medicine and agriculture. At the same time it raises many environmental and ethical issues of concern to society.

● Organisms may be genetically modified

Very many organisms have been genetically modified by humans, most of them by means of **artificial selection**. Nearly all the animals and plants used in agriculture, horticulture, transport and leisure pursuits have been bred from wild animals and plants in this way. In artificial selection, the largest and best of the organisms, or those that are the most useful for a particular purpose, are chosen. These are then used as the next generation of parents. At the same time, the less satisfactory organisms are prevented from breeding. The effect of this selection process is the relative speedy and deliberate genetic change of local populations of plants or animals into new varieties, useful to humans.

Today a new type of genetic modification is also in use, known as **genetic engineering**. Genes from one organism are transferred to the set of genes (the **genome**) of another *unrelated* organism. The process is also known as **recombinant DNA technology** or **gene technology**. The outcomes are new varieties of organisms, mostly but not exclusively of microorganisms. Microorganisms are preferred simply because they are easier to modify (page 129). Gene technology has important applications in biotechnology, medicinal drug production (pharmaceuticals industry), gene therapy, agriculture and horticulture.

Genetic engineering can generate many potential benefits for humans. But there may be hazards, too. The economic advantages may be outnumbered by environmental and ethical drawbacks or dangers. The issues require balanced and informed judgements.

I What do the terms 'genome' and 'gene' mean?

● The steps to genetic engineering

Isolating genes

The long double strand of DNA of a chromosome (Figure 5.8, page 107) carries a linear sequence of many genes, the units of inheritance. For example, there are on average 2200 genes on each human chromosome. Genes consist of between hundreds and thousands of bases, but each gene codes for a particular protein. For genetic engineering to take place, individual genes have to be isolated (and eventually identified). How can one gene be found and isolated among so many?

2 Why do we describe DNA as 'double-stranded'?

Isolating the gene from the source genome

Genetic engineering really began with the discovery of restriction endonucleases (**restriction enzymes**). These enzymes occur naturally in bacteria, where they protect the organism against DNA injected by viruses by cutting it into small pieces, thereby inactivating it. Virus DNA otherwise takes over the host cell (Figure 5.9, page 108). Restriction enzymes were so named because they *restrict* the multiplication of viruses.

Many different restriction enzymes have been discovered and purified, and today they are used widely in genetic engineering experiments. For example, a restriction enzyme is used to cut up the DNA extracted from cells of an organism known to carry a required gene. The DNA fragments so produced may be sorted on size and copied (a process known as **cloning**), and the gene identified. The later stages in the process may be carried out after the gene has been added to a 'vector' by which the gene is transferred to a receiving organism. These steps and techniques to genetic engineering are explained next.

3 How does viral DNA attempt to take over a host cell (page 100)?

Extracting and cutting up DNA

DNA may be extracted from tissue samples by mechanically breaking up the cells, filtering off the debris, and breaking down cell membranes by treatment with detergents. The protein framework of the chromosomes is then removed by incubation with a protein-digesting enzyme (protease). The DNA, now existing as long threads, can be isolated from this mixture of chemicals by precipitation with ethanol, and is thus 'cleaned'. The DNA strands are then re-suspended in aqueous, pH-buffered medium.

4 What are the products of digestion of proteins by protease enzymes?

The DNA is now chopped into fragments by a restriction enzyme. Different restriction enzymes cut at particular base sequences, called **restriction sites**. Restriction enzymes are of two main types, forming either **blunt ends** or **sticky ends** to cut fragments (Figure 6.1).

Figure 6.1
The role of restriction endonucleases (restriction enzymes).

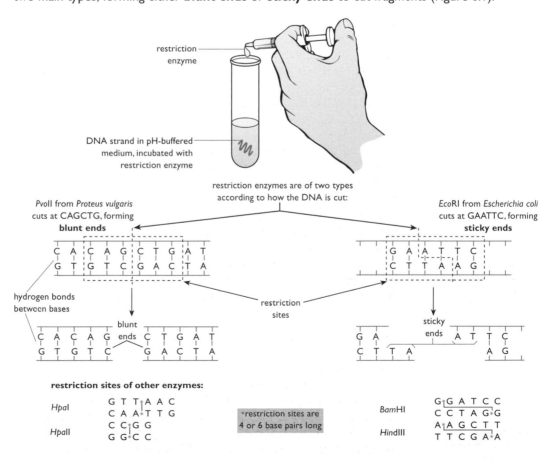

Restriction enzymes are named after the microorganisms they are found in. Roman numbers are added to distinguish different enzymes from the same microorganism.

Isolating DNA fragments

We have seen how electrophoresis is used to separate particles, including proteins and peptides (Figure 2.25, page 43), on the double basis of particle size and particle charge.

The DNA fragments carry negative charges, due to their phosphate groups, and therefore in the electric field used in electrophoresis they move towards the positive electrode (anode). Additionally, the polyacrylamide gel has a sieving effect on the DNA fragments of differing lengths, so they move through the gel at different speeds.

Plasmids as vectors and for cloning

In biology, a **vector** is an agent that transports something between one organism and another. In genetic engineering a vector is 'carrier DNA', into which a DNA fragment containing a particular gene can be inserted, and which is then used to introduce the gene into a new organism. One such vector is a bacterial plasmid.

Figure 6.2
Plasmids as vectors.

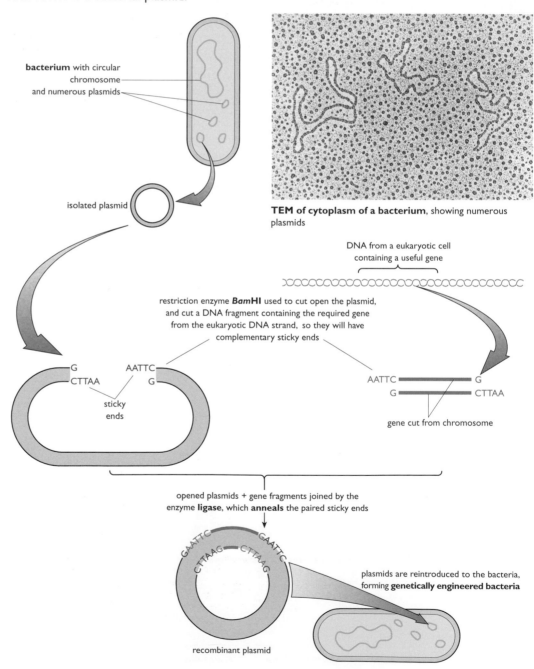

bacterium with circular chromosome and numerous plasmids

TEM of cytoplasm of a bacterium, showing numerous plasmids

isolated plasmid

DNA from a eukaryotic cell containing a useful gene

restriction enzyme **Bam**HI used to cut open the plasmid, and cut a DNA fragment containing the required gene from the eukaryotic DNA strand, so they will have complementary sticky ends

G   AATTC
CTTAA   G

sticky ends

AATTC   G
G   CTTAA

gene cut from chromosome

opened plasmids + gene fragments joined by the enzyme **ligase**, which **anneals** the paired sticky ends

GAATTC   GAATTC
CTTAAG   CTTAAG

plasmids are reintroduced to the bacteria, forming **genetically engineered bacteria**

recombinant plasmid

122

A bacterium contains two types of genetic material. One is a long double strand of DNA in the form of a ring, which we can think of as a **single, circular chromosome**. The other type of DNA takes the form of numerous smaller rings of double-stranded DNA, called **plasmids** (Figure 6.2). Plasmids are easily isolated from a bacterium, and they can be re-introduced to another bacterial cell relatively easily, too. They are therefore extremely useful as vectors. In the bacterium, plasmids copy themselves (replicate) independently of the chromosome. So any gene added to a plasmid is also copied many times (**cloned**), once it is inside a bacterial cell.

To prepare isolated plasmids as vectors, a restriction enzyme that forms 'sticky ends' is used to cut open the plasmid. The same restriction enzyme is also used to cut out the required gene from longer strands of DNA. Then the opened plasmids and the gene-containing fragments are combined together in the presence of a second enzyme, known as a **ligase**. Ligase occurs naturally in nuclei, where it will 'repair' DNA damaged in replication. Ligase catalyses the combination of complementary strands of DNA after their sticky ends have paired (a process called **annealing**).

Finally, genetically engineered plasmids are re-introduced into the bacterium. This is done by mixing bacterial cells and engineered plasmids in the presence of a salt (calcium chloride) that makes the bacterial cell walls specially permeable to plasmids. Some of the recombinant plasmids enter the cytoplasm of the bacteria.

As an alternative technique, a gene may be cloned into a bacterium using a bacteriophage as vector (Figure 6.3). This mechanism is most useful in attempts to clone larger genes (longer lengths of double-stranded DNA).

5 What property of DNA makes complementary 'sticky ends' hold together?

Figure 6.3
Bacteriophages as vectors.

Bacteriophages ('phages) are viruses that parasitise bacteria. The 'phages inject viral nucleic acid, which is taken up by the host bacterium.

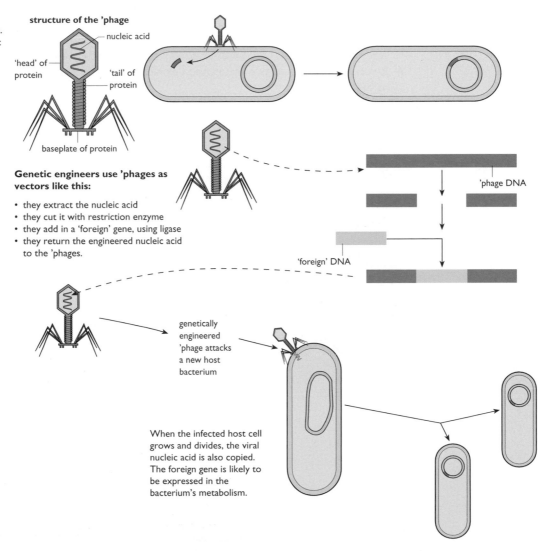

structure of the 'phage

nucleic acid

'head' of protein

'tail' of protein

baseplate of protein

Genetic engineers use 'phages as vectors like this:

- they extract the nucleic acid
- they cut it with restriction enzyme
- they add in a 'foreign' gene, using ligase
- they return the engineered nucleic acid to the 'phages.

'phage DNA

'foreign' DNA

genetically engineered 'phage attacks a new host bacterium

When the infected host cell grows and divides, the viral nucleic acid is also copied. The foreign gene is likely to be expressed in the bacterium's metabolism.

Selecting genetically engineered cells

The vector that is most commonly used is a plasmid that carries two genes for antibiotic resistance. This **R-plasmid**, as it is known, has a gene for ampicillin resistance and a gene for tetracycline resistance. Now it happens that the tetracycline-resistance gene is cut in half by a restriction enzyme called *Bam*HI (it has a restriction site within this gene), whilst the ampicillin-resistance gene is uncut. When a gene is cut it is inactivated; in this case, resistance to tetracycline is lost. This feature is used in the detection of recombinant bacteria. The process is summarised in Figures 6.4 and 6.5.

1 Restriction enzyme *Bam*HI is used to cut the genome with the wanted gene into fragments, and also to cut open the R-plasmids. This means both have complementary sticky ends.
2 DNA fragments and cut plasmids are brought together with ligase. Recombinant plasmids are formed, but only a few will contain the wanted gene. Other plasmids will have their sticky ends annealed without any DNA fragment added, or will have some other fragment annealed.
3 *E. coli* bacteria are now made to take up these plasmids. Only about 1% are found to contain recombinant DNA, and it is these bacteria alone that the genetic engineer requires. They need to be located!
4 The bacteria are cultured. This means they are plated out on nutrient agar containing the antibiotic ampicillin. Only bacteria that have taken up R-plasmids will grow here. This is because bacteria without the R-plasmid do not have the ampicillin-resistance gene.
5 The next step is **replica plating** of these ampicillin-resistant bacteria on to nutrient agar containing the antibiotic tetracycline. In replica plating an exact copy of the first plate is transferred to a second plate using a disc so that the bacterial colonies are in identical positions. All bacteria will also grow here *except* those with an inactivated tetracycline-resistance gene (they contain recombinant DNA inserted into the tetracycline-resistance gene, remember).
6 By comparison of the two plates, the colonies of bacteria *with* recombinant DNA can be located.

6 Why is a gene for antibiotic resistance inactivated when it is cut by a restriction enzyme?

Figure 6.4
Using R-plasmids as vectors.

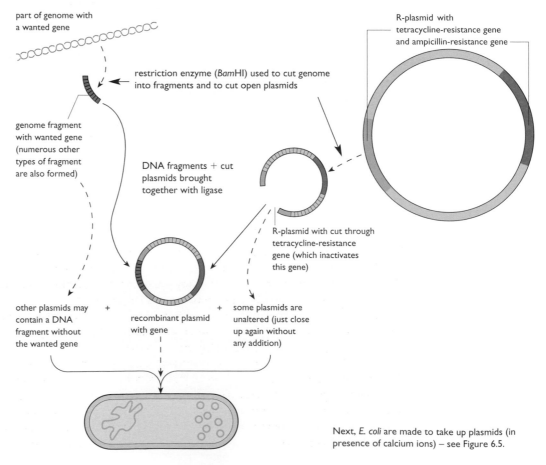

part of genome with a wanted gene

R-plasmid with tetracycline-resistance gene and ampicillin-resistance gene

restriction enzyme (*Bam*HI) used to cut genome into fragments and to cut open plasmids

genome fragment with wanted gene (numerous other types of fragment are also formed)

DNA fragments + cut plasmids brought together with ligase

R-plasmid with cut through tetracycline-resistance gene (which inactivates this gene)

other plasmids may contain a DNA fragment without the wanted gene   +   recombinant plasmid with gene   +   some plasmids are unaltered (just close up again without any addition)

Next, *E. coli* are made to take up plasmids (in presence of calcium ions) – see Figure 6.5.

124

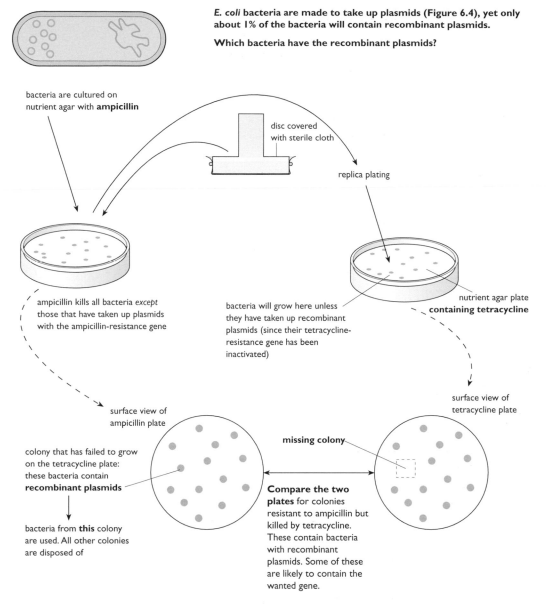

Figure 6.5
Selecting the genetically engineered bacteria.

E. coli bacteria are made to take up plasmids (Figure 6.4), yet only about 1% of the bacteria will contain recombinant plasmids.

Which bacteria have the recombinant plasmids?

bacteria are cultured on nutrient agar with **ampicillin**

disc covered with sterile cloth

replica plating

ampicillin kills all bacteria *except* those that have taken up plasmids with the ampicillin-resistance gene

bacteria will grow here unless they have taken up recombinant plasmids (since their tetracycline-resistance gene has been inactivated)

nutrient agar plate **containing tetracycline**

surface view of ampicillin plate

surface view of tetracycline plate

colony that has failed to grow on the tetracycline plate: these bacteria contain **recombinant plasmids**

missing colony

bacteria from **this** colony are used. All other colonies are disposed of

Compare the two plates for colonies resistant to ampicillin but killed by tetracycline. These contain bacteria with recombinant plasmids. Some of these are likely to contain the wanted gene.

Switching on gene action

Some of the genes in a cell's chromosomes are actively transcribed throughout the life of the cell. Others, however, are activated (we say they are **expressed**) only at a particular stage in the life of the cell, or when the substance they act on (their substrate molecule) is present. Very many genes have to be deliberately activated, as required.

One such activating mechanism found in bacteria is the **lactose operon** mechanism (Figure 6.6). This consists of a **regulator gene** and an **operator gene**, close to the genes that are regulated (known as **structural genes** – in this case, the genes for lactose-metabolising enzymes). The regulator gene codes for a repressor protein that binds to the operator gene site. The repressor protein prevents transcription of the structural gene. But if lactose is present (for example, it might become available in the medium in which the bacteria are growing), then the lactose molecule reacts with the regulator protein, preventing its binding with the operator gene. As a result, the lactose-metabolising enzyme genes are transcribed, and lactose is metabolised. Once all the lactose has been used up, the repressor molecule blocks transcription again.

Figure 6.6
'Operon' gene regulation.

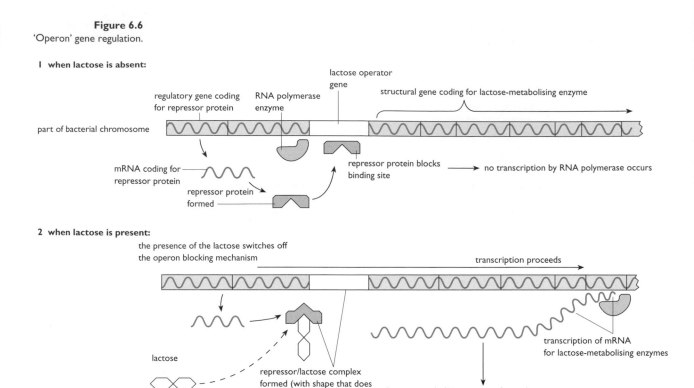

1 **when lactose is absent:**

regulatory gene coding
for repressor protein

RNA polymerase
enzyme

lactose operator
gene

structural gene coding for lactose-metabolising enzyme

part of bacterial chromosome

mRNA coding for
repressor protein

repressor protein
formed

repressor protein blocks
binding site

no transcription by RNA polymerase occurs

2 **when lactose is present:**

the presence of the lactose switches off
the operon blocking mechanism

transcription proceeds

lactose

repressor/lactose complex
formed (with shape that does
not fit on to binding site)

lactose-metabolising enzymes formed
(only whilst lactose is present)

transcription of mRNA
for lactose-metabolising enzymes

This type of mechanism occurs in prokaryotes (bacteria and cyanobacteria) only. In eukaryotes the gene-regulation mechanisms are more complicated. The principle is the same, however, in that transcription of many structural genes is regulated according to the needs of the cell.

In genetic engineering, the lactose operon mechanism (or a similar type of regulator gene) may be engineered into a bacterium, alongside the structural gene that is introduced into the genome. As a result, adding lactose to the medium in which the engineered bacteria are cultured will activate the engineered structural genes. They can be switched on by the presence of a metabolite in the medium. Thus the lactose operon and others of the same type are important tools of the genetic engineer.

Identifying a gene with a gene probe

To identify a gene by means of a gene probe, the base sequence of that gene must first be worked out. With this information, a specific **gene probe** can be made. A gene probe is a single strand of DNA with a base sequence complementary to that of the gene, so it may bind to it. For example, the gene sequence TGAGATCGT will form hydrogen bonds with a probe of base sequence ACTCTAGCA. Meanwhile, the phosphate groups in the DNA backbone of a gene probe are made with radioactive phosphorus, ^{32}P, so the presence of the probe can be detected after it has bound to the gene (by autoradiography, for example, shown in Figure 6.7).

We have seen that the DNA of cells can be cut into fragments by a restriction enzyme, and the fragments separated by gel electrophoresis. To detect a specific gene by means of its radioactive probe, the gel is treated with sodium hydroxide. The alkali breaks the hydrogen bonds of the DNA, so that it forms single strands. A nitrocellulose membrane is then pressed to the gel and picks up single strands of DNA, so that a copy of the distribution (banding) of the DNA fragments is reproduced. This blotting technique is called **Southern blotting**, after its inventor. The nitrocellulose membrane is removed and treated with a gene probe. Finally, X-ray film is laid over the membrane. When the autoradiograph is developed the presence of the gene will be shown.

The word **protocol** is often used in genetic engineering. It means 'standard procedure'. The process of identifying a gene with a gene probe is one example of a protocol.

Figure 6.7
Gene probe technology.

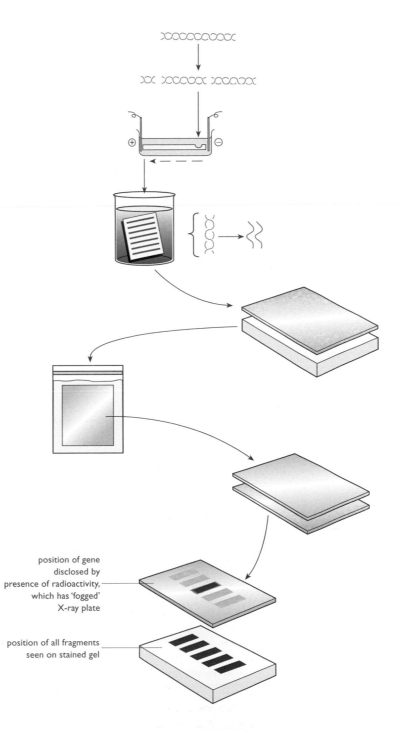

genome sliced into fragments by restriction enzyme

fragments separated by electrophoresis

electrophoresis gel treated with sodium hydroxide (this breaks the hydrogen bonds between complementary DNA strands of the fragments)

(The distribution of DNA fragments can be shown by adding dye. The dye shows the sites of all fragments, but does not indentify a single gene.)

copy of distribution of single-stranded DNA fragments taken on to nitrocellulose sheet (called **Southern blotting**)

X-ray plate applied to nitrocellulose sheet to find where the radioactively labelled gene probe has lined up with complementary gene sequence; this shows up the position of the required gene on the electrophoresis gel

radioactively labelled gene probe for required gene applied to nitrocellulose sheet (with DNA strands)

position of gene disclosed by presence of radioactivity, which has 'fogged' X-ray plate

position of all fragments seen on stained gel

● Extension   Alternative ways of obtaining copies of genes

Synthesising the gene artificially

Where we know the amino acid sequence of the protein that is coded for by a gene, the DNA code for the protein can be worked out using the universal genetic code (Figure 5.14, page 112). This has been applied successfully to a few, relatively short proteins. For example, the gene for the human growth inhibitor called somatostatin (only 14 amino acids long) and the gene for insulin have been constructed in this way. Once the base sequence of a gene is known, a copy of the gene can be produced by joining nucleotides in the required sequence. An automated machine is used. So far, the amino acid sequence of many larger proteins is not known, so the genes coding for them cannot yet be synthesised.

continued

Making a copy of the gene from its mRNA

When a gene is active in a cell, that cell produces thousands of copies of messenger RNA (mRNA, page 104), which are complementary to the gene. For example, mRNA coding for insulin can be extracted from the cells of the pancreas that produce insulin (page 259).

An enzyme obtained from a retrovirus that catalyses the production of DNA from RNA is made to act on the mRNA copies. Retroviruses contain RNA, and when they invade host cells they make DNA copies of their RNA using an enzyme called **reverse transcriptase**. This enzyme actually reverses the normal transcription step of protein synthesis (pages 112–13), and is another naturally occurring enzyme of use in genetic engineering.

The DNA copy produced by reverse transcriptase is called **cDNA**, because it is a complementary, single strand of DNA. The single-stranded cDNA may then be converted into double-stranded DNA by the use of the enzyme **DNA polymerase** (page 109). This constructs a second strand of DNA, complementary to cDNA. The cDNA and its complementary strand together make up a copy of the required gene (Figure 6.8).

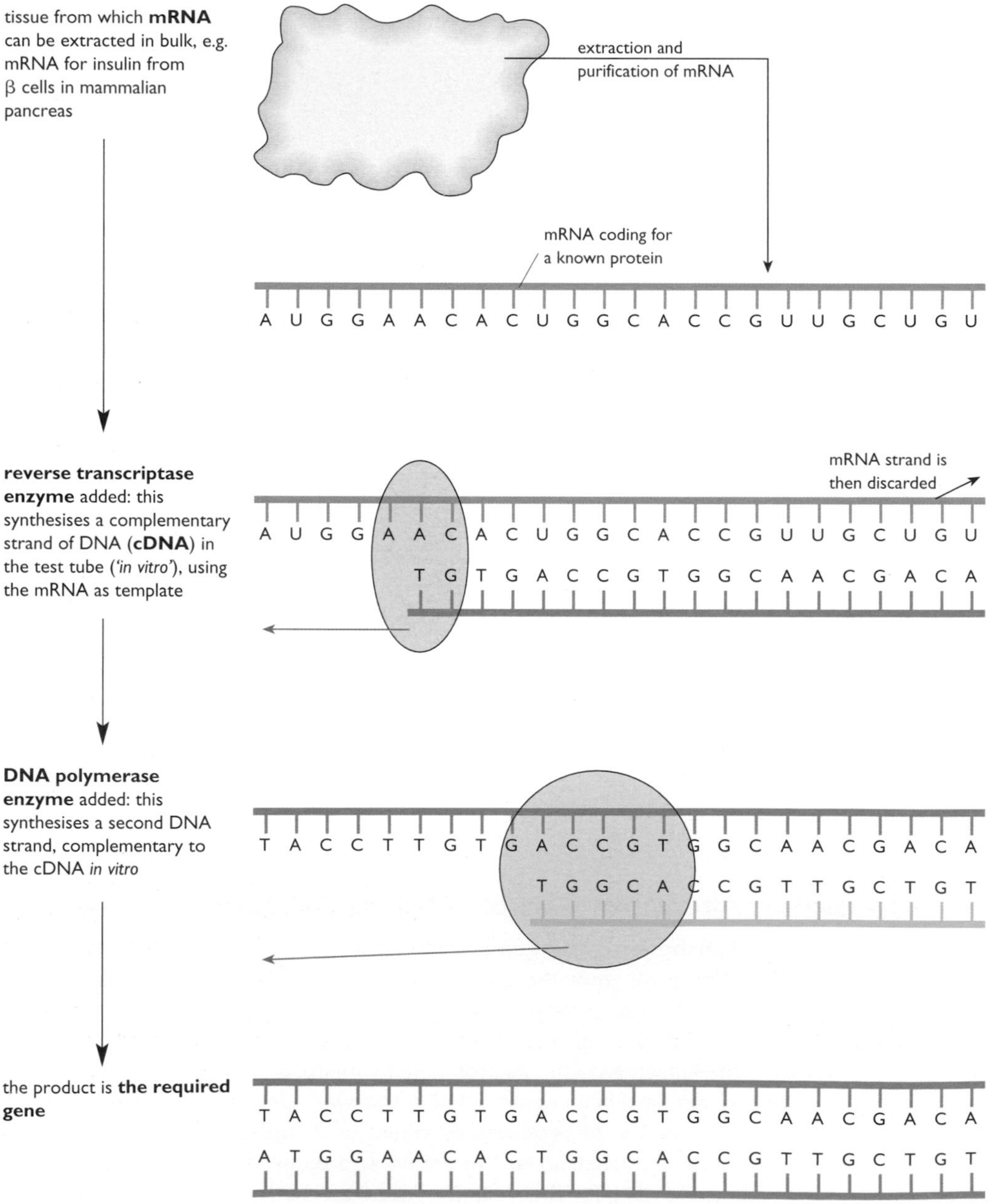

Figure 6.8
Building a gene with reverse transcriptase.

tissue from which **mRNA** can be extracted in bulk, e.g. mRNA for insulin from β cells in mammalian pancreas

extraction and purification of mRNA

mRNA coding for a known protein

A U G G A A C A C U G G C A C C G U U G C U G U

reverse transcriptase enzyme added: this synthesises a complementary strand of DNA (**cDNA**) in the test tube ('*in vitro*'), using the mRNA as template

mRNA strand is then discarded

A U G G A A C A C U G G C A C C G U U G C U G U
        T G T G A C C G T G G C A A C G A C A

DNA polymerase enzyme added: this synthesises a second DNA strand, complementary to the cDNA *in vitro*

T A C C T T G T G A C C G T G G C A A C G A C A
              T G G C A C C G T T G C T G T

the product is **the required gene**

T A C C T T G T G A C C G T G G C A A C G A C A
A T G G A A C A C T G G C A C C G T T G C T G T

7 The activity of reverse transcriptase contradicts the central dogma of molecular biology (page 114). Why is this so?

Applications of genetic engineering
Production of transformed bacteria

One of the earliest applications of the techniques of genetic engineering was in the production of bacteria containing human genes, or genes taken from other eukaryotes. A bacterium frequently selected was a strain of *Escherichia coli*. *E. coli* is commonly found in the gut of humans and other animals. Actually, it is a mutant form of *E. coli* that is used in genetic engineering, which is only able to survive in special laboratory conditions. This is an obvious safety precaution, since otherwise an 'engineered' bacterium might escape at some time in the future. It could exchange its genes with gut populations, and perhaps cause harm to humans.

Transformed bacteria were cultured in fermenters (page 91) with the transferred gene 'switched on', and there produced proteins of value in significant quantities (Figure 6.9). These were extracted and purified from the medium.

Figure 6.9
Products of value to humans produced by transformed bacteria or yeast.

8 What is the general name for a 'foreign substance' that triggers a reaction by the immune system?

human insulin

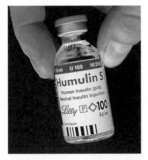

Human insulin

The production of human insulin by engineered bacteria was an important early example. Deficiency in the levels of blood insulin is one of the main causes of **diabetes** (page 261). At one time, diabetics were treated with regular injections of insulin from animals. But human insulin and insulin from animal sources are different chemically, and repeated injections of animal insulin led to allergic reactions in many patients (they were detected as 'foreign' proteins). Human insulins produced by bacteria overcame this problem for many patients.

growth hormone: a researcher taking a sample from a fermenter

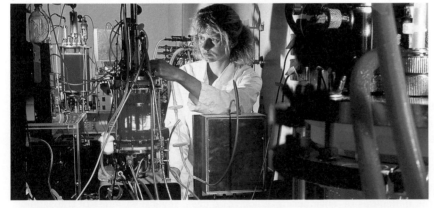

Growth hormone

Human growth hormone is a small protein that is normally produced by the pituitary gland. Abnormally low levels of human growth hormone in an individual causes **dwarfism**. Dwarfs are of normal intelligence, but are physically much smaller than most other people. Regular injections of human growth hormone may restore near-normal heights in affected individuals. Human growth hormone is produced by genetically engineered bacteria.

chymosin, a substitute for rennin in cheese manufacture, produced by genetically modified yeast

Yeast

Yeast is another microorganism that is much used for genetic engineering. Unlike bacteria, yeast is a eukaryote (it has a nucleus bound by a nuclear membrane, and DNA in its chromosomes). But like the bacteria, yeast has plasmids. It can readily accept engineered plasmids from other sources too, when the cell wall is made permeable to them (lithium salts are used for this). For example, yeast has been genetically engineered to produce human interferon (page 336) and chymosin, a substitute for rennin in cheese manufacture.

bovine somatotrophin (BST): a sample of the purified hormone

Bovine somatotrophin (BST)

BST is a growth hormone produced only by cattle. It is of similar chemical structure to human growth hormone. BST hormone is normally produced in cattle by the pituitary gland at a low, steady rate. When additional BST hormone is administered to cattle (it was injected into lactating cows every two weeks, for example), they produce far more milk. In the USA a biotechnology company has isolated the BST gene from cattle, and engineered bacteria to produce and secrete BST hormone.

BST is regularly used by US farmers to increase milk production by their herds, but at the time of writing its use in the European Union is banned. One reason for the ban is that there is already an excess of milk produced in Europe. In addition, there were fears for the health of cows made to produce excessive milk by treatment with BST over prolonged periods. Also, if BST is regularly used in cows there is a possibility that traces of the hormone may appear in milk. Human growth might be affected.

In eukaryotes

Manipulating genes in eukaryotes is a more difficult process than in prokaryotes. There are several reasons for this.

- Plasmids, the most useful vehicle for moving genes, do not occur in eukaryotes (except in yeasts). If they are introduced, they often do not survive and become replicated in a eukaryotic cell.
- Eukaryotes are diploid organisms, so two forms (alleles) for every gene must be engineered into the nucleus. Prokaryotes have a single, circular 'chromosome', so only one copy of a gene has to be engineered into their DNA.
- Transcription of eukaryotic DNA to mRNA is more complex than in prokaryotes, where it involves removal of short lengths of 'non-informative' DNA sequences within the mRNA.
- Plant walls may be impassable by gene vectors. In contrast, the bacterial wall can be crossed by plasmids (after suitable treatments).
- Machinery for triggering gene expression in bacteria is known. In eukaryotes the machinery is more complex, and is only partially understood.

Producing transgenic animals

'Transgenic' organisms have genetic material that has been artificially introduced from another organism. Despite the difficulties of 'engineering' eukaryotic cells, several varieties of transgenic animal have been produced. Transferred genes may be directly injected into cells (Figure 6.10). Alternatively, they may be incorporated into tiny particles and 'bombarded' into cells at high speed. Another method is to induce temporary tiny holes in a cell's plasma membrane by rapid, brief electrical pulses applied to the membrane (a technique known as **electroporation**), through which particles carrying genes can be introduced. Occasionally, a gene introduced by these methods becomes attached to a chromosome and is then replicated in every cell of the organism that is formed. Success rates can be quite low.

Transgenic sheep have been successfully engineered to yield rare and expensive human proteins in their milk. These may be useful as medicines. One example is a special human blood protein, known as AAT. Production of AAT in our bodies preserves the vital elasticity of our lungs. Patients with a certain rare genetic disease cannot produce AAT at all, and they develop emphysema (page 326). The chemical industry is unable to manufacture AAT on a practical scale. But the human gene for AAT production has been identified, isolated and cloned into sheep, together with a promoter gene (a sheep's milk protein promoter) attached to it. Consequently the sheep's mammary glands produce the human protein and secrete it in their milk. AAT is made available for use with patients.

9 Why is it that a gene that becomes inserted in the nucleus of a fertilised egg cell is also passed to the progeny of the animal that grows from that cell?

Figure 6.10
The cloning of transgenic sheep to secrete human AAT protein.

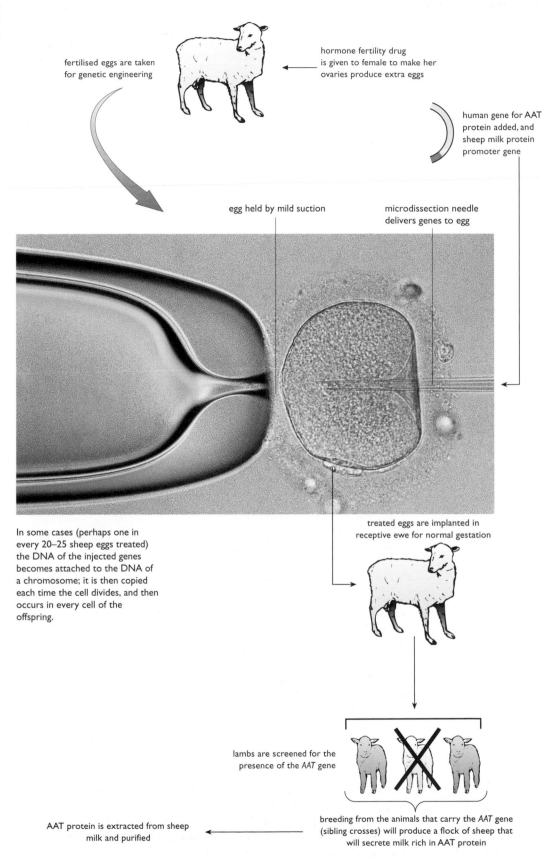

fertilised eggs are taken for genetic engineering

hormone fertility drug is given to female to make her ovaries produce extra eggs

human gene for AAT protein added, and sheep milk protein promoter gene

egg held by mild suction

microdissection needle delivers genes to egg

In some cases (perhaps one in every 20–25 sheep eggs treated) the DNA of the injected genes becomes attached to the DNA of a chromosome; it is then copied each time the cell divides, and then occurs in every cell of the offspring.

treated eggs are implanted in receptive ewe for normal gestation

lambs are screened for the presence of the *AAT* gene

AAT protein is extracted from sheep milk and purified

breeding from the animals that carry the *AAT* gene (sibling crosses) will produce a flock of sheep that will secrete milk rich in AAT protein

Figure 6.11
Transgenic plants via the Ti plasmid of *Agrobacterium*.

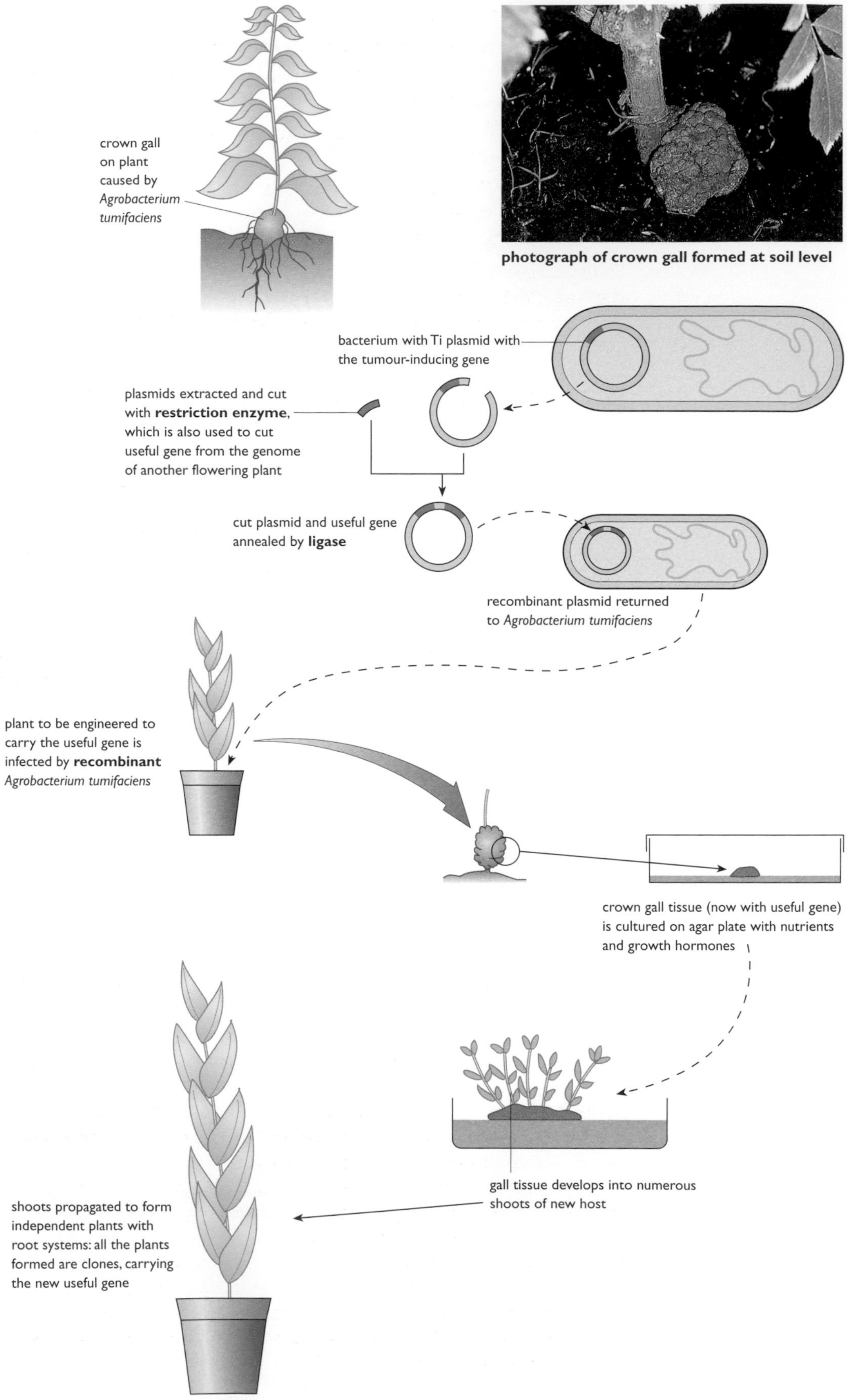

crown gall on plant caused by *Agrobacterium tumifaciens*

photograph of crown gall formed at soil level

bacterium with Ti plasmid with the tumour-inducing gene

plasmids extracted and cut with **restriction enzyme**, which is also used to cut useful gene from the genome of another flowering plant

cut plasmid and useful gene annealed by **ligase**

recombinant plasmid returned to *Agrobacterium tumifaciens*

plant to be engineered to carry the useful gene is infected by **recombinant** *Agrobacterium tumifaciens*

crown gall tissue (now with useful gene) is cultured on agar plate with nutrients and growth hormones

gall tissue develops into numerous shoots of new host

shoots propagated to form independent plants with root systems: all the plants formed are clones, carrying the new useful gene

Producing transgenic plants

Many commercially valuable plant species have been genetically engineered and field trials undertaken. The crops concerned include cotton, tobacco, oilseed rape, maize, potatoes, soya and tomatoes. The improvements achieved include:

- tolerance to herbicides: if a crop plant can inactivate a weedkiller, then weeds can be killed without harming the crop plants
- resistance to insect pests: the crop plant tissue contains a toxin lethal to insects but harmless to other animal species
- resistance to viral disease in the crop plant.

Some transgenic plants also show an improvement in crop quality. Examples include oilseed rape varieties, making the plant's oils more useful either as fuel oils or for human consumption. Another example is a variety of tomato that can be ripened on the plant to develop full flavour, without rotting quickly when picked and marketed as red fruit. (Traditionally, tomatoes are picked green and induced to ripen by treatment with the chemical ethene prior to sale. In this state they lack flavour, however, even though they look red.) Again, the plant thale cress (*Arabidopsis thaliana*) has been engineered as a cheap, renewable source of the biodegradable plastic polyhydroxybutyrate (PHB); most other plastics come from expensive petrochemicals and are slow to degrade.

Transgenic flowering plants may be formed using tumour-forming *Agrobacterium*. This soil-inhabiting bacterium sometimes invades plants (dicotyledonous plants only, page 355) at the junction of stem and root, forming a huge growth called a tumour or crown gall. The gene for tumour formation occurs in a plasmid in the bacterium, known as a **Ti plasmid** (Figure 6.11). Useful genes (for example, one that carries resistance to viral infection) may be added to this plasmid, using restriction enzyme and ligase, and the recombinant plasmid placed back into *Agrobacterium*. Then a host crop plant is infected by the modified bacterium. The gall tissue that results may be cultured into independent plants, all of which will also carry the gene for viral resistance (Figure 6.11).

10 Why will plants formed from the gall tissue contain the recombinant gene that has been added to the Ti plasmid?

In gene therapy

Genetic diseases are conditions that can be inherited, and which are caused by a specific defect in a gene. Such diseases afflict about 1–2% of the human population. Common genetic diseases include cystic fibrosis, sickle cell anaemia (page 115), Duchenne muscular dystrophy and haemophilia (page 445). These conditions mostly arise from a mutation involving a single gene. The mutant allele that causes the disease is usually recessive, so a person must be homozygous for the mutant gene for the condition to be expressed (these terms are explained in Chapter 20, page 438). (People with a single mutant allele are called 'carriers'.) For example, cystic fibrosis is due to a recessive gene on chromosome 7. Duchenne muscular dystrophy and haemophilia are due to recessive alleles on the X chromosome, so these two conditions are sex-linked.

Recent developments in genetic engineering suggest the possibility that some genetic diseases may be curable. **Gene therapy** is the use of recombinant DNA technology to overcome genetic disease, where this is thought safe and ethically sound. For example, the body may be supplied with the missing gene's product (and then periodically re-supplied). More difficult, but a permanent solution, would be to supply the missing gene to body cells in such a way that it remains permanently functional. Gene therapy is a recent, highly experimental science. It is illustrated here by reference to cystic fibrosis.

Cystic fibrosis affects the epithelial cells of the body and is the most common genetic disorder in the UK. The cystic fibrosis gene codes for a protein (called CFTR) that functions as an ion pump. The pump transports chloride ions across membranes, and water follows the ions. This is how epithelia are kept smooth and moist. In cystic fibrosis patients, the gene (*cfcf*) coding for this protein has a changed base sequence and codes either for no protein or for a faulty protein. As a result the epithelia remain dry, and a thick, sticky mucus builds up. The effects are felt in the pancreas (secretion of digestive juices) and the sweat glands (salty sweat is formed). But the life-threatening consequences arise in the lungs, which may become blocked by mucus and are prone to infection.

Gene therapy involves getting copies of the healthy gene to the cells of the lung epithelia. An aerosol spray is used, containing tiny lipid bilayer droplets (called **liposomes**) to which copies of the healthy gene are attached. Liposomes fuse with cell membrane lipids and deliver the gene to the epithelial cell (Figure 6.12). In trials the treatment seems effective, but it lasts only until the epithelial cells are routinely replaced. The treatment has to be regularly repeated. The cure can only be more permanent when it is targeted on the cells that make epithelial cells.

Figure 6.12
Cystic fibrosis; getting the healthy gene into functioning cells in the lungs.

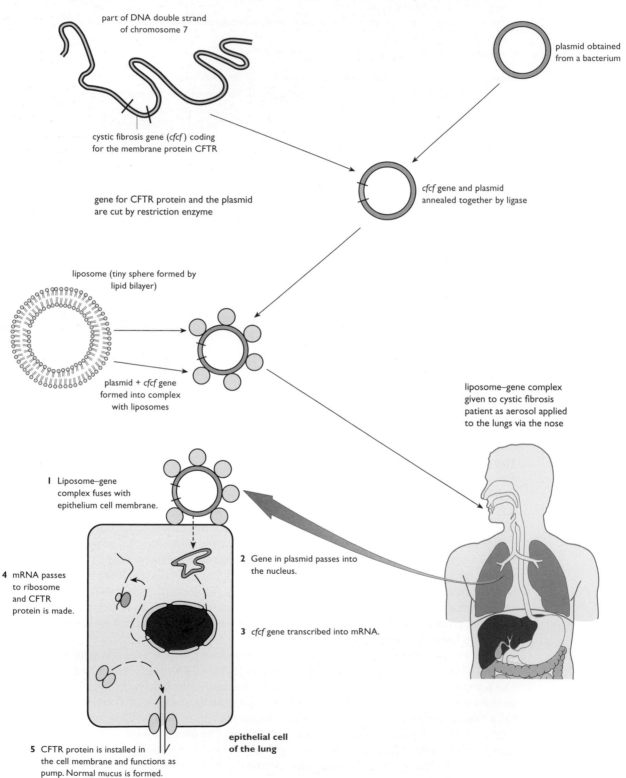

part of DNA double strand of chromosome 7

cystic fibrosis gene (*cfcf*) coding for the membrane protein CFTR

gene for CFTR protein and the plasmid are cut by restriction enzyme

plasmid obtained from a bacterium

cfcf gene and plasmid annealed together by ligase

liposome (tiny sphere formed by lipid bilayer)

plasmid + *cfcf* gene formed into complex with liposomes

liposome–gene complex given to cystic fibrosis patient as aerosol applied to the lungs via the nose

1 Liposome–gene complex fuses with epithelium cell membrane.

4 mRNA passes to ribosome and CFTR protein is made.

2 Gene in plasmid passes into the nucleus.

3 *cfcf* gene transcribed into mRNA.

5 CFTR protein is installed in the cell membrane and functions as pump. Normal mucus is formed.

epithelial cell of the lung

DNA fingerprinting

DNA 'fingerprinting' exploits the techniques of genetic engineering to identify a person from a sample of their DNA. For example, genetic fingerprinting is used to eliminate (or incriminate) suspects in crimes in which blood, tissue or body fluid samples are available. Sometimes it is used to establish relationships, typically of parentage.

The DNA of our chromosomes is unique. It includes the DNA of our genes. The bulk of our DNA does not code for proteins, however. The non-coding regions contain short sequences of bases that are repeated over and over again. Some of these sequences are scattered throughout the length of the DNA molecule, but many are joined together in major clusters. It is these major lengths of the non-coding DNA that are used in genetic fingerprinting. Everyone inherits a distinctive combination of these apparently non-functional 'repeat regions', half from their mother and half from their father. The process of 'fingerprinting' in outline is as follows.

- A sample of cells is obtained from blood, semen, hair root or body tissues, and the DNA is extracted. Where a tiny quantity of DNA is all that can be recovered, this is precisely copied first by a process called the **polymerase chain reaction** (in an automated process, the strands of the DNA are separated and copied to make duplicates of the original DNA). This produces sufficient DNA to analyse.
- The DNA is cut into small, double-stranded fragments using restriction enzyme (*Hin*fl in the UK, *Hae*III in the USA). These cut the DNA close to but not within the highly repetitive, 'nonsense' regions.
- The resulting DNA fragments are of varying lengths, and are separated by gel electrophoresis into invisible bands.
- The gel is treated with alkali to split double-stranded DNA into single strands.
- By means of 'Southern blotting' of the gel, a copy of the strands is transferred to a membrane (see page 127).
- Selected, radioactively labelled DNA probes are added to the membrane to bind to particular bands of DNA. The excess probes are washed away.
- The membrane is now overlaid with X-ray film, which becomes selectively 'fogged' by emission from the retained labelled probes.
- The X-ray film is developed, showing up the positions of the bands (fragments) to which probes have attached.

Figure 6.13
DNA profiles used to investigate parentage.

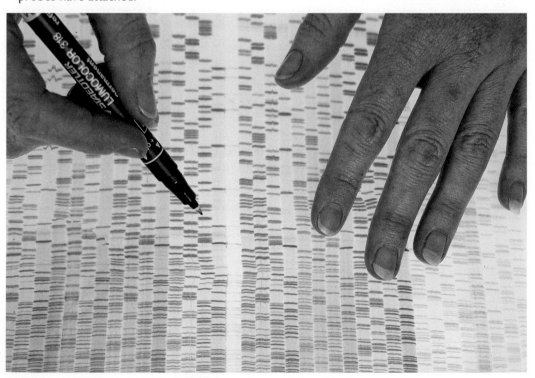

DNA profiles are produced from samples taken from the scene of the crime, from victims and suspects, and also from others who have certainly taken no part in the crime, as a control. Alternatively, if the issue is one of parentage a range of samples of DNA are analysed side by side, together with samples from possibly related people, and from 'controls' (Figure 6.13). The banding patterns are then compared. DNA profiling may eliminate innocent suspects, and identify a person or people who may be responsible (or related). It cannot prove *with absolute certainty* anyone's guilt or connection.

Issues raised by genetic engineering

Geneticists are really producing new organisms when genes are transferred between organisms. Consequently this work could become a source of hazards and it certainly generates questions – ethical, environmental and legal. The following are some examples.

- Will a gene, added to a genome, function in an unforeseen manner? Could it even trigger cancer or some other disease in the recipient, for example?
- Might an introduced gene for resistance to adverse conditions get transferred from a crop plant or farm animal into a weed species or some predator?
- Is it possible that recombinant DNA technology could transform a harmless organism, such as the human gut bacterium *E. coli*, into a harmful pathogen that could escape the laboratory and pass into the population at large?
- Is it true that there is an important over-riding principle that humans should not deliberately tamper with 'nature'?
- Genetic engineering is a costly technology that is mostly beneficial to the health and life expectancy of people of developed nations. If the funds made available for genetic engineering were largely diverted to solve more basic problems of housing, health, employment and nutrition (such as clean water supply) of the poor worldwide (and especially in the less-developed countries), would the money not benefit vastly more humans, immediately?
- In DNA fingerprinting, tiny quantities of DNA are often all that is available at scenes where DNA from other people may also be present and contaminate samples (unknown to scientist or defence counsel alike). Might the apparently clear-cut results of a DNA fingerprint analysis lead to the incrimination of the innocent?

11 Distinguish between the following pairs:

- genotype and genome
- restriction endonuclease and ligase
- 'blunt ends' and 'sticky ends'
- a bacterial chromosome and a plasmid
- reverse transcriptase and DNA polymerase
- R-plasmid and recombinant plasmid.

Skills task Prepare a case for and against the genetic engineering of food organisms.

Articles occasionally appear in the press that warn against genetically modified organisms in the food chain, sometimes with alarmist headlines.

Select such an article and then prepare the following to use in a discussion with other students:

- a concise summary of the criticisms the article makes, avoiding extremist language and any unnecessary exaggeration
- a list of any balancing arguments in favour of the genetic engineering of food plants
- a concise personal statement of your own views and preference in this issue.

SUMMARY
- In **genetic engineering**, genes are transferred from one organism to another (possibly unrelated) organism. Gene technology has many existing and future applications in agriculture, medicine, biotechnology and other industries. There are enormous **benefits** from genetic modification. But certain **potential dangers** arise, ethical, environmental and (sometimes) legal, and these may outweigh the benefits in some cases.
- Gene technology involves the cutting out, isolation, identification, transfer and multiplication (cloning) of genes. DNA strands are cut with **restriction enzymes**, which cleave the DNA at specific restriction sites (particular combinations of bases), either straight across, leaving 'blunt' ends, or 'staggered', leaving 'sticky' ends.

continued

- Genes are transferred between organisms by a DNA **vector**. Often this is a **plasmid**, a tiny ring of double-stranded DNA obtained from a bacterium. An alternative vector may be the nucleic acid of a virus.
- The gene and the vector are cut by means of the same restriction enzyme, forming compatible **sticky ends** at the cuts. Gene and plasmid are then brought together and joined (annealed), using **ligase enzyme**.
- Bacteria that have been genetically engineered to carry a new gene are identified by the use of plasmids that carry genes for resistance to two antibiotics. These plasmids are known as **R-plasmids**.
- For a gene to be active (be **expressed**, i.e. be transcribed into mRNA) a regulator mechanism (regulator gene and operator gene) normally need to be attached and activated. One example is the **lactose operon** mechanism present in certain bacteria.
- Another way of obtaining copies of genes is to **build them from nucleotides** in the correct sequence. This sequence is worked out from the amino acid sequence of the protein that the gene codes for, and by using the genetic code. Alternatively, the gene can be **constructed from the mRNA** that it codes for, using reverse transcriptase enzyme.
- **Genetically modified bacteria** are now used to make valuable products such as human insulin (for treatment of diabetics), human growth hormone and several other hormonal or enzymic products of use in medicine, agriculture and other industries.
- **Genetically modified eukaryotes** are harder to produce. (For example, they carry two copies of a gene, so the 'engineering' processes are often more difficult.) But food plants with herbicide resistance, insect resistance or improved food value have been produced. So too have sheep that will secrete certain human proteins needed in medicines.
- It is possible that the symptoms of **genetic diseases** like cystic fibrosis may be overcome by gene therapy in the future. DNA 'fingerprinting' is currently used in forensic science and in the investigations of family relationships; the results feature decisively in legal cases.

Examination questions

1 Recombinant DNA technology has been used successfully to transfer genes, thus producing organisms with new properties. An early example was the transfer of the human insulin gene to yeast. **Part** of the process for gene cloning is outlined below.

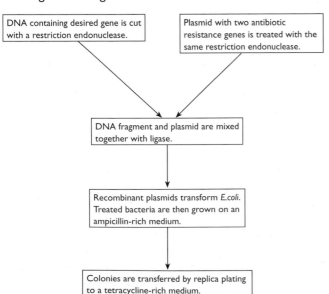

a Why is the same restriction endonuclease used to cut the DNA in both cases? (2)

b What is the function of ligase? (1)

c What can be deduced about the colonies of bacteria which can grow on the ampicillin-rich medium? (1)

d Explain the meaning of the term *replica plating*. (2)

e Colonies which also grow on the tetracycline-rich medium are discarded. Explain why these organisms are unwanted. (2)

f Suggest an alternative way of introducing the DNA into the bacterial cells. (1)

OCR (Oxford), A level, 6914, Mar 1999

2 a Make a labelled diagram to show the structure of a **named** virus. (4)

b Explain how viruses reproduce. (4)

c Certain types of viruses can be used instead of plasmids as cloning vectors.

  i What is meant by a *cloning* vector? (1)

  ii Why are viruses considered to be so useful for this purpose? (1)

OCR (Oxford), A level, 6914, June 1999

3 *Bacillus thuringiensis* produces a protein that is toxic to leaf-eating caterpillars. This protein has been used by farmers as a natural insecticide. Recently, the gene that codes for the toxin has been genetically engineered into several crop plants.

a Outline how the gene that codes for the toxin could have been isolated. (5)

The gene, once isolated, is inserted into a host plant cell either by using the bacterium *Agrobacterium tumefaciens* as a vector to infect a plant cell or using a particle gun which shoots DNA-coated pellets into a plant cell.

b i Suggest why a plasmid vector cannot be used to insert the gene into plant cells. (1)

ii Explain why it is important to insert the gene into a single isolated plant cell rather than into a cell within a whole plant. (2)

c State **two** environmental implications of genetically engineered pest resistance in plants. (2)

It has been suggested that the integration of the gene for toxin production from *B. thuringiensis* into a wide range of crop plants could result in a loss of the effectiveness of the toxin.

d Outline how this loss of effectiveness of the toxin might occur. (2)

OCR (Cambridge), A level, 4806, Mar 1999

4 The human gene for alpha-1-antitrypsin (AAT) was introduced into fertilised eggs of sheep and the eggs implanted into surrogate mothers. Some surrogates produced transgenic female animals which secreted AAT in their milk. The sequence of events is shown below.

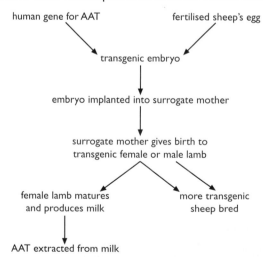

a i Explain what is meant by a *transgenic animal*. (2)

ii Describe how a transgenic embryo might successfully be implanted into a surrogate mother. (3)

In some cases the injected DNA may not be incorporated into the DNA of the fertilised egg and in others the transgenic female may not produce much AAT in her milk.

b Suggest why the transgenic females produce different quantities of AAT. (2)

Complex human proteins, such as AAT, cannot be produced by genetically engineered bacteria.

c Suggest why bacteria cannot be genetically engineered to produce complex human proteins such as AAT. (1)

A possible use of AAT is in the treatment of cystic fibrosis. AAT inhibits an enzyme, elastase, which helps to remove dead or damaged tissue in the body. In people suffering from cystic fibrosis, the frequent lung infections lead to the presence of large numbers of white blood cells, which release extra elastase, causing a potentially fatal breakdown of lung structure.

d i Describe the inheritance of cystic fibrosis. (3)

ii Explain why the sufferers of cystic fibrosis develop frequent lung infections. (2)

In a small clinical trial in 1996–97, patients with cystic fibrosis inhaled AAT into their lungs.

e Suggest how this treatment might help someone with cystic fibrosis. (2)

OCR (Cambridge), A level, 4807, Mar 1999

II
RESOURCES
FOR
LIVING

7 Feeding by digestion

STARTING POINTS ● **Nutrition** is the process by which organisms obtain energy to maintain the functions of life and matter to build and maintain their structures.
● Organisms require carbohydrates, lipids and proteins as **bulk raw materials** to build up the structures of cells and tissues and to provide energy.
● Animals (and fungi) take complex food molecules and break them down by **digestion**, to form molecules small enough to be absorbed into body cells.
● Digestion involves **hydrolytic enzymes**. Most of these are packaged for discharge from the cells in which they are produced.

● Nutrients: you take them or make them!

There is a division in the living world over how organisms obtain the materials they require for living.

Green plants actually make them! They manufacture their own nutrients, which are elaborate food molecules like sugars, amino acids and fatty acids. To do this, they use carbon dioxide and water, together with mineral ions, and they build large organic molecules from them, using the energy of sunlight. This is described as 'self-feeding', or **autotrophic nutrition**.

Most other organisms cannot do this. Instead, they rely on ready-made food in the form of other organisms, dead or alive, and the waste products of organisms. Their nutrition is described as 'different' or **heterotrophic nutrition**. Heterotrophs obtain nutrients from complex food molecules by the processes of digestion. They then absorb the products of digestion into their cells and tissues.

Figure 7.1
Interdependence in nutrition.

Organisms depend directly or indirectly on the Sun for energy and on each other for nutrients.

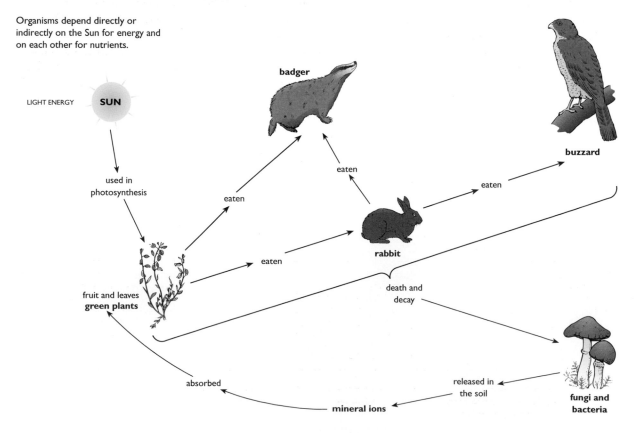

On further analysis, we can see there is complete **interdependence in nutrition** in the living world. All heterotrophs feed either on plants, or on organisms that are dependent on plants. This means that all organisms rely on energy from the Sun, directly or indirectly. Furthermore, the inorganic nutrients required by plants are released after death and decay of living things. Dead organic matter is broken down by the activities of organisms like bacteria and fungi. Their nutrition leads to the release of nutrients and ions for reuse. Inorganic nutrients are endlessly recycled in this way (Figure 7.1). Nevertheless, we need to look at heterotrophic and autotrophic nutrition independently, to see how these feeding mechanisms work.

Heterotrophic nutrition: the strategies

Heterotrophs are unable to manufacture their own foods, but rather depend on other organisms as their source of nutrients. All animals are heterotrophs, and so too are fungi and bacteria. Among the heterotrophs, however, there are three distinctive strategies for obtaining nutrients (Figure 7.2).

Saprotrophs live on decaying matter, the dead remains of organisms or their products, typically faeces. Digestion by saprotrophs occurs outside the cells, and the useful products of digestion are absorbed. Most fungi and many bacteria are saprotrophs. Yeasts, for example, are saprotrophs, living as they do on sugars on the surface of fruits and in the nectaries of flowers, and on sugar deposited in soils and elsewhere. It is saprotrophs that ultimately release inorganic molecules and mineral ions from dead organisms for reuse by plants. The ecological effect of saprotrophic nutrition is discussed in Chapter 17.

Parasites feed on living organisms on (or in) which they live for most of their life cycle. The organism parasitised is referred to as the **host**. The relationship is obviously harmful, or at least unhelpful, to the host. The parasite has a supply of nutrients on hand, but any resistance by the host has to be overcome. Movement between hosts is also a period of danger to parasites. Both plant and animal parasites exist. An example of an animal parasite is the protozoan *Plasmodium*, which lives in the blood and liver cells of humans and causes malaria. *Plasmodium* may be transferred from one host to another when a female mosquito takes a blood meal from an infected human, and later feeds on another human who is not yet infected with malaria. The effects of parasites on the host are health issues considered in Chapter 15.

Holozoic nutrition involves the taking in of organic matter, which is then digested into a suitable form for uptake into the cells of the body. This type of nutrition requires a specialised digestive system – a pouch or tube, in effect. Here the food is broken down to smaller molecules that are then absorbed. Very many organisms, including most free-living animals, have holozoic nutrition. Human nutrition is just one example.

1 What features of the nutrition of parasites and saprotrophs are common to holozoic nutrition too?
2 Why does a heap of fresh lawn mowings heat up?

Figure 7.2
Strategies of nutrition.

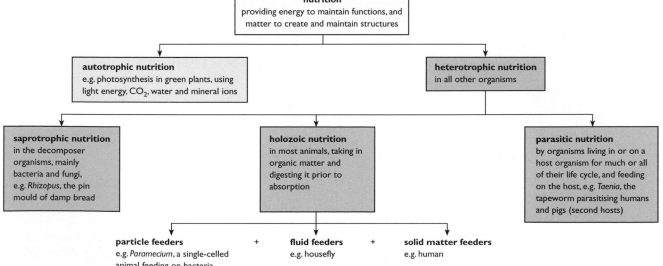

nutrition
providing energy to maintain functions, and matter to create and maintain structures

autotrophic nutrition
e.g. photosynthesis in green plants, using light energy, CO_2, water and mineral ions

heterotrophic nutrition
in all other organisms

saprotrophic nutrition
in the decomposer organisms, mainly bacteria and fungi, e.g. *Rhizopus*, the pin mould of damp bread

holozoic nutrition
in most animals, taking in organic matter and digesting it prior to absorption

parasitic nutrition
by organisms living in or on a host organism for much or all of their life cycle, and feeding on the host, e.g. *Taenia*, the tapeworm parasitising humans and pigs (second hosts)

particle feeders
e.g. *Paramecium*, a single-celled animal feeding on bacteria

+

fluid feeders
e.g. housefly

+

solid matter feeders
e.g. human

Variety in holozoic nutrition

There is such a wide variety of feeding mechanisms among holozoic organisms that it is helpful to classify them broadly. This is most conveniently done on the size or form of the food taken in.

Particle feeders take in small particles such as floating unicellular organisms or tiny multicellular organisms suspended in fresh or salt water. They gather in these particles, sieving or otherwise separating them from the surrounding water, and selectively take up the food present for digestion. Particle feeding, sometimes called **filter feeding**, is used by animals ranging from the huge baleen whales that feed on marine plankton to unicellular organisms like *Paramecium* of freshwater habitats (Figure 7.3).

Figure 7.3
Particle feeding by the 'slipper animalcule', *Paramecium*.

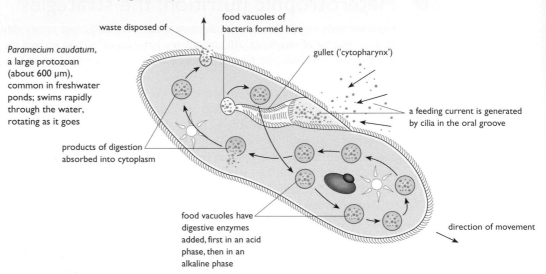

Paramecium caudatum, a large protozoan (about 600 μm), common in freshwater ponds; swims rapidly through the water, rotating as it goes

waste disposed of

food vacuoles of bacteria formed here

gullet ('cytopharynx')

a feeding current is generated by cilia in the oral groove

products of digestion absorbed into cytoplasm

food vacuoles have digestive enzymes added, first in an acid phase, then in an alkaline phase

direction of movement

Fluid feeders, on the other hand, are organisms that take in liquid food, either dissolved food or liquidised tissues. Their mouthparts are often specialised for this purpose. A wide range of such adaptations are seen, including the nectar- and pollen-collecting apparatus of the honey bee, and the blood-sucking mouthparts of the female mosquito; another example is shown in Figure 7.4. Liquidising tissues involves the injection of digestive enzymes into trapped prey, in order to reduce the solid tissues to liquid. This unusual form of fluid feeding is used by many spiders.

Figure 7.4
Fluid feeding by the house fly (*Musca domestica*).

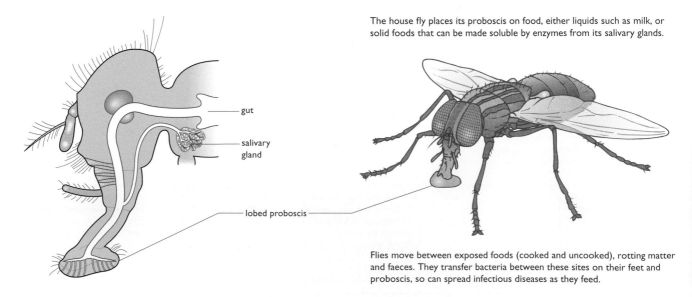

The house fly places its proboscis on food, either liquids such as milk, or solid foods that can be made soluble by enzymes from its salivary glands.

gut

salivary gland

lobed proboscis

Flies move between exposed foods (cooked and uncooked), rotting matter and faeces. They transfer bacteria between these sites on their feet and proboscis, so can spread infectious diseases as they feed.

Solid matter feeders, also known as **macrophagous feeders**, take in relatively large, solid particles. Human nutrition is a good example of macrophagous feeding. We focus on this feeding strategy in this chapter.

● Extension   Diet and feeding mechanisms may change during the life cycle

Whilst very many organisms maintain a similar diet and method of feeding throughout their life cycle, some do not. For example, insects like butterflies undergo an abrupt transition in body form during their life cycle, called **metamorphosis**. Diet and feeding mechanism also change in the process (Figure 7.5).

The juvenile or larval stage, known as a **caterpillar**, is the principal feeding and growing stage. It has biting and chewing mouthparts, and typically feeds on leaf tissue of green plants. So the caterpillar is a solid matter feeder. Its gut produces digestive enzymes that enable it to access the carbohydrates, lipids and proteins in its diet, all of which are needed for growth and development.

After a certain size and maturity is reached the caterpillar pupates. From the pupa the adult stage, a butterfly, emerges later. The **butterfly** is the dispersal and reproductive stage in the life cycle. Butterflies typically feed on the liquid nectar in flowers, which is rich in sucrose. In this fluid-feeding stage, the adult has digestive enzymes only for the release of monosaccharide sugar, which it requires for respiration to provide energy for flight and reproduction.

Figure 7.5
The life cycle and feeding mechanisms of a butterfly and a caterpillar.

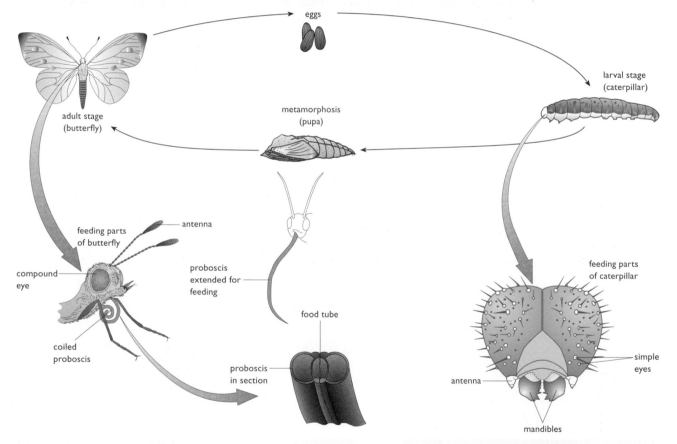

Stage in life cycle	Food	Digestive enzymes of gut				
		protease proteins ↓ amino acids	**lipase** lipids ↓ fatty acids + glycerol	**amylase** starch ↓ maltose	**maltase** maltose ↓ glucose	**sucrase** sucrose ↓ glucose + fructose
Caterpillar (larva)	Leaves	✓	✓	✓	✓	✓
Butterfly (adult)	Nectar					✓

Holozoic nutrition in mammals

In the nutrition of mammals, food is taken into a specialised structure called the **alimentary canal** or **gut**. This is a long muscular tube beginning at the mouth and ending at the anus. Along the gut are several **glands**, and the whole structure is specialised for the **movement** and **digestion** of food and for the **absorption** of the useful products of digestion.

Mechanical digestion takes place by the action of the jaws and teeth in the mouth, and through the churning action of the muscular walls that moves the food along the gut. Chemical digestion is by **enzymes**. Enzymes are secreted on to the food in the gut and these, together with enzymes in the gut lining, complete the digestion of the food.

The useful products of digestion in the gut are then **absorbed** into the body and **assimilated** into cells and tissues. Undigested matter leaves the body as faeces.

The regions of the gut and the stages to holozoic nutrition in the mammal are summarised in Figure 7.6.

A mammal has to search for the food it needs, or possibly hunts it down. Some mammals eat only plant material (these are **herbivores**, such as the rabbit), some eat only other animals (**carnivores**, such as the stoat) and others eat both animal and plant material (**omnivores**, such as the fox). Whatever is eaten, a balance of the essential nutrients is required by the body, and diet is the next issue to look into.

Figure 7.6
Mammal in sagittal section, showing the layout of the gut and the stages in holozoic nutrition.

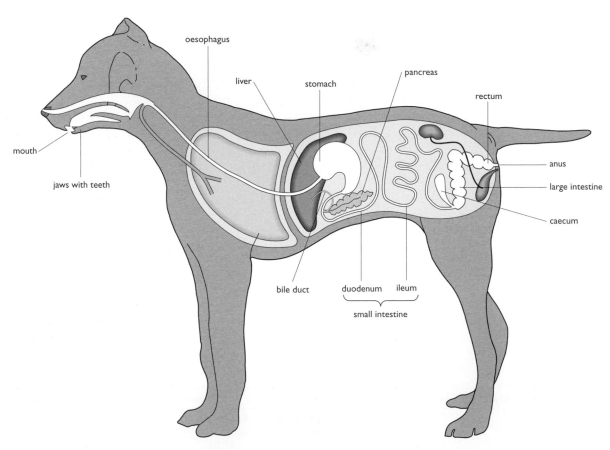

stages in holozoic nutrition:

food (large complex insoluble molecules)	mechanical digestion (teeth and muscle actions)	chemical digestion (enzymes in stomach and small intestine)	products of digestion absorbed into blood circulation in small intestine, then to cells	faeces (undigested food, dead cells from the gut and bacteria)
ingestion →	**digestion** →		**absorption** →	**egestion**
			assimilation	

The idea of diet

The food a holozoic organism consumes is described as its **diet**. A **balanced diet** consists of the essential nutrients in the correct proportions. The term is usually applied to human diets. A diet that is lacking in one or more essential nutrients, or that provides the wrong balance of nutrients, causes **malnutrition**. Malnutrition is experienced by very many humans (Chapter 15, page 322), but malnutrition is a misfortune that can befall any organism in nature – and frequently does.

The diet should provide an appropriate amount of the following six food components on a regular basis.

Metabolic fuel is normally supplied from carbohydrates and fats (lipids), but it can also be obtained from proteins. Chemical energy in all of these 'fuels' is released by respiration, but proteins must first be **deaminated**. This means that the combined nitrogen as the amino group ($-NH_2$) is removed first, before respiration occurs.

The energy value of foods is expressed in **joules** and **kilojoules** (J and kJ, 1 kJ = 1000 J). The joule is defined in terms of heat energy; 4.18 J of heat energy are required to raise 1 g of water through 1 °C. The energy typically provided by individual nutrients is estimated experimentally, using the bomb **calorimeter** (see Figure 9.1, page 192). The amounts of energy that major food substances might yield (for example, when they are completely respired) are as follows:

- carbohydrates, e.g. glucose or sucrose $\quad$ 16 kJ g^{-1}
- fats $\quad$ 37 kJ g^{-1}
- proteins $\quad$ 17 kJ g^{-1}

An earlier unit for the amount of energy in food substances was the calorie. This term may often be read on commercial packs of food (a calorie = 4.18 J).

The body's requirements for energy are determined by four factors:

- the background rate of metabolism, known as **basal metabolism**; this is the amount of energy required to maintain brain function and the rest of the body's basic metabolism 'ticking over' comfortably, at normal temperatures, when at rest in activities like heart contraction; this is the rate against which we compare the energy demands of various activities
- how **physically active** we are in work and leisure; additional energy is needed for physical work
- our **age** and the amount of **growth and repair work** the body has to support; the rapid growth of adolescence makes an additional demand of about 8 kJ per hour
- our **gender**; usually females require less than males, but in pregnancy and during lactation (breastfeeding of an infant), females' requirements are greatly increased.

In Table 7.1 the recommended daily intakes of energy and certain nutrients are compared for some categories of humans. Current eating habits are such that a significant part of our diet may be taken in the form of snacks and convenience foods, sometimes taken at a 'fast food outlet' such as a burger bar. Table 7.2 gives the food value of some familiar snacks and fast food items. Does a significant proportion of your daily requirements of energy come from snacks like these?

Table 7.1 Reference daily nutrient intakes.

Age range	Estimated average requirements for energy /kJ	Protein /g	Calcium /mg	Iron /mg	Zinc /mg	Vitamin A /µg	Thiamin /mg	Vitamin B$_6$ /mg	Folic acid /µg	Vitamin C /mg
Males:										
15–18 years	11 510	55.2	1000	11.3	9.5	700	1.1	1.5	200	40
19–50 years	10 600	55.5	700	8.7	9.5	700	1.0	1.4	200	40
Females:										
15–18 years	8830	45.0	800	14.8	7.0	600	0.8	1.2	200	40
19–50 years	8100	45.0	700	14.8	7.0	600	0.8	1.2	200	40
Pregnant	+800	+6.0				+100	+0.1		+100	+10
Lactating:										
0–4 months	+2200	+11.0	+550		+6.0	+350	+0.2		+60	+30

Data taken from Ministry of Agriculture, Fisheries and Food (1995) *Manual of Nutrition 10th edition*, pp 68–9, Tables 24 and 25 (parts).

Table 7.2
Food values of selected 'fast food' items.

Our likely daily requirements in terms of energy are between 9 and 11.5 MJ per day (see Table 7.1). One megajoule (MJ) of energy = 1000 kilojoules (kJ).

Burger King	Hamburger	1220 kJ
	French fries	880 kJ
	Apple pie	1010 kJ
Kentucky Fried Chicken	Chicken (two pieces with chips)	3280 kJ
	Spare ribs	1600 kJ
	Jacket potato	630 kJ
McDonald's	Quarter pounder	1760 kJ
	Cheeseburger	1260 kJ
	Big Mac	2270 kJ
	Hotcakes with butter and syrup	2100 kJ
	Vanilla shake	1470 kJ
Pizzaland	Cheese and tomato traditional	2940 kJ
	Deep pan special	5250 kJ
Wimpy	Chicken in a bun	1810 kJ
	Wimpy grill	2180 kJ
	Thick shake	945 kJ
Fish and chip shop	Cod fried in batter, with chips (6 oz portion)	3150 kJ
Can of Coke/lemonade		181 kJ
Diet Coke/lemonade		1.6 kJ
Mars Bar/Snicker bar		1349 kJ
Packet of crisps		564 kJ

Combined nitrogen is required for the building of proteins, and is taken in as proteins or amino acids. Dietary protein is the chief source of the 20 amino acids from which the mammals' own proteins are built up.

Vitamins are organic compounds that are only required in tiny amounts. Most function as coenzymes in the body. Vitamins cannot be manufactured in the body, so their absence from the diet tends to have marked effects, known as **deficiency diseases** (see Table 7.3).

Water, since 70–90% of the body is water.

Essential minerals include major minerals like calcium, iron and phosphate ions, which are needed for the construction of body tissues or are combined in metabolites essential for many metabolic processes. They also include the micronutrients such as manganese, which are often cofactors in the functioning of particular enzymes. The minerals we require are listed in Table 3.2 (page 58).

Roughage or **dietary fibre**, which is mostly of plant origin, consists of cellulose from cell walls. Dietary fibre cannot be digested. The value of dietary fibre is as bulk that stimulates food movement through the gut. Additionally, a high fibre diet obtained largely from fruit and vegetables is believed to reduce the risk of gut cancers and of coronary heart disease.

Table 7.3
Vitamins in the human diet.

Vitamin	Sources	Functions (and the effects of a deficiency)
Fat-soluble vitamins:		
A (retinol)	fish liver oils, animal liver, made in the body from the pigment carotene (present in leafy vegetables)	needed for healthy epithelial cells (dry skin), used to make retinal – essential for production of visual pigment rhodopsin – in rod cells (poor vision/'night blindness')
D (calciferol)	fish liver oil, butter, egg yolks; made in the skin by the action of sunlight	promotes the absorption of calcium from the intestine and reabsorption of phosphorus from urine (rickets – soft bones – in children, painful bones in adults)
E (tocopherol)	plant oils	required for the absorption of polyunsaturated fatty acids
K (phylloquinone)	dark green leafy vegetables; made by bacteria of the intestine	for the manufacture of prothrombin, a protein necessary for blood clotting, in the liver (delay in the blood-clotting mechanism)
Water-soluble vitamins:		
B_1 (thiamin)	widely distributed (meat, wholemeal bread, vegetables)	coenzyme in decarboxylation in respiration of carbohydrate (beri-beri disease, nerve degeneration)
B_2 (riboflavin)	widely distributed in foods, including milk	coenzyme in electron-transport part of respiration (deficiency rarely seen)
B_3 (niacin, nicotinic acid)	meat, yeast extract, potatoes, wholemeal bread, coffee; and made from the amino acid tryptophan	precursor of coenzymes NAD/NADP (pellagra, a skin disease)
B_5 (pantothenic acid)	most foods	component of coenzyme A molecule
B_6 (pyridoxine)	meat, fish, eggs, some vegetables	coenzyme in formation of amino acids from fatty acids
B_{12} (several cobalt-containing compounds)	liver, yeast (not in plants)	essential for nucleic acid synthesis in rapidly dividing cells (pernicious anaemia)
folic acid	liver, white fish, raw leafy vegetables	essential for nucleic acid synthesis (anaemia during pregnancy)
H (biotin)	liver, yeast, egg white; synthesised by gut bacteria	coenzyme in carboxylation, and in formation of amino acids
C (ascorbic acid)	vegetables (potatoes and green vegetables), fruits (citrus fruits)	essential for collagen fibre synthesis and healthy connective tissues (scurvy, with bleeding from gums, poor wound healing)

● **Extension**

Dietary reference values

The term **dietary reference value (DRV)** has been introduced to assess the adequacy of diets of different groups of people. DRVs are a product of three values:

- Estimated Average Requirement (EAR), an estimate of the average need for food energy or a nutrient
- Reference Nutrient Intake (RNI), the amount of a nutrient that any individual would need, even those with high needs
- Lower Reference Nutrient Intake (LRNI), the amount of a nutrient sufficient for individuals with low needs.

Tables of the values of EARs and RNIs are given in the MAFF booklet *Manual of Nutrition*, published by HMSO, where their involvement in the assessment of diets of groups of people is discussed.

Digestion

This account of the structure of the gut and the process of digestion in mammals is mostly illustrated by reference to humans (Figure 7.7). The details vary little between mammals.

Figure 7.7
The human gut.

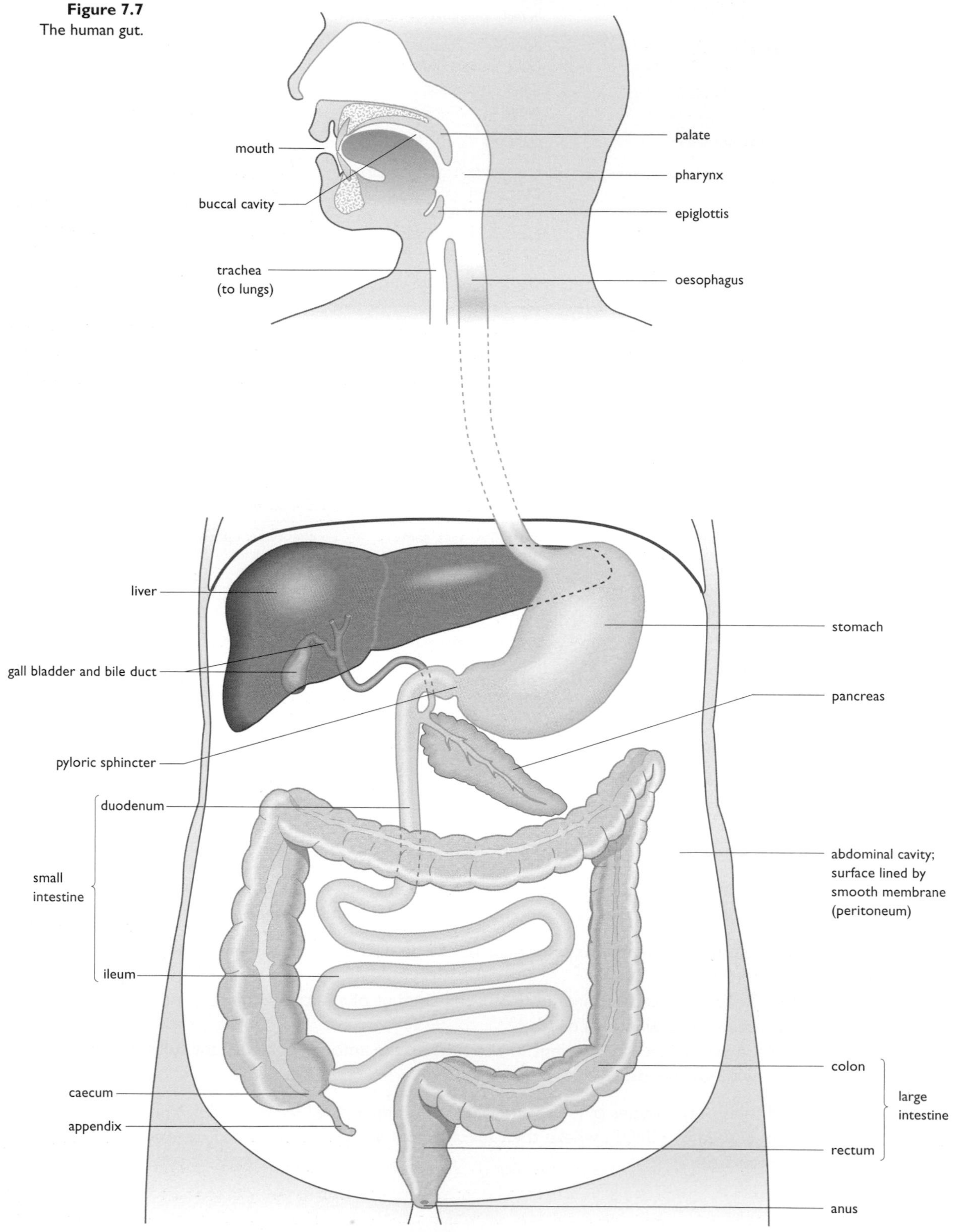

palate

pharynx

epiglottis

mouth

buccal cavity

trachea
(to lungs)

oesophagus

liver

gall bladder and bile duct

pyloric sphincter

duodenum

small
intestine

ileum

caecum

appendix

stomach

pancreas

abdominal cavity;
surface lined by
smooth membrane
(peritoneum)

colon

large
intestine

rectum

anus

The structure of the gut

The gut is a muscular and glandular tube with an opening at both ends. It is suspended by connective tissue, called mesentery, from the dorsal body wall. Running down the mesentery are the blood vessels, lymph vessels and nerves that serve the gut wall and its glands. The gut wall itself consists of four distinct layers (Figure 7.8):

- an outer covering of **fibrous connective tissue**
- external **muscle layers** (both longitudinal and circular)
- **connective tissue**, and
- the **innermost layers**, made up of glandular epithelium, connective tissue and a thin layer of muscle.

The different regions of the gut are locally specialised and structurally modified. For example, the **stomach** stores the bulk of the meal and churns up the food, as well as being the site where protein digestion begins. The stomach wall has an additional layer of muscle, alongside the basic circular and longitudinal muscle layers (see Figure 7.14, page 155). Also, the inner wall of the stomach is packed with tubular pits called **gastric glands**. These are discussed in 'Digestion in the stomach' (page 155).

The **small intestine** is specialised for digestion and absorption. It has an enormously increased surface area, through the presence of finger-like projections, called **villi**, that extend from the inner surface into the lumen. As a result, the digested food passes in close contact with cells.

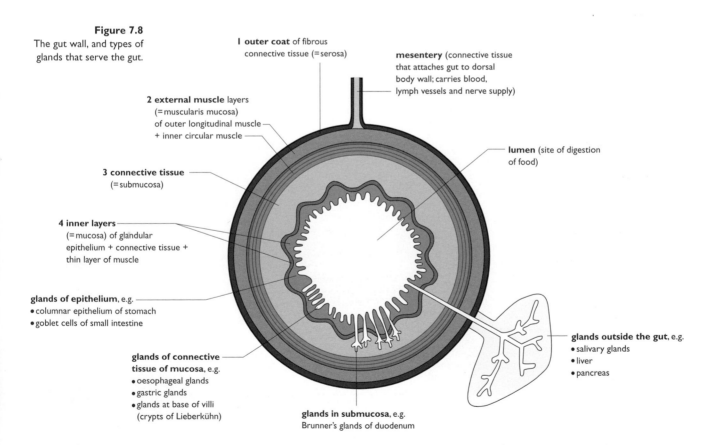

Figure 7.8
The gut wall, and types of glands that serve the gut.

1 outer coat of fibrous connective tissue (=serosa)

mesentery (connective tissue that attaches gut to dorsal body wall; carries blood, lymph vessels and nerve supply)

2 external muscle layers (=muscularis mucosa) of outer longitudinal muscle + inner circular muscle

lumen (site of digestion of food)

3 connective tissue (=submucosa)

4 inner layers (=mucosa) of glandular epithelium + connective tissue + thin layer of muscle

glands of epithelium, e.g.
- columnar epithelium of stomach
- goblet cells of small intestine

glands outside the gut, e.g.
- salivary glands
- liver
- pancreas

glands of connective tissue of mucosa, e.g.
- oesophageal glands
- gastric glands
- glands at base of villi (crypts of Lieberkühn)

glands in submucosa, e.g.
Brunner's glands of duodenum

Associated with the gut and its wall are glands of various sorts (Figure 7.8). The glands produce large quantities of watery secretions, some of which contain digestive enzymes. Different parts of the gut carry out particular steps in chemical digestion by enzymes, and secretion by the glands is coordinated with the presence of food in that region of the gut. The range of digestive enzymes is listed in Table 7.4 on page 151.

3 What are the roles of the circular and longitudinal muscle layers of the gut wall?

The processes of digestion

Figure 7.9
Chemical digestion:
the steps.

The bulk of the food taken in consists initially of insoluble molecules, too large to cross the gut wall and enter the bloodstream. Food cannot be said to have truly entered the body until it has been digested and the products absorbed across the gut wall. The changes undergone by carbohydrates, lipids and proteins during digestion are summarised in Figure 7.9 and Table 7.4.

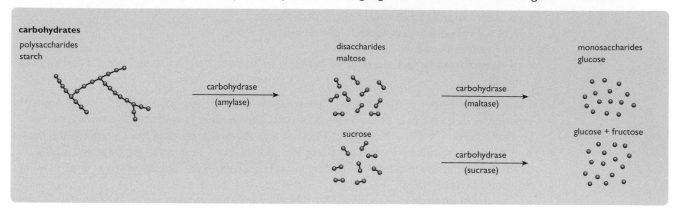

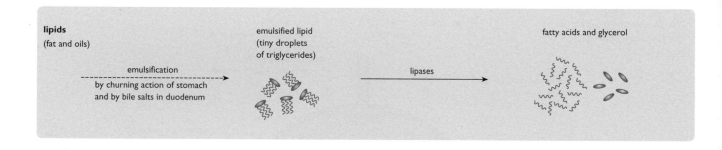

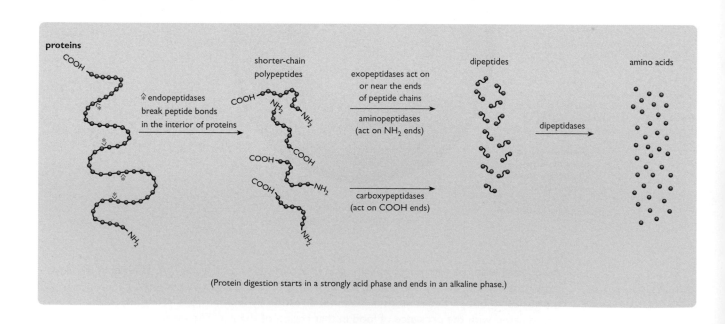

(Protein digestion starts in a strongly acid phase and ends in an alkaline phase.)

Table 7.4 Digestive secretions, sites and actions.

Secretion	Source	Site of action	pH range	Active ingredient	Substrate/effects	Products
saliva[bc]	salivary glands	mouth	6.5–7.5	amylase	starch ⟶	maltose
gastric juice[b]	gastric glands	stomach	2.0	hydrochloric acid, *activates* pepsin rennin (*young mammals only*)	pepsinogen[a] ⟶ proteins ⟶ milk protein ⟶	pepsin polypeptides coagulated
bile[bc]	liver	duodenum	(alkaline)	bile salts (*not an enzyme*)	emulsification of lipids	
intestinal juice[bc]	crypts of Lieberkühn	duodenum	7.0	enteropeptidase (*enzyme activator*)	trypsinogen[a] ⟶	trypsin
	Brunner's glands[bc]	duodenum	7.0	no enzymes		
pancreatic juice[bc]	pancreas	duodenum and ileum	7.0	amylase protease e.g. trypsin and chymotrypsin *trypsin activates* peptidases lipases nuclease	starch ⟶ proteins ⟶ chymotrypsinogen[a] ⟶ peptides ⟶ triglycerides ⟶ nucleic acids ⟶	maltose polypeptides chymotrypsin amino acids fatty acids and glycerol nucleotides
	surface (microvilli) and interior of epithelial cells of villi	ileum	8.5	peptidases maltase sucrase lactase nucleotidase	dipeptides ⟶ maltose ⟶ sucrose ⟶ lactose ⟶ nucleotides ⟶	amino acids glucose glucose and fructose glucose and galactose pentose sugar, phosphate and bases

[a] Endopeptidases are secreted in inactive form, and are activated.
[b] Mucus is an ingredient of these secretions.
[c] Alkaline hydrogencarbonate ions are a component of these secretions.

Protection of the gut lining

All the digestive juices contain **mucus**, which is also secreted by the cells of the epithelium along the entire length of the gut. Mucus is a lubricating secretion that adheres to the cell lining of the gut and coats the food, protecting the alimentary canal from mechanical damage and self-digestion. Mucus contains a globular protein to which short-chain polysaccharides are added before mucus is secreted, making a glycoprotein. When secreted, if they come into contact with water, glycoproteins swell up to become sticky and gel-like (Figure 7.10).

Figure 7.10 Protection of the gut by mucus.

Mucus is secreted by epithelial cells throughout the gut: here the columnar epithelium of the stomach lining is secreting mucus copiously.

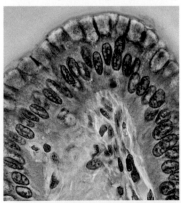

section through stomach epithelium, HP (phase contrast)

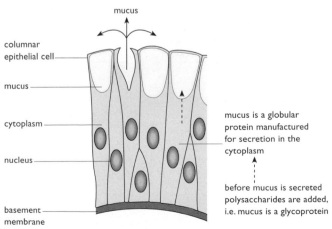

mucus

columnar epithelial cell

mucus

cytoplasm

nucleus

basement membrane

mucus is a globular protein manufactured for secretion in the cytoplasm

before mucus is secreted polysaccharides are added, i.e. mucus is a glycoprotein

Digestion in the mouth

In the mouth, the lips, tongue and teeth work together to take in food, and move it about the mouth. The teeth of the lower jaw work against the teeth of the fixed upper jaw. This chewing action of the teeth, known as **mastication**, greatly increases the surface area of the food for the later actions of digestive enzymes. It also makes the food easier to swallow (Figure 7.11).

The temporary holding of food in the mouth is made possible by presence of the **palate**. This is a horizontal plate of bone and cartilage that divides the mouth from the nasal cavity in mammals. Because of the palate, breathing can continue without interruption whilst the food is being chewed. Consequently, the teeth of mammals are able to carry out specialised tasks. The **incisors** are the front teeth, chisel-shaped for cutting, the **canines** are pointed teeth, for grasping and tearing, the **premolars** have cusps on the surface of the crown, and are for chewing, and the **molars** are the large back teeth with four cusps, and are used for grinding and chewing. The positions of the teeth in the jaws and structure of human teeth are shown in Figure 7.12.

In a small way, chemical digestion also starts in the mouth, in that the saliva contains a starch-digesting enzyme, **amylase**. The main component of saliva is mucus, however, and the role of saliva is to lubricate the food and help bind it into a soft ball called a **bolus**, which is then passed to the back of the mouth for swallowing.

Figure 7.11
The mouth: structure and function.

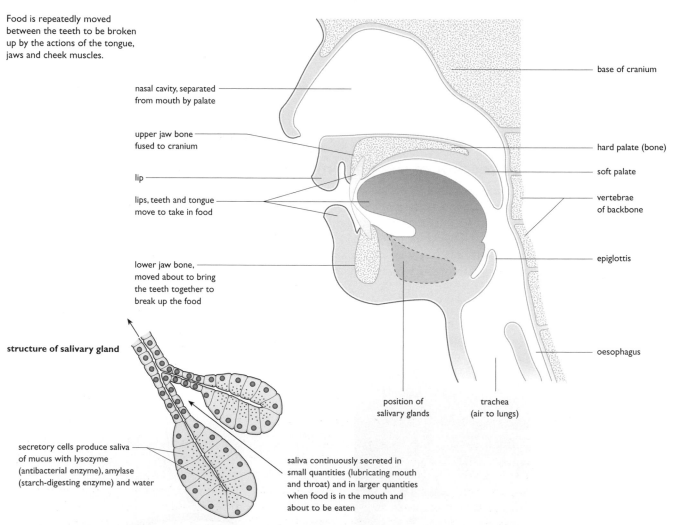

Food is repeatedly moved between the teeth to be broken up by the actions of the tongue, jaws and cheek muscles.

base of cranium

nasal cavity, separated from mouth by palate

upper jaw bone fused to cranium

hard palate (bone)

soft palate

lip

vertebrae of backbone

lips, teeth and tongue move to take in food

lower jaw bone, moved about to bring the teeth together to break up the food

epiglottis

oesophagus

structure of salivary gland

secretory cells produce saliva of mucus with lysozyme (antibacterial enzyme), amylase (starch-digesting enzyme) and water

saliva continuously secreted in small quantities (lubricating mouth and throat) and in larger quantities when food is in the mouth and about to be eaten

position of salivary glands

trachea (air to lungs)

Secretion of saliva is controlled by reflex actions (page 275):
• triggered when food is present in the mouth
• triggered by sight, smell or thought of food, and learned through experience (known as a **conditioned reflex**).

Figure 7.12
Teeth, and the permanent
dentition of a human.

molar tooth in section

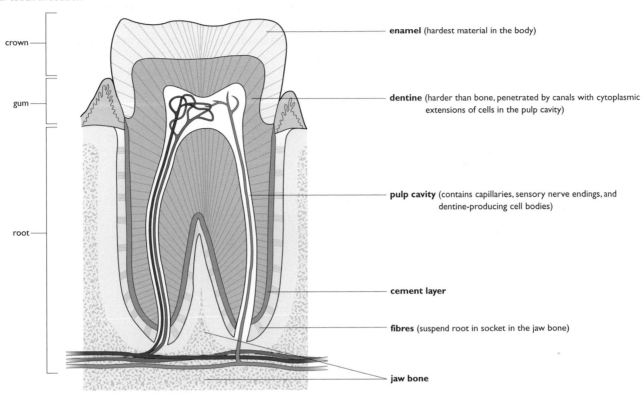

crown

enamel (hardest material in the body)

gum

dentine (harder than bone, penetrated by canals with cytoplasmic
extensions of cells in the pulp cavity)

root

pulp cavity (contains capillaries, sensory nerve endings, and
dentine-producing cell bodies)

cement layer

fibres (suspend root in socket in the jaw bone)

jaw bone

side view of the teeth in one half of the upper and lower jaws

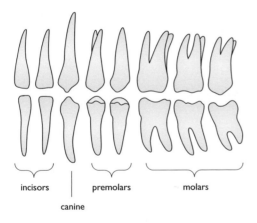

incisors

canine

premolars

molars

surface view of teeth of the lower jaw

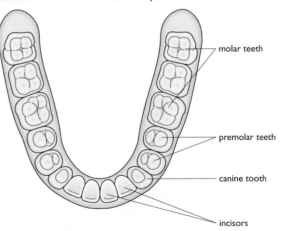

molar teeth

premolar teeth

canine tooth

incisors

● **Extension**   Starch agar to detect carbohydrase activity

A dilute solution of starch with agar can be poured into a Petri dish when warm and allowed to
cool, forming a **starch agar plate**. This can be used to investigate carbohydrase activity. 'Wells'
in the starch agar, cut with a cork borer, can be filled with different enzyme solutions. The
amylase present digests the starch in the surrounding agar. Later, when the plate is flooded with
iodine, a colourless 'halo' occurs around wells where starch digestion has occurred, and the
remainder of the starch agar plate turns dark blue. The more amylase present, the larger the halo.

This technique can be used to investigate amylase in different regions of the gut of a freshly
killed cockroach. Alternatively, different species of germinating seed can be halved and laid on
the intact starch agar surface for a given time.

The movement of food along the gut

The food bolus is propelled along the gut by a wave of muscular contraction and relaxation, known as **peristalsis**. Circular muscles in the gut wall in front of the bolus relax, whilst those just behind it contract. This is how the bolus travels down the oesophagus, into the stomach, and on through the entire gut. Movement of bolus from mouth to stomach is summarised in Figure 7.13. The oesophagus wall secretes copious quantities of mucus into the lumen, lubricating the passage of the bolus.

Figure 7.13
Movement of food from mouth to stomach.

movement of food from the mouth

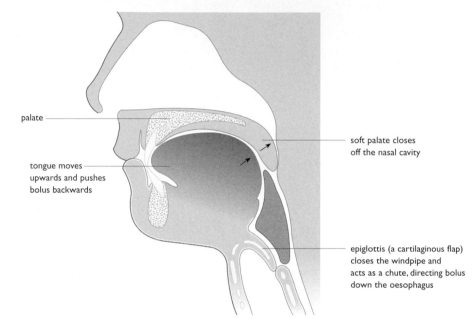

palate

tongue moves upwards and pushes bolus backwards

soft palate closes off the nasal cavity

epiglottis (a cartilaginous flap) closes the windpipe and acts as a chute, directing bolus down the oesophagus

movement of food down the oesophagus

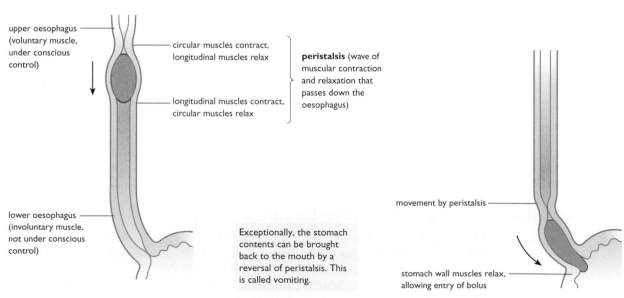

upper oesophagus (voluntary muscle, under conscious control)

circular muscles contract, longitudinal muscles relax

longitudinal muscles contract, circular muscles relax

peristalsis (wave of muscular contraction and relaxation that passes down the oesophagus)

lower oesophagus (involuntary muscle, not under conscious control)

Exceptionally, the stomach contents can be brought back to the mouth by a reversal of peristalsis. This is called vomiting.

movement by peristalsis

stomach wall muscles relax, allowing entry of bolus

Digestion in the stomach

The human stomach is a J-shaped muscular bag located high in the abdominal cavity, below the diaphragm and liver. In the absence of food the stomach wall is contracted, but it becomes distended by a large meal. The stomach has a maximum capacity of about 5 dm³. Its wall has an additional layer of muscle (Figure 7.14) which helps with the mechanical churning action.

Present in the wall of the stomach are millions of tiny pits called **gastric glands**, formed by intuckings of the gastric epithelium. The cells in the gastric glands make and secrete the contents of the gastric juice. About 600 cm³ of gastric juice is secreted per meal; secretion is coordinated with the presence of food (see Figure 7.21, page 161).

One of the components of gastric juice is **hydrochloric acid** (strength 0.15 M) at about pH 1. This is sufficient to create an acid environment (pH 1.5–2.0) for the contents of the bolus: this is the optimum pH for the protein-digesting enzymes of the gastric juice. The hydrochloric acid also kills bacteria, and it aids the absorption of iron and calcium ions, among other useful effects. It also converts prorennin into rennin and pepsinogen to pepsin (see below).

Two **endopeptidase** enzymes are formed in the gastric glands. Endopeptidases (*endo-* means 'within') catalyse the breakdown of proteins at numerous points within the protein chain (Figure 7.9, page 150). If these were secreted in their active forms they would digest the proteins of the cells that formed them (this is known as self-digestion or 'autolysis'). Instead, the endopeptidase **pepsin** is secreted as an inactive precursor called pepsinogen, and is activated by the hydrochloric acid in the gastric juice. Pepsin breaks protein chains into shorter-length polypeptides by hydrolysing peptide linkages between tyrosine and phenylalanine residues. Another protein-digesting enzyme (a protease) is produced only in the gastric glands of young mammals. This is **rennin**, which is also secreted in an inactivated form called prorennin. The conversion of prorennin is also triggered by hydrochloric acid. Rennin starts the digestion of the milk protein caseinogen by coagulating it. In the coagulated form, milk protein is digested by pepsin. Milk forms the complete diet of very young mammals.

4 What is the main role of the mucus secreted in:
  a the stomach,
  b the oesophagus?
5 Why is it essential that the protease enzymes of digestion are secreted in inactive forms?

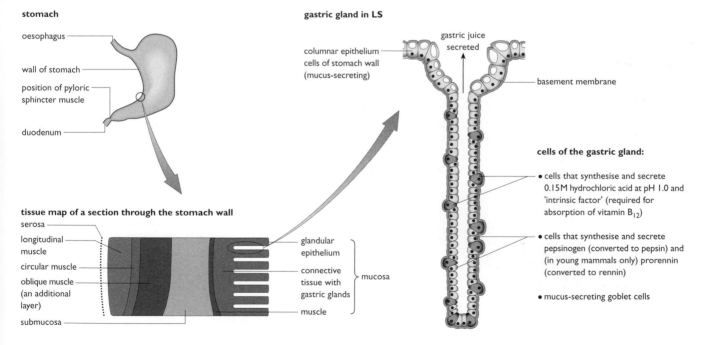

stomach
- oesophagus
- wall of stomach
- position of pyloric sphincter muscle
- duodenum

tissue map of a section through the stomach wall
- serosa
- longitudinal muscle
- circular muscle
- oblique muscle (an additional layer)
- submucosa
- glandular epithelium
- connective tissue with gastric glands — mucosa
- muscle

gastric gland in LS
- columnar epithelium cells of stomach wall (mucus-secreting)
- gastric juice secreted
- basement membrane

cells of the gastric gland:
- cells that synthesise and secrete 0.15M hydrochloric acid at pH 1.0 and 'intrinsic factor' (required for absorption of vitamin B₁₂)
- cells that synthesise and secrete pepsinogen (converted to pepsin) and (in young mammals only) prorennin (converted to rennin)
- mucus-secreting goblet cells

Figure 7.14
Gastric glands, structure and function.

The whole stomach epithelium is richly supplied with mucus-secreting cells, and goblet cells in the gastric glands also secrete mucus. Mucus bathes the interior lining of the stomach, protecting it from both the hydrochloric acid and the digestive enzymes in the gastric juices.

As the food is mixed with gastric juice and churned by muscle action it becomes a semiliquid called **chyme**. The churning action of the stomach is an important part of the mechanical digestion process. A typical meal may spend up to 4 hours in the stomach.

Digestion in the duodenum

Exactly how long food remains in the stomach depends on the amount of protein and lipid in the meal. If food has a high protein or lipid content its entry to the duodenum is delayed, and will only occur in small amounts at a time. But eventually periodic relaxations of the pyloric sphincter muscle allow quantities of chyme to pass into the duodenum, the first region of the small intestine.

In humans the small intestine is about 5 metres long, of which the **duodenum** makes up about 30 cm. The rest is known as the **ileum**. The whole small intestine is a relatively thin-walled region of the gut, but in the duodenum the submucosa is thrown into inwardly projecting folds. These folds are absent from the ileum. Throughout its entire length, the innermost layer of the small intestine is formed into vast numbers of finger- or leaf-like projections called **villi**. Between the villi are the intestinal glands known as the **crypts of Lieberkühn**. Here there is a steady production of new epithelial cells. These cells migrate up on to the villi, replacing the short-lived epithelial cells. Damaged epithelial cells fall off into the contents of the intestine (but still play a part in digestion). In the duodenum there are additional small rounded glands called Brunner's glands. Secretions of both the crypts of Lieberkühn and Brunner's glands coat the epithelium with mucus and alkaline salts. These secretions are an important defence against damage by the acid chyme, as it enters from the stomach.

The villi are lined by simple **columnar epithelium** with numerous **goblet cells**, which also secrete mucus. Each villus contains a **capillary network**, which connects with the blood circulation, and a **lymph vessel** that connects with the lymphatic system. The villi present a huge surface area in contact with food, and contraction and relaxation of the smooth muscle of the villi (the **muscularis mucosa**) moves them through the passing chyme. A further mechanism increases the contact surface area greatly: this is provided by the outer surfaces of the epithelial cells, which are thrown into tiny **microvilli** (about two thousand per cell). This feature is called a **brush border** because under the light microscope the villi look like the bristles of a brush. The interior of the small intestine is thus clearly adapted for absorption (see Figure 7.16).

Secretions in the small intestine

Bile from the bile duct, and the **pancreatic juice** from the pancreas, enter the duodenum (Figure 7.15). The arrival of these secretions is coordinated with the delivery of chyme from the stomach. Both fluids have important roles in continuing digestion.

Bile is a yellow-green, mucous fluid containing the bile salts, bile pigments, cholesterol and salts. It is produced in the liver. Bile is strongly alkaline, and plays a major part in neutralising the acidity of the chyme. It also lowers the surface tension of large fat globules, causing them to break into tiny droplets, a process called **emulsification**. This speeds digestion by lipase later on. Bile itself contains no enzymes.

Figure 7.15
Chyme meets bile, pancreatic juice and 'intestinal juice'. In the disease **pancreatitis**, the digestive enzymes become active inside the pancreas cells, and break down the gland. Digestive enzymes then appear in the blood, rather than in the duodenum.

the duodenum

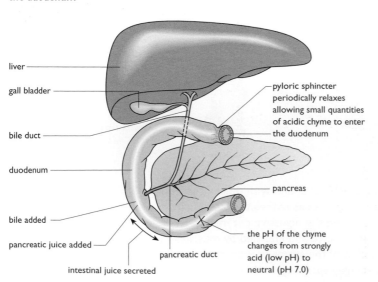

liver
gall bladder
bile duct
duodenum
bile added
pancreatic juice added
intestinal juice secreted
pancreatic duct

pyloric sphincter periodically relaxes allowing small quantities of acidic chyme to enter the duodenum

pancreas

the pH of the chyme changes from strongly acid (low pH) to neutral (pH 7.0)

mixing the chyme

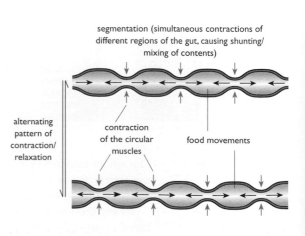

segmentation (simultaneous contractions of different regions of the gut, causing shunting/ mixing of contents)

alternating pattern of contraction/ relaxation

contraction of the circular muscles

food movements

Pancreatic juice is an alkaline fluid that contains several enzymes. These include an **amylase** that catalyses the hydrolysis of starch to maltose, a **lipase** that catalyses the hydrolysis of fats to fatty acids and glycerol, and protein-digesting enzymes (**proteases**) in inactive forms. One is trypsinogen, which is activated to the enzyme **trypsin** by another enzyme – enteropeptidase, secreted by the epithelial cells in the villi. Another is chymotrypsinogen. This is activated to **chymotrypsin** by trypsin. Both these enzymes hydrolyse proteins to polypeptides. Also present in pancreatic juice are several other **peptidases** that hydrolyse the release of tripeptides, dipeptides and free amino acids. A **nuclease** is also present, catalysing the hydrolysis of nucleic acid to nucleotides.

The chyme is thoroughly mixed with bile and pancreatic juice here, by a form of peristalsis called 'segmentation' (Figure 7.15).

Figure 7.16
The small intestine: the absorption surface.

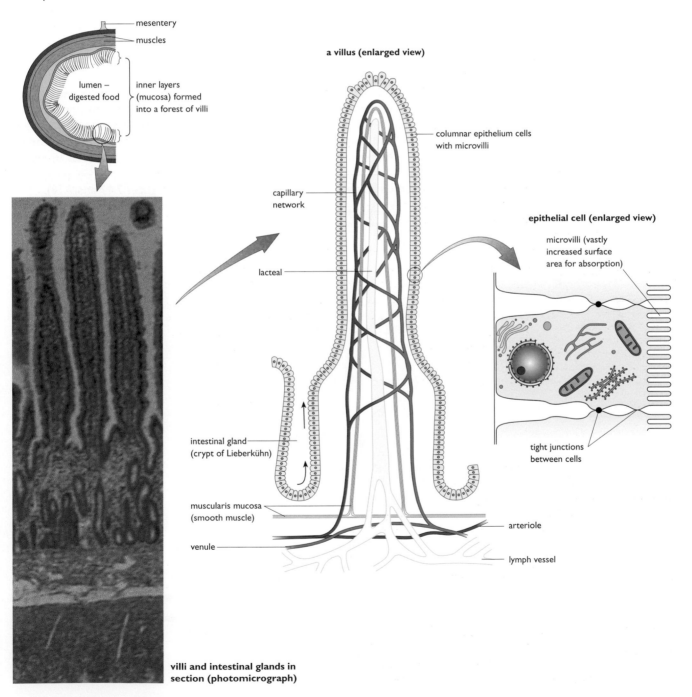

part of ileum in cross-section

- mesentery
- muscles
- lumen – digested food
- inner layers (mucosa) formed into a forest of villi

a villus (enlarged view)

- columnar epithelium cells with microvilli
- capillary network
- lacteal
- intestinal gland (crypt of Lieberkühn)
- muscularis mucosa (smooth muscle)
- venule
- arteriole
- lymph vessel

epithelial cell (enlarged view)

- microvilli (vastly increased surface area for absorption)
- tight junctions between cells

villi and intestinal glands in section (photomicrograph)

Digestion in the ileum

The digestive processes begun in the duodenum by the pancreatic enzymes continue in the ileum. Here, too, are additional sources of enzymes operating on the chyme. Some of these are enzymes released by **disintegration of epithelial cells** that have been dislodged from the villi and fallen into the chyme. (Remember, the epithelial cells are short-lived. Cells of the intestinal glands continually migrate out on to the villi to replace them.)

The other source of enzymes is the **outer surface of the epithelial cells**, where they are bound to the membrane of the microvilli. These enzymes catalyse the final stages of protein and carbohydrate digestion as they transport the products of digestion across the plasma membrane, into the epithelial cells. The combined effects of all these enzymes complete digestion.

● Absorption in the small intestine

Very little uptake occurs in the gut before the food reaches the small intestine. Drugs such as aspirin and alcohol are absorbed as they enter the gut, however, and absorption of them is completed in the stomach. Water is taken up by osmosis; whilst this may happen anywhere along the gut, much water is absorbed in the large intestine.

The products of digestion, mostly monosaccharide sugars, amino acids, fatty acids and glycerol, together with various vitamins and mineral ions, are absorbed as they make contact with the epithelial cells of the villi. The process is efficient because the small intestine has a huge surface area, due to the vast number of villi, together with the presence of very many thousands of microvilli (Figure 7.16). Epithelial cells expend energy in the active transport process by which most of the products of digestion are taken into the cells. Transport involves protein 'pump' molecules in the plasma membrane, activated by reaction with ATP (Figures 7.17 and 7.18).

Figure 7.17
The completion of carbohydrate digestion.

In the lumen of the gut, enzymes have converted most carbohydrates to disaccharides, and some to monosaccharides, e.g. glucose.

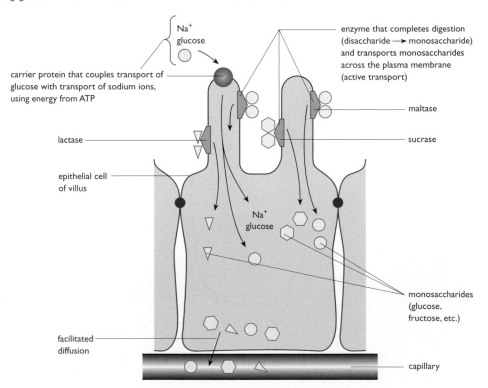

Figure 7.18
The completion of
protein digestion.

In the lumen of the gut, enzymes have converted proteins to short-chain peptides, dipeptides and some amino acids.

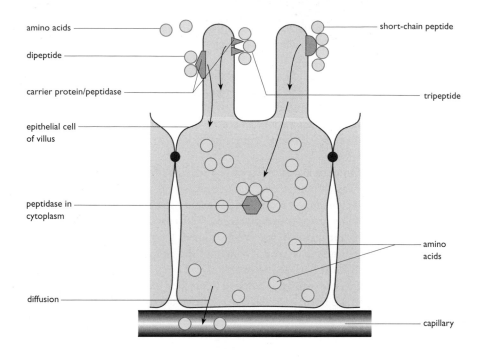

amino acids

dipeptide

carrier protein/peptidase

epithelial cell
of villus

peptidase in
cytoplasm

diffusion

short-chain peptide

tripeptide

amino
acids

capillary

Assimilation

The fate of absorbed nutrients is termed **assimilation**. In the first stage of assimilation, absorbed nutrients are transported from the intestine (Figure 7.19).

Figure 7.19
Transport of nutrients
from the intestine.

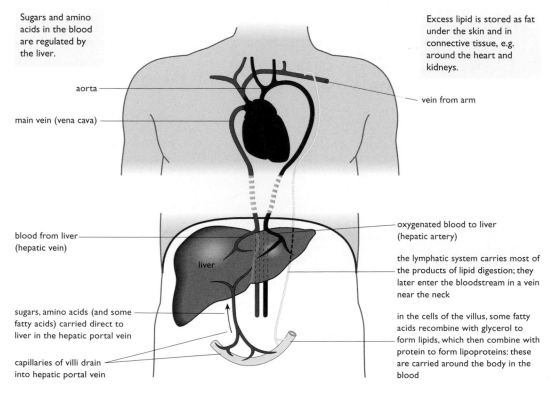

Sugars and amino acids in the blood are regulated by the liver.

Excess lipid is stored as fat under the skin and in connective tissue, e.g. around the heart and kidneys.

aorta

main vein (vena cava)

vein from arm

blood from liver
(hepatic vein)

oxygenated blood to liver
(hepatic artery)

liver

the lymphatic system carries most of the products of lipid digestion; they later enter the bloodstream in a vein near the neck

sugars, amino acids (and some fatty acids) carried direct to liver in the hepatic portal vein

in the cells of the villus, some fatty acids recombine with glycerol to form lipids, which then combine with protein to form lipoproteins: these are carried around the body in the blood

capillaries of villi drain into hepatic portal vein

Sugars are passed into the capillary network, and from here they are transported via the **hepatic portal vein** to the liver (Figure 7.20). The liver maintains a constant level of blood sugar. This is done by converting excess sugar to glycogen, in which form it can be stored. If the blood sugar falls, as it does in vigorous exercise, glycogen reserves are converted back to glucose.

In the liver, glucose is also used in the synthesis of metabolites for growth and other body activities.

Amino acids are also passed into the capillary network, and transported via the hepatic portal vein to the liver. These amino acids contribute to the pool from which new proteins are made in cells and tissues all over the body. Metabolically active tissues and rapidly growing organisms require a large supply of amino acids for protein synthesis. But any excess amino acids received by the body cannot be stored. Instead, they are deaminated in the liver (see Figure 12.14, page 263).

Fats are absorbed as fatty acids and glycerol. Fatty acids pass easily through the lipid bilayer of the plasma membrane; active transport is not a necessity for them. Most fatty acids and glycerol molecules then recombine to form triglycerides (= lipids), and these lipids then combine with proteins to form **lipoproteins**. This reaction occurs in the smooth endoplasmic reticulum and Golgi apparatus of the epithelial cells. Lipoproteins pass out of the epithelial cells by exocytosis, and enter the lacteals. From here the lymphatic system delivers them directly into the blood circulation outside the heart.

Fats are stored in adipose tissue (for example, below the skin) and in connective tissues all over the body, especially around the kidney and heart. When fats and lipids are required in metabolism the fat stores are drawn upon, and they are converted back to fatty acids and glycerol. Muscles will respire glucose if it is available, but they are equally efficient at respiring fatty acids.

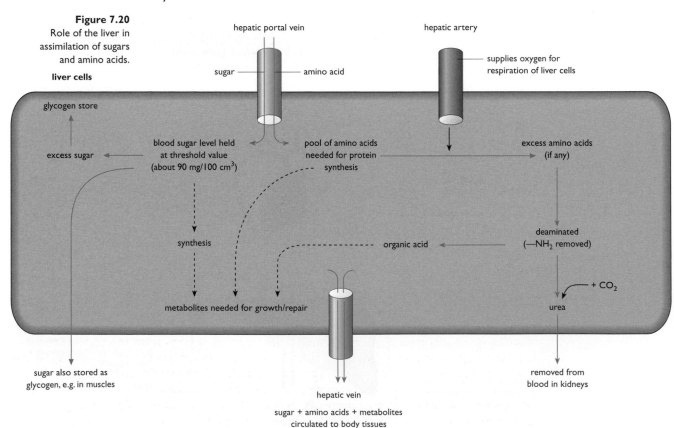

Figure 7.20
Role of the liver in assimilation of sugars and amino acids.

● Extension   Control of secretion

The secretion of digestive juices is coordinated with the presence of food in that part of the gut. This coordination is regulated by nervous or hormonal mechanisms, or both. For example, saliva, which mainly aids swallowing, is produced by a reflex action triggered by the sight, smell, taste or thought of food (Figure 7.21).

Figure 7.21
The control of gastric secretion.

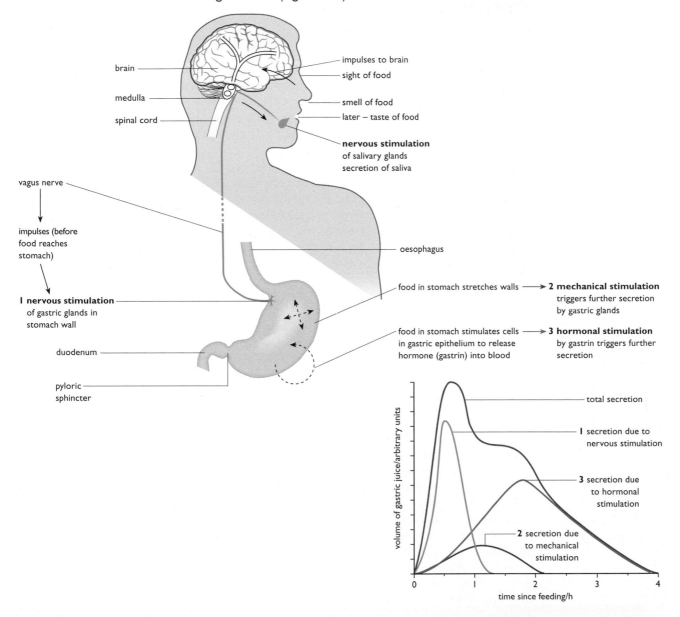

Control of the secretion of **gastric juice** is more complex. As with saliva, the sight or smell of food can trigger secretion by the gastric glands, even before food is taken into the mouth. When the arrival of food in the stomach stretches the stomach wall, this mechanical stimulation triggers further secretion of gastric juice by reflex action. At the same time, cells in the stomach lining are stimulated to secrete a hormone, gastrin, into the bloodstream. On reaching the gastric glands via the blood circulation, this again stimulates further secretion of gastric juice. The contributions of these components to the regulation of gastric juice secretion are shown in the graph in Figure 7.21.

Control of secretions in the duodenum (pancreatic juice and bile) are regulated by hormones (**secretin** and **cholecystokinin**) produced by cells in the wall of the duodenum.

Role of the large intestine

The large intestine consists of the caecum and appendix (a cul-de-sac region), the colon and the rectum. The colon has no villi, but the surface area for absorption is increased by numerous folds. Waves of peristalsis carry the remains of meals into the colon and the caecum. The appendix is largely by-passed. By this stage of the digestion process, most of the useful products of digestion have been absorbed. What remains is the undigested matter (such as plant fibre), mucus, dead intestinal cells, bacteria, some mineral ions and water. Water is an important component of our diet, and many litres of water are also secreted on to the chyme in the form of digestive juices.

Bacteria flourish here as conditions in the colon are ideal for their growth. Mostly they appear to neither help nor harm us. This sort of relationship is described as **commensalism**. On the other hand, some species of bacteria in the gut are beneficial in that they are a source of vitamins (such as vitamin K). At the same time as releasing these vitamins, the bacteria obtain nutrients and a favourable environment. Close association relationships with mutual advantages, like this, are described as **mutualism**.

In the colon, water and mineral salts (such as Na^+ and Cl^- ions) are absorbed. What remains of the meal is now referred to as **faeces**. Bacteria make up about 50% of the faeces, and some of these microorganisms produce gases and substances with unpleasant odours. Bile pigments (excretory products formed from the routine breakdown of red cells), which were added in the duodenum, colour the faeces uniformly.

The rectum is a short muscular tube that terminates at the anus. Discharge of faeces from the body at the anus is controlled by sphincter muscles.

Digestion of cellulose in herbivores

Cellulose is the most abundant organic compound in the biosphere; it makes up more than 50% of all organic carbon. Its origin is as plant cell walls. As such, cellulose is a major component of the diet of all herbivores. Mammals do not produce the enzyme cellulase, so herbivorous and omnivorous mammals cannot digest cellulose. Many bacteria, fungi and protozoa do produce cellulases, however. Herbivorous mammals exploit this facility of microorganisms in order to digest the cellulose in their diet. For example **ruminants** (cows and sheep) have a four-chambered 'stomach' (Figure 7.22). The first three compartments are modified forms of the lower oesophagus. The first compartment, the rumen, is in effect a large fermentation vat, and this is where these animals get their name. The rumen contains microorganisms able to digest cellulose. The final compartment is the true stomach.

Digestion of the cellulose in grass by a ruminant begins with the actions of the mechanical grinding of premolars and molars in the mouth. Later on, in the cycle of fermentation, grass is also regurgitated to the mouth from the rumen for further grinding. Meanwhile, much of the sugars released by cellulase during fermentation in the rumen is turned into organic acids. Sugars and organic acids are the major source of energy for the ruminant, and they are absorbed immediately they are formed, through the rumen wall. The microorganisms present also synthesise their own amino acids and proteins from inorganic nitrogen (nitrate ions and ammonia). When, later, the contents of the rumen pass on to the true stomach, protein digestion commences. At this stage, ruminants digest the microorganisms as an additional source of protein.

Non-ruminant herbivores (e.g. horses and rabbits) house cellulose-digesting microorganisms much further along the gut, in their enlarged caecum and appendix. Undigested food passes into this cul-de-sac, and cellulose is converted into organic acids under anaerobic conditions.

In the horse, the products of caecum digestion are moved to the large intestine by reverse peristalsis, and are absorbed here. Compared with the intestine of ruminants, the horse has a restricted area for absorption, and the bulk of the excess microorganisms are not themselves digested after the fermentation stage. In the rabbit, on the other hand, the faeces egested during the night are eaten as they emerge and pass through the entire gut again. Hard dry pellets are then discharged in the daytime.

Figure 7.22
Digestion of cellulose by a ruminant.

Ruminants (cows and sheep) have:
• teeth and jaws that are adapted for the cropping and grinding up of grass
• a four-chambered stomach where microorganisms are housed.

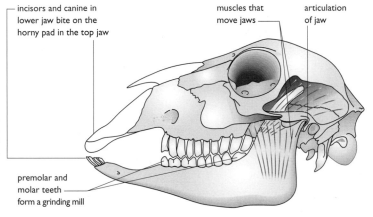

incisors and canine in lower jaw bite on the horny pad in the top jaw

muscles that move jaws

articulation of jaw

premolar and molar teeth form a grinding mill

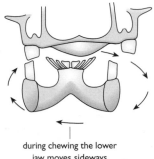

during chewing the lower jaw moves sideways

LS of molar tooth

surfaces of tooth worn down to have sharp (enamel) ridges

dentine

pulp cavity

teeth grow throughout life; entry to root remains open and unrestricted

nutrients brought to cells of dentine, allowing growth

the stages of cellulose digestion

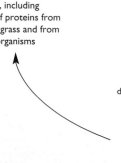

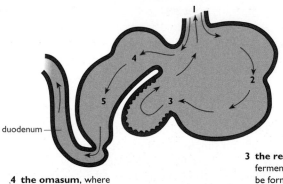

1 the mouth: grass is cropped, ground up by premolars and molars, mixed with saliva and swallowed

5 the abomasum, the true stomach: normal digestion starts here, including digestion of proteins from ground-up grass and from the microorganisms

2 the rumen, a fermentation 'vat' where under anaerobic conditions bacterial 'flora' produce cellulases that turn cellulose into glucose and organic acids, which are absorbed into the blood; ciliates feed on bacteria here

duodenum

4 the omasum, where water is reabsorbed

3 the reticulum, where fermented grass returns to be formed into a ball and sent back to the mouth for further grinding ('chewing the cud')

Saprotrophic nutrition

Saprotrophic organisms feed on dead matter, causing decay. Saprotrophs secrete enzymes on to their food source, and digestion occurs outside the organism. The useful products of digestion are absorbed. Most bacteria and fungi have saprotrophic nutrition. One example is the pin mould *Rhizopus*, which grows on damp organic matter such as mouldy bread or decaying fruit. The structure and nutrition of *Rhizopus* are shown in Figure 7.23.

Figure 7.23
Structure and nutrition of *Rhizopus*.

Rhizopus is called a 'pin mould' because of the tiny sporangia that grow up all over the food source as soon as it is established.

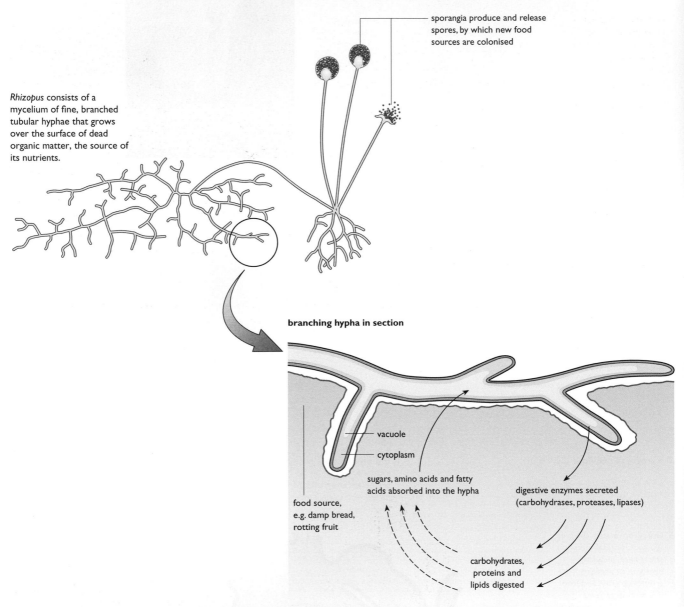

sporangia produce and release spores, by which new food sources are colonised

Rhizopus consists of a mycelium of fine, branched tubular hyphae that grows over the surface of dead organic matter, the source of its nutrients.

branching hypha in section

vacuole

cytoplasm

sugars, amino acids and fatty acids absorbed into the hypha

food source, e.g. damp bread, rotting fruit

digestive enzymes secreted (carbohydrases, proteases, lipases)

carbohydrates, proteins and lipids digested

The complex organic matter of all dead organisms and their waste products are broken down by saprotrophs, and simpler substances are released. For example, the fresh dung of herbivorous animals is colonised by a whole succession of fungi, starting with quick-growing pin moulds such as *Mucor*, which feeds on simple carbohydrates, amino acids and fatty acids present. The fungi that subsequently flourish here feed on the increasingly insoluble organic matter (Figure 7.24). This includes cellulose and, later, the lignin of xylem and fibres and the waxes, all remains of the plant matter the herbivore ate. In a similar fashion, a dead tree trunk is slowly decomposed by a succession of microorganisms, ending with fungi able to enzymically digest the long-dead heartwood at the centre of the trunk (Figure 7.24).

Figure 7.24
Saprotrophic fungi of dung and rotting wood.

spore-producing structures growing on dung
The fungal mycelia grow over the surface of the dung.

spore-producing structure of a bracket fungus (*Polyporus betulinus*) growing on dead birch wood
The fungal mycelium grows in the heartwood of the dead tree.

6 In what ways is the nutrition of yeast made use of in human food production?

7 Distinguish between the following pairs:

- heterotroph and autotroph
- trachea and oesophagus
- dentine and enamel
- herbivore and omnivore
- molars and canines
- vitamins and minerals
- pepsin and trypsin
- villi and microvilli
- bile and pancreatic juice
- absorption and assimilation.

Yeasts (*Saccharomyces*) are saprotrophic unicellular fungi that grow on the surface of plants or in the soil – anywhere that sugar occurs naturally (Figure 7.25). Yeasts feed on sugars and produce alcohol and carbon dioxide as waste products. Consequently, they have long been of great economic importance in brewing and baking. Today they are also used in genetic technology for two main reasons:

- they are easily cultured in fermenters
- they contain plastids in their cytoplasm similar to those of bacterial cells, so they are eukaryotes that can be genetically modified relatively easily (page 129).

Figure 7.25
Yeast (*Saccharomyces*), a saprotroph of sugary solutions.

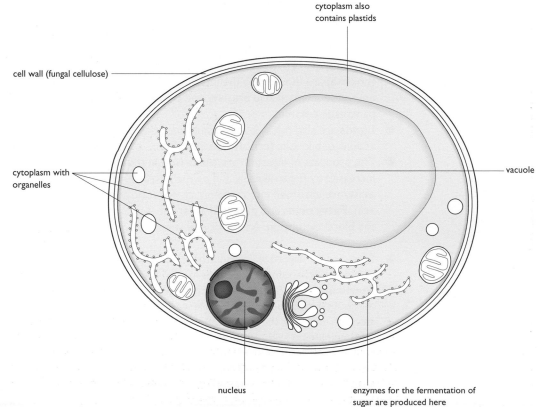

cytoplasm also contains plastids

cell wall (fungal cellulose)

cytoplasm with organelles

vacuole

nucleus

enzymes for the fermentation of sugar are produced here

● **Skills task**   Make a list of the snacks (drinks, chocolate bars and between-meal, fast food snacks) you eat during a typical day.
   Then, using the table of energy values (Table 7.2) and your likely total energy requirements per day (Table 7.1), work out what percentage of your daily energy requirements is made up of snacks.

SUMMARY
● **Autotrophs** (e.g. green plants) manufacture their own nutrients from simple, inorganic substances, whereas **heterotrophs** break down complex inorganic molecules to obtain nutrients. Heterotrophs are ultimately dependent on autotrophs for their nutrients. All animals are heterotrophs.

● **Holozoic nutrition** is the taking in of organic matter in the form of other animals or plants (or both) into a digestive system where the food is broken down to molecules that can be absorbed. Holozoic nutrition is a form of heterotrophic nutrition. It is the feeding strategy of mammals, including humans.

● A **balanced diet** consists of appropriate amounts of **metabolic fuel** in the form of carbohydrates and lipids (and possibly proteins), **combined nitrogen** (as amino acids or proteins) for the manufacture of proteins, **vitamins**, **water**, essential **mineral ions** and **roughage**.

● **Digestion** occurs in the alimentary canal or **gut**, which is a long muscular tube with an opening at both ends (mouth and anus). Mechanical digestion is brought about by the teeth and the churning actions of the gut. Chemical digestion is brought about by **enzymes** secreted on to the broken-up food in particular regions of the gut, under carefully controlled conditions of pH.

● **Mucus** is secreted on to the food throughout the gut to lubricate movements and protect the gut walls. For example, mucus is an ingredient of saliva, and helps bind the food for swallowing. Once swallowed, the food is moved by a wave of muscle contractions (**peristalsis**) to the stomach.

● **Proteins** are broken down to amino acids, starting in the stomach. Protease enzymes in the gastric juice work in the acid environment of the stomach, but proteases in the pancreatic juice work in the neutral/alkaline conditions of the small intestine. The amino acids are eventually absorbed in the small intestine.

● **Carbohydrates** are mostly digested in the small intestine. When the stomach contents (**chyme**) are moved into the intestine, alkaline bile from the liver/gall bladder helps to neutralise stomach acid present, and create the more neutral environment required for pancreatic enzymes.

● **Lipids** are also digested in the small intestine, after being converted to tiny droplets by actions of bile salts (**emulsification**).

● The products of digestion are **absorbed** in the small intestine. Here the surface area is vastly increased by finger-like villi and by the microvilli of the epithelial cells. **Sugars** and **amino acids** are absorbed into the capillary network, and carried to the liver by the hepatic portal vein. **Fatty acids** and **glycerol** enter the lacteals, and are carried by the lymphatic system to the blood circulation. Absorption of water and mineral ions is completed in the large intestine.

● Secretions of digestive juices in the gut are **coordinated** with the presence of food by both nervous mechanisms (reflex actions) and hormonal mechanisms.

● **Ruminants** (cows and sheep) are herbivorous mammals that exploit the exclusive ability of microorganisms to produce cellulose-digesting enzymes. Ruminants have a four-chambered stomach, in which they ferment chewed-up grass. In this way they obtain the sugars, organic acids and amino acids which the microorganism's metabolism produces.

● **Saprotrophic organisms** (mainly fungi and bacteria) feed on dead organic matter, causing delay. Enzymes are secreted outside the organism, and the useful products of digestion are absorbed. Saprotrophs have an important role in cycling nutrients for reuse by autotrophs.

● Examination questions

1 The small intestine in humans is 5 to 6 metres long. Along its length it is thrown into circular folds each approximately 10 mm high. The mucosa is modified to create finger-like processes known as villi, each of which is between 0.5 and 1.5 mm tall and contains capillaries and a lacteal. The columnar epithelial cells making up the surface of the villi are covered in microvilli. These projections, 1 μm long, incorporate several enzymes including exopeptidases and carbohydrases such as maltase. The epithelial cells are joined together by 'tight junctions', ridges which span the space between the adjacent membranes and match complementary grooves in the other membrane. These not only link the two cells involved, but also obliterate the intercellular space.

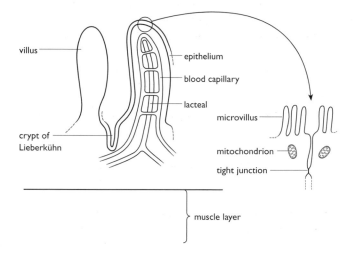

a Describe, in detail, the function of the capillaries and lacteal in each villus. (4)
b Explain how the structure of the wall of the small intestine is adapted for its functions. (6)
c Amylase is secreted into the lumen of the gut, but maltase is attached to the surface of the epithelial cells. Suggest the importance of this difference. (2)
NEAB, AS/A level, Module BY10, Mar 1998

2 The flow chart represents the breakdown of starch in the human gut.

starch —amylase→ maltose —maltase→ glucose

a Name **two** organs which produce amylase in humans. (1)
b Describe how the release of amylase from each of these organs is controlled. (3)
c Describe the precise location of maltase in the human gut. (2)
AQA(AEB), A level, Module 0607/1, June 1999

3 The drawing shows a section through the human stomach wall.

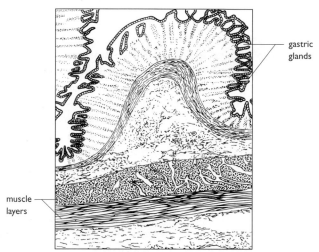

(Reproduced from *Atlas of Histology*, Freeman and Bracegirdle, reprinted by permission of Heinemann Educational Publishers, a division of Reed Educational & Professional Publishing Ltd)

a Describe **one** function of the muscle layers in the stomach wall. (1)
b i Name the type of protein-digesting enzyme secreted by the gastric glands. (1)
 ii Describe the function of this type of enzyme. (2)
 iii Name the hormone which stimulates the release of this enzyme. (1)
c Explain briefly why a different enzyme is required for the digestion of each type of food substance. (2)
NEAB, AS/A level, Module BY03, Mar 1998

4 The secretion of digestive juices into the mammalian gut is controlled by the endocrine and nervous systems. Complete the table about the secretion of digestive juices.

Stimulus that triggers secretion	Effect	Digestive juice secreted
....	parasympathetic nerve stimulates salivary gland	saliva
contact of food with stomach lining	.... secreted	gastric juice
contact of food with duodenum lining	cholecystokinin secreted	....
contact of food with duodenum lining	.... secreted	alkaline fluid from pancreas

(4)
AQA(NEAB), A level, Paper 1/Sections A & B, June 1999

5 a If you were given a sample of milk and you were asked to demonstrate that it contained proteins:

    i what practical test could you use? (1)

    ii what result would you expect to observe? (1)

b Apples normally contain some reducing sugars and some non-reducing sugars. If you had already proved the presence of the reducing sugars and removed these from an apple extract, what practical test could you use to indicate the presence of the **non-reducing** sugars? Indicate what you would expect to observe for a positive result. (2)

c If you were given a mixture of glucose solution and a polysaccharide suspension and you were asked to separate the two carbohydrate components:

    i what practical technique could you use? (1)

    ii what particular material or apparatus would you require to enable the separation to occur? (1)

OCR (Oxford), A level, 6910, June 1999

6 Read through the following passage, which refers to hormonal coordination of the functioning of the alimentary canal in humans, and then write on the dotted lines the most appropriate word or words to complete the account.

The presence of partially digested food in the stomach causes the secretion of the hormone .... which stimulates the secretion of gastric juice. On entering the duodenum, the acidic chyme stimulates the secretion of .... This travels in the .... and causes the release into the duodenum of an alkaline pancreatic secretion. The release of an enzyme-rich pancreatic secretion is caused by the hormone .... which also causes contraction of the .... (5)

London, A level, Module HB3, June 1999

8 Plant nutrition

STARTING POINTS
● Green plants manufacture glucose by **photosynthesis**, using the raw materials carbon dioxide and water and energy from sunlight. Oxygen is produced as a waste product.
● **Chloroplasts** are the photosynthetic organelles. Chloroplasts contain chlorophyll, which is needed for the transfer of light energy into chemicals like glucose during photosynthesis.
● Feeding relationships of organisms are shown in **food chains** and food webs. Green plants are primary producers; all other organisms are dependent on green plants and the energy from sunlight, directly or indirectly.

Introducing photosynthesis

Green plants use the energy of sunlight to produce **sugars** from the inorganic raw materials **carbon dioxide** and **water**, by a process called **photosynthesis**. The waste product is **oxygen**. Photosynthesis takes place mainly in cells of the leaves of plants, in specialised organelles called **chloroplasts**. Here, the energy of light is trapped by the green pigment **chlorophyll**, and becomes the chemical energy in molecules such as **glucose** and **ATP**.

Sugar formed in photosynthesis may temporarily be stored as **starch**, but sooner or later most is used in metabolism. For example, plants manufacture other carbohydrates, together with the lipids, proteins, growth factors and all other metabolites they require. For this they additionally need certain **mineral ions**, which are absorbed from the soil solution. The energy used to take in the ions required and to drive the syntheses of the other metabolites comes from the respiration of sugar. Figure 8.1 is a summary of photosynthesis and its place in plant nutrition.

1 In what form is the carbohydrate produced in photosynthesis:
a first formed in the leaf,
b transported in the phloem, and
c used in metabolism?

Figure 8.1
Photosynthesis and its place in plant nutrition.

photosynthesis: a summary

The process in the chloroplast can be summarised by the equation:

carbon + water + LIGHT   chlorophyll   organic   + oxygen
dioxide   ENERGY →————→ compounds,
                   in chloroplast   e.g. sugars

raw materials   *energy*   *products*   *waste*
                source   *product*

$$6CO_2 + 6H_2O + light \xrightarrow[\text{in chloroplast}]{\text{chlorophyll}} C_6H_{12}O_6 + 6O_2$$

plant nutrition: a summary

energy from sunlight   THE LEAF

carbon + water dioxide   photosynthesis in chloroplasts in leaf cells → oxygen + glucose

sugar is transported as sucrose between leaf and rest of plant

THE REST OF THE PLANT

oxygen from the air

oxygen

carbon dioxide

glucose

respiration

ions → ← energy

carbon dioxide in air   loss of water vapour   oxygen diffuses into the atmosphere

storage carbohydrates, fats and waxes

cellulose, and other wall-forming compounds

proteins, enzymes, cytoplasm

vitamins, hormones and growth factors

ROOTS

water

ions actively absorbed

The wider significance of photosynthesis

The importance of photosynthesis *to the green plant* is that it provides the energy-rich sugar molecules from which the plant builds its other organic molecules. The metabolism of the green plant is sustained by the products of photosynthesis. But photosynthesis has wider significance as well.

- The feeding relationships between organisms are represented in **food chains** (page 366). Food chains begin with green plants, or parts of plants. Plants are the primary producers in the food chain; other organisms feed on them. Some (the herbivores) do so directly. Others do so indirectly, by feeding on the herbivores or on organisms that themselves feed on herbivores. So virtually all life, including human life, is dependent upon green plant nutrition.
- Green plants also maintain the **composition of the atmosphere**. For example, the amount of carbon dioxide removed by plants in photosynthesis each day is almost equal to the amounts added to the air from respiration and from the burning of fossil fuels. This is a part of the carbon cycle (Figure 18.11, page 396).
- Photosynthesis is also the *only* natural process that releases oxygen into the atmosphere. All oxygen present in the air (about 21%) has come there as a waste product of photosynthesis.

It was an environmentalist who summarised our dependence on green plants in the phrase *'Have you thanked a green plant today?'*!

The leaf as a factory for photosynthesis

The leaf is the plant organ specialised for photosynthesis (Figure 8.2). The leaf **blade** is attached to the stem by the **stalk**, and held in such a way that most of the leaf cells receive plenty of light. The blade is a thin structure with a large surface area; it may be divided up into leaflets (as in a clover leaf) or entire (like an oak leaf). The outermost layer of a leaf is a tough, protective

Figure 8.2
The structure of a leaf.

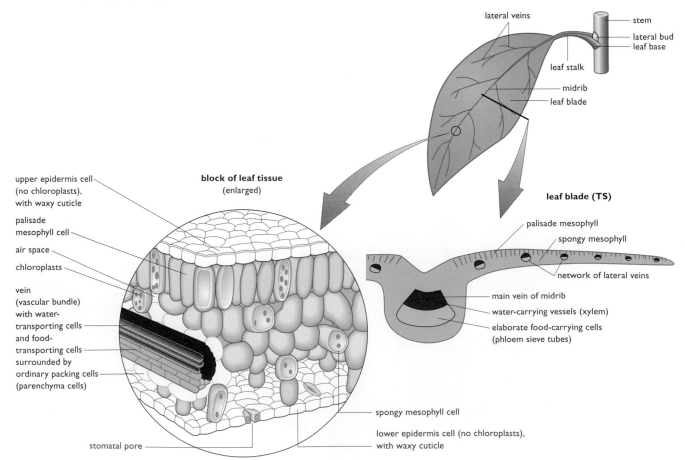

block of leaf tissue (enlarged)

upper epidermis cell (no chloroplasts), with waxy cuticle

palisade mesophyll cell

air space

chloroplasts

vein (vascular bundle) with water-transporting cells and food-transporting cells surrounded by ordinary packing cells (parenchyma cells)

stomatal pore

spongy mesophyll cell

lower epidermis cell (no chloroplasts), with waxy cuticle

lateral veins

stem

lateral bud

leaf base

leaf stalk

midrib

leaf blade

leaf blade (TS)

palisade mesophyll

spongy mesophyll

network of lateral veins

main vein of midrib

water-carrying vessels (xylem)

elaborate food-carrying cells (phloem sieve tubes)

epidermis, made of a single layer of cells. The epidermis supports the leaf by binding together the leaf tissues, counteracting the hydrostatic pressure of all the turgid cells of the leaf. It contains tiny pores called **stomata**, which allow gaseous exchange. Most of the pores are on the lower epidermis, although they are also found in stems and in parts of flowers.

Inside the leaf, a midrib with a system of branching veins supports the leaf tissue. No photosynthetic cell is more than a few cells away from a vein. Each vein contains a compact **vascular bundle**, which consists of water-carrying cells (**xylem vessels**) above and food-carrying cells (**phloem sieve tubes**) below. The vascular bundles of leaves connect via the leaf stalk with those in the stem and root. Their roles are to supply water to all cells, and to transport the products of photosynthesis to sites of storage, active growth or repair.

A **stoma** (*plural*, stomata) consists of two almost sausage-shaped **guard cells** (Figure 8.3). Guard cells are able to separate so as to form a pore between them. All diffusion of gases (oxygen, carbon dioxide, water vapour) into and out of the leaf occurs through the stomatal pores. The pores tend to be open in the light and closed in the dark, but close also even in the light if the leaves become severely wilted. In fact, when the guard cells are fully turgid the stomata are open, but when the guard cells are flaccid, they close (Chapter 11, page 242).

Figure 8.3
The distribution and structure of stomata.

VS of a stoma (photomicrograph)

the lower surface of a leaf (photomicrograph)

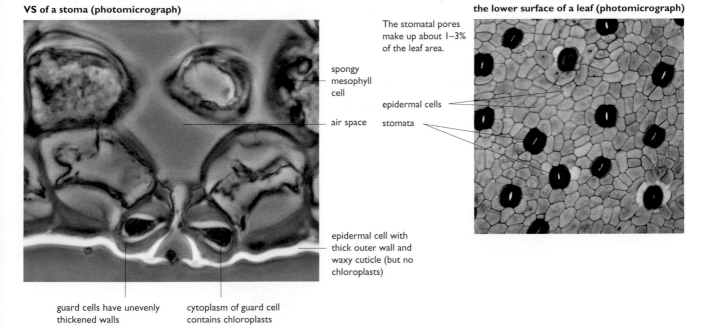

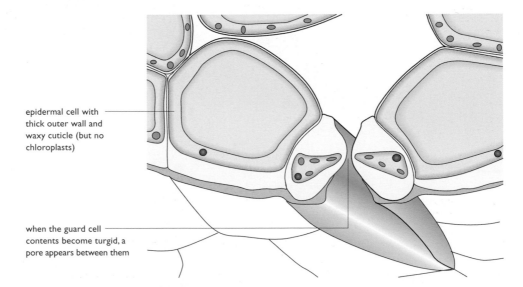

The adaptations of the palisade mesophyll cell

The palisade mesophyll cell (see Figure 8.2) is the site of photosynthesis in the green plant. The epidermis above is more or less transparent and has a thick waxy **cuticle**. This reduces loss of water by evaporation from the outer surface, in sunlight. The palisade cells below the epidermis are elongated, with their long axis perpendicular to the leaf surface. The cytoplasm of palisade cells is packed full of chloroplasts, and both the cell shape and positioning of the chloroplasts ensure they receive maximum illumination. In fact the chloroplasts move about (**cyclosis**) and become arranged in the part of the cytoplasm that is best illuminated at the time. There is a large permanent vacuole in the centre of the cell (a reservoir of water), which keeps the cytoplasm against the cell wall. Around the palisade cells are interconnecting **air spaces**, helping with gaseous exchange. The air spaces connect with those in the rest of the leaf. Carbon dioxide diffuses into the palisade cells and into the chloroplasts, down a concentration gradient. Oxygen diffuses away. The cellulose wall is fully permeable to dissolved substances. Water travels from the water-transporting **xylem** in the vascular bundle to the palisade cells, and sugars pass back to the **phloem sieve tubes**. The position and role of palisade cells in the working leaf are summarised in Figure 8.4.

2 Give three ways in which the green leaf is adapted for the efficient absorption of carbon dioxide.

Figure 8.4
The functioning leaf.

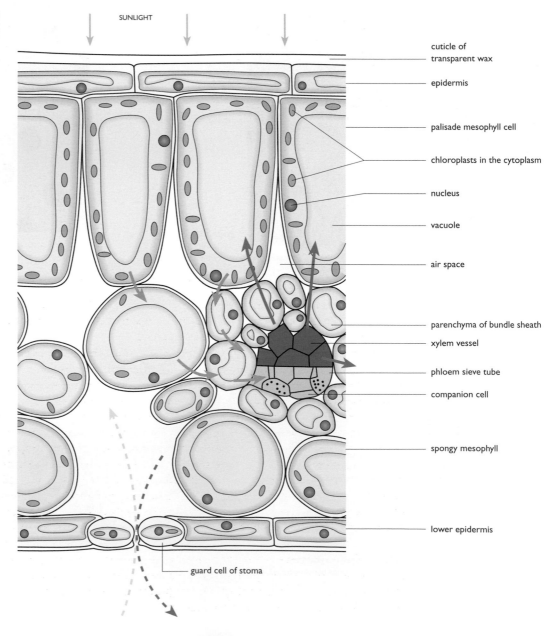

SUNLIGHT

cuticle of transparent wax

epidermis

palisade mesophyll cell

chloroplasts in the cytoplasm

nucleus

vacuole

air space

parenchyma of bundle sheath

xylem vessel

phloem sieve tube

companion cell

spongy mesophyll

lower epidermis

guard cell of stoma

Key

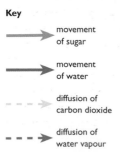

movement of sugar

movement of water

diffusion of carbon dioxide

diffusion of water vapour

Chloroplast structure

The chloroplasts are the organelles in which photosynthesis takes place. Chloroplasts are biconvex discs, about 4–10 µm long and 2–3 µm wide (Figure 8.5). They are found in the mesophyll cells of leaves, in the guard cells of the stomata and in the cells of the outer part (the cortex) of green plant stems. A single palisade mesophyll cell may contain up to 50 chloroplasts.

Studies by electron microscopy show there is a double membrane around the chloroplast, and that the inner of these membranes intucks at various points to form a system of branching membranes. These membranes are called **thylakoids**. The thylakoid membranes of the chloroplast are organised into flat, compact, circular piles, called **grana** (*singular*, granum), and between them are loosely arranged tubular membranes, suspended in a watery matrix called the **stroma**. Chlorophyll, the group of photosynthetic pigments that absorb light energy, occurs in the grana. Also suspended in the stroma are starch grains, lipid droplets and ribosomes.

Figure 8.5
The structure of the chloroplast and the position of the photosynthetic pigments.

palisade cell

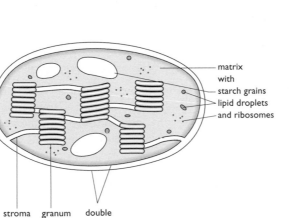

chloroplasts

chloroplast (diagrammatic view)

matrix
with
starch grains
lipid droplets
and ribosomes

stroma   granum   double
membrane

grana (stereogram)

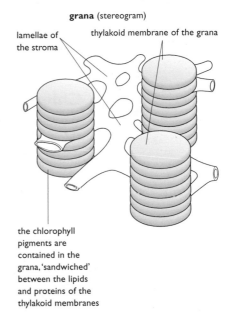

lamellae of
the stroma

thylakoid membrane of the grana

the chlorophyll pigments are contained in the grana, 'sandwiched' between the lipids and proteins of the thylakoid membranes

Separating out the photosynthetic pigments

Chlorophyll pigments are not soluble in water but they will dissolve in organic solvents like propanone (acetone). The composition of a solution of chlorophyll extracted from leaves can be investigated by the technique of chromatography.

Chromatography allows us to separate tiny quantities of components of mixtures in very small samples, and then to identify them or use the isolated components for further investigations. It is an ideal technique for separating the components of a mixture of biologically active molecules because often only small samples can be obtained for analysis.

The process of chromatography involves a stationary phase, the chromatogram, which may be absorptive paper in paper chromatography (Figure 8.6), powdered solid in column chromatography, or a thin film of dried solid in thin-layer chromatography. In paper or thin-layer chromatography, the mixture to be separated must be dissolved in an appropriate solvent and is then loaded on to the chromatogram at a spot near one edge, and allowed to dry. The edge of the chromatogram is then introduced into a suitable chromatography solvent, and the solvent is allowed to travel through the stationary phase, passing through the loaded spot, by capillarity. Because the substances being separated have different solubilities in the solvent and also interact with the stationary phase to differing degrees, they move through the chromatogram at different rates. Before the solvent itself reaches the opposite end of the chromatogram, the process is stopped and the chromatogram dried. Coloured components of the mixture form clearly defined bands or spots on the chromatogram. The presence of components that are not coloured has to be identified; various techniques are available.

3 Why is chromatography a useful technique for the investigation of cell biochemistry?

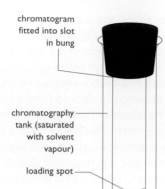

Figure 8.6
Chromatographic
separation of
chlorophyll pigments.

paper chromatography in progress

chromatogram
fitted into slot
in bung

chromatography
tank (saturated
with solvent
vapour)

loading spot

chromatography
solvent

The distance a particular substance
moves up the chromatogram
relative to its solvent front is
constant. This value is known as
the **Rf value**:

$$Rf = \frac{\text{distance moved by substance}}{\text{distance moved by solvent}}$$

The Rf value of
chlorophyll $a = 0.65$, and that of
chlorophyll $b = 0.45$

using a solvent of 9 parts
petroleum ether to 1 part 90%
aqueous propanone (acetone).

chromatogram

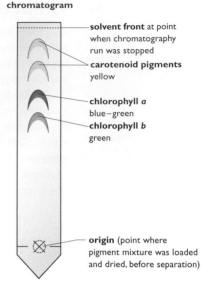

solvent front at point
when chromatography
run was stopped

carotenoid pigments
yellow

chlorophyll *a*
blue–green

chlorophyll *b*
green

origin (point where
pigment mixture was loaded
and dried, before separation)

Chlorophyll pigments in the chloroplast

Figure 8.7
The structure of
chlorophyll.

The chlorophyll of the green leaf is a mixture of pigments. Two are chlorophylls, known as
chlorophyll *a* and **chlorophyll** *b*, and the others belong to a group of compounds called

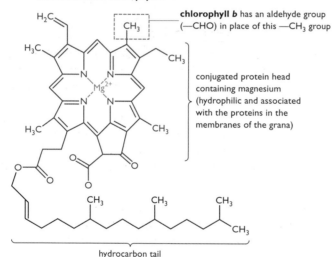

the structure of chlorophyll *a*

chlorophyll *b* has an aldehyde group
(—CHO) in place of this —CH₃ group

conjugated protein head
containing magnesium
(hydrophilic and associated
with the proteins in the
membranes of the grana)

hydrocarbon tail
(hydrophobic and occurs folded, associated with the lipid of the membranes)

carotenoids. The chemistry of the chlorophylls is
particularly important because these pigments are
directly involved in the energy-transfer processes in
the chloroplasts. Their structure is shown in Figure
8.7. The other pigments are described as **accessory
pigments** because they have the role of passing the
light energy they absorb to chlorophyll, before it takes
part in photosynthesis.

The chlorophyll pigments in the grana are
'sandwiched' between the lipids and proteins of the
thylakoid membranes. This is because chlorophylls are
'head and tail' molecules. Their heads are hydrophilic
and associate with proteins in the thylakoid
membranes. The tails are hydrophobic and associate
with lipids in the membranes. Also found here, with
the pigments, are the enzymes and electron-carrier
molecules involved in the steps of photosynthesis
where light energy becomes chemical energy
(discussed later in this chapter).

The absorption and action spectra of chlorophyll

White light consists of a roughly equal mixture of all the visible wavelengths, namely violet, blue,
green, yellow, orange and red. Chlorophyll is a mixture of pigments that largely absorbs the
component wavelengths of white light *except* green, which it transmits or reflects (hence its green
colour). Now the issue is: how much of each wavelength does it absorb (the absorption spectrum),
and which of these wavelengths are most effective in photosynthesis (the action spectrum)?

The **absorption spectra** of chlorophyll pigments are obtained by measuring their absorption
of violet, blue, green, yellow, orange and red light, in turn. The results are plotted as a graph
showing the amount of light absorbed by the pigments over the wavelength range of visible light
(Figure 8.8).

The **action spectrum** for photosynthesis is obtained by projecting light of these same
wavelengths, in turn, on to photosynthesising plant matter, and measuring the rate of
photosynthesis. This can be done using aquatic pondweed, in an apparatus like that shown in

Figure 8.9. The gas evolved by a green plant in the light is largely oxygen, and the volume given off in a unit of time is a measure of the rate at which it is photosynthesising. The rate of photosynthesis at different wavelengths is plotted on a graph on the same scale as the absorption spectrum.

Comparison of absorption and action spectra shows that the wavelengths of light most strongly absorbed by chlorophyll pigments, largely red and blue, are also the wavelengths that cause photosynthesis. We can tell this because the absorption and action spectra match quite well. This means that red and blue light must provide most energy for photosynthesis.

Figure 8.8
The absorption spectra and action spectrum of chlorophyll.

absorption spectra
the amount of light absorbed by each pigment, measured at each wavelength

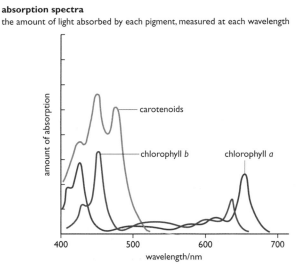

action spectrum
the amount of photosynthesis occurring at each wavelength

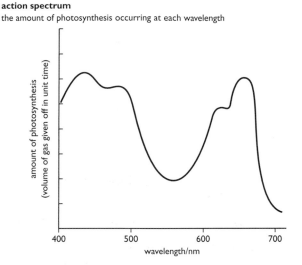

Measuring the rate of photosynthesis

The rate of photosynthesis can be measured with an **Audus microburette** (Figure 8.9). The experiment requires a freshly cut shoot of pondweed, such as *Elodea*, which when inverted produces a vigorous stream of gas bubbles from the base. The bubbles tell us the pondweed is actively photosynthesising. The pondweed is placed in a dilute solution of sodium hydrogencarbonate, which supplies the carbon dioxide (as HCO_3^- ions) required by the plant for photosynthesis. The quantity of gas evolved in a given time, say 30 minutes, is collected and measured by drawing the gas bubble into the capillary tube, and measuring its length. This length is then converted to a volume. This method can be used to measure the effects on the rate of photosynthesis of:

• light intensity (by varying the distance between light source and the apparatus)
• carbon dioxide concentration (by varying the concentration of hydrogencarbonate ions), and
• temperature (by varying the temperature of the dilute hydrogencarbonate solution).

Figure 8.9
Measuring the rate of photosynthesis with an Audus microburette.

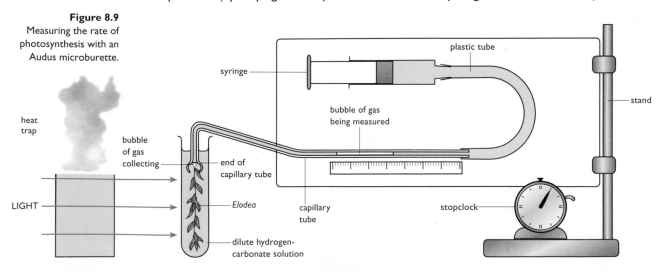

Factors affecting the rate of photosynthesis

Carbon dioxide concentration and light intensity

A limited supply of either carbon dioxide or light would limit the overall rate of photosynthesis, since both are essential for photosynthesis. The effects of separately limiting carbon dioxide concentration and light intensity, using shoots of pondweed in a microburette apparatus, are shown in Figure 8.10. (It is impossible in a practical way to limit the supply of water in order to show that its absence would also limit the rate of photosynthesis, since water makes up so much of the total plant substance.)

The effect of a shortage of any essential factor in photosynthesis is to limit the overall rate. This factor is then described as the **limiting factor**, for obvious reasons. So, if a plant has a plentiful supply of carbon dioxide, but the light is set at a very low intensity, then light is limiting. If the light intensity is raised, the plant immediately photosynthesises faster. Had the carbon dioxide concentration been raised instead, the rate would have stayed the same, since carbon dioxide was not the rate-limiting factor at the time.

Figure 8.10
Carbon dioxide and light intensity as limiting factors.

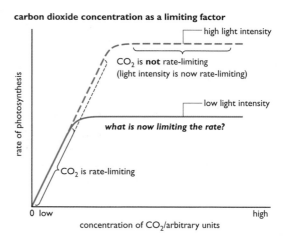

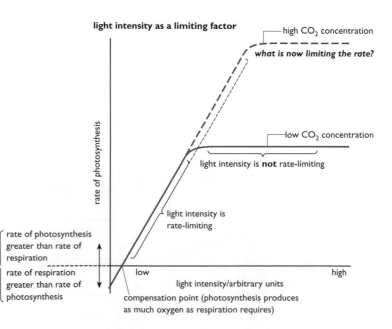

Photosynthesis occurs only in the light. Respiration goes on all the time, and oxygen is taken in by the plant for respiration.

Figure 8.11
Intensive glasshouse farming.

With plants outside the laboratory the limiting factor will change, probably with the time of day and the conditions. For example, at dawn light will be the limiting factor. Later, in maximum sunlight, the carbon dioxide supply may limit the rate of photosynthesis. With commercial crops grown intensively in glasshouses (Figure 8.11) where environmental conditions are controlled, the limiting effects of light intensity or carbon dioxide concentration can be reduced or removed (by additional lighting, or by enriching the atmosphere with carbon dioxide gas), improving productivity.

● Extension   The effect of temperature on the rate

The effect of temperature on the rate of photosynthesis, under controlled laboratory conditions, is especially interesting. One effect of increasing temperature, say from 10 °C to 30 °C, *actually depends upon the light intensity*. Under low light intensities, a rise in temperature has little effect. Under higher intensities, the rise in temperature increases the rate of photosynthesis significantly. This relationship is shown in Figure 8.12.

Figure 8.12
The effect of temperature on the rate of photosynthesis.

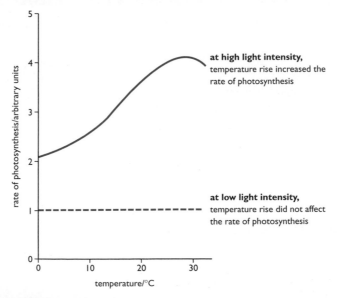

The graph in Figure 8.12 has been interpreted as showing that photosynthesis is made up of two sequential reactions: a **light-dependent reaction** (which, like all photochemical events, is unaffected by temperature) and a **light-independent reaction** (which, like all biochemical steps catalysed by enzymes, is temperature-sensitive). This idea was confirmed when photosynthesis was investigated in detail by biochemical techniques. The two stages that make up photosynthesis are what we look at next.

The process of photosynthesis in the chloroplast

4 Why is 'light-independent reaction' a better name than 'dark reaction'?

Photosynthesis is a complex set of many reactions that take place in illuminated chloroplasts only, and by which water and carbon dioxide are converted to sugar and oxygen in the light. The series of reactions can be divided into two stages (Figure 8.13).

1 The **'light reaction'** or **light-dependent stage**, in which light energy is used to split water, removing hydrogen and adding it to NADP, forming NADPH and H^+ (also known as reduced NADP or $NADPH_2$). At the same time ATP is generated from ADP and phosphate, also using energy from light. This is known as **photophosphorylation**. Oxygen is given off as a waste product of the light reaction. This stage occurs in the **grana** of the chloroplasts.

2 The **Calvin cycle** or **light-independent stage**, in which sugars are built up using carbon dioxide and the energy of ATP and reduced NADP ($NADPH + H^+$). This stage occurs in the **stroma** of the chloroplast in the light, because it requires a continuous supply of the products of the light reaction.

   The Calvin cycle has also been called the 'dark reaction', because it is not a photochemical step (it does not *itself* need light energy), and has characteristics different from those of a light or photochemical reaction. This can be misleading, however, because it is just one part of photosynthesis, and photosynthesis only occurs in the light.

Figure 8.13
The two reactions of photosynthesis in chloroplasts: inputs and outputs.

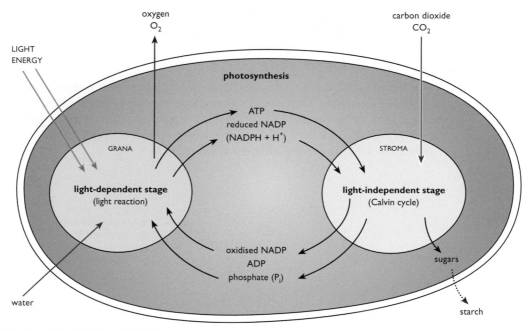

The structure of NADP is almost identical to that of NAD of respiration (NADP has an additional P_i group attached). NADP is the **hydrogen acceptor** of photosynthesis.

● Extension   The light-dependent stage in the grana

In the light-dependent stage of photosynthesis, energy from sunlight excites certain electrons in the chlorophyll molecules, and these excited electrons bring about the splitting (**photolysis**) of water, the formation of ATP and the reduction of NADP.

The reactions of the light-dependent stage occur in reaction centres called **photosystems** (**photosystem I** and **photosystem II**, Figure 8.14). Here, carotenoids and chlorophyll molecules (and other molecules) occur. The light energy that falls on to the photosystems is 'funnelled' to two central chlorophyll molecules, energising particular electrons there. It is these **excited electrons** (called **high energy electrons**) that are released from their chlorophyll molecules and bring about the reactions of the light-dependent stage.

continued

- The **excited electrons from photosystem II** are passed via the electron-carrier molecules to fill the electron gaps in photosystem I. In transit, the energy of these electrons is used to produce ATP from ADP and P_i. The process is called ***photophosphorylation*** because it is light energy that brings about the reaction.
- The electron gap in photosystem II is filled by electrons from the photolysis of water.
- The **excited electrons from photosystem I** are passed to oxidised NADP, two at a time, together with a hydrogen ion (from the splitting of water). Reduced NADP is formed, and this is the other essential product of the light-dependent stage.

In summary: using light energy, electrons are caused to flow from water, via photosystem II and photosystem I to NADP, forming reduced NADP. ATP is generated from ADP and P_i, also using energy from light. By these sequences of reactions, happening repeatedly at great speed throughout every second of daylight, the products of the light reaction are formed.

The ATP and reduced NADP do not accumulate, however. They are used to drive the Calvin cycle in the stroma, just outside the grana. Here carbohydrate is formed using carbon dioxide. Then the ADP, P_i and oxidised NADP diffuse back (by facilitated diffusion) for re-formation in the light-dependent stage.

Figure 8.14
Photosystem I and II and the light-dependent stage (Z diagram).

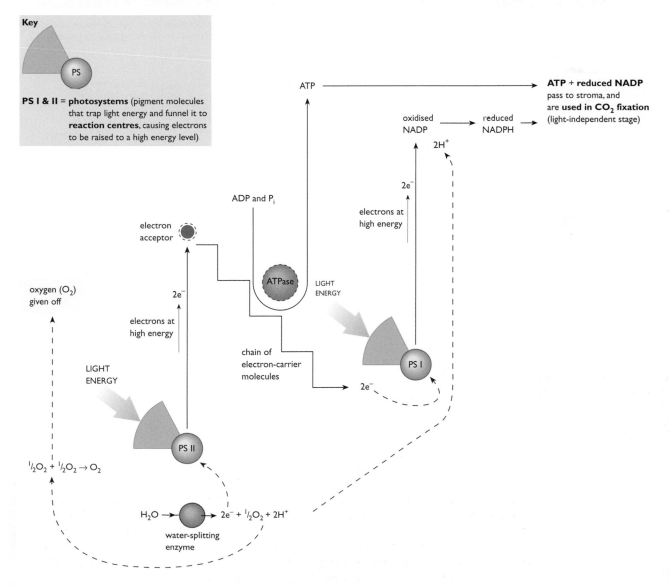

Key

PS I & II = photosystems (pigment molecules that trap light energy and funnel it to **reaction centres**, causing electrons to be raised to a high energy level)

● Extension Studying the light-dependent reaction with isolated chloroplasts

Chloroplasts can be isolated from green plant leaves and suspended in buffer solution (page 481) of the same concentration as the cytosol (an isotonic buffer). Isolated chloroplasts can be used to investigate the reactions of photosynthesis. For example, isolated chloroplasts can be shown to produce oxygen from water, when illuminated. They do so *provided* the natural electron-acceptor enzymes/carrier molecules are present. In the research laboratory, a sensitive piece of apparatus called an oxygen electrode is used to detect the oxygen given off by a sample of chloroplasts.

Alternatively, a hydrogen acceptor that changes colour when it is reduced can be used. The dye known as DCPIP is an example. DCPIP does no harm when added to chloroplasts in a suitable buffer solution, and its blue colour disappears when it is reduced. The splitting of water by light energy (photolysis) is the source of hydrogen that turns DCPIP colourless.

The photolysis of water and the reduction of the dye is represented by the equation:

$$2DCPIP + 2H_2O \rightarrow 2DCPIPH_2 + O_2$$

Figure 8.15
The reducing activity of isolated chloroplasts.

Figure 8.15 shows the steps to isolation of chloroplasts and the investigation of their reducing activity.

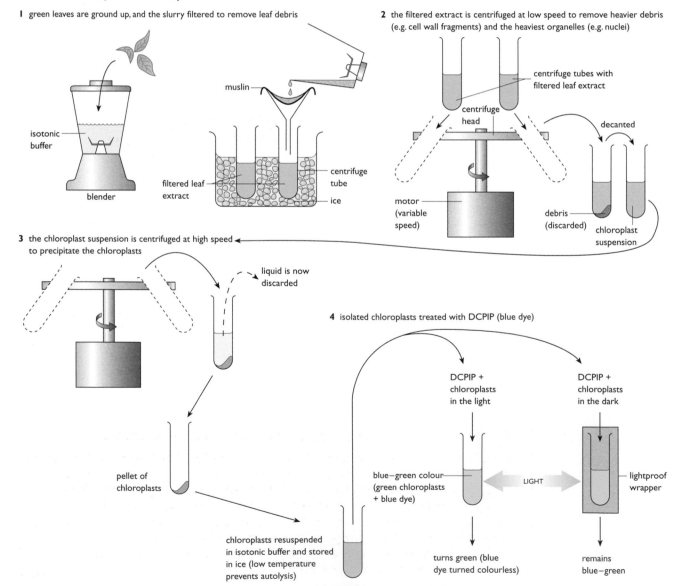

1 green leaves are ground up, and the slurry filtered to remove leaf debris

isotonic buffer

blender

muslin

filtered leaf extract

centrifuge tube

ice

2 the filtered extract is centrifuged at low speed to remove heavier debris (e.g. cell wall fragments) and the heaviest organelles (e.g. nuclei)

centrifuge tubes with filtered leaf extract

centrifuge head

motor (variable speed)

decanted

debris (discarded)

chloroplast suspension

3 the chloroplast suspension is centrifuged at high speed to precipitate the chloroplasts

liquid is now discarded

pellet of chloroplasts

chloroplasts resuspended in isotonic buffer and stored in ice (low temperature prevents autolysis)

4 isolated chloroplasts treated with DCPIP (blue dye)

DCPIP + chloroplasts in the light

DCPIP + chloroplasts in the dark

blue–green colour (green chloroplasts + blue dye)

LIGHT

lightproof wrapper

turns green (blue dye turned colourless)

remains blue–green

● **Extension**   The light-independent stage

Carbon dioxide readily diffuses into the chloroplast, where it is built up into sugars in a cyclic process called the **Calvin cycle** (Figure 8.16). In the Calvin cycle, carbon dioxide is combined with an acceptor molecule in the presence of a special enzyme, **ribulose bisphosphate carboxylase** (**Rubisco** for short). This reaction goes on in the stroma of the chloroplasts. The stroma is packed full of Rubisco, which makes up the bulk of the protein in a green plant. It is probably the most abundant enzyme present in the living world.

The acceptor molecule is a five-carbon sugar, ribulose bisphosphate (referred to as RuBP). Carbon dioxide is added to RuBP in a process known as **fixation**. The product is not a six-carbon sugar, but two molecules of a three-carbon compound, glycerate-3-phosphate (GP). GP is then reduced to a three-carbon sugar, triose phosphate. Some of the triose phosphate is converted into the products of photosynthesis, such as glucose, or into amino acids and fatty acids. The glucose may be immediately respired or stored as starch until required. But the bulk of triose phosphate is converted to more RuBP acceptor molecules, enabling fixation of carbon dioxide to continue.

Figure 8.16
A summary of the Calvin cycle in the stroma.

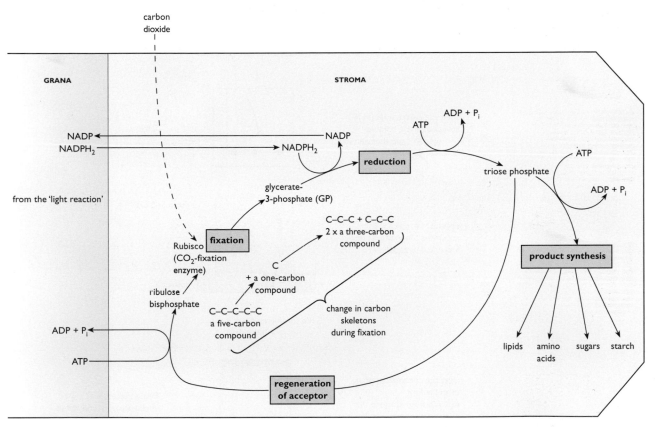

● **Extension**   Radioactive isotopes in the investigation of a metabolic pathway

The reactions of the Calvin cycle can be shown by the use of **radioactively labelled carbon dioxide** ($^{14}CO_2$) in a series of 'feeding' experiments. Labelled carbon dioxide is introduced briefly to the air supplied to a culture of unicellular green plants actively photosynthesising in the light. The radioactive carbon dioxide is taken up by the cells, and becomes fixed into all the products of photosynthesis, just as the ordinary carbon dioxide of the air ($^{12}CO_2$) is. Samples of the culture are then harvested at regular intervals, starting from the time the labelled carbon dioxide is fed. The metabolites are extracted from the harvested cells in each timed sample and separated by two-way chromatography (Figure 8.17).

continued

The sequence of carbon-containing compounds in which radioactivity appears is the path of carbon in photosynthesis, from the first-labelled glycerate-3-phosphate, to all the various intermediates and products.

This method of investigating a metabolic pathway has been widely applied in the biochemical study of life processes.

Figure 8.17
Analysis of radioactive metabolite samples by two-way paper chromatography.

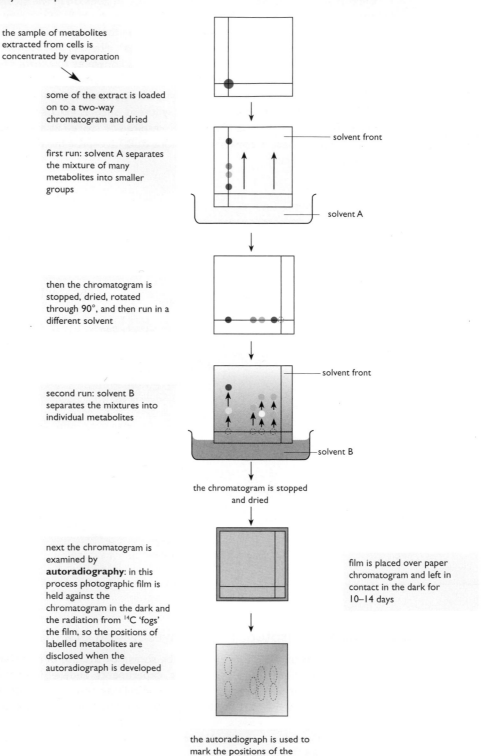

the sample of metabolites extracted from cells is concentrated by evaporation

some of the extract is loaded on to a two-way chromatogram and dried

first run: solvent A separates the mixture of many metabolites into smaller groups

solvent front

solvent A

then the chromatogram is stopped, dried, rotated through 90°, and then run in a different solvent

second run: solvent B separates the mixtures into individual metabolites

solvent front

solvent B

the chromatogram is stopped and dried

next the chromatogram is examined by **autoradiography**: in this process photographic film is held against the chromatogram in the dark and the radiation from ^{14}C 'fogs' the film, so the positions of labelled metabolites are disclosed when the autoradiograph is developed

film is placed over paper chromatogram and left in contact in the dark for 10–14 days

the autoradiograph is used to mark the positions of the labelled metabolites

Photosynthesis in tropical and subtropical plants

Many tropical grasses and plants of tropical and subtropical origins, such as sugar cane, sorghum and maize (*Zea mays*), are able to fix carbon dioxide in their photosynthesis by an *additional* mechanism. In these natural environments, light is not a limiting factor, but the concentration of carbon dioxide may become limiting in full sunlight. An additional fixation mechanism delivers a higher concentration of carbon dioxide to the chloroplasts where photosynthetic fixation occurs. By this mechanism, full advantage is taken of the available light, and as a result more sugar is produced by the chloroplasts.

The plants with this mechanism are called **C₄ plants**, to separate them from all other green plants that fix carbon dioxide only by the Calvin cycle and produce a three-carbon sugar (triose phosphate) as the first main product (these are called **C₃ plants**). C₄ plants have a different arrangement of the photosynthetic cells in their leaves. Here, the main photosynthetic cells (called **bundle sheath cells**) are surrounded by **mesophyll cells** where carbon dioxide is fixed into a four-carbon organic acid; this is called the Krantz anatomy.

In C₄ plants in the light, a C₄ organic acid is formed in the mesophyll cells, but is moved into the bundle sheath cells as soon as it is formed. In the bundle sheath cells it breaks down, releasing additional carbon dioxide to be fixed by the Calvin cycle (Figure 8.18). This is additional to the carbon dioxide that diffuses into the bundle sheath cells from the atmosphere.

As a result of this mechanism, C₄ plants operate extremely efficiently at the high temperatures and high light intensities found in tropical and subtropical regions of the globe.

Figure 8.18
Photosynthesis in the maize leaf.

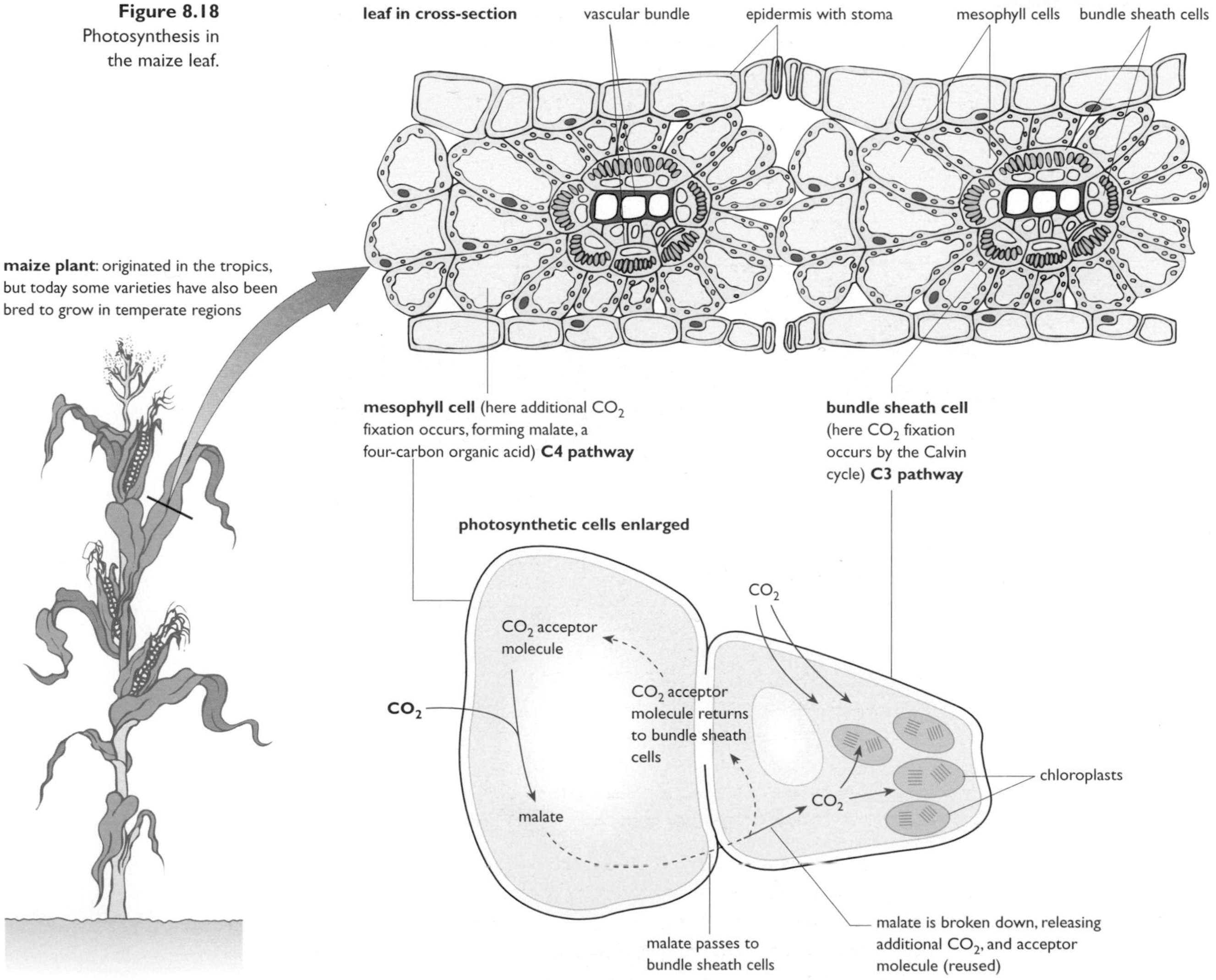

maize plant: originated in the tropics, but today some varieties have also been bred to grow in temperate regions

leaf in cross-section vascular bundle epidermis with stoma mesophyll cells bundle sheath cells

mesophyll cell (here additional CO₂ fixation occurs, forming malate, a four-carbon organic acid) **C4 pathway**

bundle sheath cell (here CO₂ fixation occurs by the Calvin cycle) **C3 pathway**

photosynthetic cells enlarged

CO₂ acceptor molecule

CO₂ acceptor molecule returns to bundle sheath cells

CO₂

CO₂

chloroplasts

malate

CO₂

malate passes to bundle sheath cells

malate is broken down, releasing additional CO₂, and acceptor molecule (reused)

183

Photosynthesis and plant metabolism

As we have seen, the first sugar produced in photosynthesis is a three-carbon compound, **triose phosphate**. Some of this product is immediately converted into the acceptor molecule for more carbon dioxide fixation, by the Calvin cycle. The remainder is converted into the carbohydrate products of photosynthesis, mainly glucose and starch, or into intermediates that are the starting points for all the other metabolites the plant requires. By **intermediate** we mean all the substances of a metabolic pathway from which the end-product is assembled.

Glucose is also the substrate for respiration. By **substrate** we mean a molecule which is the starting point for a biochemical pathway, and a substance that forms a complex with an enzyme (thereby getting the pathway up and running). The intermediates of respiration are also starting points for the synthesis of other metabolites. In other words, the biochemical pathways of both photosynthesis and respiration interact to supply metabolism with the intermediates required. These include:

- specialist carbohydrates, such as sucrose for transport and cellulose for cell walls
- lipids, including those in membranes
- amino acids and proteins, including those in membranes and as enzymes
- nucleic acids, growth factors, vitamins, hormones and pigments.

The fates of the products of photosynthesis are summarised in Figure 8.19.

Figure 8.19
What happens to the products of photosynthesis.

Key
— photosynthesis
— (Calvin cycle)
— respiration pathway (glycolysis + Krebs cycle)
— formation of essential metabolites

CO_2

acceptor molecule (RuBP)

three-carbon phosphorylated sugar (glycerate-3-phosphate)

three-carbon phosphorylated sugar (triose phosphate)

pyruvate

acetyl coenzyme A

phosphorylated six-carbon sugars

glycerol

fatty acids

organic acids of the Krebs cycle

ion uptake from soil NO_3^-

glucose   sucrose   starch, cellulose

carbohydrates

lipids

α-ketoglutarate

NH_3

transamination

proteins ← all other amino acids ← glutamate

184

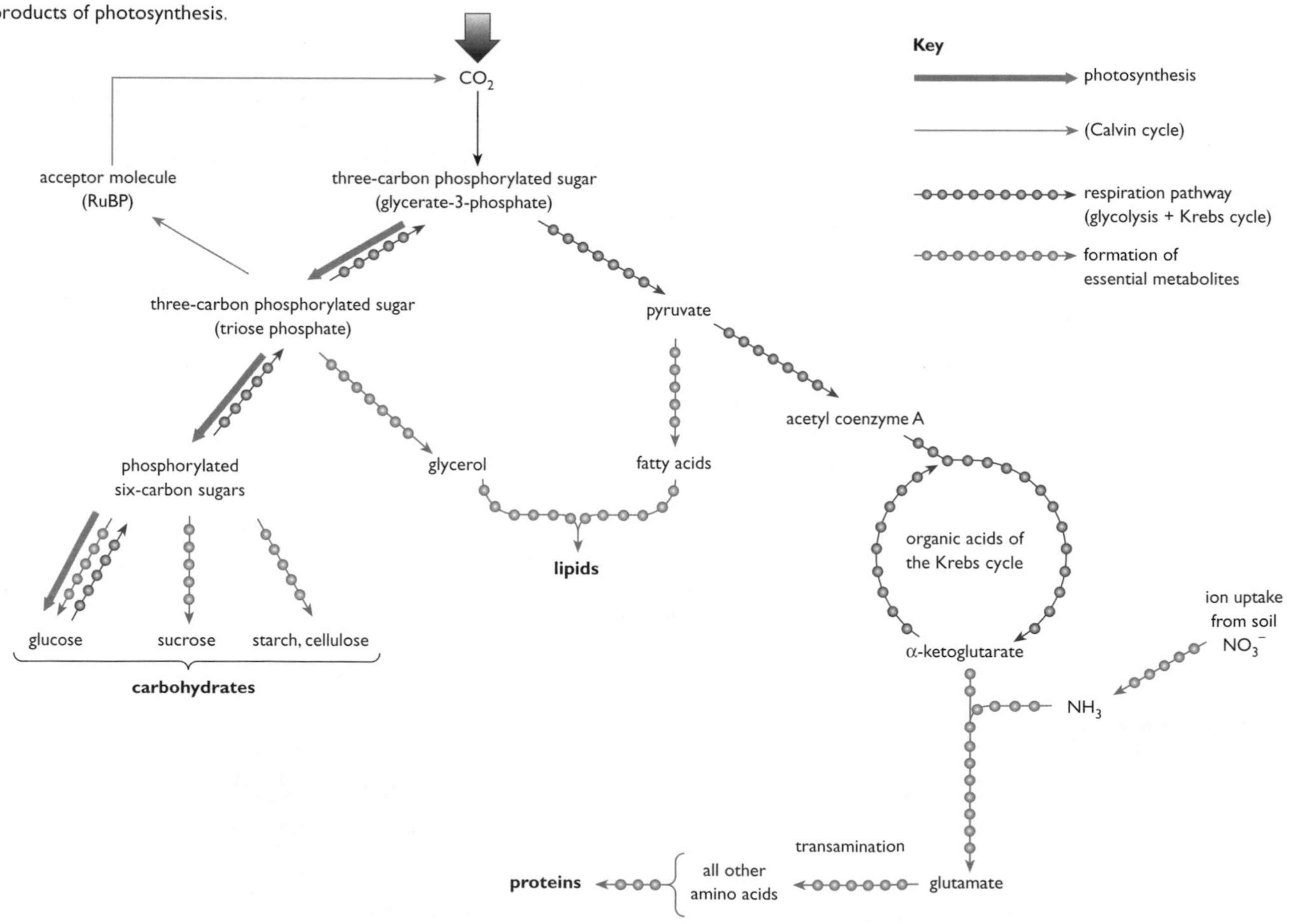

● **Extension**   Autotrophic nutrition

Autotrophic organisms make all the organic food they require from inorganic molecules, using an external source of energy. By contrast, animals and fungi need organic food molecules to supply the energy and materials they require (**heterotrophic nutrition**, described in Chapter 7).

Photosynthesis is one form of autotrophic nutrition. The autotrophs fall into two distinct groups, according to the source of energy used to build carbon dioxide into carbohydrates.

* **Photosynthetic organisms** use light energy. This group include the autotrophs we are most familiar with – the **green plants**, the **algae** (page 350) and the photosynthetic bacteria (the **cyanobacteria**, page 349). In these organisms carbon dioxide and water are combined in the light to produce sugar, and oxygen is the waste product.

    The **purple sulphur bacteria** are a different group of organisms, which also require light energy to build sugars from carbon dioxide. In these bacteria, however, hydrogen sulphide replaces water as the source of hydrogen. The waste product they form is sulphur, rather than oxygen. Many of the sulphur deposits in the Earth's crust have their origin in the metabolism of these bacteria.

* **Chemosynthetic organisms** are unable to use light energy. Instead, they catalyse a specific reaction in order to make available the free energy they need to synthesise organic compounds from carbon dioxide and water.

    For example, the **nitrifying bacteria** of the soil oxidise ammonium ions to nitrites, or nitrites to nitrates. Both these reactions provide the bacteria with energy needed to synthesise carbohydrates. The nitrifying bacteria have an important role in the nitrogen cycle (page 371).

    Other chemosynthetic organisms include the **iron bacteria**, which are sometimes used in industry in the extraction of metal from low grade ores.

● Mineral ions for metabolism

The metabolites that a plant requires for its growth, development and repair activities come from photosynthesis and respiration. However, there is another ingredient, namely **mineral ions**, needed for the production of these essential metabolites.

Some mineral ions are needed in relatively large quantities, and these are called the **macronutrients**. A good example is the nitrate ion, which is a form of combined nitrogen that plants absorb in quantity and use in the synthesis of amino acids.

Other mineral ions are required only in tiny amounts (more of them might well be poisonous). These are called the **micronutrients** or trace elements. An example is the copper(II) ion (Cu^{2+}), which is a component of enzymes of the photosynthetic photosystems. Examples of these two groups of essential minerals are listed here (Table 8.1), but a full list of mineral ions required by living things is given in Table 3.2 (page 58). Harvesting depletes the soil of ions, and these need to be replaced in the soil solution (Figure 8.20).

Table 8.1
Some mineral ions essential for plant metabolism.

Mineral ion	Uses
Some macronutrients:	
nitrogen as nitrate (NO_3^-)	required for amino acid synthesis
phosphorus as phosphate (PO_4^{3-})	required for ATP, nucleic acids and phospholipids
magnesium as magnesium ion (Mg^{2+})	required for chlorophyll, and for ATPase enzyme
Some micronutrients:	
manganese as manganese ion (Mn^{2+})	for carboxylase enzymes
molybdenum as molybdenum ion (Mo^{3+})	for nitrate reductase enzyme

Figure 8.20
Ions are taken up from the soil for plant metabolism and growth. When harvesting of crops occurs, the soil is depleted of ions, which may be returned to the soil with artificial fertilisers or by using farmyard manure.

Wheat yields in the UK have increased greatly during the past 50 years. This is because of the use of improved varieties of wheat, barley, oats and maize. Also, the practice of providing essential mineral ions to the soil of arable farms, by the regular and timely application of fertilisers, has been essential. Minerals lost from the soil during crop growth and harvesting have been entirely restored.

Artificial fertilisers provide minerals in a form that is immediately or quickly made available to the growing plants. The minerals present in the fertiliser granules mostly dissolve speedily and are taken up by the roots from the soil solution. Consequently, these fertilisers are applied at the start of peak growing periods of crop plants, usually after weed plants have been killed off. This minimises the loss of soluble fertilisers to competitor weeds or into the water table below. Modern plant varieties mostly require relatively high levels of ions at key times in their growth in order to provide exceptional yields at the end of the season.

Farmyard manure (particularly from the housing of herds of cows in sheltered yards over winter) may be spread on to arable fields and ploughed in. Saprotrophic organisms in the soil break down the dung and straw, releasing mineral ions. These are taken up by the crop plants as they grow. Decay of manure is a slow process, and ions are released over an extended period, not necessarily when most required by the crop plant. However, the organic matter normally leads to a build-up of the soil structure, improving aeration and drainage. Soil rich in organic matter is darker in colour and absorbs more heat; yet it retains water well. However, manure may increase the weed seeds present in the soil.

5 What cells of a plant root are best able to absorb ions from the soil solution, and why?

Absorption of mineral ions for plant metabolism

The source of mineral ions for plants is the soil solution. This is a layer of water that surrounds the individual soil particles. It contains very many different ions, most in quite low concentrations. Plants can take up ions from the soil solution through their roots, mostly if not entirely in a specialised region of the root, near the root tip. This is called the region of **root hairs**.

Root hairs form just behind the region where growth in length of the root takes place. These hairs are extremely delicate structures, tiny extensions of the outermost layer of cells. If they were formed where the root was still pushing its way between the soil particles, the root hairs would be quickly torn off. Further back, the root becomes impervious, and the outer layers of living cells, root hairs included, are sloughed off. So root hairs are found only in this particular part of the root (Figure 8.21).

Figure 8.21
The region of uptake in roots.

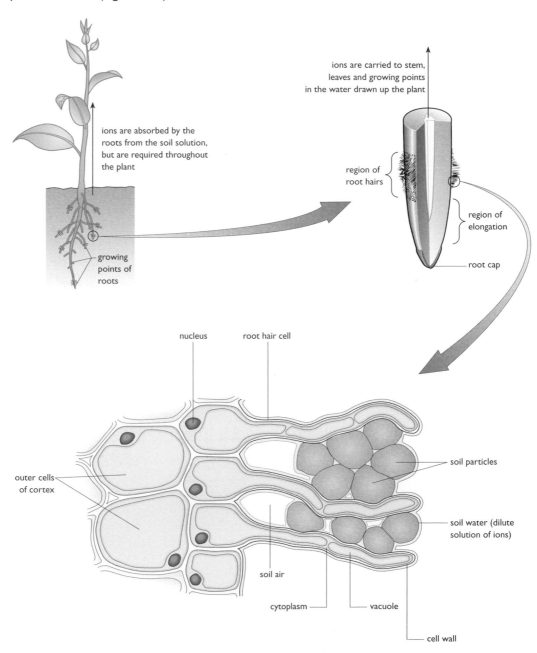

ions are absorbed by the roots from the soil solution, but are required throughout the plant

growing points of roots

ions are carried to stem, leaves and growing points in the water drawn up the plant

region of root hairs

region of elongation

root cap

nucleus   root hair cell

outer cells of cortex

soil particles

soil water (dilute solution of ions)

soil air

cytoplasm   vacuole

cell wall

Water is taken up from the soil and mineral ions are absorbed at the root hairs, but entirely different mechanisms are used. Water uptake is discussed on page 245. Ions are taken up selectively, by an active process, using energy from respiration. This means that the ions that are useful are selected, and ions not required by the plant are largely ignored. Uptake occurs by means of protein pumps in the plasma membrane of the root hair cells (Figure 8.22). Protein pumps are specific for particular ions, so if an ion is required, the particular transport protein is produced by the cells and built into the cell membranes. If the required ion is available in the soil solution, it can be pumped into the cell even if there is a higher concentration in the cell already.

Figure 8.22
The active uptake of ions by a protein pump.

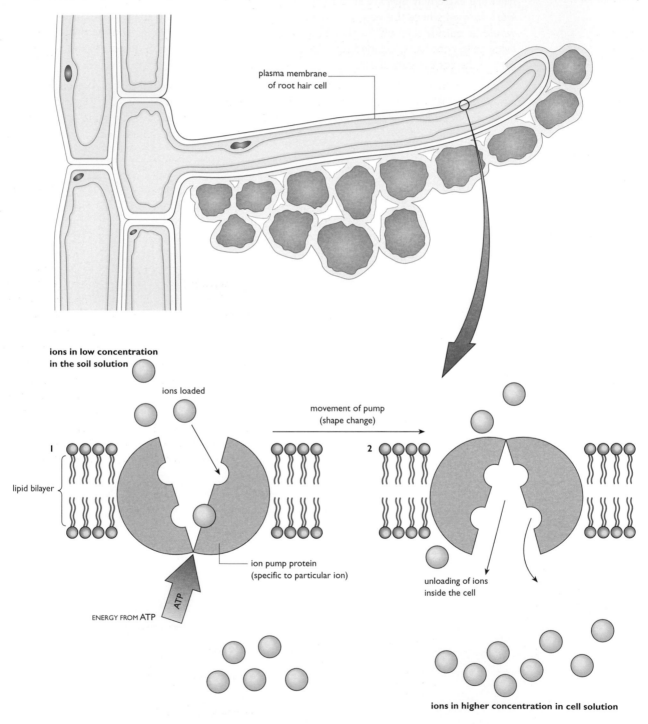

Protein synthesis in plants

For protein synthesis, amino acids are required. Plants make all their own amino acids, using combined nitrogen such as nitrate ions (but they can use ammonium ions as well), together with some of the organic acids formed as intermediates in respiration and other metabolic processes. The steps are summarised in Figure 8.23.

The **first step** is the reduction of nitrate to the ammonium ion. This occurs in the roots of most plants, at or near the site of absorption from the soil solution.

Then, in the **second step**, the ammonium ion is immediately combined with an organic acid, called α-ketoglutaric acid. (Since organic acids are always slightly ionised in cell solutions, we refer to them as their ion. For example, the organic acid α-ketoglutaric acid exists in cells as α-ketoglutarate, so this is what it is called.) When an ammonium ion is added to α-ketoglutarate, glutamate (glutamic acid) is the amino acid formed.

This biochemical step is the only initial 'entry point' of combined nitrogen into plant metabolites. All other amino acids are formed from other amino acids by a process called **transamination**. Transamination is the **third step**. This involves switching the amino group from an amino acid to an organic acid, forming a different amino acid. A specific transamination enzyme is involved in the formation of each amino acid.

$$\text{amino acid (1)} + \text{organic acid (2)} \xrightarrow{\textit{transaminase enzyme}} \text{organic acid (1)} + \text{amino acid (2)}$$

For example,

$$\text{glutamic acid} + \text{pyruvic acid} \rightarrow \text{α-ketoglutaric acid} + \text{alanine}$$

Amino acids are transported around the plant in the sieve tubes of the phloem, and collect at the growing points of the plant. These include the tips of stems and roots, young leaves, lateral buds, young flowers and in ripening seeds. Here a 'pool' of amino acids accumulates in the cells where protein synthesis occurs. This pool contains the 20 amino acids from which the complete range of cell proteins are synthesised. Amino acids are condensed together by peptide bonds, at ribosomes in the cytoplasm. The sequence of amino acids is dictated by messenger RNA (Chapter 5, page 112).

6 Which organelle in the cytoplasm is the site of protein synthesis?

7 Distinguish between:
- photosynthesis and chemosynthesis
- chlorophyll and chloroplast
- mesophyll and epidermis
- grana and stroma
- absorption spectrum and action spectrum
- leaf veins and vascular bundles
- light-dependent and light-independent steps
- photolysis and photophosphorylation.

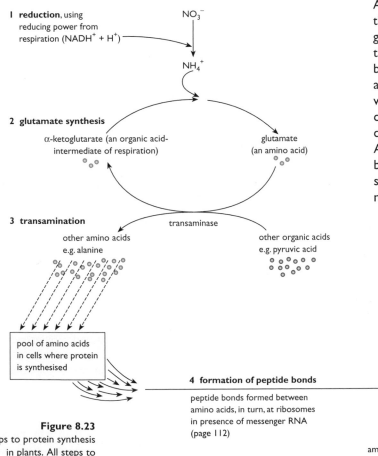

Figure 8.23
Steps to protein synthesis in plants. All steps to protein synthesis require metabolic energy, as ATP.

● **Skills task**   Using the Audus microburette (Figure 8.9), measurements were made of the rate of photosynthesis under conditions of both high light intensity and low light intensity, over a temperature range of 10–25 °C. The results were:

| | Temperature /°C | | | |
	10	15	20	25
rate of photosynthesis /cm³ per minute				
high light intensity	1.0	3.3	5.2	7.3
low light intensity	0.4	0.7	1.1	1.5

1 Present the data in a single, fully labelled graph designed to make clear the difference in the effect of temperature under differing light intensities.
2 Under conditions of high light intensity, what is the likely limiting factor?

SUMMARY
- **Photosynthesis** is the process by which green plants manufacture carbohydrates from carbon dioxide and water, using energy from sunlight. Oxygen is the waste product. Photosynthesis takes place in specialised organelles, **chloroplasts**, most of which occur in the palisade mesophyll cells of the leaves.
- Plants use the products of photosynthesis, mostly sugar, to manufacture the other carbohydrates, lipids, proteins and other substances they require. They also use selected **mineral ions**, absorbed from the soil.
- Plant nutrition is described as **autotrophic** (self-feeding). Photosynthesis sustains all living things, since all organisms feed on plants or plant products, directly or indirectly.
- The **leaf** is the factory for photosynthesis, holding palisade cells in favourably illuminated positions and supplying them with water from the xylem vessels, and with carbon dioxide by diffusion from the air. The products of photosynthesis for export from the leaf are carried away in the sieve tubes in the phloem.
- The **chloroplast** is an organelle with a double membrane. The inner membrane intucks to form the membrane systems of the chloroplast (**thylakoid membranes**). These are arranged in compact, circular piles called **grana**, around which are loosely arranged membranes called the **stroma**.
- The photosynthetic pigment **chlorophyll** traps light energy. It is a mixture of pigments, and occurs sandwiched between the membranes of the grana. The components of chlorophyll can be separated by chromatography.
- Photosynthesis, a complex process, can be divided into two linked steps. The **light-dependent stage** occurs in the grana, and results in the formation of reduced coenzyme NADP and ATP. It involves the photolysis of water and the release of oxygen. The **light-independent stage** occurs in the stroma, and involves the fixing of carbon dioxide to form carbohydrate, using the products of the light-dependent stage.
- The **rate of photosynthesis** in water plants is measured in terms of the volume of oxygen-enriched gas given off in the light. The volume of gas produced under different conditions can be measured in an Audus microburette.
- **Amino acids** are formed by the reduction of nitrate ions and the reaction of the resulting ammonium ions with a specific organic acid of the Krebs cycle (page 197), to form glutamate. All other amino acids are formed by **transamination**. Amino acids are condensed together by peptide linkages to form proteins.
- Some autotrophic organisms use energy from a chemical reaction rather than light energy to reduce carbon dioxide to carbohydrate. These organisms are all bacteria, and they do not contain chlorophyll. They are described as **chemotrophic**.

● Examination questions

I The diagram below shows the structure of a chloroplast, as seen using the electron microscope.

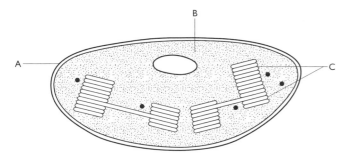

a Name the parts labelled A, B and C. (3)

b The actual length of this chloroplast is 2.5 μm. Calculate the magnification of this diagram. Show your working. (2)

London, AS/A level, Module B2, June 1996

2 The statements in the table below refer to the light-dependent and light-independent (dark) reactions of photosynthesis.

If a statement is correct for the process, place a tick (✓) in the appropriate row and if it is incorrect, place a cross (✗) in the appropriate row. (5)

Statement	Light-dependent reaction	Light-independent reaction
oxygen produced		
carbon dioxide fixed		
occurs in stroma		
uses NADPH and H^+		
produces ATP		

London, AS/A level, Module B2, June 1996

3 An experiment was carried out to investigate the effect of light intensity on the rate of photosynthesis of an aquatic plant, using the apparatus shown in the diagram below.

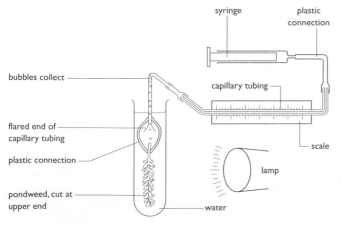

a State **two** environmental conditions, other than light intensity, which would need to be controlled. For each condition, describe how control could be achieved. (4)

b The plant was allowed to carry out photosynthesis for 10 minutes. Describe how you would use the apparatus to determine the volume of oxygen produced by the plant during this 10 minute period. (4)

c Using this apparatus, the volume of oxygen produced after 10 minute periods of photosynthesis was determined at different light intensities. The results of this investigation are shown in the graph below. (3)

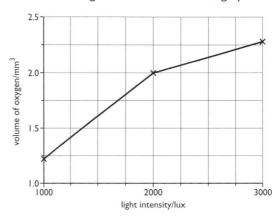

Comment on the results of this investigation.

London, AS/A level, Module B2, Jan 1998

4 a i Where in the chloroplast does the light-independent stage of photosynthesis occur?

ii Describe briefly what happens in this stage of photosynthesis. (4)

A sample of *Chlorella* (a unicellular organism) was allowed to photosynthesise at high and very low carbon dioxide levels. The graph shows the concentrations of glycerate-3-phosphate (GP) and ribulose bisphosphate (RuBP) during the investigation.

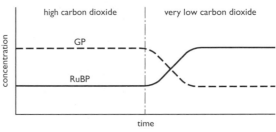

b Account for the different concentrations of RuBP during the whole course of the investigation. (3)

c Explain why the concentration of GP falls when the level of carbon dioxide is reduced. (1)

d Give **two** conditions which should be kept constant throughout the investigation. (1)

NEAB, A level, Paper 1/Sections A & B, June 1996

9 Respiration

STARTING POINTS
- Organisms need usable **energy** to maintain cells and carry out their activities and functions.
- **Respiration** is a process that takes place in every living cell, making energy available.
- In respiration requiring oxygen – **aerobic respiration** – sugar is oxidised to carbon dioxide and water.
- Respiration in the absence of oxygen – **anaerobic respiration** – is also known as **fermentation**.
- Aerobic respiration is much more **energy-efficient** than fermentation.

Living things need energy

Living organisms need energy to build, maintain and repair body structures, and for activities such as nutrition, excretion, sensitivity, movement and reproduction. Specifically, all organisms require **usable energy** for:

- the reactions of metabolism, and especially for the steps by which complex molecules are built up (**anabolism**), such as protein synthesis
- the **active transport** of molecules and ions across membranes, carried out by membrane pumps
- **movements** in and by organisms, including those due to muscle contractions and the beating of cilia and flagella
- formation and **secretion** of substances from cells, including digestive enzymes and hormones
- cell division, and the formation and maintenance of all the organelles of the cytoplasm.

Respiration provides energy from food substances

Energy is made available in cells by the breakdown of food substances, principally carbohydrates like glucose. Food molecules are made in cells (**autotrophic nutrition**, Chapter 8) or taken into cells following digestion (**heterotrophic nutrition**, Chapter 7). Different types of food molecules contain different amounts of energy (page 145). The total amount of energy that can be released from food substances is measured in a calorimeter (Figure 9.1).

Figure 9.1
A calorimeter for measuring the energy value of foods.

The food sample is completely oxidised by burning it in oxygen.

The energy released is transferred to the water jacket.

The rise in temperature of the water is measured.

The energy value of the food is calculated using the fact that it takes 4.2 J of heat energy to raise 1 g of water by 1°C.

The energy values of foods are published in tables, and those of manufactured and packaged foods may be recorded on the wrapping.

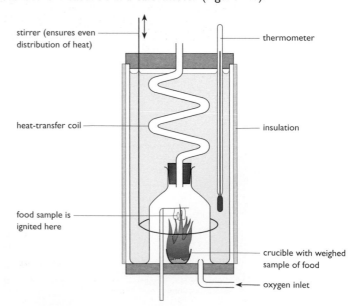

stirrer (ensures even distribution of heat)

thermometer

heat-transfer coil

insulation

food sample is ignited here

crucible with weighed sample of food

oxygen inlet

The process by which energy is made available from food substances like glucose is called **respiration**. Respiration occurs in all organisms and every living cell, all the time. The biochemical steps to the breakdown of sugar in the cell are known as **cellular respiration**. Cellular respiration is the subject of this chapter. As a result of the reactions of cellular respiration, gases must be exchanged between cells and the environment, and this is known as **gaseous exchange**. Gaseous exchange is a process we will look at in the next chapter.

The process of cellular respiration

Cellular respiration involving **oxygen** is described as **aerobic respiration**. Most animals and plants and very many microorganisms respire aerobically most, if not all of the time. We will examine aerobic respiration first.

In aerobic respiration, sugar is oxidised to carbon dioxide and water and much energy is made available. The steps to aerobic respiration can be summarised by a single equation. This equation is equivalent to a balance sheet of inputs (the raw materials) and outputs (the products), but it tells us nothing about the steps:

$$\text{glucose} + \text{oxygen} \rightarrow \text{carbon dioxide} + \text{water} + \text{ENERGY}$$
$$C_6H_{12}O_6 + 6O_2 \rightarrow 6CO_2 + 6H_2O + \text{ENERGY}$$

Sometimes aerobic respiration is compared to combustion – for example, people may talk about 'burning up food' in respiration. In fact this comparison is unhelpful (Figure 9.2). In combustion the energy in fuel is released in a one-step reaction, as heat. Such a violent change would be disastrous for body tissues. Cellular respiration consists of a very large number of small steps, each catalysed by a specific enzyme. Because energy in respiration is transferred in small quantities, much of it can be made available, and may be trapped in the energy currency molecule ATP. Some energy is still lost as heat in each step, however.

Figure 9.2
Combustion and respiration compared.

glucose burning in air

sprinter completing a race

energy change in burning

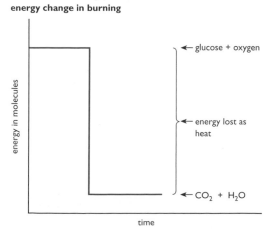

energy in molecules

← glucose + oxygen

← energy lost as heat

← CO$_2$ + H$_2$O

time

energy change in cellular respiration

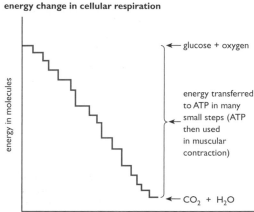

energy in molecules

← glucose + oxygen

energy transferred to ATP in many small steps (ATP then used in muscular contraction)

← CO$_2$ + H$_2$O

time

ATP, the universal energy currency

Energy made available within the cytoplasm (the fluid parts, the cytosol, and the organelles) is transferred to a molecule called **adenosine triphosphate (ATP)**. This molecule is spoken of as **energy currency**, because like money it is constantly recycled. ATP is a nucleotide (page 48) with an unusual feature: it carries a sequence of three phosphate groups linked together (Figure 9.3). ATP may lose both its outer phosphate groups (usually only one at a time). ATP is a relatively small, soluble organic molecule. It occurs in cells at a concentration of 0.5–2.5 mg cm^{-3}.

Like many organic molecules of its size, ATP contains a good deal of chemical energy locked up in its structure. What makes ATP special as a reservoir of stored chemical energy, is its role as a common intermediate between energy-yielding reactions and energy-requiring reactions. Energy-yielding reactions (**exergonic reactions**, page 75) include many of the individual steps in respiration. Energy-requiring reactions (**endergonic reactions**) include the synthesis of cellulose from glucose, and the synthesis of proteins from amino acids.

The important features of ATP are as follows:

- it is universal to all living things
- it can move easily between cytosol and organelles by diffusion
- it can take part in very many reactions of metabolism
- it can deliver energy in relatively small amounts, sufficient to drive individual reactions
- it is involved in energy-requiring reactions and in the energy-releasing steps of respiration
- it is the source of energy for most biological processes.

Figure 9.3
ATP, ADP and AMP.

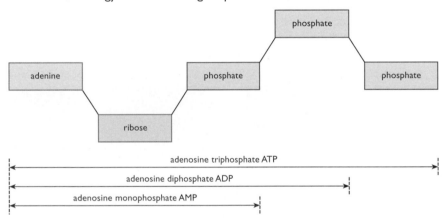

The ATP–ADP cycle and metabolism

In cells, ATP is formed from adenosine diphosphate (ADP) and phosphate ion (P$_i$) using energy from respiration. If you have studied photosynthesis already you will know that ATP is also formed in the chloroplasts of green plants in steps known as photophosphorylation, using light energy.

In the presence of enzymes, ATP participates in energy-requiring reactions. The free energy available in ATP is approximately 30–34 kJ mol^{-1}. Some of this energy is lost as heat in a reaction, but much free energy is made available to do useful work, more than sufficient to drive a typical endergonic reaction of anabolism.

- Sometimes ATP reacts with water (a hydrolysis reaction) and is converted to ADP and P$_i$. Direct hydrolysis of the terminal phosphate groups like this happens in muscle contraction, for example.
- Mostly, ATP reacts with other metabolites and forms phosphorylated intermediates. ADP and P$_i$ become available for reuse as metabolism of these intermediates continues (Figure 9.4). For example, in the first reactions of aerobic respiration, ATP reacts with hexose sugars to form phosphorylated sugars. These compounds are reactive in ways that glucose alone is not. The phosphate groups are released later in the respiration pathway.
- ATP is sometimes (but rarely) hydrolysed to AMP in metabolism. We will note this event when it arises.

I Give three reasons why ATP is an efficient energy currency molecule.

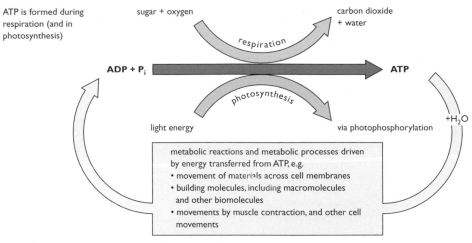

Figure 9.4
The
$ATP \rightarrow ADP + P_i$
cycle.

The three stages of aerobic respiration
==

The aerobic respiration of glucose is a major metabolic pathway. It is a sequence of about 25 individual reactions, each with a specific enzyme. As with any metabolic pathway, the product of one step becomes the substrate for the next reaction, and immediately forms an enzyme–substrate complex (page 79) with the enzyme for that next reaction.

The reactions of aerobic respiration conveniently fall into three main stages, known as:

- glycolysis
- the Krebs cycle
- oxidative phosphorylation.

The products of each of these stages are shown in Figure 9.5.

Figure 9.5
The stages of aerobic respiration.

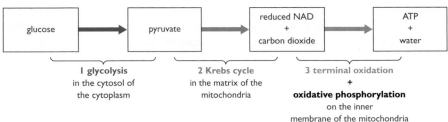

The three stages of aerobic respiration need to be understood in more detail, but the chemistry of the individual reactions is unimportant. It is helpful, however, to identify two types of chemical change that occur frequently in aerobic respiration.

Redox reactions
--

In aerobic respiration, glucose is oxidised to carbon dioxide, but at the same time, oxygen is reduced to water. Tissue respiration is a series of oxidation–reduction reactions, so described because when one substance in a reaction is oxidised another is automatically reduced. The short-hand name for **red**uction–**ox**idation reactions is **redox reactions** (page 483). In biological oxidation, oxygen atoms may be added to a compound; alternatively, hydrogen atoms may be removed. For example, in respiration all the hydrogen atoms are gradually removed from glucose. They are added to hydrogen acceptors, usually a substance known as **NAD** (nicotinamide adenine dinucleotide, page 49), which itself is reduced. We can write this addition of hydrogen to its carrier as:

$$NAD + 2H \rightarrow NADH_2$$

but what actually happens is:

$$NAD^+ + 2H \rightarrow NADH + H^+$$

Many of the reactions of aerobic respiration are redox reactions (Figure 9.6).

Figure 9.6
Respiration as a
redox reaction.

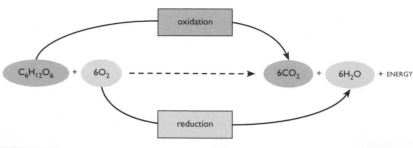

oxidation

$C_6H_{12}O_6$ + $6O_2$ ---------→ $6CO_2$ + $6H_2O$ + ENERGY

reduction

oxidation involves:
• addition of oxygen
• removal of hydrogen
• loss of electrons
• release of energy

reduction involves:
• removal of oxygen
• addition of hydrogen
• gain of electrons
• uptake of energy

Decarboxylation reactions

2 What types of reactions
are catalysed by:
a dehydrogenases,
and
b decarboxylases?

Decarboxylation is the removal of carbon from organic compounds by the formation of carbon dioxide. For example, glucose contains six carbon atoms. All six are removed at different stages of respiration, one at a time, and given off as carbon dioxide. A specific decarboxylase enzyme is involved in each reaction. The first decarboxylation in aerobic respiration occurs in the reaction linking glycolysis with the Krebs cycle, when pyruvate is converted to a two-carbon molecule. The other decarboxylation reactions of aerobic respiration occur in steps in the Krebs cycle.

The stages of respiration

Glycolysis

In glycolysis, one molecule of **glucose** is oxidised to two molecules of **pyruvate**, the salt of a three-carbon organic acid. In summary, this change involves 'glucose-splitting', hence its name (glyco-lysis). All the enzymes that catalyse the reactions of glycolysis are dissolved in the cytosol, and glycolysis occurs in the cytoplasm, outside the mitochondria. The process falls into three steps, summarised in Figure 9.7.

Figure 9.7
Glycolysis in summary.

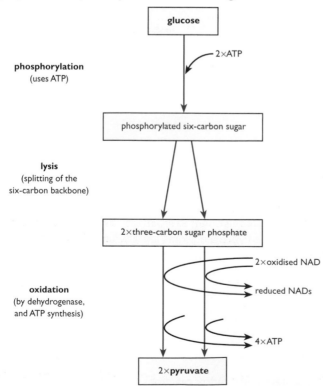

phosphorylation
(uses ATP)

lysis
(splitting of the
six-carbon backbone)

oxidation
(by dehydrogenase,
and ATP synthesis)

glucose

2×ATP

phosphorylated six-carbon sugar

2×three-carbon sugar phosphate

2×oxidised NAD

reduced NADs

4×ATP

2×**pyruvate**

Firstly, glucose is phosphorylated. Glucose is a relatively unreactive molecule, and the reactions with ATP activate it for subsequent reactions.

Secondly, the phosphorylated six-carbon sugar is split into two three-carbon sugar phosphates. This is the critical feature of glycolysis. (Incidentally, the intermediates of this stage are the same as those in the Calvin cycle of photosynthesis, page 181.)

Thirdly, the three-carbon sugar is converted to pyruvate. This involves oxidation by dehydrogenation, and reduced NAD is formed. Also, sufficient free energy is released to trigger the formation of two molecules of ATP. Consequently, for each molecule of glucose metabolised, four molecules of ATP are produced. This is a net gain of two ATPs in glycolysis. However, when the reduced NAD formed in this stage is later oxidised (in the final steps to aerobic respiration – terminal oxidation), additional molecules of ATP are formed (see Table 9.1 opposite).

Krebs cycle

The pyruvate ions first diffuse across the double membrane of the mitochondria, into the matrix (Figure 9.11, page 200). There pyruvate is immediately decarboxylated and oxidised to an acetyl group. Oxidation occurs by removal of hydrogen, and reduced NAD is formed. The acetyl group combines with a coenzyme called **coenzyme A**, forming **acetyl coenzyme A**. The production of acetyl coenzyme A from pyruvate is a **link reaction**, connecting glycolysis to reactions of the Krebs cycle (Figure 9.8).

The acetyl coenzyme A enters the Krebs cycle by reacting with a four-carbon organic acid (oxaloacetate, OAA). The products of this reaction are a six-carbon acid (citrate) and coenzyme A, which is released. Citrate is then metabolised and converted back to the four-carbon acid by the reactions of the Krebs cycle. These involve the following changes:

- two molecules of carbon dioxide are given off, in separate decarboxylation reactions
- a molecule of ATP is formed
- three molecules of reduced NAD are formed
- one molecule of another hydrogen acceptor (FAD, flavin adenine dinucleotide) is reduced.

Because glucose is converted to two molecules of pyruvate in glycolysis, the whole Krebs cycle sequence of reactions 'turns' twice for every molecule of glucose that is respired.

Figure 9.8
The Krebs cycle in summary (the Krebs cycle is also known as the citric acid cycle, or the tricarboxylic acid cycle).

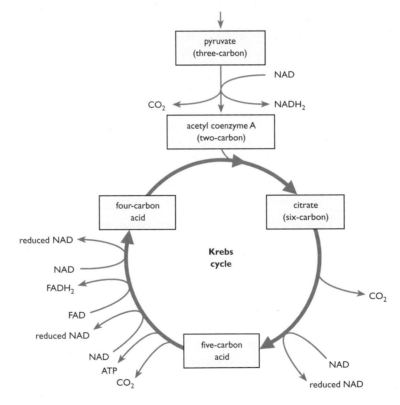

Now we are in a position to summarise the changes to the molecule of glucose that occurred in the reactions of glycolysis and the Krebs cycle. Table 9.1 shows a 'budget' of the products of glycolysis and two turns of the Krebs cycle.

Table 9.1
Net products of aerobic respiration of glucose at the end of the Krebs cycle.

	CO_2	ATP	Reduced NAD	Reduced FAD
glycolysis	0	2	2	0
link reaction (pyruvate → acetyl CoA)	2	0	2	0
Krebs cycle	4	2	6	2
Total	$6CO_2$	4ATP	10 reduced NAD	2 reduced FAD

3 How does the absence of oxygen in respiring tissue switch off the Krebs cycle and terminal oxidation?

Terminal oxidation (and oxidative phosphorylation)

The removal of pairs of hydrogen atoms from various intermediates of the respiratory pathway has been a feature of several of the steps in glycolysis and the Krebs cycle. On most occasions oxidised NAD was converted to reduced NAD (but, once in the Krebs cycle, FAD was reduced).

Now, in this final stage of aerobic respiration, the hydrogen atoms (or their electrons) are transported along a series of carriers, from the reduced NAD (or FAD), to be combined with oxygen to form water. As electrons are passed between the carriers in the series, energy is released. Release of energy in this manner is controlled, and the energy can be used by the cell. The energy is transferred to ADP and P_i, forming ATP. Normally, for every molecule of reduced NAD that is oxidised (that is, for every pair of hydrogen atoms) three molecules of ATP are produced. The process is summarised in Figure 9.9. The total yield from aerobic respiration is 38 ATP molecules per molecule of glucose respired.

Figure 9.9
Terminal oxidation and the formation of ATP: a summary.

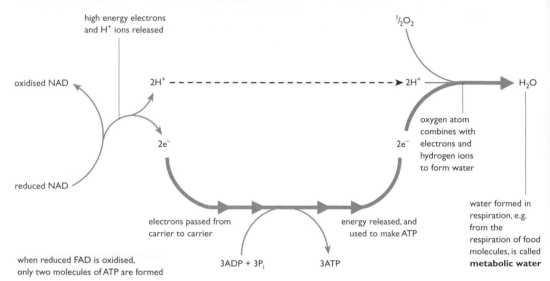

● Extension   The enzymes and carriers of terminal oxidation

When hydrogen atoms are removed from compounds of the glycolysis pathway and the Krebs cycle (respiratory intermediates) and transferred to NAD, the reactions are catalysed by enzymes called **dehydrogenases**. Each dehydrogenase of the respiratory pathway is specific to a particular intermediate molecule. A dehydrogenase enzyme works with NAD as a coenzyme (Figure 4.6, page 80).

Reduced NAD is then oxidised by the terminal oxidation pathway. As the first carrier of the pathway accepts hydrogen (or its electron), it becomes reduced. As the hydrogen (or electron) is passed to the next carrier, the first is reoxidised. Thus passage along the terminal oxidation chain is another example of a redox reaction. Only at the end of this process do the electrons and hydrogen ions finally combine with oxygen to form water.

The carriers of the terminal oxidation chains are an interesting group of compounds whose chemistry is well understood. Many are substances called **cytochromes**. This molecule has a chemical structure very similar to that of chlorophyll, but in cytochrome an iron atom replaces the magnesium atom of chlorophyll (Figure 8.7, page 174). Cyanide will react with the iron of cytochromes, and if this happens, electron-transport reactions and ATP synthesis are blocked (cyanide is an inhibitor of cytochromes). The result for any aerobically respiring tissue is disastrous. For example, in a human who has ingested cyanide, the supply of fresh ATP to muscles almost instantly stops. As a result the heart and breathing muscles become locked in immobility, with fatal consequences.

Fats and proteins as respiratory substrates

In addition to glucose, **fats** (lipids) are also commonly used as respiratory substrates. When fats are about to be respired they are broken down to fatty acids and glycerol. The glycerol is converted into triose phosphate and enters the glycolytic stage of respiration. Fatty acids are broken into two-carbon fragments and fed into the Krebs cycle via acetyl coenzyme A (Figure 9.10). Vertebrate muscle is well adapted to the respiration of fatty acids in this way, and they are just as likely as glucose to be the respiratory substrate.

If there is an excess of **proteins** in the diet, the excess amino acids produced on digestion may also be used as respiratory substrates. First the amino group is removed (the process is called **deamination**, and occurs in the liver, page 261). The amino group is combined with carbon dioxide to form urea, which is excreted from the body. What remains, the carbon 'skeleton' of the amino acid, is an organic acid. Organic acids enter the Krebs cycle.

Mammals will always respire excess amino acids in this way because they cannot store proteins. By contrast, plants do not normally respire proteins, but rather store them for later use – in seeds, for example.

Figure 9.10
Fats and proteins as alternative respiratory substrates.

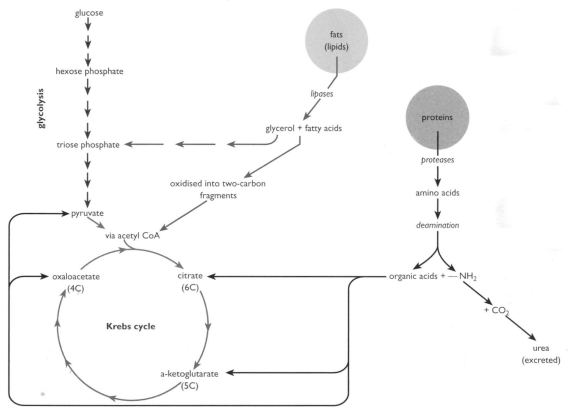

Respiration as a source of intermediates

The main role of respiration is to provide a pool of ATP, which is used to drive the endergonic reactions of synthesis. But the compounds of the glycolysis pathway and the Krebs cycle (respiratory intermediates) may also serve as the starting points of synthesis of other metabolites needed in the cells and tissues of the organism. For example:

- hexose phosphates are built into polysaccharides like **starch** and **cellulose** and into **sucrose**
- three-carbon sugar phosphates (triose phosphate) may be metabolised into **glycerol**
- acetyl coenzyme A may be converted to **fatty acids**
- the five-carbon acid of the Krebs cycle (α-ketoglutarate) is converted to the amino acid **glutamate**
- pyruvate, together with organic acids of the Krebs cycle, are converted to **amino acids** by transamination (transfer of amino groups from other amino acids, typically from glutamate).

The sites of respiration

The glycolytic enzymes occur in the cytosol of the cytoplasm, where glycolysis takes place. But the products of glycolysis (pyruvate and the reduced NAD) pass into the mitochondria by facilitated diffusion. The enzymes of the link reaction (pyruvate to acetyl coenzyme A) and of the Krebs cycle itself (Figure 9.8) occur in the matrix of the mitochondria. Meanwhile, the reduced NAD (and FAD) are oxidised by the hydrogen transport chain carriers, which are located on the inner membrane of the mitochondria, the surface area of which is greatly extended by the cristae. ATP is formed here, and then diffuses to all parts of the cell. Both ADP and ATP pass through the mitochondrial membranes by facilitated diffusion.

Figure 9.11 summarises the sites of respiration in cells.

Figure 9.11
The sites of respiration in cells.

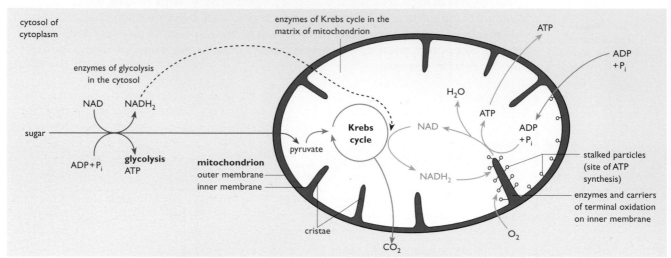

Anaerobic respiration/fermentation

In the absence of oxygen many organisms (and sometimes certain tissues in organisms that have been deprived of sufficient oxygen) will continue to respire by a process known as fermentation or **anaerobic respiration**, at least for a short time.

If deprived of oxygen, flowering plants may respire by **alcoholic fermentation** (as, for example, in the cells of roots in waterlogged soil):

glucose $\rightarrow$ ethanol + carbon dioxide + ENERGY
$C_6H_{12}O_6 \rightarrow 2CH_3CH_2OH + 2CO_2$ + ENERGY

Vertebrate muscle tissue can respire anaerobically too, but in this case lactic acid is formed instead of ethanol. **Lactic acid fermentation** occurs in muscle fibres, but only when the demand for energy for contractions is too great to be met fully by aerobic respiration. In lactic acid fermentation the sole waste product is lactic acid:

glucose $\rightarrow$ lactic acid + ENERGY
$C_6H_{12}O_6 \rightarrow 2CH_3CHOHCOOH$ + ENERGY

Obligatory anaerobes

Just a few organisms respire *only* in the absence of oxygen. One such is the tetanus bacillus *Clostridium tetani*, which causes 'lock-jaw' (Figure 9.12). The bacterium lives in oxygen-free environments where there are organic chemicals available as nutrients, such as deep, sealed wounds with much dead tissue (little blood supply), and among the faeces in the lower gut of many animals. Its spores are found in faeces, soil and dust. It produces a toxin that, when released inside wounds and carried around the body in the circulation, causes muscular spasm. Spasms may affect the whole body, but are likely to make jaw movements and breathing difficult. Tetanus is prevented by an initial vaccination, supported by a 'booster' injection every few years.

Figure 9.12
The lock-jaw bacterium and its effects.

Clostridium tetani, **TEM** (x 24000)

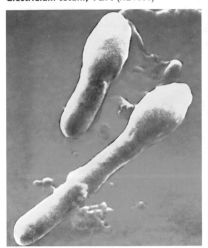

patient with tetanus

Many species of yeast (*Saccharomyces*) respire anaerobically, even in the presence of oxygen. Human communities have exploited the respiration of yeast for many thousands of years in the production of ethanol ('alcohol'). Ethanol is produced by fermenting sugar solutions, such as malt extract obtained from germinated barley and then fortified with additional sugar. Commercial beer production is carried out in deep, open tanks, as part of a largely automated industrial process (Figure 9.13).

Figure 9.13
An industrial plant for the production of ethanol by fermentation.

open fermentation tank

The pathways of fermentation

The respiratory pathways of alcoholic and lactic acid fermentation are shown in Figure 9.14. When oxygen is not available, glycolysis continues and pyruvate accumulates, at least initially. However, terminal oxidation and the Krebs cycle cannot take place because the aerobic oxidation of reduced NAD is now blocked. In a tissue in which reserves of oxidised NAD run out, glycolysis will also cease.

In fact, in both the alternative fermentation pathways, reduced NAD is oxidised in other reactions. In effect, oxygen is replaced as the hydrogen acceptor. The hydrogen acceptor in alcoholic fermentation is ethanal, and in lactic acid fermentation it is pyruvate. Glycolysis can therefore continue.

The total energy yield in terms of ATP generated in both alcoholic and lactic acid fermentation is limited to the net two molecules of ATP generated in glycolysis per molecule of glucose respired.

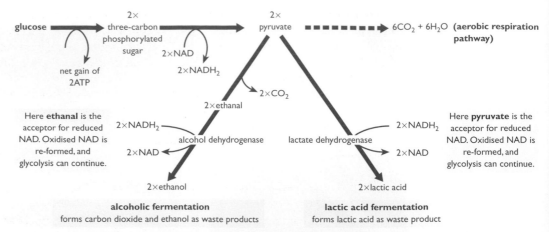

Figure 9.14
The respiratory pathways of anaerobic respiration.

Anaerobic respiration is less efficient than aerobic respiration

Anaerobic respiration is wasteful of respiratory substrate. The useful product is a tiny quantity of ATP only, when compared with the ATP yield from aerobic respiration of the same quantity of respiratory substrate. Also, the waste products (ethanol or lactic acid) contain much unused chemical energy. For example, ethanol is a very good fuel in its own right.

Lactic acid and ethanol may also be harmful to organisms if they accumulate. Organisms may, however, be able to tap the energy locked up in the waste products of fermentation by converting them back to sugar, which can then be respired. For example, in the vertebrate body, lactic acid is eventually converted back to glucose in the liver. Yeast, on the other hand, cannot metabolise ethanol, which makes it an industrially useful organism in ethanol production.

4 Name two products of anaerobic respiration in muscle.

Investigating respiration

The rate of respiration of an organism is an indication of its demand for energy. Respiration rate, the uptake of oxygen per unit time, is measured by means of a **respirometer**. A respirometer is a form of manometer, because it detects changes in the volume of a gas. So respiration rates are investigated by **manometry**.

A **simple respirometer** is shown in Figure 9.15. Once the screw clip has been closed, respiration by organisms enclosed in the chamber alters the composition of the gas there. Soda lime is also placed in the chamber, to remove carbon dioxide gas as it is released by the respiring organism. Consequently only oxygen uptake causes a change in the volume of gas in the apparatus. The bubble of coloured liquid in the attached capillary tube will move in response. The change in volume of the gas can be estimated by measuring the movement of the manometric fluid during the experiment.

Figure 9.15
A simple respirometer.

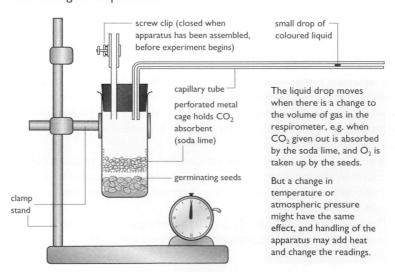

With a **differential respirometer** (Figure 9.16), the sources of error arising from the simple manometer are eliminated by having a control chamber connected by a U-tube manometer to the respirometer chamber. External temperature or pressure changes act equally on both sides of the manometer and cancel out. In this apparatus, the volume of gas absorbed per unit time is given by readings on the syringe.

The differential respirometer is used with a water bath. By repeating readings at a range of different temperatures, the effect of temperature on respiration can be measured. Data such as Figure 9.17 can then be obtained with this equipment.

Why does temperature affect the rate of respiration? Remember that the enzymes of respiration are proteins. All proteins are denatured by higher temperatures (page 84), although the temperature at which they are denatured varies widely. For example, some bacteria live successfully in hot springs where the temperature may approach that of boiling water.

From the graph in Figure 9.17 we can work out the temperature at which significant denaturing of respiratory enzymes in the organisms used in this experiment takes place. Below this, temperature rises cause respiration rate to speed up.

Figure 9.16
A differential respirometer.

A simple apparatus for measuring respiration rate accurately:

• the apparatus is set up as shown, and allowed to stand in the water bath until the whole apparatus is at the same temperature
• clips A and B are closed
• the respiring organisms give off CO_2 and absorb O_2
• the CO_2 is absorbed by the soda lime, so only the volume changes due to O_2 uptake cause the manometer fluid to move to the right
• after a fixed time the syringe is adjusted to level the fluid in the two arms of the manometer, and the volume of O_2 absorbed is read off on the syringe
• any change in pressure or temperature during the experiment affects the respirometer tube and the thermo-barometer tube equally.

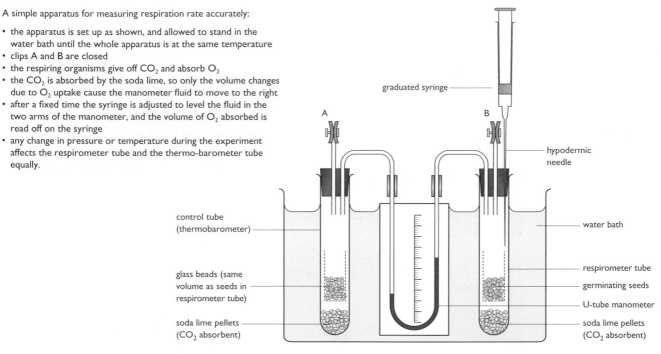

graduated syringe

A   B

hypodermic needle

control tube (thermobarometer)

water bath

glass beads (same volume as seeds in respirometer tube)

respirometer tube

germinating seeds

U-tube manometer

soda lime pellets (CO_2 absorbent)

soda lime pellets (CO_2 absorbent)

Figure 9.17
The effect of temperature on respiration rate.

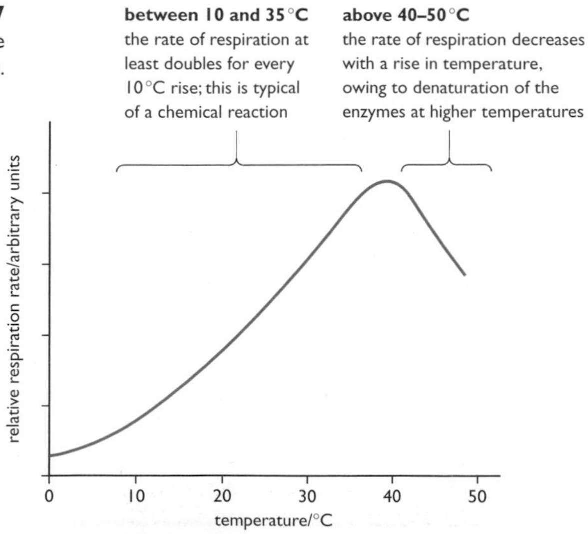

between 10 and 35°C
the rate of respiration at least doubles for every 10°C rise; this is typical of a chemical reaction

above 40–50°C
the rate of respiration decreases with a rise in temperature, owing to denaturation of the enzymes at higher temperatures

relative respiration rate/arbitrary units

0   10   20   30   40   50
temperature/°C

Respiratory quotient

The **respiratory quotient** (RQ) is the ratio of the amount of carbon dioxide produced to the amount of oxygen taken in by an organism in a given time, that is:

$$RQ = \frac{CO_2 \text{ produced}}{O_2 \text{ taken in}}$$

Knowing the RQ can be useful because it indicates which substrates are being respired. For example, when hexose sugars are respired aerobically the reaction is:

$$C_6H_{12}O_6 + 6O_2 \rightarrow 6CO_2 + 6H_2O$$

So the RQ is:

$$\frac{6CO_2}{6O_2} = 1.0$$

On the other hand, when fatty acids are respired aerobically, the reaction is:

$$C_{18}H_{36}O_2 + 26O_2 \rightarrow 18CO_2 + 18H_2O$$

and the RQ is:

$$\frac{18CO_2}{26O_2} = 0.7$$

The RQ due to fat respiration (RQ = 0.7) is significantly lower than that due to carbohydrate respiration (RQ = 1.0). This is because fats have a greater proportion of hydrogen relative to oxygen (they are a more highly reduced form of respiratory substrate than are sugars). More oxygen is required for the respiration of fats.

Despite this clear difference in values from different respiratory substrates, however, RQ studies are of only limited usefulness. An organism such as a germinating seed does not usually respire only a single respiratory substance. Many organisms are found to have an RQ of 0.8–0.9, perhaps because both hexose sugars and fatty acids are being respired, in varying proportions.

5 Distinguish between the following pairs:

- respiration and gaseous exchange
- anabolism and catabolism
- aerobic and anaerobic respiration
- glycolysis and the Krebs cycle
- endergonic and exergonic reactions
- oxidation and reduction
- substrate and intermediate
- ATP and NAD
- dehydrogenation and decarboxylation
- lactic acid fermentation and alcoholic fermentation.

● **Skills task**

The respiratory quotient (RQ) of two species of germinating seeds was measured at 2 day intervals after germination:

	Day 2	4	6	8	10
seedling A	0.65	0.35	0.48	0.68	0.70
seedling B	0.70	0.91	0.98	1.0	1.0

Plot a graph to compare the changes in RQ of the two species during early germination. Comment as fully as you can on the possible substrates being respired.

SUMMARY
- **Respiration** is a cellular process in which **energy is transferred** from nutrients, such as glucose, to the cellular machinery. Energy is required to do **useful work**, such as the transport of metabolites across membranes and the driving of anabolic reactions, and to allow movements in organisms.
- In **aerobic respiration**, glucose is completely oxidised to carbon dioxide and water, with the release of a large amount of energy. In **anaerobic respiration**, glucose is partially oxidised with the release of much less energy.
- **ATP** is the **universal energy currency molecule** by which energy is transferred to do useful work. ATP is a soluble molecule, formed in the mitochondria but able to move into the cytosol by facilitated diffusion. It diffuses freely about cells.

continued

The stages of aerobic respiration are:

- **glycolysis**, in which glucose is converted to pyruvate
- the **Krebs cycle**, in which pyruvate is metabolised, carbon dioxide is given off and oxidised NAD (or FAD) is reduced
- **terminal oxidation** and **oxidative phosphorylation**, in which reduced NAD (and FAD) are oxidised and water is formed, together with most of the ATP produced in respiration.

Glycolysis occurs in the cytoplasm, but the Krebs cycle is located in the matrix of mitochondria and terminal oxidation occurs on the cristae.
- In addition to hexose sugars, fats and proteins may be used as **respiratory substrates**.
- Respiratory metabolism is also a source of **intermediates**, from which various macromolecules and other substances required for the structure and function of the organism may be synthesised.
- In anaerobic respiration, the products are either **lactate** (in lactic acid fermentation, typically found in vertebrate muscle) or **ethanol** and **carbon dioxide** (in alcoholic fermentation, found in yeast and in plants under anaerobic conditions).
- The **rate of respiration** can be measured manometrically, in a respirometer. The **respiratory quotient** is the ratio of the amount of carbon dioxide evolved to the amount of oxygen absorbed, in a given time. RQ is an indicator of the respiratory substrate.

● Examination questions

1 The diagram below shows an outline of anaerobic respiration in muscle.

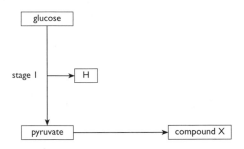

a i State what happens to the hydrogen, removed during stage 1. (2)
ii Identify compound **X**. (1)
b Explain why it is necessary to convert pyruvate to compound **X**. (2)

London, AS/A level, Module B/HB1, Jan 1998

2 The diagram shows some of the processes that occur within a mitochondrion and some of the substances that enter and leave it.

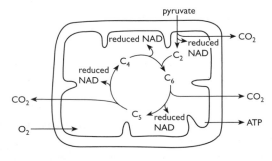

a Name the process that:
i produces pyruvate in the cytoplasm
ii produces reduced NAD and carbon dioxide in the matrix of the mitochondrion. (2)
b Describe how ATP is produced from reduced NAD within the mitochondrion. (3)

NEAB, A level, Paper 1/Sections A & B, June 1997

3 The diagram below shows some of the stages in anaerobic respiration in a muscle.

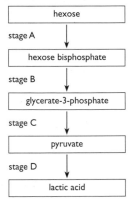

a i Name the process shown by stages A to C. (1)
ii State where in a cell this process occurs. (1)
b i Give **two** uses of ATP in cells. (2)
ii At which of the stages shown in the diagram is ATP used? (1)
c NADH + H$^+$ is a reduced coenzyme which is involved in anaerobic respiration. At which of the stages shown is NADH + H$^+$ oxidised? (1)

London, AS/A level, Module B/HB1, Jan 1997

4 A student investigated the effect of temperature on the rate of respiration of maggots. This was measured by calculating the rate of oxygen uptake, using a respirometer. The apparatus was set up as shown in the diagram below.

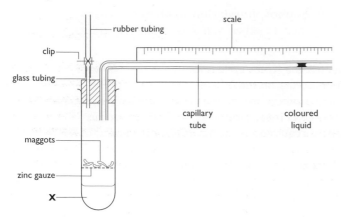

a **i** Name a suitable chemical to be used at **X**. (1)
   ii Explain the purpose of chemical **X**. (1)

The apparatus was placed in a water bath at 25 °C with the clip open. After 10 minutes the clip was closed and the position of the liquid in the capillary tube was recorded at 5 minute intervals. The results obtained are shown in the diagram below.

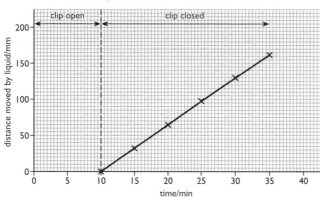

b Explain
   i why the apparatus was left for 10 minutes before closing the clip (2)
   ii why the liquid moved after the clip was closed. (1)

The capillary tube had a cross-sectional area of 2.5 mm².
c Calculate the rate of oxygen uptake, in mm³ per minute, between 20 and 30 minutes. Show your working. (2)
d Explain how the results would be expected to differ if the investigation was carried out at 15 °C. (2)

Another student carried out the same investigation under exactly the same conditions, except that a different mass of maggots was used.
e Explain what the students needed to do in order to be able to compare their results. (1)

The student carried out the investigation with some green leaves to compare their rate of respiration with that of the maggots.
f State **two** precautions that the student should have taken in order to make a valid comparison. (2)

UCLES, AS/A level, 4802, June 1998

5 The diagram below shows some of the reactions in a cell which occur during aerobic respiration.

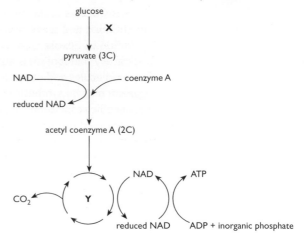

a **i** Identify pathways **X** and **Y**. (2)
   ii State precisely where pathway **X** occurs. (1)
b Explain why one of the enzymes involved in the conversion of pyruvate to acetyl coenzyme A is called pyruvate dehydrogenase. (2)
c State what is meant by the term *decarboxylation*. (1)

Bacteria are found naturally in raw milk. As they multiply, their metabolic activities and waste products can cause the milk to spoil. The amount of respiration which is taking place can provide the basis for a test to check on the freshness of milk.

If oxygen is excluded from a stoppered tube containing raw milk and methylene blue, hydrogen ions can be transferred to methylene blue, which acts as a hydrogen acceptor. The methylene blue is reduced, restoring the white colour to the mixture. If the stopper is then removed, and the tube is shaken vigorously, the blue colour reappears.

d Explain why the blue colour reappears when the tube is shaken after the stopper is removed. (2)

The milk which we drink has normally been pasteurised. This involves heating the milk to a high temperature for a short period of time.

e Explain what would happen if the same test for freshness described above was carried out using pasteurised milk. (2)
f Suggest **two** reasons why milk should be kept in a refrigerator. (2)

UCLES, AS/A level, 4802, June 1997

10 Gaseous exchange

STARTING POINTS
● Organisms take in gases from the environment, and give out gases to the environment. The process is known as **gaseous exchange**.
● Gaseous exchange in cells occurs by **diffusion**.
● When cells are **respiring aerobically**, oxygen is taken in and carbon dioxide is given out.
● When green plant cells are **photosynthesising**, carbon dioxide is taken in and oxygen is given out.
● Many organisms have a specialised **respiratory surface** through which gaseous exchange occurs.

● Gaseous exchange in cells occurs by diffusion

Many animal and plant cells respire aerobically. For this cells must take in oxygen from their environment and give out carbon dioxide, by a process called **gaseous exchange** (Figure 10.1). Respiration is a continuous process in all living cells, producing energy. In green plant cells in the light, photosynthesis also occurs. For this, carbon dioxide is taken in from their environment and oxygen is given out, which is the reverse of respiration. In a green plant cell in the light, photosynthesis is so fast that gaseous exchange due to photosynthesis completely masks that due to aerobic respiration.

The exchange of gases between cells and the environment takes place by **diffusion**. For example, in cells respiring aerobically there is a higher concentration of oxygen outside the cells than inside, and so there is a net inward diffusion of oxygen. By contrast, in a cell that is photosynthesising, there is a higher concentration of oxygen inside than outside, and there is a net outward diffusion of oxygen. Wherever such differences in concentrations occur, there is net diffusion from the higher to the lower concentration.

Figure 10.1
Gaseous exchange in cells.

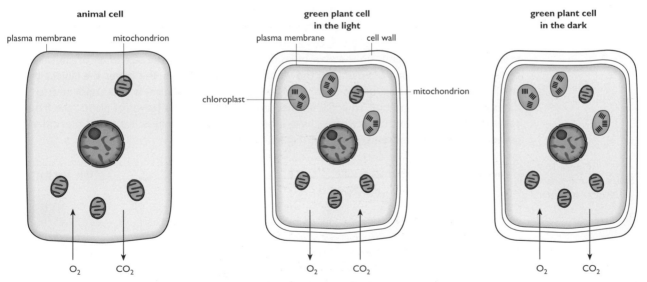

What speeds up diffusion?

The rate of diffusion depends on several factors. For example, an increase in temperature speeds up the random movements of molecules and so speeds up diffusion. In living things, however, temperature is normally quite low and fairly constant. In practice, temperature is not an important factor in deciding the diffusion rate here. Within biological systems the following three factors effectively determine the rate of diffusion in practice.

- The **surface area** of the organism available for gaseous exchange, which is called the **respiratory surface**. The greater this surface area, the greater is the rate of diffusion. In a single cell, the respiratory surface is the whole plasma membrane.
- The **difference in concentration**: a rapidly respiring organism will have a very much lower concentration of oxygen in the cells and a higher than normal concentration of carbon dioxide. Some cells and tissues have quite low rates of respiration, others have high rates (Table 10.1). The greater the gradient in concentration across the respiratory surface, the greater is the rate of diffusion.
- The **length of the diffusion path**: the shorter the diffusion path, the greater is the rate of diffusion. So the respiratory surface must be as thin as possible.

The relationship of these factors is summarised by **Fick's Law of diffusion**. This states that:

$$\text{rate of diffusion} \propto \frac{\text{surface area} \times \text{difference in concentration}}{\text{length of diffusion pathway}}$$

This law can be applied to see how the rate of diffusion in living systems will vary under particular conditions.

Table 10.1
The rate of respiration varies in different cells.

Relatively low respiration rate	Relatively high respiration rate
starch storage cells in the cortex of the plant stem	growing cells at root tip, also active in reducing NO_3^- ions to NH_4^+ ions for use in amino acid synthesis
long-term lipid storage cells in mammals, e.g. in adipose tissue under skin	voluntary muscle cells, whilst they are contracting

The respiratory surface

Size and shape of organisms

1 List three characteristics of an efficient respiratory surface. Give a reason why each influences diffusion.

The size and shape of an organism influence its gaseous exchange. The amount of gas an organism needs to exchange is largely proportional to its *volume* (the bulk of respiring cells). But the amount of exchange that can occur is proportional to the *surface area* over which diffusion takes place. For example, the surface area of a single-celled organism is very large in relation to the amount of cytoplasm it contains. Here the surface of the cell is sufficient for efficient gaseous exchange, because the sites of respiration in the cytoplasm are never very far from its surface.

The rather geometrically shaped 'organisms' in Figure 10.2 illustrate how the surface area/volume ratio depends on the **size** of an organism. Increasing the size of an organism lowers the surface area per unit of volume of the whole structure. That is, the larger the object the smaller is its surface area/volume ratio. But the **shape** of an organism is also important to diffusion of gases in and out. Thin, flat shapes, such as those of the leaves of plants, the fronds of seaweed and the bodies of flatworms, have a large surface area/volume ratio and therefore their gaseous exchange is extremely efficient (Figure 10.3).

Figure 10.2
Size, shape and surface area/volume ratio.

organism	'spheroid'		'cuboid'		'thin and flat'	
and type	small	large	small	large	small	large
dimensions/mm (diameter/mm)	(1)	(4)	1 × 1 × 1	4 × 4 × 4	2 × 1 × 0.5	16 × 8 × 0.5
volume/mm³	0.5	33.5	1	64	1	64
surface area/mm²	3	50	6	96	7	280
SA/V ratio	3/0.5 = 6	50/33.5 = 1.5	6/1 = 6	96/64 = 1.5	7/1 = 7	280/64 = 4.4

Amoeba, a large, single-celled animal (protozoan), living in pond water and feeding on the tiny protozoa around it. Food is taken into food vacuoles. Gases are exchanged over the whole body surface.

Size = about 400 μm

Ulva, the sea lettuce, an anchored or free-floating seaweed. It floats near the surface of water and photosynthesises in the light. Gases are exchanged over the whole body surface.

Size = about 5–15 cm long, about 30–35 μm thick

Dugesia tigrina, a free-living flatworm found in ponds under stones or leaves or gliding over the mud. It feeds on smaller animals and fish eggs. It is a very thin animal that exchanges gases over the whole body surface.

Size = about 20 mm

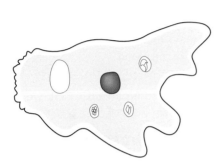

Figure 10.3
Organisms with gaseous exchange through their external surfaces.

Respiratory systems in animals

Many of the cells of larger animals are too far from the body surface to receive enough oxygen by diffusion alone. In addition, many such animals have developed an external surface that provides protection to the body: examples include watertight outer coverings, and tough or hardened skins. These outer surfaces are unsuitable for gaseous exchange, and the organism requires an alternative respiratory surface. Active organisms have an increased metabolic rate, too, and the demand for oxygen in their cells is higher than in sluggish and inactive organisms. So we find that for many reasons, larger, active animals have specialised organs for gaseous exchange (Figure 10.4).

Figure 10.4
Examples of specialised respiratory systems in animals.

specialised respiratory systems have:
- a large surface area in a small space
- a ventilation mechanism to maintain the supply of air or oxygenated water

and may have:
- an internal transport system to deliver oxygen to tissues
- a respiratory pigment to improve the efficiency of transport

gills:
- internal or external
- compact, but with a large surface area
- blood circulates between gills and body
- water forced over gills by muscle action

lungs:
- internal, with a large surface area
- blood circulates between lungs and body
- air drawn into and out of lungs by muscle action

tracheae:
- internal tubes that divide and reach the cells of the body
- air moves mostly by diffusion but may be pumped by simple 'bellows' mechanism

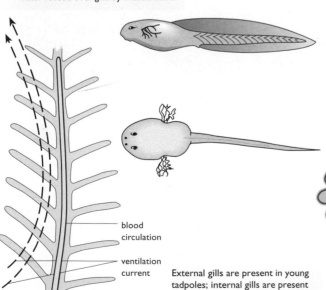

blood circulation

ventilation current

External gills are present in young tadpoles; internal gills are present in older tadpoles and in fish.

ventilation current

blood circulation

Lungs are typical of mammals and other vertebrates.

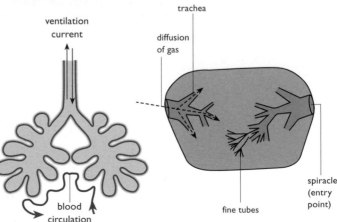

trachea

diffusion of gas

spiracle (entry point)

fine tubes

Tracheae are present in many insects.

Specialised, efficient respiratory surfaces in animals take various forms, such as gills, or lungs, or a tubular system (tracheae) that carries air to the most actively respiring organs (Figure 10.4). All these systems provide a large, thin surface area, suitable for gaseous exchange. In addition, conditions for diffusion are often improved by three refinements:

- a **ventilation mechanism** – a pumping mechanism that moves the respiratory medium (water or air) over the gills, or into and out of the lungs or tubes, so maintaining the concentration gradient for diffusion
- a **blood circulation system** – a means of speeding up the removal of dissolved oxygen from the respiratory surface as soon as it has diffused in, so maintaining the concentration gradient
- a **respiratory pigment** that increases the gas-carrying ability of the blood.

The second and third of these are considered in more detail in the next chapter.

Later in this chapter we will look at some specialised respiratory systems in detail. First, we need to think about the issues of gaseous exchange in air and in water.

Gaseous exchange in air, and the problem of water loss

Terrestrial (land-living) organisms obtain oxygen from the air, and air contains almost 21% oxygen gas. But diffusion within an organism occurs in solution, so the first step in oxygen uptake is the dissolving of oxygen gas in the film of water that covers the respiratory surface. As a consequence, the respiratory surface must be kept moist. ('Being moist' is not a requirement of diffusion in principle, but it is necessary for diffusion in solution.)

Because the respiratory surface is always moist, water vapour will evaporate as gaseous exchange occurs. We can see immediately that an efficient respiratory surface in a terrestrial organism carries with it the risk of being dried out by loss of water vapour (Figure 10.5). Most terrestrial animals need frequent access to water, and animal behaviour is often adapted to overcome the dangers resulting from water scarcity. This is illustrated by the responses of the earthworm and the garden snail to times of drought (Figure 10.6).

Figure 10.5
Water balance and water loss in gaseous exchange in humans.

Exhaled air is saturated with water vapour: an invisible component except in freezing weather or when breathed on to a very cold surface.

The water balance of the body: about 3 dm³ is taken in and lost daily.

About 10–15% of this total is lost from the lungs.

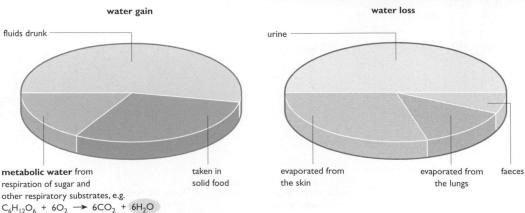

water gain

fluids drunk

water loss

urine

metabolic water from respiration of sugar and other respiratory substrates, e.g.
$C_6H_{12}O_6 + 6O_2 \rightarrow 6CO_2 + 6H_2O$

taken in solid food

evaporated from the skin

evaporated from the lungs

faeces

Figure 10.6
Gaseous exchange in the earthworm and the snail.

The **earthworm** moves and feeds in damp soils. It exchanges gases over its whole body surface, which is thin-skinned, moist and well supplied with blood capillaries.

The **garden snail** has a body partly protected by a shell, which also houses a lung chamber where gases are exchanged. In the daytime and in dry weather, the snail moves to a sheltered position and withdraws into its shell.

The earthworm's habitat is the soil: it does not normally expose itself above ground except in darkness, and in wet or humid conditions.

The snail feeds at night, moving slowly over damp soil.

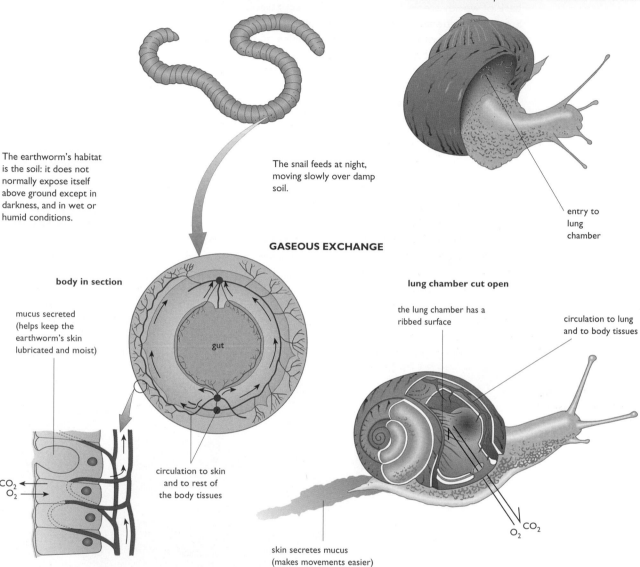

entry to lung chamber

GASEOUS EXCHANGE

body in section

mucus secreted (helps keep the earthworm's skin lubricated and moist)

gut

CO_2
O_2

circulation to skin and to rest of the body tissues

lung chamber cut open

the lung chamber has a ribbed surface

circulation to lung and to body tissues

O_2 CO_2

skin secretes mucus (makes movements easier)

In drought, the earthworm retreats to lower layers of the soil, curls up tightly and becomes inactive, with minimal respiration.

WHEN WATER BECOMES SCARCE

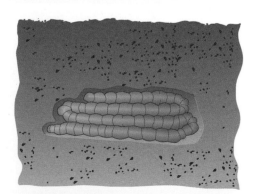

In drought, the snail seals itself into its shell with a layer of chalky mucus through which some gaseous exchange can occur, with a minimum of water loss.

The respiratory surface of plants

The outer surfaces of most terrestrial plants are protected against water loss – for example, by the presence of a waxy cuticle on the outer surface of leaves and non-woody stems, and by the bark of woody stems. These plants carry on gaseous exchange over the surface area of the cells around the air spaces within their leaves and elsewhere. Gases in all the air spaces of the leaves are exchanged with the environment by diffusion through tiny pores called stomata (Figure 8.4, page 172). Inevitably, water vapour diffuses out here too.

All plants are dependent on a supply of water being available to them where they grow. Very many plants show some degree of adaptation that will hinder or reduce water loss from their leaves. For example, leaves may trap a layer of moist air outside the stomata in many tiny hairs on the leaf surface. The bodies of plants that have adapted and evolved to survive in extremely dry conditions may be more drastically modified. Some leaves will roll up to enclose the surface with stomata when the leaf water content is low (Figure 10.7). These and other mechanisms reduce the water vapour concentration gradient between the leaf interior and the air outside, and so powerfully reduce diffusion of water vapour from the leaf.

Figure 10.7
The leaf of marram grass: protection against water loss.

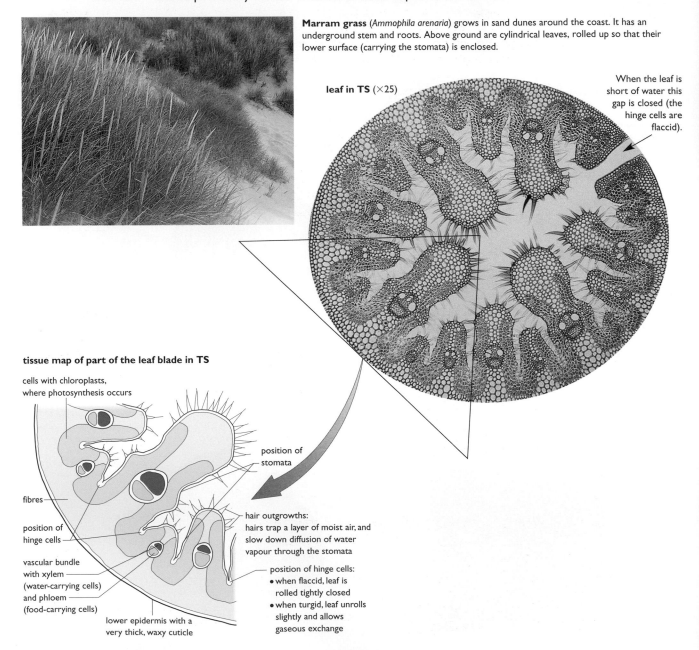

Marram grass (*Ammophila arenaria*) grows in sand dunes around the coast. It has an underground stem and roots. Above ground are cylindrical leaves, rolled up so that their lower surface (carrying the stomata) is enclosed.

leaf in TS (×25)

When the leaf is short of water this gap is closed (the hinge cells are flaccid).

tissue map of part of the leaf blade in TS

cells with chloroplasts, where photosynthesis occurs

fibres

position of hinge cells

vascular bundle with xylem (water-carrying cells) and phloem (food-carrying cells)

lower epidermis with a very thick, waxy cuticle

position of stomata

hair outgrowths:
hairs trap a layer of moist air, and slow down diffusion of water vapour through the stomata

position of hinge cells:
• when flaccid, leaf is rolled tightly closed
• when turgid, leaf unrolls slightly and allows gaseous exchange

Gaseous exchange in water: the issue of oxygen solubility

Oxygen gas is only slightly soluble in water, perhaps about 0.8% by volume – even less at higher temperatures. Obviously, much less oxygen is available to aquatic organisms per unit volume of medium than to those living on land. Large aquatic plants such as the seaweeds, with a plant body that is a thin, extensive frond, have a very large surface area/volume ratio; this is typical of aquatic plants.

Aquatic animals that are highly mobile and consequently have a high respiration rate, such as the trout (freshwater) or the herring (marine), maintain a continuous flow of water over their gills. They also have an especially efficient exchange mechanism between blood and water at the gill surface. The functioning of the gills of the bony fish is considered next.

Gaseous exchange in a bony fish

Figure 10.8
Bony fish: mouth, pharynx and gill region, and the ventilation mechanism.

Fish obtain oxygen from water by means of **internal gills**. The structure of the gills of a bony fish, such as a herring, is shown in Figures 10.8 and 10.9. You can see that the bony fish have four pairs of gills, supported by a bony arch. Each gill has two rows of **filaments** arranged in a V-shape. Filaments are extremely thin structures carrying rows of thin-walled **gill plates** on both surfaces. The gill filaments are flanked by a tough, muscular flap of skin, the **operculum**. The operculum protects the gills and is partly responsible for the continuous flow of water over them.

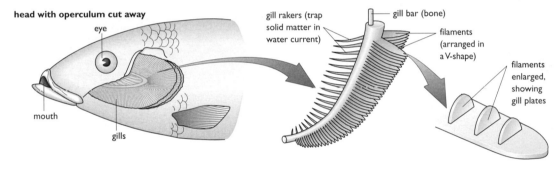

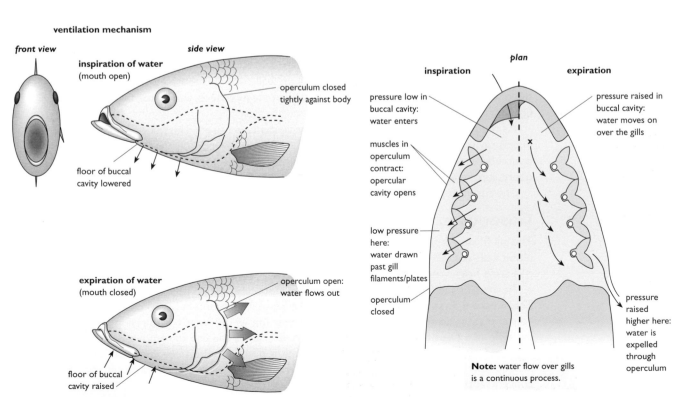

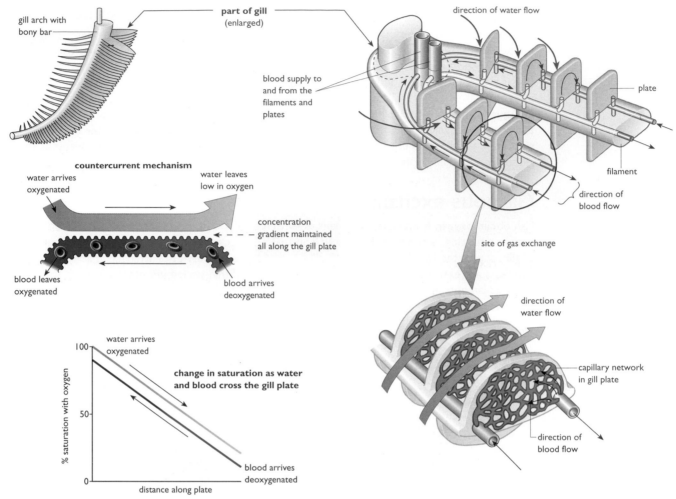

Figure 10.9
Gill structure and gaseous exchange by a counter-current mechanism.

Ventilation of the gills

As the fish's mouth opens, the floor of the buccal cavity is lowered. This lowers pressure in the buccal cavity relative to outside, and water flows in. At this stage the operculum is closed tight against the body, but muscles in the operculum wall contract, causing the operculum to bulge and the opercular cavity to enlarge. This lowers the pressure here, and water flows over the gill filaments, between the plates, into the opercular cavity.

As the mouth closes, the floor of the buccal cavity is raised. This increases the pressure in the buccal cavity and water continues to flow over the gills. Pressure is now even higher in the opercular cavity, and continues to rise above the external pressure. Consequently, the operculum opens and water passes out.

The result of the opening and closing of the mouth is a continuous flow of water over the gills.

Gaseous exchange in the gills

The gill filaments and plates are thin walled and richly supplied with blood capillaries. The red blood cells contain haemoglobin, which enables the blood to carry oxygen very efficiently. The gills are a bright red colour.

At the gills the stream of water and the flow of blood run in opposite directions (Figure 10.9). This means that as water flows over the gill surface it encounters blood of a lower oxygen concentration, so gaseous exchange occurs over the whole length of the gill plates. This is an example of a **countercurrent mechanism**. It enables the fish to remove 80–90% of the dissolved oxygen from water. (If blood and water flowed in the *same* direction, the blood could pick up only 50% of the available oxygen, and net diffusion into the blood would stop at this concentration.)

Gaseous exchange in insects

Although insects are quite small terrestrial animals, they generally have a high level of metabolic activity. We can expect this in organisms that have (very unusually) mastered two modes of locomotion! Insects have both wings and legs attached to the thorax. Most are fast and efficient at both running over surfaces and flying in the air.

An insect has a segmented body, surrounded and protected by a tough **external skeleton** (an **exoskeleton**) made of chitin. This material is impervious to oxygen. Air reaches the tissues of the insect's body via a branching system of fine tubes called **tracheae** (Figure 10.10).

Tracheae open to the exterior at valves called **spiracles**. Typically, an adult insect has two pairs of spiracles in the thorax, and eight pairs in the abdomen. Large 'trunk' tracheal tubes run along and across the body in most segments. Smaller tracheae branch from this system, and end as fine **tracheoles** – tiny blind tubes ending between the cells of the tissues.

Air moves through the tracheal system by diffusion. The endings of the tracheoles have thin, permeable walls, and oxygen diffuses readily through these walls into respiring cells. Movement of air in the tubes may be accelerated by compression and expansion movements, particularly of the thorax, caused by contractions of the flight muscles. Additionally, some insects have a system of 'bellows' or air sacs built into the tracheal system. These are worked by body movements due to locomotion, and speed the flow of gases through the tracheae.

Figure 10.10
The tracheal system for gaseous exchange in insects.

layout of the tracheal system (air sacs not shown)

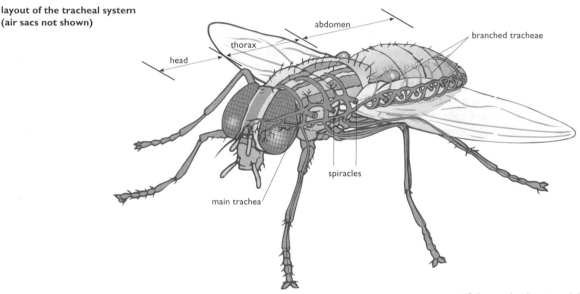

part of the tracheal system (drawing)

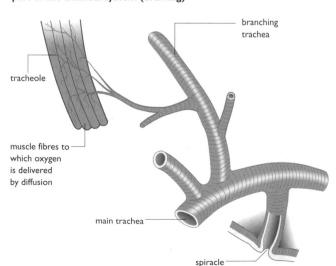

part of the tracheal system (photomicrograph)

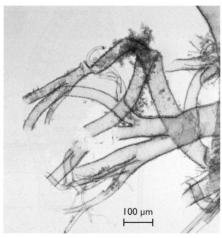

The main tracheae have rings of chitin thickening in their walls, preventing collapse.

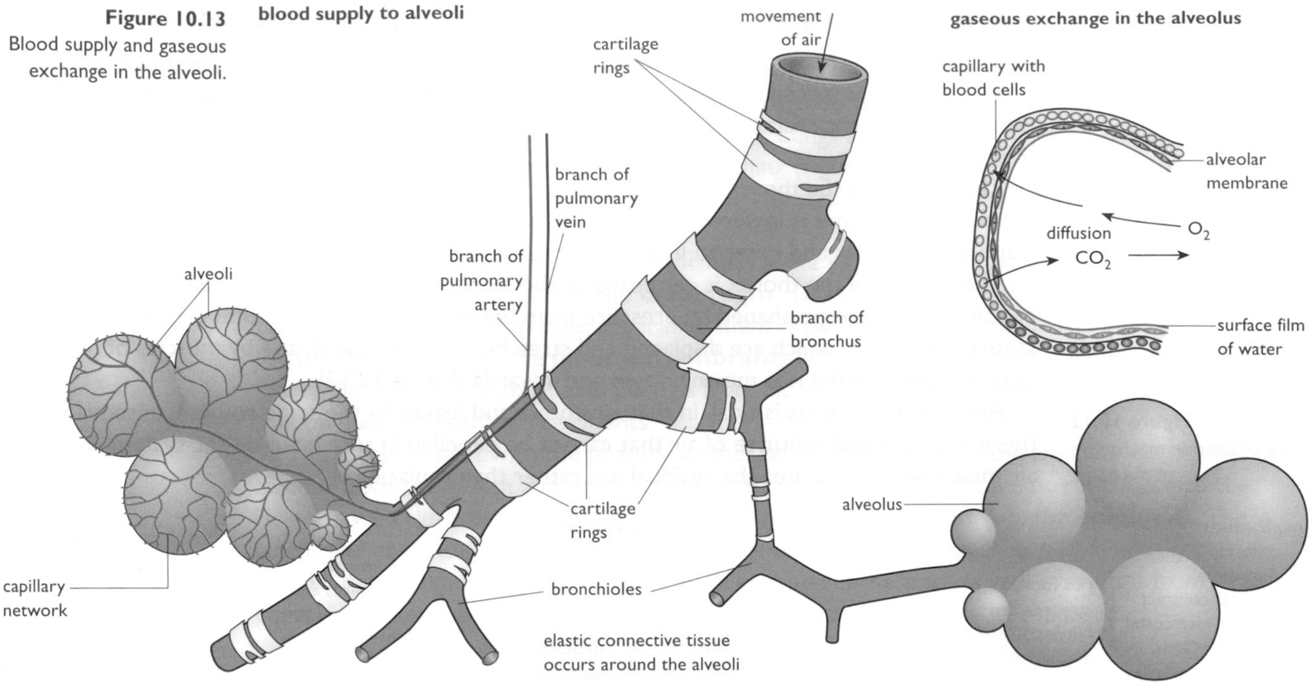

Figure 10.13
Blood supply and gaseous
exchange in the alveoli.

Figure 10.13
Blood supply and gaseous
exchange in the alveoli.

Alveolar structure and gaseous exchange

There are some 700 million alveoli present in our lungs, providing a total surface area of about
70 m². This is an area 30–40 times that of the body's external skin. The wall of an alveolus is one cell
thick, formed by pavement epithelium. Lying very close is a capillary, the wall of which is also
composed of a single, flattened (endothelium) cell. The combined thickness of walls separating air
and blood is typically 2–4 µm. The capillaries are extremely narrow, just wide enough for red cells to
squeeze through, so red cells are close to or touching the capillary walls (Figures 10.13 and 10.14).

Blood arriving in the lungs is low in oxygen (it has a lower *partial pressure* of oxygen than the
alveolar air, see Table 10.2) but high in carbon dioxide (it has a partial pressure of carbon dioxide
higher than the alveolar air). As blood flows past the alveoli, gaseous exchange occurs by
diffusion. Oxygen dissolves in the surface film of water and then diffuses across into the blood
plasma and the red cells, where it combines with haemoglobin to form oxyhaemoglobin. At the
same time, carbon dioxide diffuses from the blood into the alveolus (Figure 10.14).

Table 10.2
The composition of air
in the lungs.

	Inspired air	Alveolar air	Expired air
oxygen	20%	14%	16%
carbon dioxide	0.04%	5.5%	4.0%
nitrogen	79%	81%	79%
water vapour	variable	saturated	saturated

In a mixture of gases, each component gas exerts a pressure that is proportional to how
much of it is present. So the concentration of a gas may be quoted as its **partial pressure**,
expressed as kilopascals (kPa). The partial pressure of oxygen is written as pO_2 and that of
carbon dioxide as pCO_2.

At sea level, the atmospheric pressure is 101.3 kPa. Using the figures in Table 10.2, we may
say that the partial pressure of oxygen in the air at sea level is:

$$pO_2 = \frac{101.3}{100} \times 20 = 20.3 \text{ kPa}$$

but in the alveolus the partial pressure of oxygen is only:

$$pO_2 = \frac{101.3}{100} \times 14 = 14.2 \text{ kPa}$$

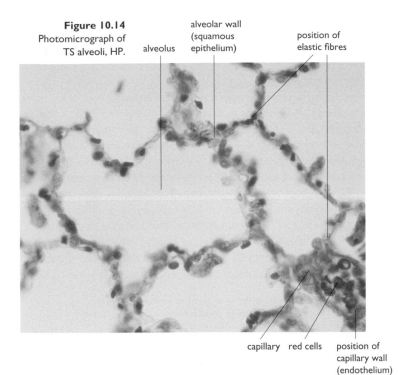

Figure 10.14
Photomicrograph of
TS alveoli, HP.

alveolus

alveolar wall
(squamous
epithelium)

position of
elastic fibres

capillary   red cells   position of
capillary wall
(endothelium)

Investigating human breathing

The volume of air breathed in and out during normal, relaxed, rhythmical breathing is referred to as the **tidal volume**, and is typically 400–500 cm³. However, our potential for extra large intakes (**maximum inspiratory capacity**) and extra large expirations of air (**expiratory reserve volume**) when required, together make up our **vital capacity**. Vital capacity is about 4.5 dm³. To this volume we must add the **residual volume**, to arrive at the total capacity of our lung system, typically about 6 dm³.

The changes in lung volume during breathing can be studied using apparatus called a **spirometer** (Figure 10.15). With the spirometer chamber filled with air, we can investigate the capacity of the lungs when breathing at different rates. With the spirometer chamber filled with oxygen, and with the carbon dioxide that is exhaled absorbed by soda lime, we can estimate oxygen consumption.

Figure 10.15
Investigating breathing with
a spirometer.

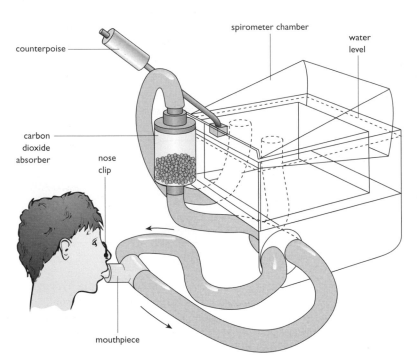

counterpoise

spirometer chamber

water
level

carbon
dioxide
absorber

nose
clip

mouthpiece

The movements of the lid of the airtight spirometer chamber are recorded by a position transducer, connecting box and microcomputer. The results (e.g. inspiratory capacity and tidal volume) are printed out using appropriate control software.

A recording spirometer is used to analyse the pattern of change in lung volume during breathing.

human lung capacity

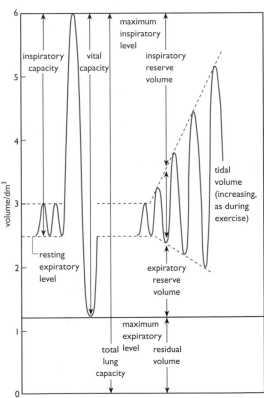

Control of human breathing

The breathing rate is controlled by the **respiratory centre**, which is situated in the medulla of the hindbrain (Figure 13.17, page 289). Here two adjacent and interacting groups of nerve cells (neurones), known as the **inspiratory centre** and the **expiratory centre** respectively, send rhythmic nerve impulses to the muscles of the ribs and diaphragm to bring about ventilation movements.

Breathing occurs automatically (involuntarily) by **reflex action**, but its rate is also continually adjusted. On average, we normally breathe about 15 times per minute. Since the tidal volume is typically 400 cm³, the volume of air taken into the lungs in 1 minute (**ventilation rate**) is about 6 dm³. We can however consciously override this breathing rate with messages sent from the cerebral hemispheres, as when we prepare to shout or sing, or play woodwind or brass instruments!

Breathing rates may be adjusted without conscious thought, too. This happens during increased physical activity, when our voluntary muscles use much more oxygen and more carbon dioxide is produced and transported in the blood. The main stimulus that controls breathing is the **concentration of carbon dioxide in the blood**. To a lesser extent, lowered oxygen concentration is also a factor. Blood carbon dioxide levels are detected by the chemoreceptors present in the medulla of the hindbrain and also in the carotid arteries and aorta (Figure 10.16).

Figure 10.16
The control of ventilation rate.

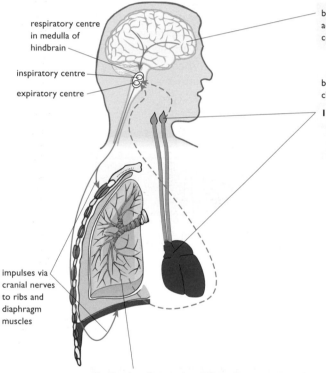

respiratory centre in medulla of hindbrain

inspiratory centre

expiratory centre

impulses via cranial nerves to ribs and diaphragm muscles

breathing takes place automatically by involuntary reflex action, which can be overridden by impulses from the cerebral hemispheres, e.g. when talking or singing

breathing rate is continually adjusted to meet the body's changing needs, e.g. different levels of physical activity:

1 when breathing too slowly or when very physically active, **chemoreceptors** in the medulla, carotid artery and aorta detect rising CO_2 concentration: impulses trigger faster/deeper breathing

2 when breathing too heavily, **stretch receptors** in the lungs detect the stretching: impulses suppress inspiration

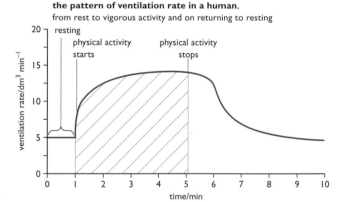

the pattern of ventilation rate in a human, from rest to vigorous activity and on returning to resting

resting

physical activity starts

physical activity stops

When carbon dioxide levels increase, as they do during strenuous physical activity, the hydrogen ion detectors (carbon dioxide forms acidic solutions) and the carbon dioxide detectors send impulses to the inspiratory centre. This centre sends additional impulses to the intercostal muscles and diaphragm, increasing their contraction rates.

In the cycle of breathing movements, each inflation of the lungs stimulates the stretch receptors in the bronchioles and alveoli, and these send impulses to the expiratory centre. These temporarily inhibit the inspiratory centre and inspiratory movements stop. The lungs then relax and, because of the elasticity of lung tissue, expiration follows. At this point the stretch receptors are no longer stimulated, so (temporarily) neither is the expiratory centre. Inspiration starts again, and the cycle of events is repeated. This reflex also protects the lungs from excessive stretching during panting or very deep breathing.

After strenuous exercise stops the concentration of carbon dioxide in the blood falls (and the concentration of oxygen rises). These changes are detected and the ventilation rate responds accordingly.

3 What is the difference between tidal volume and vital capacity of the lungs?

4 If the concentration of carbon dioxide were to build up in the blood of a mammal, why would this be harmful?

Protection of the lungs

The trachea and bronchi are lined by ciliated epithelium with **goblet cells** that secrete mucus. The mucus moistens the lining, raising the water content of incoming air to saturation point. It also traps most of the dust particles present in the air we breathe. These particles might otherwise irritate and damage the delicate alveoli walls. The cilia beat the stream of mucus with trapped particles out of the lungs and up the trachea to the pharynx. In the alveoli themselves, dust particles that do arrive are mopped up by the **dust cells** (macrophages) present (Figure 10.17).

Figure 10.17
Protection of the lungs.

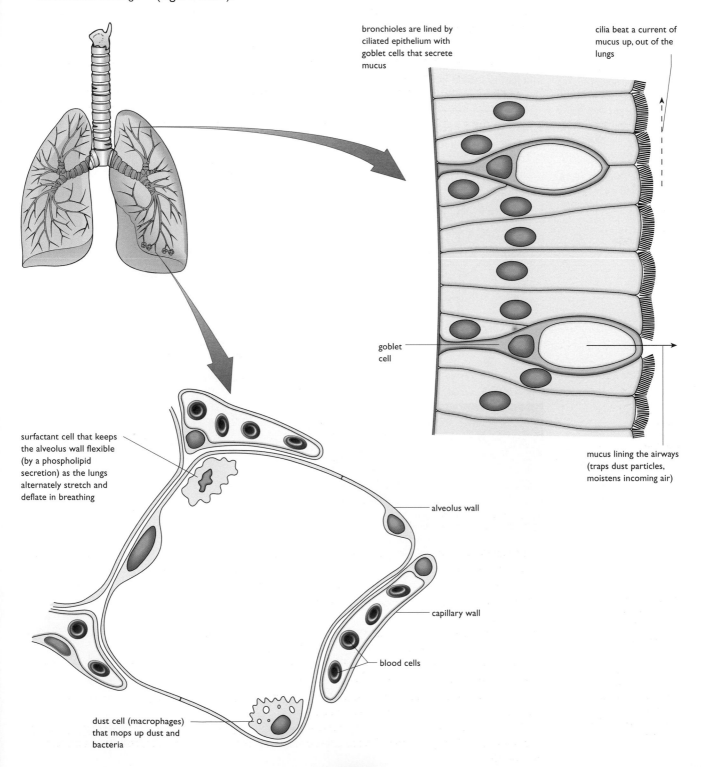

bronchioles are lined by ciliated epithelium with goblet cells that secrete mucus

cilia beat a current of mucus up, out of the lungs

goblet cell

mucus lining the airways (traps dust particles, moistens incoming air)

surfactant cell that keeps the alveolus wall flexible (by a phospholipid secretion) as the lungs alternately stretch and deflate in breathing

alveolus wall

capillary wall

blood cells

dust cell (macrophages) that mops up dust and bacteria

Gaseous exchange in plants

5 Distinguish between the following pairs:

- inspiration and expiration
- gill rakers and gill filaments
- operculum and pharynx
- epiglottis and trachea
- surfactant cells and dust cells
- chemoreceptors and stretch receptors
- bronchiole and alveolus
- thorax and abdomen
- xylem and phloem
- cuticle and epidermis.

Plants also respire aerobically, their cells taking in oxygen and producing carbon dioxide. The volume of oxygen produced in the leaf cells in full daylight more than meets the requirements for respiration by all cells of the plant, and oxygen is given out by the leaves. In the dark, no photosynthesis occurs and all plant cells take in oxygen and give out carbon dioxide.

Gaseous exchange in plants occurs by diffusion. Plants have evolved shapes and structures that facilitate this. Most gas enters and leaves plants via stomata in the epidermis of leaves and of herbaceous (non-woody) stems. In the trunks of woody plants (trees and shrubs), gaseous exchange also occurs through small, powdery patches in the bark, called **lenticels** (Figure 10.18).

Air spaces abound in plants; most living cells have contact with air in this way. The air spaces of leaves are continuous and connect with those of stems and roots. Oxygen diffuses into the air spaces through stomata (and lenticels) and carbon dioxide diffuses out. The pathway of diffusion in a leaf is shown in Figure 8.4, page 172. Oxygen also enters the root tissue by diffusion from the soil.

We have already noted that terrestrial organisms lose water by evaporation from any surface where gaseous exchange occurs. In plants, water vapour diffuses out through stomata and lenticels. We will look into water loss from leaves, by diffusion through stomata, in Chapter 11.

Figure 10.18
Gaseous exchange in a woody plant.

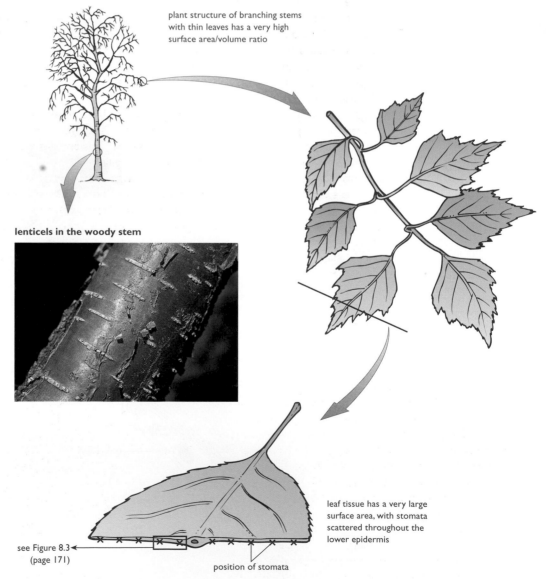

plant structure of branching stems with thin leaves has a very high surface area/volume ratio

lenticels in the woody stem

leaf tissue has a very large surface area, with stomata scattered throughout the lower epidermis

see Figure 8.3 (page 171)

position of stomata

222

⬤ **Skills task** Assume that the composition of the air (approximately 20% oxygen, 80% nitrogen) is approximately the same at sea level (atmospheric pressure = 101.3 kPa), at 5000 m above sea level (atmospheric pressure = 54.0 kPa) and at 10 000 m (atmospheric pressure = 26.4 kPa). What is the partial pressure of oxygen at these altitudes? Table 10.2 (page 218) may help your calculations.

SUMMARY
⬤ **Gaseous exchange** is the exchange of gases between an organism and its environment. Gaseous exchange is needed to supply the needs of aerobic respiration and photosynthesis.
⬤ The factors that determine the **rate of gaseous exchange** in organisms are:

• the size of the surface area for gaseous exchange
• the concentration difference across the respiratory surface
• the thickness of the respiratory surface.

⬤ Small organisms have a very high **surface area/volume ratio**, and tend to carry out gaseous exchange over the whole surface area. The surface area/volume ratio falls as the size increases, but is larger in flatter/thinner structures.
⬤ In living things **gases diffuse in solution**, and the respiratory surface is moist so that the gas dissolves easily as the first step. Water vapour is consequently lost from respiratory surfaces in terrestrial organisms.
⬤ Many animals have compact bodies, are mobile and have a protected external surface to the body. They often have specialised **respiratory organs** such as lungs or gills or a system of tubes (tracheae) carrying air to body cells. Gaseous exchange may be further facilitated by a **ventilation mechanism** to move air or oxygenated water over the respiratory surface, a **blood circulation system** and a **respiratory pigment** for the efficient transport of oxygen.
⬤ Organisms carrying out gaseous exchange in water have access to very little dissolved oxygen (0.8% by volume), compared with about 21% oxygen in air. Bony fish have a countercurrent mechanism in their extensive **gills**. This ensures that 80–90% of dissolved oxygen in water is absorbed as it flows over the gills.
⬤ In mammals gaseous exchange occurs in the **lungs**, which are extremely efficient organs of gaseous exchange. They are housed in the airtight thorax, which moves rhythmically to ventilate the lungs. The circulation system transports oxygen all over the body, in combination with the respiratory pigment haemoglobin, present in red cells.
⬤ Plants carry out gaseous exchange between their living cells and the air spaces between them, which are continuous throughout the plant. Gases enter and leave stems and leaves through the pores in **stomata**, through the **lenticels** in woody stems, and through the cell walls of young root tips.

⬤ # Examination questions

1 **a** Tench are freshwater fish found in water with a low oxygen content. The structure of their gills and the direction of water flow over the gills makes them particularly efficient at removing oxygen from the water.
    Describe and explain how efficient uptake of oxygen by gills is achieved in a fish such as tench. (6)

b Describe how ventilation is controlled in mammals. (3)

c The diagram shows the arrangement of the respiratory surface in the lungs of birds.
  i Give **one** similarity and **one** difference between the *gas exchange surface* of a bird and that of a mammal. (2)
  ii During inhalation in birds, some air passes through the bronchial system into the air sacs. During exhalation the air may pass out by the same route. Suggest how this increases the efficiency of oxygen uptake. (1)

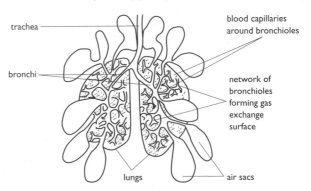

AQA(NEAB), AS/A level, Module BY03, June 1999

2 The drawing shows structures in the breathing system of an insect.

   a Name the structures labelled **A** and **B**. (2)

   b Describe the mechanism by which the respiratory surfaces of an insect are ventilated. (2)

   c Structure **X** has bands of thickening. Suggest the functions of these. (1)

   d Give **two** features which the respiratory surfaces of an insect and a mammal have in common. (2)

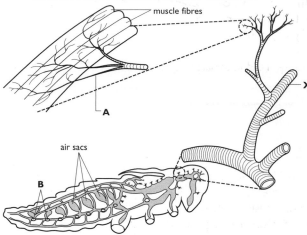

NEAB, AS/A level, Module BY03, Mar 1998

3 There are many different species of annelid worm. Some are very small, only a few millimetres in length. Others, such as lugworms, are much larger. The drawing shows a lugworm and part of one of its gills.

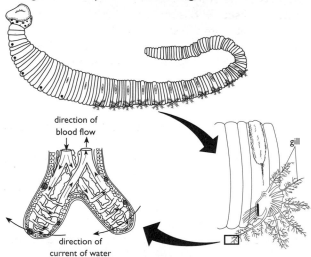

   a Smaller species of annelid do not have gills. Explain why these small worms do not need gills to obtain sufficient oxygen. (2)

   b In many of the lugworm gills, the blood flows in the opposite direction to the current of water passing over them. Explain the advantage of this arrangement. (2)

   c Explain **two** ways, other than that described in part **b**, in which the structure of a lugworm gill is adapted for efficient gas exchange. (2)

   d Explain why water is always lost from the gas exchange surfaces of terrestrial organisms. (2)

The table shows the ratio of the amount of water lost to the amount of oxygen gained for two terrestrial animals, an annelid worm and an insect.

Organism	Ratio:	mass of water lost/mg g^{-1} min^{-1} / volume of oxygen taken up/cm^3 g^{-1} min^{-1}
annelid worm		2.61
insect		0.11

   e Both the annelid and the insect take up oxygen at a rate of 2.5 cm^3 g^{-1} min^{-1}. Calculate the rate at which water would be lost in meeting these requirements in:
   i the annelid;
   ii the insect. (2)

   f Give **two** explanations as to why the rate of water loss during gas exchange is very low in most insects. (4)

   g Annelids like the lugworm have blood which contains haemoglobin. The graph shows the oxygen dissociation curves for lugworm haemoglobin and for human haemoglobin.

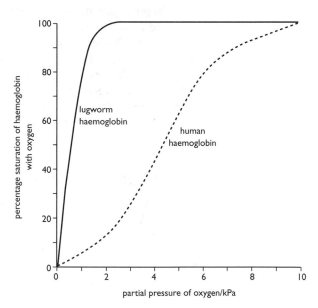

   i During exercise, the rate of respiration of muscle cells increases. Explain what causes human haemoglobin to unload more oxygen to these cells. (4)

   ii The lugworm lives in a burrow in the sand on the seashore. When the tide is out, water bringing a fresh supply of oxygen no longer flows through the burrow. Suggest how the lugworm's haemoglobin allows it to survive in these conditions. (2)

AQA(AEB), A level, Module 3, June 1999

Internal transport

STARTING POINTS ● Cells require a supply of **nutrients** and **water**, and most require **oxygen**. Their **waste products** must be disposed of.
● Across a large, multicellular organism, movement of substances by diffusion alone is not sufficient, and an **internal transport system** is required.
● In **mammals**, internal transport is by a system of vessels through which blood is pumped and circulated to all parts of the body.
● In **plants**, water and nutrients are transported in separate systems of vessels, and there is no pump or circulation.

The need for transport

Living cells require supplies of water and nutrients such as glucose and amino acids, and most need oxygen. The waste products of cellular metabolism have to be removed, too. In very small organisms, internal distances (the lengths of diffusion pathways) are small. So most nutrients and other molecules can move efficiently by **diffusion**, although some substances have to cross membranes by **active transport**.

In larger organisms these mechanisms alone are insufficient. An internal transport system is required to service the needs of the cells. These internal transport systems are examples of **mass flow**. The more active an organism is, the more nutrients are likely to be required by cells, and so the greater is the need for an efficient system for internal transport. Larger animals have a **blood circulatory system** that links the parts of the body and makes resources available where they are required. In flowering plants the **vascular tissues** distribute the products of photosynthesis from the leaves to the sites of metabolism and storage, and water and ions from the roots to the aerial system (the stem and leaves). The internal transport systems of mammals and flowering plants are fundamentally different, so we will consider them in detail, separately.

Transport in mammals

Mammals have a **closed circulation** in which **blood** is pumped by a powerful, muscular **heart** and circulated in a continuous system of tubes, the **arteries**, **veins** and **capillaries**, under pressure. The heart has four chambers, and is divided into right and left sides. Blood flows from the right side of the heart to the lungs, then back to the left side of the heart. From here it is pumped around the rest of the body and back to the right side of the heart. As the blood passes twice through the heart in every single circulation of the body, this is called a **double circulation**. The double circulatory system of mammals is shown in Figure 11.1, alongside alternative systems. Looking at these other systems can help us understand the features of the mammalian circulation.

Fish also have a closed circulation, but here blood flows only once through the heart in every circulation of the body. This condition is known as a **single circulation**. This means that the blood pressure lost in passing through the gills is not re-established before the oxygenated blood is distributed to the respiring tissues.

Insects have an **open circulation**. Blood is pumped out by a long, tubular heart into spaces in the body cavity called **sinuses**, where it bathes the body organs directly, but under very low pressure. From the body organs the blood re-enters the heart through openings controlled by valves and is recirculated. At the same time, in the adult insect air is delivered to the respiring tissues via a system of tubes called tracheae (see Figure 10.10, page 215).

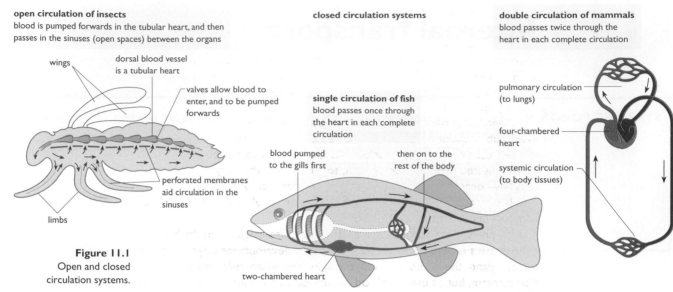

open circulation of insects
blood is pumped forwards in the tubular heart, and then passes in the sinuses (open spaces) between the organs

wings

dorsal blood vessel is a tubular heart

valves allow blood to enter, and to be pumped forwards

perforated membranes aid circulation in the sinuses

limbs

closed circulation systems

single circulation of fish
blood passes once through the heart in each complete circulation

blood pumped to the gills first

then on to the rest of the body

two-chambered heart

double circulation of mammals
blood passes twice through the heart in each complete circulation

pulmonary circulation (to lungs)

four-chambered heart

systemic circulation (to body tissues)

Figure 11.1
Open and closed circulation systems.

The major **advantages** of the mammalian double circulation over those of the fish and of insects are that:

* there is simultaneous high pressure delivery of oxygenated blood to all regions of the body
* oxygenated blood reaches the respiring tissues undiluted by deoxygenated blood.

In discussing the mammalian blood circulation, we will take the human circulation as the example.

> 1 In an open circulation there is 'little control over circulation'. What does this mean?

The transport medium: the blood

Blood is a special tissue of several different types of cell suspended in a liquid medium called **plasma**. The composition of human blood is shown in Figure 11.2.

Plasma is a straw-coloured, slightly alkaline liquid, consisting mainly of **water**. It is the medium for the continuous exchange of substances by cells and tissues throughout the body. Dissolved in the plasma are **nutrients** on their way from the gut or liver to all the cells. Excretory products are also transported in solution, chiefly **urea** from the liver to the kidneys. So too are **hormones**, from the ductless (endocrine) glands where they are formed and released to the tissues and organs.

Figure 11.2
The components of the blood.

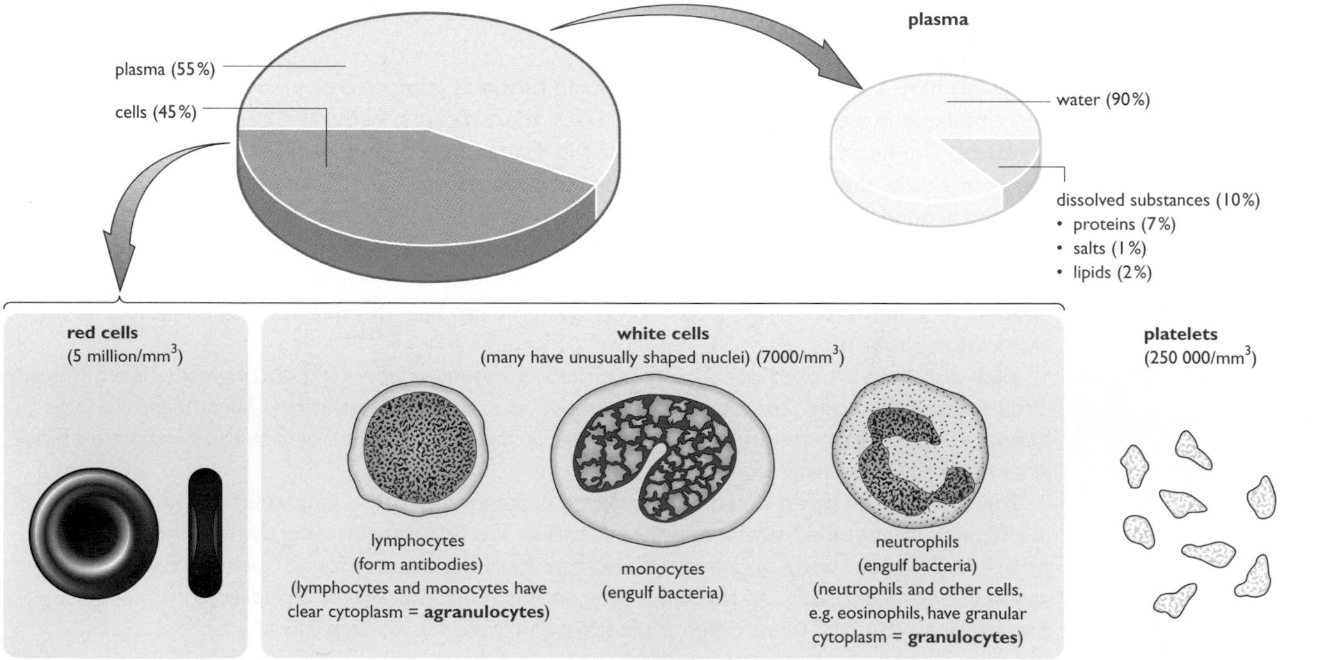

plasma (55%)

cells (45%)

plasma

water (90%)

dissolved substances (10%)
* proteins (7%)
* salts (1%)
* lipids (2%)

red cells
(5 million/mm³)

white cells
(many have unusually shaped nuclei) (7000/mm³)

lymphocytes
(form antibodies)
(lymphocytes and monocytes have clear cytoplasm = **agranulocytes**)

monocytes
(engulf bacteria)

neutrophils
(engulf bacteria)
(neutrophils and other cells, e.g. eosinophils, have granular cytoplasm = **granulocytes**)

platelets
(250 000/mm³)

The plasma also contains **dissolved proteins**. The principal blood protein is albumin, which has the role of regulating the water potential of the blood. The presence of dissolved albumin stops too much water leaving at the capillaries by osmosis, and helps in the return of fluids, too (Figure 11.13, page 236). Albumin and other globulins (proteins) also assist in the transport of lipids and iron in the plasma. Other blood proteins are the immunoglobulins, which are antibodies (page 337), and fibrinogen and prothrombin, which are components of the blood-clotting mechanism (page 337).

Suspended in the plasma are the **blood cells**. Most of these are **red cells** – about 5 million in every cubic millimetre of blood. The red cells are formed in the bone marrow tissue. When first formed, each red cell has a nucleus. As it develops this nucleus is lost, and is largely replaced by the conjugated protein haemoglobin, together with the enzyme carbonic anhydrase. Mature red cells have only one role: transporting respiratory gases in the blood. The life-span of working red cells is only about 120 days, after which they are broken down and replaced. Most of their components are retrieved and reused.

Also present are some **white cells**. These also originate in the bone marrow, but they retain their nucleus (Figure 11.3). In the growth and development stage, white cells may migrate to the thymus gland, the lymph nodes or the skin. The white cells do not necessarily function in the bloodstream, but all use the blood circulation as a means of moving through the body. Many leave the bloodstream by migrating between the cells of the capillary wall. There are several different types of white cell, all of which play a part in the body's defences (page 336). Most are quite short-lived. The white cells that are particularly important are:

- the **lymphocytes**, which form antibodies
- the **monocytes**, which are phagocytic (meaning they ingest bacteria or cell fragments); these include the macrophages in the alveoli of the lungs, for example
- the **granulocytes**, which are concerned with defence against infection; one group, the **neutrophils**, also destroy bacteria by phagocytosis.

Finally the blood contains **platelets**, best described as cell fragments. They are tiny packages of cytoplasm containing vesicles of substances that, when released, have a role in the blood-clotting mechanism.

Figure 11.3
Examining a blood smear.

preparing a blood smear for staining

Once the smear has dried, it is usually double-stained.

The first stain is selected to dye the cytoplasm of white cells. The second stain will dye the nuclei. When coloured in this way, the few white cells in a blood sample are easy to find.

This technique might be used in a hospital pathology laboratory to search for abnormalities in the blood cells.

The taking of blood samples and the handling of human blood in school and college laboratories are **forbidden** because of the remote danger of infection from hepatitis and AIDS viruses. The technique shown here is used in the manufacture of prepared slides by a laboratory supplier, and is carried out under proper sterile procedures.

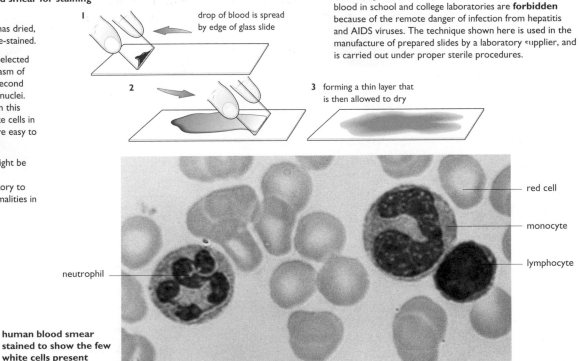

1 drop of blood is spread by edge of glass slide

2

3 forming a thin layer that is then allowed to dry

red cell

monocyte

lymphocyte

neutrophil

human blood smear stained to show the few white cells present (×4500)

The plumbing of the circulation system: arteries, veins and capillaries

There are three types of vessel in the circulation system: **arteries**, which carry blood away from the heart, **veins**, which carry blood back to the heart, and **capillaries**, which are fine networks of tiny tubes linking arteries and veins. Both arteries and veins have strong, elastic walls, but the walls of the arteries are very much thicker and stronger than those of the veins. The strength of the walls comes from the collagen fibres present, and the elasticity is due to the elastic and involuntary (smooth) muscle fibres.

Blood leaving the heart is under high pressure, and travels in waves or pulses, following each heart beat. By the time the blood has reached the capillaries it is under very much lower pressure, without a pulse. This difference in blood pressure accounts for the differences in the walls of arteries and veins. Figure 11.4 shows an artery and vein in section, and Table 11.1 details the wall structures of the vessels. Because of the low pressure in veins there is a possibility of backflow here. Veins have valves at intervals that prevent this (Figure 11.5).

Figure 11.4
The structure of the walls of arteries, veins and capillaries.

TS artery and vein, LP (×20)

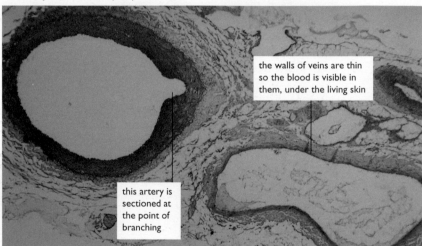

the walls of veins are thin so the blood is visible in them, under the living skin

this artery is sectioned at the point of branching

In sectioned material (as here), veins are more likely to appear squashed, whereas arteries are circular in section.

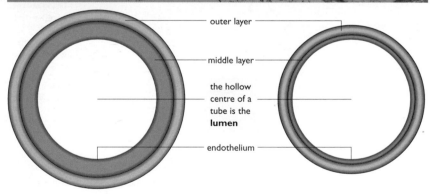

outer layer

middle layer

the hollow centre of a tube is the **lumen**

endothelium

Table 11.1
Differences between arteries, veins and capillaries.

	Artery	Capillary	Vein
outer layer: collagen fibres	present	absent	present
middle layer: elastic fibres and involuntary (smooth) muscle fibres	thick layer	absent	thin layer
endothelium: pavement epithelium	present	present	present
valves	absent	absent	present

Figure 11.5
The valves in veins
(especially common in the
veins of the limbs).

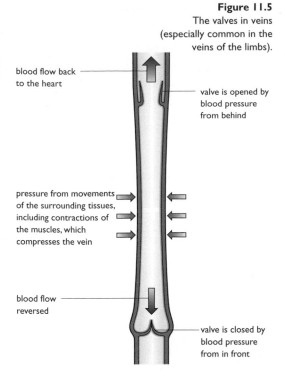

blood flow back
to the heart

valve is opened by
blood pressure
from behind

pressure from movements
of the surrounding tissues,
including contractions of
the muscles, which
compresses the vein

blood flow
reversed

valve is closed by
blood pressure
from in front

The arrangement of arteries, capillaries and veins in the body

The right side of the heart pumps deoxygenated blood to the lungs. The arteries serving the lungs and the veins from the lungs form the **pulmonary circulation**. The left side of the heart pumps oxygenated blood to the body via the **systemic circulation**.

In the systemic circulation, each organ is supplied with blood from the left side of the heart by an artery that branches from the main aorta. Inside each organ the artery branches, forming numerous **arterioles** (smaller arteries). The smallest arterioles supply the capillary networks. Capillaries drain into **venules** (smaller veins), and venules join to form veins. Finally, the veins join the vena cava that carries blood back to the right side of the heart. The branching sequence in the circulation is therefore:

aorta → artery → arteriole → capillary → venule → vein → vena cava

Figure 11.6 shows the main arteries and veins in the human circulation. Many arteries and veins are named after the organs they serve. Blood is supplied to the liver via the hepatic artery, but the liver also receives blood directly from the small intestine via a vein called the hepatic portal vein. This brings much of the products of digestion, after they have been absorbed into the capillaries of the villi (Figures 7.17, 7.18 and 7.20, pages 158, 159 and 160).

Figure 11.6
The layout of the
human circulation.

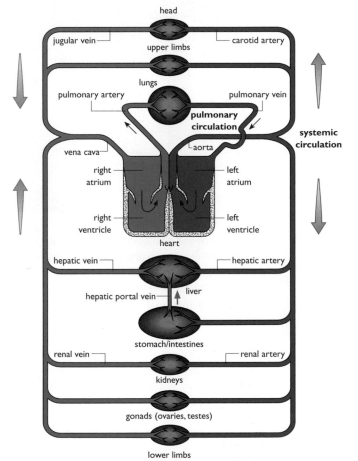

head

jugular vein

carotid artery

upper limbs

lungs

pulmonary artery

pulmonary vein

pulmonary circulation

systemic circulation

vena cava

aorta

right atrium

left atrium

right ventricle

left ventricle

heart

hepatic vein

hepatic artery

hepatic portal vein

liver

stomach/intestines

renal vein

renal artery

kidneys

gonads (ovaries, testes)

lower limbs

The circulatory system as shown here is simplified, e.g. limbs, lungs, kidneys and gonads are paired structures in the body.

The heart as a pump

The human heart is the size of a clenched fist. It lies in the thorax, between the lungs and beneath the breast bone (sternum). The heart is a hollow organ with a muscular wall, and is contained in a tightly fitting membrane, the pericardium. This strong, non-elastic sac anchors the heart within the thorax, and it prevents over-filling of the heart with blood. Within the pericardium is fluid, which reduces friction between the beating heart muscle and the surrounding tissues.

The wall of the heart is supplied with oxygenated blood from the aorta via coronary arteries. All muscle tissue consists of fibres that are able to shorten by a half to a third of their length. Chapter 14 describes how the muscles that move parts of our body (voluntary muscles) work. Cardiac muscle functions similarly. It consists of cylindrical branching columns of fibres, uniquely forming a three-dimensional network. This allows contractions in three dimensions, unlike those of voluntary muscles. The fibres have a single nucleus, are striped or striated, and are surrounded by sarcolemma (muscle plasma membrane) (Figure 11.7). They are exceedingly well supplied by mitochondria and capillaries. The fibres are connected by special junctions called intercalated discs. These discs transmit the impulse to contract to all cells simultaneously. The impulse to contract is generated within the heart muscle itself (it is said to have a **myogenic origin**), *not* by nervous stimulation (a **neurogenic origin**). Heart muscle fibres contract rhythmically from their formation until they die.

Figure 11.7
Cardiac muscle fibres.

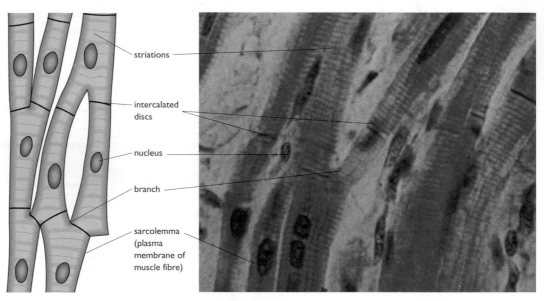

striations

intercalated discs

nucleus

branch

sarcolemma (plasma membrane of muscle fibre)

The cavity of the heart is divided into four **chambers** (Figure 11.8). The chambers of the right side of the heart are completely separate from those of the left side. The upper chambers are thin-walled and are called **atria** (*singular*, atrium). These receive blood into the heart. The two lower chambers are thick-walled and called **ventricles**. The muscular wall of the left ventricle is much thicker than that of the right ventricle, but the volumes of the right and left sides (the quantities of blood they contain) are identical. The ventricles pump blood out of the heart.

The direction of blood flow through the heart is maintained by valves. The valves of the heart prevent backflow of the blood. You see all the valves of the heart in action in the drawings in Figure 11.9 (page 232). The **atrio-ventricular valves** are large valves that separate the upper and lower chambers. The edges of these valves are supported by tendons anchored to the muscle walls of the ventricles below, which prevent the valves from folding back due to pressure from the ventricles. The valves on the right and left sides of the heart are individually named: the one on the right side is the **tricuspid valve**, and that on the left the **bicuspid** or mitral valve.

Valves of a different type separate the ventricles from the pulmonary artery (right side) and aorta (left side). These are pocket-like structures called **semilunar valves**, rather similar to the valves found in veins.

Figure 11.8
The structure of the heart.

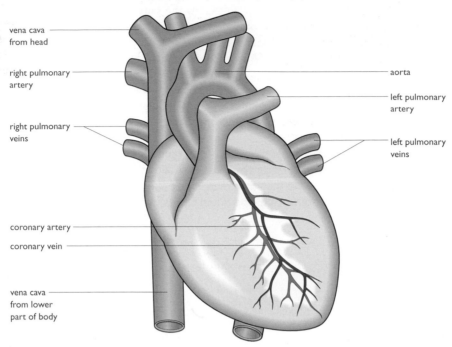

heart viewed from the front of the body with pericardium removed

vena cava from head

right pulmonary artery

right pulmonary veins

coronary artery

coronary vein

vena cava from lower part of body

aorta

left pulmonary artery

left pulmonary veins

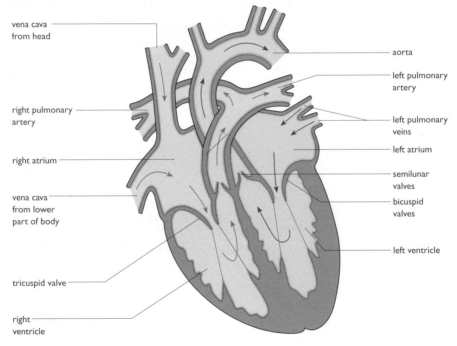

heart in LS

vena cava from head

right pulmonary artery

right atrium

vena cava from lower part of body

tricuspid valve

right ventricle

aorta

left pulmonary artery

left pulmonary veins

left atrium

semilunar valves

bicuspid valves

left ventricle

The cardiac cycle

The cardiac cycle is the sequence of events of a heart beat, by which blood is pumped all over the body. The heart beats about 75 times per minute, so each cardiac cycle is about 0.8 seconds long. This period of 'heart beat' is divided into two stages, called **systole** and **diastole**. In the systole stage heart muscle contracts, and during the diastole stage it relaxes. When the muscular walls of a chamber of the heart contract, the volume of the chamber decreases. This increases the pressure on the blood, and forces the blood to a region where pressure is lower. Valves prevent blood flowing backwards to a region of low pressure, so blood always flows on through the heart.

Look at the steps in Figure 11.9. This illustrates the cycle on the left side of the heart only, but both sides function together, in exactly the same way.

Start with contraction of the atrium (**atrial systole**, about 0.1 s). As the walls of the atrium contract, blood pushes past the atrio-ventricular valve into the ventricles, where the contents are under low pressure. (Any backflow of blood is prevented by the semilunar valves.)

The atrium now relaxes (**atrial diastole**, about 0.7 s).

Next the ventricle contracts (**ventricular systole**, about 0.3 s) and contraction of the ventricles is very forceful indeed. The high pressure this generates slams shut the atrio-ventricular valve and opens the semilunar valves, forcing blood into the aorta. Another 'pulse' has been generated.

This is followed by relaxation of the ventricles (**ventricular diastole**, about 0.5 s).

Each contraction of cardiac muscle is followed by relaxation and elastic recoil. The changing pressure of blood in the atria, ventricles, pulmonary artery and aorta (shown in the graph in Figure 11.9) automatically opens and closes the valves.

Figure 11.9
The cardiac cycle (only the left side of the heart is shown).

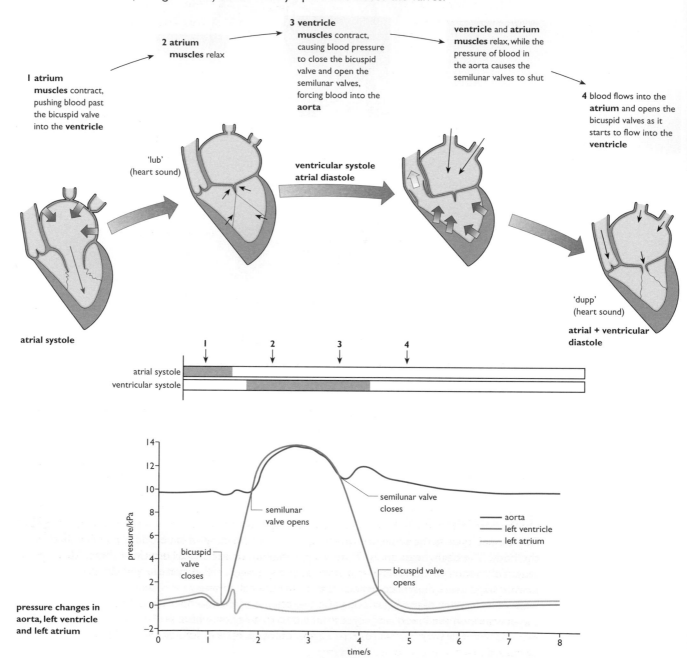

1 **atrium muscles** contract, pushing blood past the bicuspid valve into the **ventricle**

2 **atrium muscles** relax

3 **ventricle muscles** contract, causing blood pressure to close the bicuspid valve and open the semilunar valves, forcing blood into the **aorta**

ventricle and **atrium muscles** relax, while the pressure of blood in the aorta causes the semilunar valves to shut

4 blood flows into the **atrium** and opens the bicuspid valves as it starts to flow into the **ventricle**

'lub' (heart sound)

ventricular systole atrial diastole

'dupp' (heart sound)

atrial systole

atrial + ventricular diastole

atrial systole
ventricular systole

pressure changes in aorta, left ventricle and left atrium

aorta
left ventricle
left atrium

semilunar valve opens

semilunar valve closes

bicuspid valve closes

bicuspid valve opens

pressure/kPa

time/s

● **Extension** Blood pressure and its measurement

By blood pressure we mean the pressure of the blood flowing through the arteries. This is quoted as two values, since blood flows in the arteries as a pulse. High pressure is produced by ventricular systole, and is followed by low pressure at the end of ventricular diastole. To measure these two values an inflatable cuff **sphygmomanometer** is used with a **stethoscope**, as shown in Figure 11.10. The three steps are as follows.

1 The cuff is inflated and blood flow is monitored in the arm (brachial) artery at the elbow. Inflation is continued until there is no sound (= no flow of blood).
2 Air is now allowed to escaped from the cuff, slowly, until blood can just be heard spurting through the constriction point in the artery. This pressure at the cuff is recorded, for it is equal to the maximum pressure created by the heart (**systolic pressure**).
3 Pressure in the cuff is allowed to drop until the blood can be heard flowing constantly. This is the lowest pressure the blood falls to between beats (**diastolic pressure**).

Figure 11.10
Measuring blood pressure.

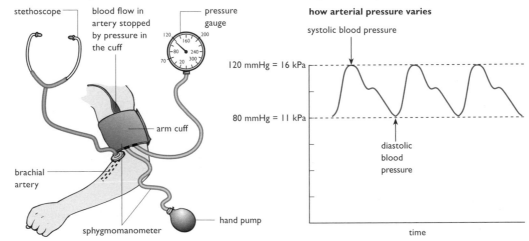

The **pascal** (Pa) and its multiple the **kilopascal** (kPa) are generally used by scientists to measure pressure, but in medicine the older unit of pressure, 'millimetre of mercury' (mmHg) is still used.
(1 mmHg = 0.13 kPa)

● **Extension** Cardiac output

The volume of blood pumped from the heart depends upon two factors:

• how fast the heart beats (the **heart rate**)
• how much blood is pumped out per beat (the **stroke volume**).

The **cardiac output**, the amount of blood flowing from the heart, is given by:

cardiac output = stroke volume × heart rate

A typical stroke volume is about 80 cm³ of blood. This is the volume of blood despatched both through the pulmonary circulation (to the lungs) and through the systemic circulation (to the rest of the body) with every heart beat.

The stroke volume of the heart can and does change; it increases with exercise, for example. During intense physical activity, the body restricts the flow of blood to the gut. As a result, blood flow to the skeletal muscle is enhanced, and blood flow back to the heart increases. Increased blood flowing into the heart stretches the cardiac muscle fibres as they are about to contract. Cardiac muscle responds by contracting more strongly during systole, and an increased volume of blood is pumped out per unit of time. As a result, the volume of blood flow back to the heart is further increased, and the heart is slightly stretched and distended. Note that, whilst the distribution of blood to skeletal muscles and gut may be varied, the supply to the brain, heart muscle and kidneys is maintained at a high level at all times.

By this process, regular exercise under aerobic muscle conditions (page 312) results in a permanent increase in output, which is maintained even when resting. Thus a 'trained' heart at rest has a greater stroke volume and can therefore pump the same quantity of blood as an untrained heart, but at a lower heart rate.

Origin of the heart beat

The heart beat originates in a structure in the muscle of the wall of the right atrium, called the **sino-atrial node** (SAN, or pacemaker). Muscle fibres radiating out from the SAN conduct the impulses to the muscles of both atria, triggering atrial systole. Then a second node, the **atrio-ventricular node**, lying at the base of the right atrium, picks up the excitation and passes it to the ventricles through modified muscle fibres called the **Purkyne tissue**. Ventricular systole is then triggered. After every contraction, cardiac muscle has a period of insensitivity to stimulation, known as a **refractory period** (in effect, a period of enforced non-contraction), while the heart refills with blood. This period is a relatively long one in heart muscle, and enables the heart to beat throughout life.

The heart's own rhythm, set by the SAN, is about 50 beats per minute, but conditions in the body can override this basic rate and increase heart performance.

Control of heart rate

The action of the SAN (pacemaker) is modified according to the needs of the body. For example, it is increased during physical activity, from the 75 beats a minute of the 'at rest' heart, up to 200 beats a minute in very strenuous exercise. How is the pacemaker regulated? Look at Figure 11.11 now.

Nervous control of the heart is by reflex action. The heart receives impulses from the **cardiovascular centre** in the medulla of the hindbrain, via two nerves:

- a **sympathetic nerve**, part of the sympathetic system, which speeds up the heart
- a branch of the **vagus nerve**, part of the parasympathetic nervous system, which slows down the heart.

Since the sympathetic nerve and the vagus nerve have opposite effects we say they are **antagonistic**.

Figure 11.11
Control of heart rate.

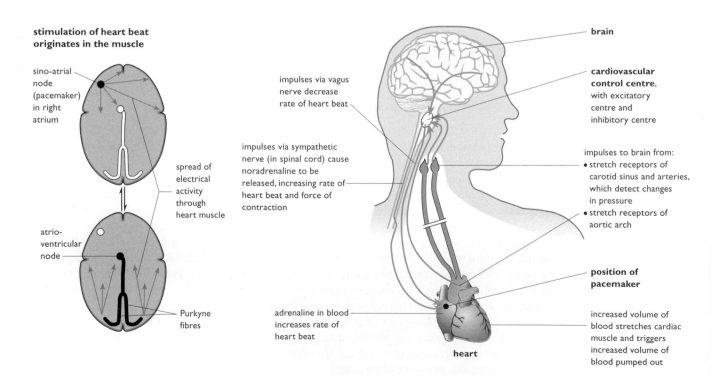

how the activity of the pacemaker is regulated

forebrain (e.g. cerebral hemispheres, hypothalamus) may send sensory impulses, e.g. in anticipation of physical effort or over an attack of 'road rage'

stimulation of heart beat originates in the muscle

sino-atrial node (pacemaker) in right atrium

spread of electrical activity through heart muscle

atrio-ventricular node

Purkyne fibres

impulses via vagus nerve decrease rate of heart beat

impulses via sympathetic nerve (in spinal cord) cause noradrenaline to be released, increasing rate of heart beat and force of contraction

adrenaline in blood increases rate of heart beat

brain

cardiovascular control centre, with excitatory centre and inhibitory centre

impulses to brain from:
• stretch receptors of carotid sinus and arteries, which detect changes in pressure
• stretch receptors of aortic arch

position of pacemaker

increased volume of blood stretches cardiac muscle and triggers increased volume of blood pumped out

heart

Nerves supplying the **cardiovascular centre** bring impulses from stretch receptors in the walls of the aorta, carotid arteries and the right atrium, whenever blood pressure at these positions changes. When blood pressure is high in the arteries, the cardiovascular centre sends impulses to the heart via the vagus nerve, and these slow down the heart rate. When blood pressure is low, the rate of heart beat is increased.

The rate of heart beat is also influenced by impulses from the higher centres of the brain. For example, emotion, stress and anticipation of events can all cause impulses from the sympathetic nerve to speed up heart rate. In addition, the hormone **adrenaline**, which is secreted by the adrenal glands and carried in the blood, causes the pacemaker to increase the heart rate (Chapter 13).

2 During vigorous activity the heart beats more quickly. What causes this raised heart rate, and how is it brought about?

Exchange in the tissues

Formation of tissue fluid

Tissue fluid is formed from the plasma, components of which escape from the blood and pass between the cells in most of the tissues of the body. Red cells and many of the blood proteins are retained in the capillaries. Tissue fluid plays an important part in the delivery of nutrients to cells, and the removal of waste products.

The walls of the capillaries are selectively permeable to many components of the blood plasma, including glucose and mineral ions. Nutrients like these, which are in low concentration in the tissues, diffuse from the plasma (Figure 11.12). There are also tiny gaps in the capillary walls, varying in size in different parts of the body, which ease the formation of tissue fluid. The pressure of the blood (hydrostatic pressure generated as the heart beats) drives fluid out. Meanwhile, the proteins and some other components are retained in the blood. These soluble substances maintain an osmotic gradient, so some of the water forced out by hydrostatic pressure returns to the blood by osmosis all along the capillary. Initially, however, there is a net outflow because the hydrostatic pressure is greater than fluid movement due to the osmotic gradient (Figure 11.13).

Figure 11.12
Exchange between blood and cells via tissue fluid.

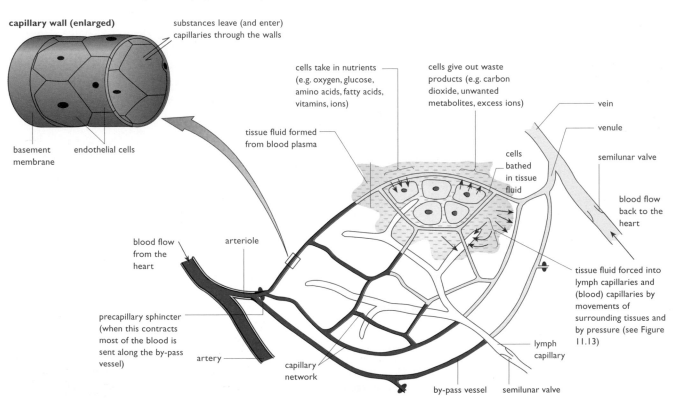

capillary wall (enlarged)

substances leave (and enter) capillaries through the walls

basement membrane

endothelial cells

cells take in nutrients (e.g. oxygen, glucose, amino acids, fatty acids, vitamins, ions)

cells give out waste products (e.g. carbon dioxide, unwanted metabolites, excess ions)

tissue fluid formed from blood plasma

cells bathed in tissue fluid

vein

venule

semilunar valve

blood flow back to the heart

blood flow from the heart

arteriole

precapillary sphincter (when this contracts most of the blood is sent along the by-pass vessel)

artery

capillary network

lymph capillary

by-pass vessel

semilunar valve

tissue fluid forced into lymph capillaries and (blood) capillaries by movements of surrounding tissues and by pressure (see Figure 11.13)

Figure 11.13
Forces for exchange
in capillaries.

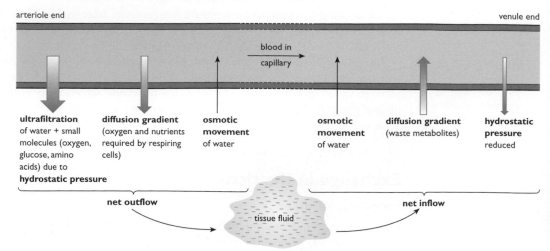

Blood proteins, particularly the albumins, cannot escape; they maintain the water potential of
the plasma, preventing excess loss of water and assisting the return of fluid to the capillaries.

arteriole end   venule end

blood in
capillary

ultrafiltration
of water + small
molecules (oxygen,
glucose, amino
acids) due to
hydrostatic pressure

diffusion gradient
(oxygen and nutrients
required by respiring
cells)

**osmotic
movement**
of water

**osmotic
movement**
of water

diffusion gradient
(waste metabolites)

**hydrostatic
pressure**
reduced

net outflow

net inflow

tissue fluid

Return of tissue fluid to the circulation

Further along the capillary there is a net inflow of tissue fluid to the capillary. Hydrostatic
pressure has now fallen as fluid is lost from the capillaries. Water also returns by osmosis, and a
diffusion gradient carries unused metabolites and excretory material back into the blood.

Not all tissue fluid returns to the blood capillaries. Some enters the **lymph capillaries**.
Molecules too large to enter lymph capillaries can pass into the lymph system at tiny valves in
their walls. Liquid is moved along these capillaries by compression caused by body movements,
and backflow is prevented by valves. Lymph finally drains back into the blood circulation in veins
close to the heart.

3 What components of
the blood are not
found in tissue fluid?

Transport of oxygen and carbon dioxide

Oxygen

Each red cell contains about 280 million molecules of **haemoglobin**. The haemoglobin molecule
is built of four interlocking sub-units. Each of these is composed of a large, globular protein with
a non-protein haem group attached, containing iron. One molecule of oxygen will combine with
each haem group, at the concentration of oxygen found in our lungs. This means each
haemoglobin molecule is able to transport four molecules of oxygen:

haemoglobin + oxygen $\rightarrow$ oxyhaemoglobin
Hb   + $4O_2$ HbO_8

Figure 11.14 shows the relationship between haemoglobin and oxygen as the concentration of
oxygen around the haemoglobin molecule changes (oxygen concentration is expressed as its
partial pressure, in kPa). This is called an **oxygen dissociation curve**. The curve is S-shaped.
This tells us that the first oxygen molecule attaches with difficulty. Once it has done so, however,
the second combines more easily, and so on until all four are attached and the molecule is
saturated.

Most haemoglobin molecules are fully saturated at a partial pressure of oxygen of only 8 kPa.
In respiring tissue the oxygen partial pressure is much lower, owing to aerobic respiration.
Oxyhaemoglobin will dissociate if the partial pressure is less than 8 kPa, releasing oxygen
molecules to respiring tissues.

In respiring cells the concentration of carbon dioxide is high, so it is interesting to see what
effect carbon dioxide concentration has on the loading and unloading of oxygen by haemoglobin.
In fact, an increased carbon dioxide concentration shifts the oxygen dissociation curve markedly
to the right (Figure 11.15). That is, where the carbon dioxide concentration is high (obviously in
the actively respiring cells), oxygen is released from oxyhaemoglobin even more readily. This
very useful outcome is known as the **Bohr effect**.

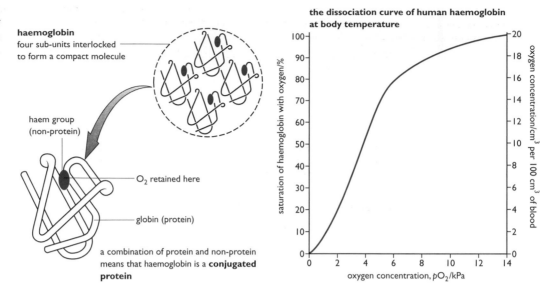

Figure 11.14
The structure of haemoglobin and its affinity for oxygen.

haemoglobin
four sub-units interlocked to form a compact molecule

haem group (non-protein)

O_2 retained here

globin (protein)

a combination of protein and non-protein means that haemoglobin is a **conjugated protein**

the dissociation curve of human haemoglobin at body temperature

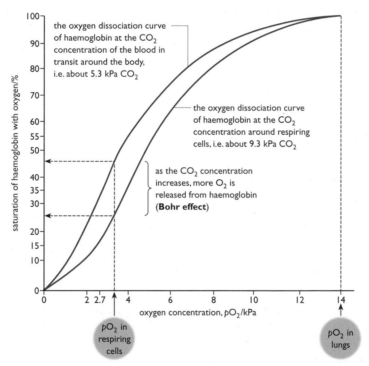

Figure 11.15
How carbon dioxide favours release of oxygen in respiring tissues.

the oxygen dissociation curve of haemoglobin at the CO_2 concentration of the blood in transit around the body, i.e. about 5.3 kPa CO_2

the oxygen dissociation curve of haemoglobin at the CO_2 concentration around respiring cells, i.e. about 9.3 kPa CO_2

as the CO_2 concentration increases, more O_2 is released from haemoglobin (**Bohr effect**)

pO_2 in respiring cells

pO_2 in lungs

Carbon dioxide

Carbon dioxide is transported in the blood (in the plasma and in red cells) as hydrogencarbonate ions:

$$CO_2 + H_2O \xrightarrow{\text{carbonic anhydrase}} HCO_3^- + H^+$$

The enzyme **carbonic anhydrase**, which catalyses this reaction, is present in the red cells. You can see that hydrogen ions are one of the products. The hydrogen ions released become associated with haemoglobin. In effect, the respiratory pigment molecules act as a buffer for H^+, preventing the blood from becoming acidic (Figure 11.16).

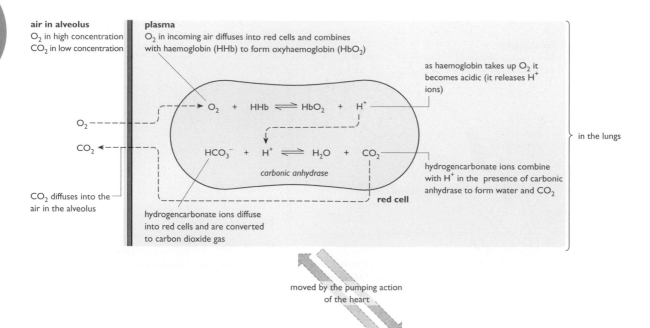

air in alveolus
O_2 in high concentration
CO_2 in low concentration

plasma
O_2 in incoming air diffuses into red cells and combines
with haemoglobin (HHb) to form oxyhaemoglobin (HbO_2)

as haemoglobin takes up O_2 it
becomes acidic (it releases H^+
ions)

O_2

CO_2

O_2 + HHb $\rightleftharpoons$ HbO_2 + H^+

in the lungs

HCO_3^- + H^+ $\rightleftharpoons$ H_2O + CO_2

carbonic anhydrase

hydrogencarbonate ions combine
with H^+ in the presence of carbonic
anhydrase to form water and CO_2

CO_2 diffuses into the
air in the alveolus

hydrogencarbonate ions diffuse
into red cells and are converted
to carbon dioxide gas

red cell

moved by the pumping action
of the heart

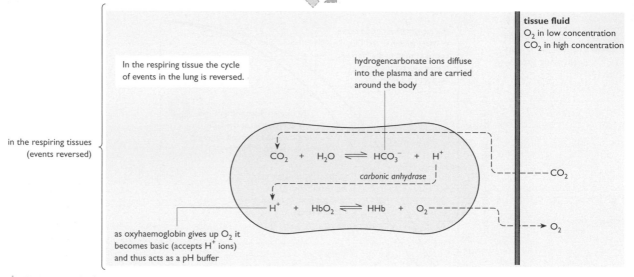

tissue fluid
O_2 in low concentration
CO_2 in high concentration

In the respiring tissue the cycle
of events in the lung is reversed.

hydrogencarbonate ions diffuse
into the plasma and are carried
around the body

in the respiring tissues
(events reversed)

CO_2 + H_2O $\rightleftharpoons$ HCO_3^- + H^+

carbonic anhydrase

CO_2

H^+ + HbO_2 $\rightleftharpoons$ HHb + O_2

O_2

as oxyhaemoglobin gives up O_2 it
becomes basic (accepts H^+ ions)
and thus acts as a pH buffer

Figure 11.16
The transport of oxygen
and carbon dioxide
between lungs and
respiring tissues.

The roles of the blood circulation system

The blood circulation has roles in the body's defence against disease (Chapter 15), in internal communication (Chapter 13), and in the maintenance of a constant internal environment (Chapter 12), as well as being the transport system of the body. The transport roles of the blood circulation are summarised in Table 11.2.

Table 11.2
Transport roles of the
blood circulation.

Function in organism	Transport role of circulation
tissue respiration	transporting **oxygen** to all tissues, and **carbon dioxide** back to the lungs
hydration	transporting **water** to all the tissues
nutrition	transporting **nutrients** (sugars, amino acids, lipids, vitamins) and inorganic **ions** to all cells
excretion	transporting **waste products** of metabolism to kidneys, lungs, sweat glands and liver
temperature regulation	distribution of **heat**
development and coordination	transporting **hormones** from endocrine glands to target organs

● **Extension** Fetal haemoglobin and myoglobin as different respiratory pigments

Figure 11.17 (left)
The blood circulation in the human fetus.

Figure 11.18 (right)
The oxygen dissociation curves of fetal haemoglobin and myoglobin.

The fetus obtains oxygen from its mother's blood through the placenta, where the maternal and fetal circulations come very close together (Figure 11.17 and see Chapter 19). The haemoglobin of the adult mammal and the haemoglobin in the fetal circulation differ slightly in their chemistry.

Fetal haemoglobin has a higher affinity for oxygen (Figure 11.18). This means that it combines with oxygen more readily than does the maternal haemoglobin at the same partial pressure. It is essential that fetal haemoglobin has this property, given that the only access to an oxygen supply for the fetus is via the placenta. If the haemoglobin of the fetus had a *lower* affinity than that of its mother's haemoglobin, oxygen would pass from the fetus to the mother.

In the fetus the functions of the adult lungs, liver, kidneys and gut are carried out by the placenta. The fetus is connected to the placenta by the umbilicus.

The fetal circulation is modified to deliver nutrients from the placenta to growing tissues, and waste products back to the placenta.

vessel (**ductus arteriosus**) diverts blood from lungs to aorta

hole between atria (**foramen ovale**) diverts blood (oxygenated) to aorta

vessel (**ductus venosus**) diverts blood away from liver to heart

umbilical vein

umbilical artery

placenta – here fetal and maternal blood come close together, and nutrients and waste products are exchanged

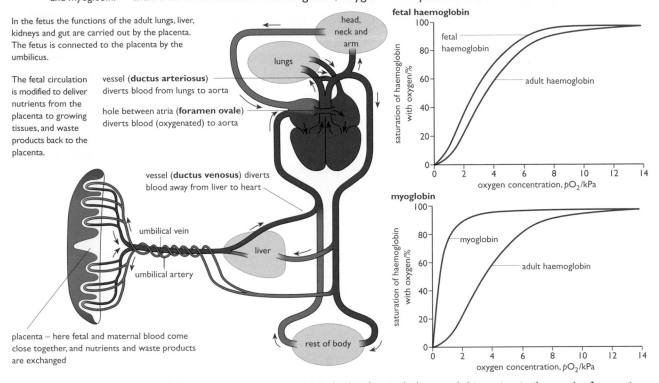

Myoglobin is a respiratory pigment built of a single haem–globin unit, similar to the four units in haemoglobin. It is found only in muscle cells. Myoglobin has a much higher affinity for oxygen than haemoglobin (Figure 11.18), so in normal conditions in muscle, myoglobin is saturated with oxygen. It functions as an oxygen store. When muscle is very active for a prolonged period, the oxygen concentration in the muscle tissue may fall below 0.5 kPa, and oxymyoglobin will dissociate to supply oxygen for aerobic respiration to continue (aerobic muscle conditions). Finally, if contraction continues and all the myoglobin has yielded its oxygen, then muscle tissue will switch to anaerobic respiration by lactic fermentation (page 200) and muscle contraction can continue.

● **Extension** Hypertension – dangerously raised blood pressure

Our blood pressure (Figure 11.10, page 233) depends on our age, but a reading of 18.6/12.0 kPa (140/90 mmHg) is at the threshold of hypertension. At 21.3/12.6 kPa (160/95 mmHg) blood pressure is dangerously high.

Causes of hypertension include atherosclerosis (page 323), kidney disease (page 269), and excessive secretion by the adrenal glands (aldosterone causes retention of salt and water by the kidneys, page 267). The main **danger** from hypertension is to the working of the heart, brain and kidneys.

The **treatment** of hypertension includes tackling obesity by dieting, and reduction of salt intake. Smokers are advised to stop. **Beta-blocking drugs** may be prescribed to block the adrenaline receptors at the sympathetic terminals of heart muscle (stimulation by the sympathetic nerve increases heart rate and force of contraction (Figure 11.11, page 234), thereby raising blood pressure).

Transport in plants

Internal transport within plants also occurs by mass flow, but here there is no pumping organ. Two separate tissues take part in transport in plants. Water and many ions travel in the **xylem**. Xylem is a system of vessels connected end to end to form non-living tubes, originally made from living cells. Manufactured foods (mainly sugar and amino acids) are carried in a living tissue, the **phloem**. Phloem consists of cells called sieve tubes and companion cells. The xylem and phloem are collectively known as the **vascular tissue**, and they occur together in the **vascular bundles** that branch throughout the plant body and serve roots, stems, leaves and growing points (buds) (Figure 11.19).

Structure of the herbaceous plant

In the herbaceous (non-woody) plant, the vascular tissue of the root occurs in a single, central vascular bundle or **stele**. At the base of the stem this vascular tissue is reorganised into several vascular bundles arranged around the outside of the stem. The bundles contain xylem and phloem, with **fibres** (Figure 11.20). Fibres are long, narrow, pointed cells that have thickened walls but no living contents. The walls of both xylem and fibres are strengthened with lignin. Together, they give mechanical strength to the bundles. Vascular bundles help support the plant as well as being the sites of transport. Smaller bundles, called **leaf traces**, branch from the main bundles, pass up the leaf stalks and connect with the network of bundles in the veins. Veins support the delicate leaf tissues, as well as supplying water and carrying sucrose to the rest of the plant.

Figure 11.19
The distribution of xylem and phloem tissue in the flowering plant.

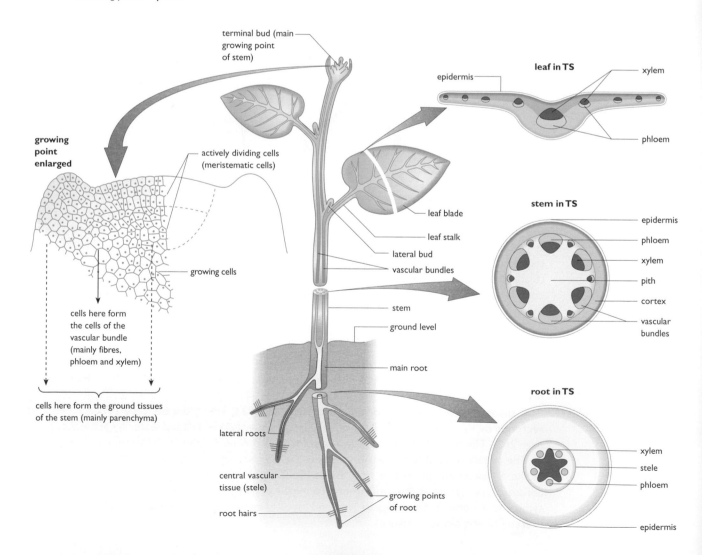

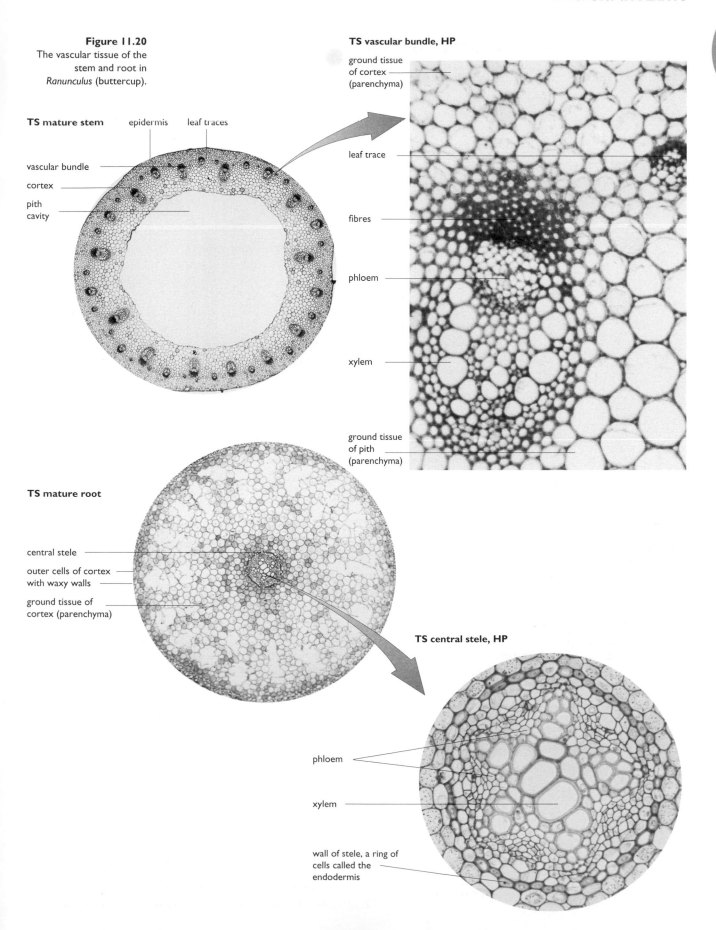

Figure 11.20
The vascular tissue of the
stem and root in
Ranunculus (buttercup).

TS vascular bundle, HP

ground tissue
of cortex
(parenchyma)

leaf trace

fibres

phloem

xylem

ground tissue
of pith
(parenchyma)

TS mature stem

epidermis   leaf traces

vascular bundle

cortex

pith
cavity

TS mature root

central stele

outer cells of cortex
with waxy walls

ground tissue of
cortex (parenchyma)

TS central stele, HP

phloem

xylem

wall of stele, a ring of
cells called the
endodermis

Transpiration and the movement of water through the plant

Transpiration is the process by which water is lost as vapour from the aerial parts of plants. In leaves, water evaporates from the cell walls, and the vapour accumulates in the air spaces and diffuses out through the open stomata. As water evaporates the leaf cells are cooled. Water is drawn by osmosis from the xylem vessels of the leaf veins to replace the lost water. As a consequence, a stream of water is drawn up through the plant; many litres are moved in this way on a hot day (Figure 11.21).

Figure 11.21
The site of transpiration.

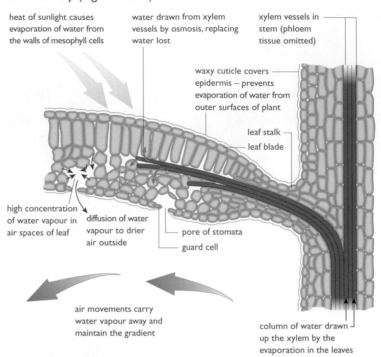

heat of sunlight causes evaporation of water from the walls of mesophyll cells

water drawn from xylem vessels by osmosis, replacing water lost

xylem vessels in stem (phloem tissue omitted)

waxy cuticle covers epidermis – prevents evaporation of water from outer surfaces of plant

leaf stalk

leaf blade

high concentration of water vapour in air spaces of leaf

diffusion of water vapour to drier air outside

pore of stomata

guard cell

air movements carry water vapour away and maintain the gradient

column of water drawn up the xylem by the evaporation in the leaves

The opening and closing of stomata

Stomata tend to be open in the light and closed in the dark. The stomata open when water is absorbed by guard cells from the surrounding cells of the epidermis, and so become fully turgid. As a result of the high internal pressure and because of the shape of the guard cell walls, a pore opens between the guard cells. The pore closes up again when the guard cells become flaccid (Figure 11.22 and also see Figure 8.3, page 171). This happens if the plant wilts from lack of water, for example.

How is turgidity caused in guard cells?

The guard cells contain chloroplasts, and they are the only type of cell in the epidermis to do so.

Figure 11.22
Opening and closing of stomata.

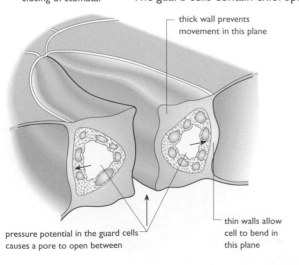

thick wall prevents movement in this plane

pressure potential in the guard cells causes a pore to open between

thin walls allow cell to bend in this plane

But opening is *not* due to the accumulation of sugar by the photosynthesising guard cells in the light, for this is far too slow a change to account for opening. Also stomata often open well before sunrise (Figure 11.23). In fact in many species of plant, the guard cells open and close to an internal rhythm. They open and close at the same times in every 24 hour cycle. The mechanism of opening appears to be as follows:

- the **accumulation of potassium ions** in the cytoplasm of the guard cells; these ions are absorbed from the surrounding cells by active transport, using energy from ATP
- the conversion of starch, previously produced and stored in the chloroplasts of the guard cells, to the soluble **organic acid malate**; starch does not act osmotically, but malate ions do.

242

Figure 11.23
The mechanism and timing of stomatal opening and closing.

Malate ions and potassium ions accumulate and cause the water potential of the guard cells to become much more negative. Net osmotic uptake of water follows, and, as the guard cells become turgid, the pore opens between them. This process is reversed just before it closes.

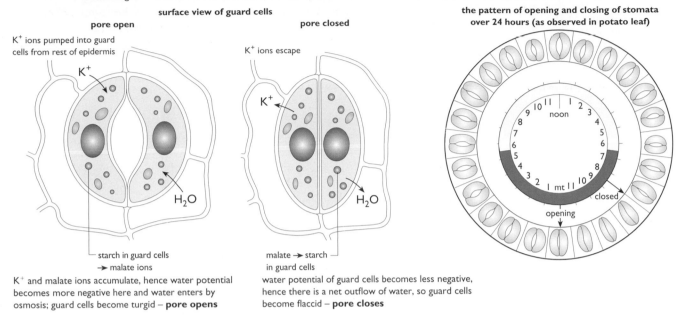

surface view of guard cells

pore open

K⁺ ions pumped into guard cells from rest of epidermis

K⁺

H₂O

starch in guard cells → malate ions

K⁺ and malate ions accumulate, hence water potential becomes more negative here and water enters by osmosis; guard cells become turgid – **pore opens**

pore closed

K⁺ ions escape

K⁺

H₂O

malate → starch in guard cells

water potential of guard cells becomes less negative, hence there is a net outflow of water, so guard cells become flaccid – **pore closes**

the pattern of opening and closing of stomata over 24 hours (as observed in potato leaf)

noon

closed

opening

The movement of water through the plant

The three routes of water movement through plant cells and tissues, shown in Figure 11.24, are as follows:

4 What environmental conditions may lead to stomatal closure in the light?

5 What is the difference between the symplast and the apoplast?

Figure 11.24
How water moves across plant cells.

• **Mass flow** through the interconnecting 'free' spaces between the cellulose fibres of the plant cell walls. This free space in cellulose makes up about 50% of the wall volume. This pathway, entirely avoiding the living contents of cells, is called the **apoplast**. It is a highly significant route for water moving about the plant. The apoplast also includes the water-filled spaces of dead cells and the hollow xylem vessels.

• **Diffusion** through the cytoplasm of cells, and via the cytoplasmic connections between cells (the **plasmodesmata**). This route is called the **symplast**. The plant cells are packed with many organelles, which offer resistance to the flow of water. This pathway is therefore not the major one.

• **Osmosis** from vacuole to vacuole of the cells, driven by a gradient in water potential. This is not a significant pathway of water transport across the plant, but it is the means by which individual cells absorb water.

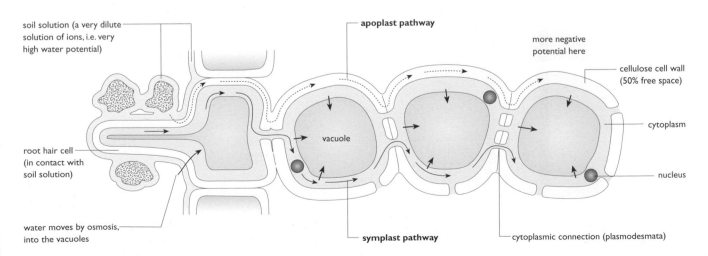

soil solution (a very dilute solution of ions, i.e. very high water potential)

apoplast pathway

more negative potential here

cellulose cell wall (50% free space)

cytoplasm

vacuole

root hair cell (in contact with soil solution)

nucleus

water moves by osmosis, into the vacuoles

symplast pathway

cytoplasmic connection (plasmodesmata)

Water movement in the xylem

The evaporation of water in the aerial parts of plants applies a tension to the water column in the xylem vessels. Water is drawn (literally 'pulled') up the stem by the transpiration stream (Figure 11.25). This water column is continuous in the xylem running from the region of water absorption in the roots to the highest leaves and buds of the stem. The cohesion of all the water molecules (the tensile strength of the water) holds the column together, and the water adheres to the sides of the xylem vessels and does not 'break'.

Figure 11.25
The pathway of water movement from soil to leaf.

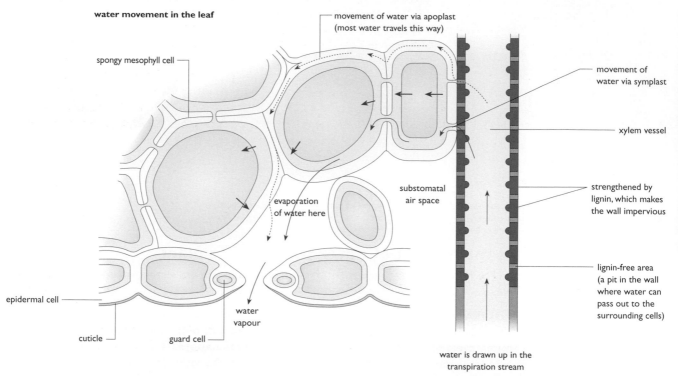

water movement in the leaf

movement of water via apoplast
(most water travels this way)

spongy mesophyll cell

movement of water via symplast

xylem vessel

substomatal air space

strengthened by lignin, which makes the wall impervious

lignin-free area (a pit in the wall where water can pass out to the surrounding cells)

evaporation of water here

epidermal cell

cuticle

guard cell

water vapour

water is drawn up in the transpiration stream

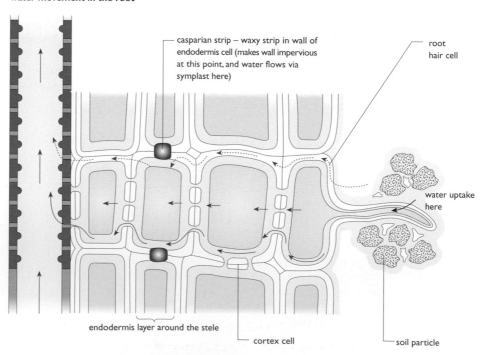

water movement in the root

casparian strip – waxy strip in wall of endodermis cell (makes wall impervious at this point, and water flows via symplast here)

root hair cell

water uptake here

endodermis layer around the stele

cortex cell

soil particle

We know this is the way water travels up a stem, firstly because xylem vessels are reinforced against collapse on the inside by rings or layers of very tough lignin added to the cellulose there. Secondly, when the stem is damaged and the xylem punctured, air rushes into the xylem column, rather than water squirting out. Water in the xylem is under tension, not under pressure.

Water uptake

Water is absorbed into the roots in the root tips and in the region of root hairs. Only in this region is the root able to absorb, because elsewhere the outer cells of the root have walls that are made waxy (therefore waterproof) by the addition of suberin.

Water travels across the root cortex mainly by the apoplast pathway (Figure 11.24), but outside the central stele of the root it passes through the endodermis layer. This is a layer of cells that surround the stele. They have a waxy strip in their walls. As a consequence, all water passes into the endodermis, and travels by the symplast at this point. Thereafter, the bulk of water returns to the apoplast pathway and travels in and through the xylem to the aerial parts. Water passes out of xylem vessels at pits (lignin-free areas) in the walls, to the surrounding cells (Figure 11.26). Most water is delivered via this transpiration stream during the hours of daylight, and is evaporated.

Figure 11.26
The structure of xylem tissue.

photomicrograph of xylem tissue in LS

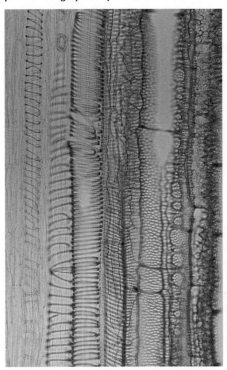

drawing of xylem vessels in TS and LS

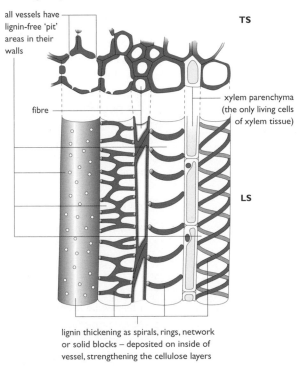

all vessels have lignin-free 'pit' areas in their walls

TS

fibre

xylem parenchyma (the only living cells of xylem tissue)

LS

lignin thickening as spirals, rings, network or solid blocks – deposited on inside of vessel, strengthening the cellulose layers

Factors affecting the rate of transpiration

Any factor that affects the process of evaporation also affects the rate of transpiration. In the environment of plants these factors include:

- the **humidity** of the air, for in conditions of low humidity (i.e. dry air) more water will evaporate
- the **temperature**, because heat energy drives evaporation
- **air movement**, since wind carries away the water vapour that diffuses from the leaf, thus maintaining the concentration gradient; plants transpire more water on a windy day than on a still one
- an adequate **water supply** to the leaves, for if the leaves become flaccid the stomata close.

The effects of these factors on transpiration in a leafy shoot can be investigated by means of the **potometer** (Figure 11.27).

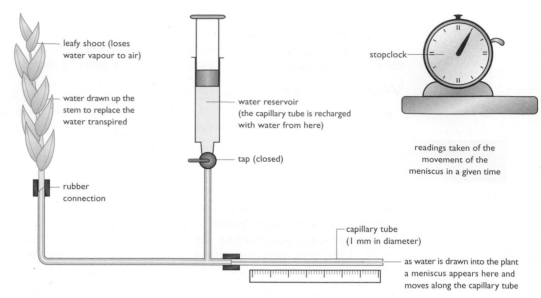

Figure 11.27
A potometer is used to investigate transpiration.

Does transpiration have a role?

Transpiration is a direct consequence of plant structure, plant nutrition and the mechanism of gaseous exchange in leaves. In effect, the living plant is a 'wick' that steadily dries the soil around it. Put like this, transpiration is an unfortunate consequence of plant structure and metabolism, rather than a valuable process!

But one effect of evaporation is that the leaf cells are cooled in the light. Furthermore, the stream of water travelling up from the roots passively carries the dissolved ions that have been actively absorbed from the soil solution in the root hairs and are required in the leaves and growing points of the plant. So transpiration has two roles: cooling the plant in sunlight, and moving mineral ions up the stem.

Translocation

Translocation is the movement of manufactured food (sugars and amino acids, mainly) in the phloem. **Sugars** are made in the leaves (in the light) by photosynthesis and transported as sucrose. The first-formed leaves, once established, transport sugars to sites of new growth (new stem, new leaves and new roots). In older plants, sucrose is increasingly transported to sites of storage, such as the cortex of roots or stems, and also seeds and fruits.

Meanwhile, **amino acids** are mostly made in the root tips, where nitrates are absorbed. The plant uses the nitrates in the synthesis of amino acids. After their manufacture, amino acids are transported to sites where proteins are synthesised. These are in the buds, young leaves, young roots and in developing fruits.

Figure 11.28
Bark ringing and its effects on stem transport.

How do we know translocation occurs in phloem?

Bark ringing is the technique of stripping a ring of the living tissues (bark, cortex and phloem) from all around a woody stem (Figure 11.28). It has been carried out experimentally in the past, but it is a very destructive process since it almost certainly kills the tree. In very severe winters, deer and rabbits sometimes do great harm to unprotected young woodland trees by gnawing the bark for the nutrients, and accidentally completely 'ringing' them.

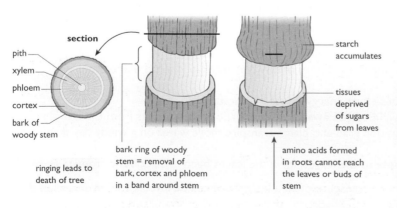

In stems ringed in summer months, sugars from the leaves accumulate above the ring as starch, and the roots are deprived of carbohydrate. Water transport from roots to leaves continues because the xylem is unharmed, but the bark-ringing treatment will eventually kill the plant because phloem cannot function and the roots are deprived of sugar from the leaves.

Transport of sugars in phloem is demonstrated by 'feeding' **radioactively labelled carbon dioxide** ($^{14}CO_2$) to a mature leaf of a green plant in the light. Sugar produced in this leaf is 'labelled' with the radioactive carbon. Movement of this sugar can be followed by autoradiography (page 182) of thin sections of the stem. The autoradiograph, when developed, shows the presence of radioactivity in the phloem.

Alternatively, the **aphids** that feed on the contents of the phloem in the growing regions of the stem have been exploited, using their mouthparts as micropipettes (Figure 11.29). The aphid's mouthparts are always inserted precisely in the phloem. After killing an aphid *in situ* (using a stream of carbon dioxide gas as anaesthetic), the aphid's proboscis can be cut whilst leaving the mouthparts in place. The mouthparts then exude phloem sap, which may be collected and analysed for radioactive sugar.

Figure 11.29
Using radioactive carbon to investigate phloem transport.

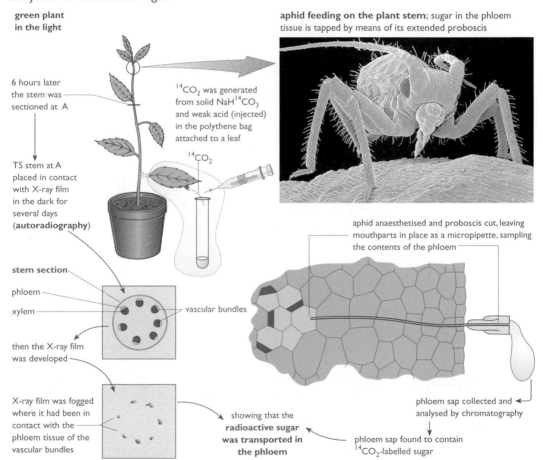

green plant in the light

aphid feeding on the plant stem; sugar in the phloem tissue is tapped by means of its extended proboscis

6 hours later the stem was sectioned at A

$^{14}CO_2$ was generated from solid $NaH^{14}CO_3$ and weak acid (injected) in the polythene bag attached to a leaf

$^{14}CO_2$

TS stem at A placed in contact with X-ray film in the dark for several days (**autoradiography**)

aphid anaesthetised and proboscis cut, leaving mouthparts in place as a micropipette, sampling the contents of the phloem

stem section

phloem

xylem

vascular bundles

then the X-ray film was developed

phloem sap collected and analysed by chromatography

X-ray film was fogged where it had been in contact with the phloem tissue of the vascular bundles

showing that the **radioactive sugar was transported in the phloem**

phloem sap found to contain $^{14}CO_2$-labelled sugar

Phloem structure and phloem transport

Phloem tissue consists of sieve tube elements and companion cells (Figure 11.30). **Sieve tubes** are narrow, elongated elements, connected end to end to form tubes. The end walls, known as **sieve plates**, are perforated by pores. The cytoplasm of a mature sieve tube has no nucleus, nor many of the other organelles of a cell either. However, each sieve tube is connected to a **companion cell** via plasmodesmata. The companion cells are believed to service and maintain the cytoplasm of the sieve tube in some way.

Phloem is a living tissue, and has quite a high rate of aerobic respiration during transport. The mechanism of transport of manufactured food in the phloem is not fully understood, but it is known that transport is an active process, using energy from metabolism. Phloem transport requires living phloem cells, and may occur in either direction in stem, leaves and roots.

● Extension   A theory of phloem transport

According to the **mass flow hypothesis**, solutes flow through the phloem from a region of high hydrostatic pressure to a region of low hydrostatic pressure. Hydrostatic pressure is high in and around cells where sugar is formed in the light (mesophyll cells of the leaf, for instance), because here the presence of sugar lowers the water potential (makes it more negative, page 65). Consequently water flows in, raising the hydrostatic pressure. This is called a 'source' area.

Hydrostatic pressure is low in cells where sugar is converted to starch and stored (such as ground tissue cells of the stem and root). Here the removal of sugar raises the water potential (makes it less negative) and water flows away. Starch storage cells like these are called 'sink' areas.

Evidence for and against the mass flow hypothesis of phloem transport from 'source' to 'sink' areas in the plant by hydrostatic pressure is summarised in Figure 11.30.

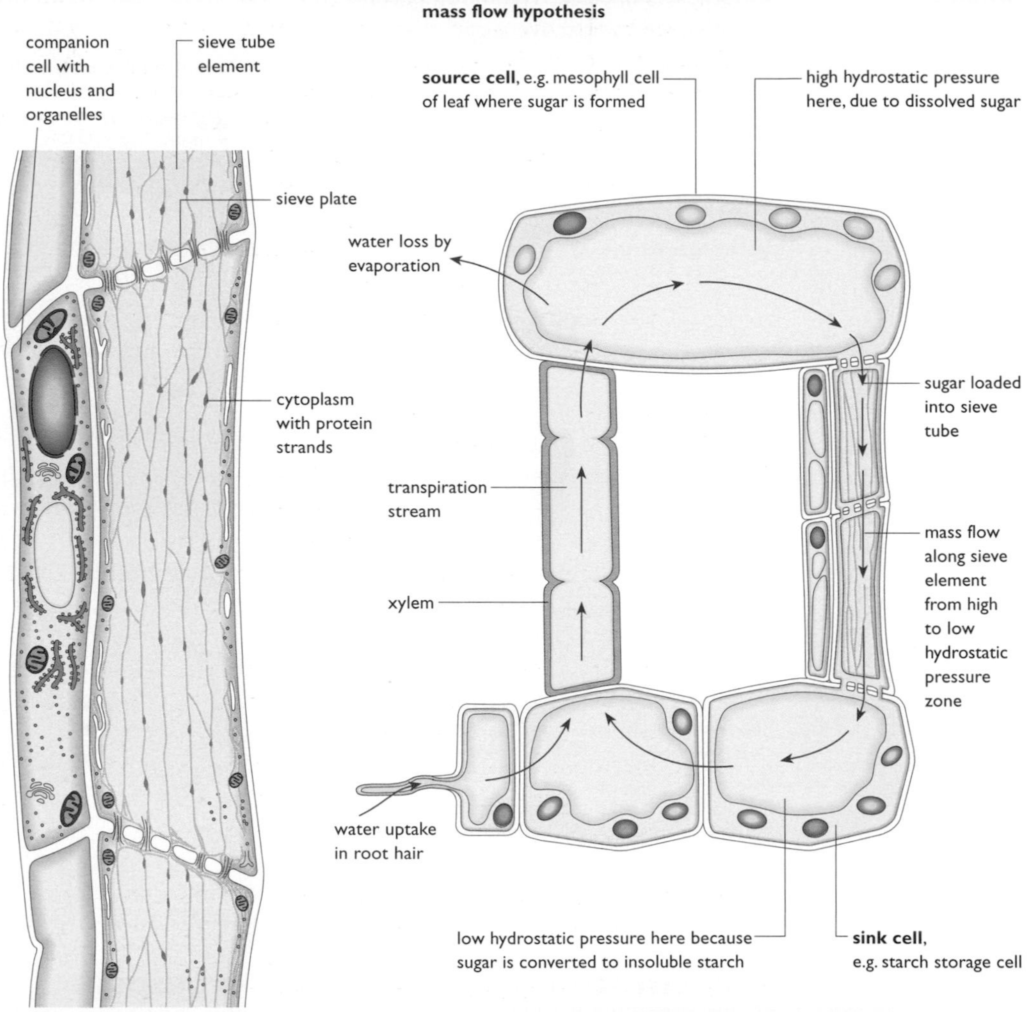

Figure 11.30
Phloem tissue and the mass flow hypothesis.

6 Distinguish between the following pairs:

- single and double circulations
- atria and ventricles
- vena cava and aorta
- diastole and systole
- arterioles and venules
- haemoglobin and myoglobin
- transpiration and translocation
- guard cell and subsidiary cell
- turgid and flaccid
- vascular bundle and stele
- diffusion and active uptake
- sieve tubes and companion cells.

Mass flow theory: evidence for theory	evidence against theory
contents of sieve tubes are under pressure, and sugar solution exudes if phloem is cut	phloem tissue carries manufactured food to various destinations simultaneously, rather than to the greatest 'sink'
appropriate gradients between 'source' and 'sink' tissues do exist	sieve plates are a barrier to mass flow, and might be expected to have been 'lost' in the course of evolution if mass flow is the mechanism of phloem transport

● **Skills task** In high mountain environments the atmospheric pressure is low. In these special conditions, normal breathing removes carbon dioxide from the blood, but the partial pressure of oxygen may be too low to fully saturate haemoglobin. The result may be a condition known as mountain sickness. However, humans living at these altitudes are **adapted**, and visiting humans become **acclimatised** with time.

Using websites as your sources, investigate this condition and the body's likely responses. Make concise notes to use for a group discussion on the main adaptations of natives and acclimatisation in visitors that enable them to carry out gaseous exchange without undue stress at high altitude. Record the sources of information used.

SUMMARY
- Mammals have a **closed circulation**, in which blood is pumped by a muscular heart through a continuous network of tubes, the **arteries**, **veins** and **capillaries**. It is a **double circulation**, in that blood goes twice through the heart in every complete circulation. The pulmonary circuit is to the lungs, supplied by the right side of the heart. The systemic circulation is to the rest of the body, supplied by the left side of the heart.
- Blood consists of a straw-coloured fluid, the **plasma**, and **blood cells**. Human red cells are without a nucleus, contain haemoglobin and transport oxygen. White cells combat disease. They are circulated by the blood to locations in the body where they act.
- The **heart** is a hollow, muscular organ of four chambers. The right and left halves of the heart are completely separate. The upper chambers, the **atria**, have relatively thin walls. The walls of the lower chambers, the **ventricles**, are much thicker. The direction of blood flow through the heart is maintained by **valves**.
- The cycle of changes of a heart beat, known as the **cardiac cycle**, lasts about 0.8 s. It consists of alternate contraction (**systole**) and relaxation (**diastole**). Atrial systole precedes ventricular systole, and both are followed by periods of diastole that partly overlap. Then atrial systole commences again.
- The heart beat originates in the heart itself (**myogenic origin**), at the **sino-atrial node** (SAN or pacemaker), in the upper wall of the right atrium. This activates the atrial muscle to contract and triggers the **atrio-ventricular node**, which carries the 'contract' signal on to the ventricles. The activity of the pacemaker is modulated from the cardiovascular control centre in the medulla of the brain. Impulses from the cerebral hemispheres, or involuntary reflexes from stretch receptors in arteries outside the heart, or hormone action can all alter heart beat rate.
- The roles of the **blood circulation** are in defence against disease, in the maintenance of a constant internal environment and in the transport of respiratory gases, water, nutrients, waste products, heat and hormones.
- **Haemoglobin**, a conjugated protein, and the enzyme **carbonic anhydrase** occur in red cells and together affect the transport of respiratory gases. Oxygen is transported as oxyhaemoglobin. Carbon dioxide is converted to hydrogencarbonate ions and transported in red cells and plasma.
- Internal transport within plants also occurs by mass flow, but here there is no pumping organ, and two separate tissues are involved in transport. Water and ions travel in the **xylem**, a system of vessels connected end to end to form non-living tubes. Manufactured foods are carried in a living tissue, the **phloem**, consisting of sieve tubes and companion cells. The xylem and phloem make up the **vascular bundles** that branch throughout the plant body and serve roots, stems, leaves and growing points (buds).
- Water is drawn up the stem by a force generated in the leaves by the evaporation of water vapour from the aerial system (**transpiration**). Water moves from the soil to the aerial system by a gradient in water potential.
- Transport of manufactured food in the phloem is an active process, requiring living phloem cells. According to the **mass flow hypothesis**, solutes flow through the phloem from a region of high hydrostatic pressure to a region of low hydrostatic pressure. Hydrostatic pressure is high in cells where sugar is formed ('source' areas) but low where sugar is converted to starch ('sink' areas).

● Examination questions

I The graphs below show the changes in pressure in the aorta and in the left and right ventricles of the heart, during the cardiac cycle. Time 0 indicates the start of atrial contraction.

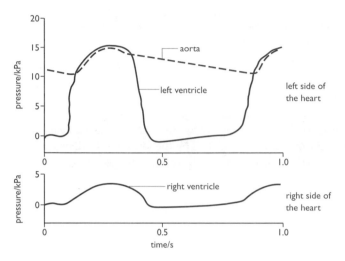

a Compare the changes in pressure in the left ventricle with those in the right ventricle, giving reasons for the differences. (4)

b Compare the changes in the pressure in the aorta with those in the left ventricle, giving reasons for the differences. (3)

c On the graph of changes in pressure in the aorta and left ventricle, show by means of an arrow when the aortic semilunar valve closes. (1)

d Cardiac muscle is described as myogenic. Explain how the cardiac cycle is coordinated within the heart. (4)

London, A level, Module B3, June 1998

2 In plants, phloem tissue is responsible for the transport of organic solutes such as sucrose and amino acids. The diagram shows transverse sections of two plant organs labelled **X** and **Y**.

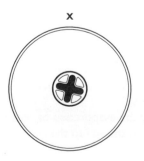

a i State which section is that of a root, and give a reason for your answer. (1)
ii On the diagram, label clearly the position of phloem tissue in **both** sections. (2)

Sucrose is made by photosynthesising cells in leaves, and some of this is used in the roots. The mass flow hypothesis, involving sources and sinks, is currently the most widely accepted mechanism by which organic materials are translocated in the phloem.

The mass flow mechanism operates due to a mass flow of solution as a result of differences in hydrostatic pressure in sources (leaves) and sinks (roots), due to sucrose production and use.

b i State how the production of sucrose by leaf cells will affect the hydrostatic pressure of these cells. (1)
ii What would lower the hydrostatic pressure? (1)

A demonstration of the mass flow mechanism was set up in the laboratory. The diagram shows the apparatus set up as the demonstration model. In the model, **A** represents a leaf and contains a highly concentrated sucrose solution. **B** represents a root and contains a weak sucrose solution. The rest of the vessel contains water.

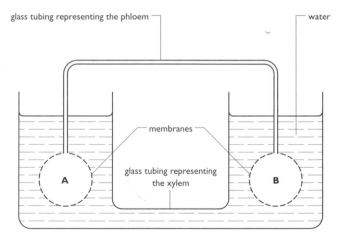

c With reference to this diagram,
i state **one** essential property of the membranes surrounding **A** and **B** (1)
ii explain how the model illustrates the process of translocation (4)
iii suggest **one other** possible sink region that **B** could represent. (1)

UCLES, A level, 4804, Nov 1996

III

COORDINATION AND CONTROL

The internal environment

STARTING POINTS
● Living things face **changing** and sometimes **hostile environments**; often environmental conditions decide where an organism can survive.
● Some animals are able to keep their internal conditions almost **unchanged** despite the changing environment around them. These organisms are **'regulators'**.
● 'Regulators' are more likely than 'non-regulators' to be found in a **wide variety of habitats**.
● 'Regulator' organisms maintain their **internal environment** in a steady state by a process called **homeostasis**.

● A constant internal environment

Environmental change is a fact of life. Conditions around organisms change all the time – some slowly, others dramatically. For example, temperature on land changes quickly when it is in direct sunlight, but the temperature of water exposed to sunlight changes only very slowly (page 55). How do organisms respond to environmental changes?

Some animals are able more or less to maintain their internal environment and their normal activities at a constant level, whatever the external conditions are like. We can call these organisms **'regulators'**. For example, mammals and birds maintain a high and almost constant body temperature over a very wide range of external temperatures. Their bodies are at or close to the optimum temperature for the majority of the enzymes that drive their metabolism. Their muscles contract efficiently, and the nervous system coordinates responses precisely, even when external conditions are unfavourable. They are better able to avoid danger, and perhaps they also benefit from the vulnerability of prey organisms that happen to be **'non-regulators'**. So regulators may have greater freedom in choosing where to live. They can exploit more habitats with differing conditions than can 'non-regulators' (Figure 12.1).

Figure 12.1
Homeostasis in mammals.

Mammals are a comparatively recent group in terms of their evolutionary history, yet they have successfully settled in significant numbers in virtually every type of habitat on Earth. This success is directly linked to their ability to control their internal environment by homeostasis.

polar bear on an ice flow

otter in fresh water

camels in the desert

whale in the sea

bat in the air

body temperature**

concentration of respiratory gases in blood (pCO_2, pO_2)•

glucose level of blood**

pressure of blood in arteries•

mammals examples of homeostasis by negative feedback

water content of blood**

heart rate•

pH of blood**

concentration of essential ions**

• = issue discussed in other chapters
** = examples explained here

Homeostasis is the name we give to the maintenance of a constant internal environment. Homeostasis simply means 'staying the same'. Mammals are excellent examples of animals that hold their internal conditions stable (Figure 12.1). A mammal's internal environment is essentially the blood circulating in the body and the tissue fluid formed from it, that bathes the cells, delivering nutrients and removing waste products. But how is this environment kept constant?

Negative feedback, the mechanism of homeostasis

Figure 12.2
Negative feedback, the mechanism.

Negative feedback is one type of control mechanism in which the condition being regulated is brought back to a set value as soon as it is detected to have parted from it. We see examples of this type of control in a laboratory water bath (or in a home central heating system) (Figure 12.2). Analysis of the first example will reveal to us the essential components.

components of a negative feedback control system

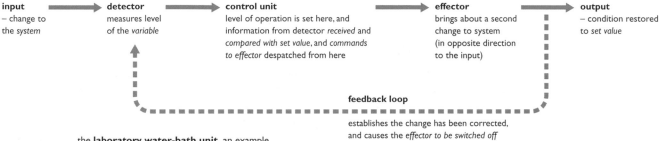

input
– change to the *system*

detector
measures level of the *variable*

control unit
level of operation is set here, and information from detector *received* and *compared with set value*, and *commands to effector* despatched from here

effector
brings about a second change to system (in opposite direction to the input)

output
– condition restored to *set value*

feedback loop
establishes the change has been corrected, and causes the *effector to be switched off*

the **laboratory water-bath unit**, an example of a self-regulating system

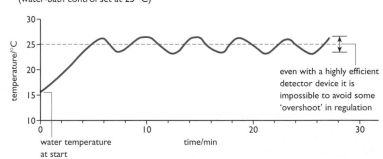

control unit with on/off switch, and set-point scale

temperature sensor

heat/water stirrer

pattern of change to water-bath temperature (water-bath control set at 25 °C)

even with a highly efficient detector device it is impossible to avoid some 'overshoot' in regulation

water temperature at start

A negative feedback system first requires a **detector** device to measure the value of the variable (for example, the water temperature of a water bath). It transmits this information to a **control unit**. The control unit compares the data from the detector with a desired **pre-set value** (in this case, the desired temperature of water in the water bath). When the value is below the required value the control unit activates an **effector device** (here a water heater in the water bath) so that the temperature starts to increase. Once the water reaches the set temperature, the detector then transmits a new set of data to this effect to the control box, which in response then switches off the effector (water heater). How precisely the variable is maintained (that is, how close to the desired value) depends on the sensitivity of the detector; negative feedback control systems typically have some degree of 'overshoot', however.

In mammals, regulation of body temperature, of blood sugar level, and of the water and ion content of the blood and tissue fluid (osmoregulation) are good examples of homeostasis in operation. The detectors are specialised cells, either in the brain or in other organs such as the pancreas. The effectors are organs such as the skin, liver and kidneys. Information passes between them via the nervous system, or via hormones (the endocrine system), or both. These systems precisely regulate the internal environment.

Temperature regulation

The regulation of body temperature, known as **thermoregulation**, involves controlling the amount of heat lost and heat gained through the skin surface. Heat may be transferred between an animal and the environment by **convection**, **radiation** and **conduction**. The body loses heat by **evaporation**. These heat transfer processes are summarised in Figure 12.3.

Figure 12.3
How heat is transferred between organism and environment.

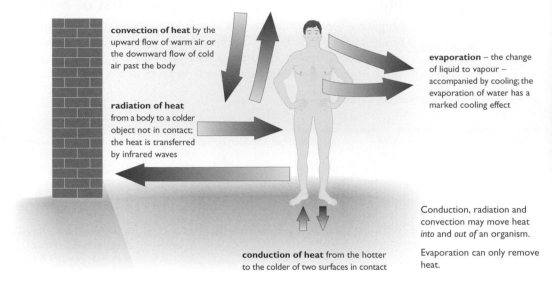

convection of heat by the upward flow of warm air or the downward flow of cold air past the body

radiation of heat from a body to a colder object not in contact; the heat is transferred by infrared waves

evaporation – the change of liquid to vapour – accompanied by cooling; the evaporation of water has a marked cooling effect

conduction of heat from the hotter to the colder of two surfaces in contact

Conduction, radiation and convection may move heat *into* and *out of* an organism.

Evaporation can only remove heat.

Body temperature of fish and reptiles

Fish are completely unable to regulate body temperature. The huge gill surface area over which water moves continuously for gaseous exchange (Figure 10.9, page 214) is also an efficient heat exchanger! In fishes, the temperature inside the body is approximately the same as the temperature of their surroundings. This is because any body heat above that of the surroundings is quickly lost to the water. In relation to thermoregulation, fish are good examples of 'non-regulators'.

On the other hand, air-breathing land animals like reptiles do have a crude form of control of body temperature, at least whilst they are active and alert. Lizards and snakes are good examples (Figure 12.4). Here, control is exercised by behavioural changes to take in heat as needed, exploiting any heat available in the external environment. In the morning, the animals 'bask' in sunlight to warm up. Then for the remainder of the day they move into and out of sunlight to absorb more or less heat according to their need. At night and over winter, their body temperature drops to that of the environment, and they become sluggish or even totally inactive.

Figure 12.4
Thermoregulation in an ectotherm.

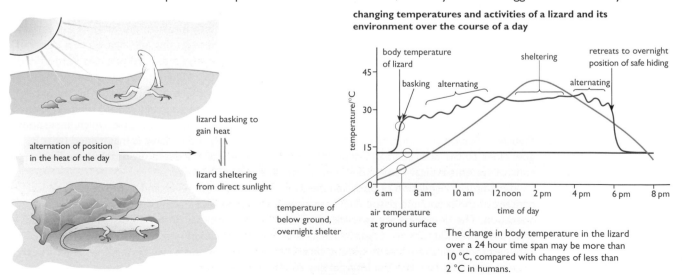

lizard basking to gain heat

alternation of position in the heat of the day

lizard sheltering from direct sunlight

changing temperatures and activities of a lizard and its environment over the course of a day

body temperature of lizard

basking   alternating

sheltering

retreats to overnight position of safe hiding

alternating

temperature of below ground, overnight shelter

air temperature at ground surface

time of day

The change in body temperature in the lizard over a 24 hour time span may be more than 10 °C, compared with changes of less than 2 °C in humans.

An animal with this form of thermoregulation is called an **ectotherm**, meaning 'outside heat'. During warm days an ectotherm may achieve a closely regulated body temperature. However, the kinds of places where ectotherms can live is typically more restricted, as is their lifestyle. They are also extremely vulnerable to mammal and bird predators during cold times. Reptiles are found commonly in only a few of the wide range of habitats that mammals have mastered.

(Notice that an older term, 'cold blooded', to describe fish and reptile body temperature, is now avoided, as is the term 'warm blooded' for birds and mammals.)

Thermoregulation in mammals

Mammals maintain a high and relatively constant body temperature. They achieve this by using the heat energy generated by metabolism within their bodies, or by generating additional heat in their muscles when cold, and carefully controlling the loss of heat through the skin. An animal with this form of thermoregulation is called an **endotherm**, meaning 'inside heat'. Birds as well as mammals have perfected this mechanism. For example, humans hold their inner body temperature ('core temperature') just below 37 °C. In fact, in a human who is in good health the body's inner temperature varies only between about 35.5 and 37.0 °C within a 24 hour period (Figure 12.5). When the external temperature is low, however, only the temperature of the trunk is held constant. The body temperature falls progessively from the trunk towards the ends of the limbs.

Figure 12.5
Body temperature of a human.

body temperature over a 48 hour period

The body temperatures shown were taken with the thermometer under the tongue. Although this is a region close to the body 'core', temperatures here may be altered by eating/drinking, and by the breathing in through the mouth of cold air, for example. More accurate values are obtained by taking the rectal temperature.

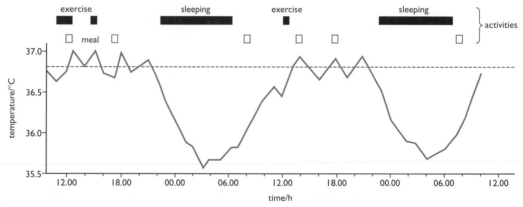

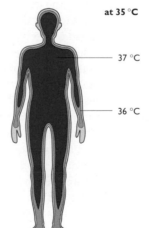

temperature distribution in environments at 20 °C and at 35 °C

The lines, **isotherms**, connect sites of equal temperature. The shaded area is the core, and around this the temperature varies according to the temperature of the surrounding air (**ambient temperature**).

Heat production in the human body

The major sources of heat in endotherms are the biochemical reactions of metabolism, which generate heat as a waste product. From the site of production, this heat reaches the rest of the body through the blood vessels. The organs of the body vary greatly in the amount of heat they yield. For example, the liver is extremely active metabolically, but most of its metabolic reactions require an input of energy (that is, they are **endothermic** reactions), so little energy is lost as heat. In consequence, the liver is more or less thermally neutral.

1 What does it mean to say most reactions in liver cells are endothermic?

The bulk of our body heat (over 70%) comes from the other abdominal organs – mainly from the heart and kidneys, but also from the brain and lungs. In contrast, when the body is at rest, the skeleton, muscles and skin, which make up over 90% of the body mass, produce less than 30% of the body heat (Figure 12.6). Of course, in times of intense physical activity, the skeletal muscles generate a great deal of heat as a waste product of respiration and contraction.

Figure 12.6
Heat production in the body at rest.

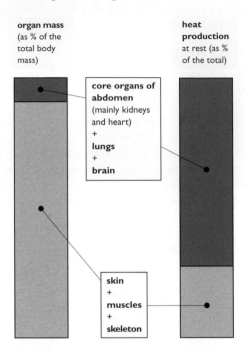

The role of the skin in thermoregulation

Heat exchanges occur at the skin. The outer layer of the skin, the **epidermis**, consists of stratified epithelium. The cells in its basal layer (called the **Malpighian layer**) constantly divide, pushing the cells above them towards the skin surface. These upper cells are progressively flattened, and the cell contents turn into keratin. The outermost layer of cells is constantly being rubbed off.

Below this layer is the **dermis**. This is a much thicker layer that consists of elastic connective tissue. In the dermis are found blood capillaries, the hair follicles with hair erector muscles, and the sweat glands. The sense receptors and sensory nerve endings are also found in this layer, and these are especially numerous in certain parts of the skin, which are consequently extremely sensitive. The sensory receptors send impulses to the central nervous system (CNS), via the sensory nerves (page 287).

At the base of the dermis is a layer of **adipose tissue**. In a mammal, this is one of the major sites of fat storage. This tissue has a limited blood supply and is a poor conductor of heat, so it insulates internal organs against heat loss. Aquatic mammals that inhabit cold waters, such as whales and seals, have an extremely thick layer of fat stored below the skin (known as blubber), which they maintain throughout life. Terrestrial mammals that remain active through the unfavourable season of the year also tend to build up their fat here, mostly as a food store.

The amount of heat loss at the skin may be varied, for example:

- at **capillary networks**: the arteriole supplying them is widened (**vasodilation**) when the body needs to lose heat, but constricted (**vasoconstriction**) when it needs to retain heat
- by the **hair erector muscles**: these contract when heat must be retained but relax when more heat needs to be lost
- by the **sweat glands**, which produce sweat only when the body needs to lose more heat.

These mechanisms are shown in Figure 12.7.

structure of the skin

sweat duct

sensory receptor
(free nerve ending)

epidermis

dermis

hair
hair follicle
cornified layer
(**dead cells**)
granular layer
(**living cells**)
Malpighian layer
skin capillary
sebaceous gland
connective tissue of dermis
hair erector muscle
root of hair (papilla)
sweat gland
sensory nerve fibre
adipose tissue (fat store)

role of the sweat glands in regulating heat loss through the skin is under control of the hypothalamus

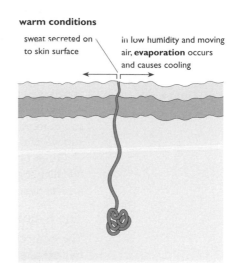

warm conditions

sweat secreted on to skin surface

in low humidity and moving air, **evaporation** occurs and causes cooling

role of capillaries in regulating heat loss through the skin

In skin that is especially exposed (e.g. outer ear, nose, extremities of the limbs) the capillary network is extensive, and the arterioles supplying it can be dilated or constricted, under control of the hypothalamus.

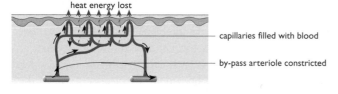

warm conditions

heat energy lost

capillaries filled with blood

by-pass arteriole constricted

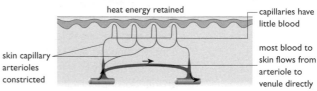

cold conditions

heat energy retained

capillaries have little blood

skin capillary arterioles constricted

most blood to skin flows from arteriole to venule directly

role of the hair in regulating heat loss through the skin

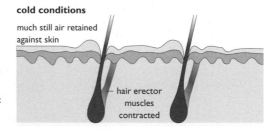

warm conditions

little still air retained against skin

hair erector muscles relaxed

The hair erector muscles may be contracted or relaxed, under control of the hypothalamus.

still air is a poor conductor of heat

cold conditions

much still air retained against skin

hair erector muscles contracted

Figure 12.7
The skin and temperature regulation.

Other mechanisms in thermoregulation

The metabolic rate can change

If a mammal's body experiences persistently cold conditions then its heat production is increased. The rate of heat release in an organism at rest is dependent on its **basal metabolic rate** (**BMR**). This is under the control of two hormones. In the short term, an increase in the rate of basal metabolism is brought about by the actions of the hormone **adrenaline**, which is secreted by the adrenal glands. In the longer term it is regulated by the actions of **thyroxine**, which is secreted by the thyroid glands (see Figure 13.20, page 292).

A specialised site of metabolic heat production is tissue known as **brown fat**, which is found in patches in the thorax of many mammals. The role of brown fat is solely to generate heat. When tissue is stimulated by sympathetic nerves, respiration of glucose formed from surrounding fat reserves is speeded up. The ATP formed in the brown fat cells is immediately hydrolysed (page 194) to ADP and P_i, and all the free energy of the reaction is released as heat and circulated by the blood.

In a persistently hot environment the metabolic rate is reduced.

Behaviour change

Under chilly conditions the heat output from the body muscles increases. An animal's posture is continuously maintained by sustained contractions of the skeletal muscles, which contributes to the basal rate of heat production. These contractions are quite distinct from those that cause movement, and they can be increased, thereby raising heat production all over the body. In cold conditions, also, non-coordinated contractions of skeletal muscles may be triggered. This type of muscle activity, which we recognise as 'shivering', raises muscle heat production about five times above the basal rate.

Panting is also a very efficient method of losing heat. It is used by mammals with a pronounced snout. In this method, air is drawn in through the nose and mouth and expelled over the moist surface of the tongue. As heat is lost by evaporation from the tongue, the body cools.

Other behavioural changes used to regulate heat include moving to a cooler or hotter place, huddling together with other individuals, or becoming vigorously active to generate even more muscle heat. In addition, in humans, the amount of clothing a person is wearing can be adjusted.

The hypothalamus as the control centre

The 'control box' for temperature regulation in mammals is a region of the forebrain called the **hypothalamus** (Figure 13.17, page 289). It is called the 'thermoregulation centre', and it consists of a 'heat loss centre' and a 'heat gain centre' (Figure 12.8). Temperature-sensitive nerve cells (**neurones**) are situated in the hypothalamus. They detect changes in the temperature of the blood flowing through the brain. The thermoregulation centre of the hypothalamus also receives information via sensory nerves from temperature-sensitive receptors located in the skin and in many internal organs.

The hypothalamus communicates with the rest of the body via the autonomic nervous system (ANS) (page 288), and this is how the body temperature is regulated. For example, when the body temperature is **lower than normal**, the heat gain centre inhibits activity of the heat loss centre; impulses are sent to the skin, hair erector muscles, sweat glands and elsewhere that decrease heat loss (for instance, by causing vasoconstriction of skin capillaries) and increase heat production (for instance, by causing shivering, and enhanced 'brown fat' respiration). When the body temperature is **higher than normal** the heat loss centre inhibits the heat gain centre activity. Impulses are sent to the skin, hair erector muscles, sweat glands and elsewhere that increase heat loss (for instance, by causing vasodilation of skin capillaries) and decrease heat production.

Figure 12.8
Temperature regulation of the body by the hypothalamus.

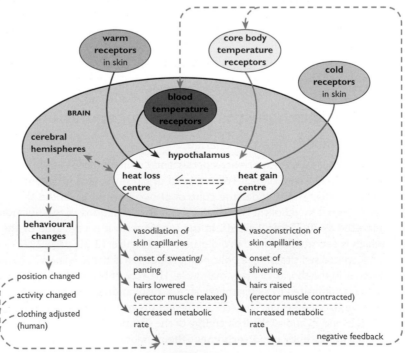

Regulation of blood glucose level

Transport of the monosaccharide glucose to all cells is a key function of the blood circulation. In humans, the **normal level of blood glucose** is about 90 mg of glucose/100 cm³ of blood, but this can vary. For example, during an extended period without food, or after prolonged and heavy physical activity, the blood glucose level may drop to as low as 70 mg. After a meal rich in carbohydrate has been digested, the blood glucose level may rise to 150 mg.

The maintenance of a constant level of this sugar in the blood plasma is important for two reasons.

- Respiration is a continuous process in all living cells. To maintain their metabolism, cells need a regular supply of glucose, which can be quickly absorbed across the cell membrane. Glucose is the principal fuel used for respiration (Figure 9.7, page 196). Most cells (including the muscle) hold additional glucose reserves in the form of glycogen, which is quickly converted to glucose during prolonged physical activity; however, glycogen reserves may be used up quickly. In the brain, glucose is the only fuel the cells can use and there are no glycogen reserves held there at all.

   If our blood glucose falls below 60 mg/100 cm³ a condition called **hypoglycaemia** develops. If this is not quickly reversed, the person may faint. If the body and brain continue to be deprived of adequate glucose levels, then convulsions and hypoglycaemic coma follow, which can be fatal.
- An abnormally high concentration of blood glucose, known as **hyperglycaemia**, is also a problem. Since high concentrations of any soluble metabolite lower the water potential of the blood plasma, water is drawn out of the cells and tissue fluid by osmosis, back into the blood. As the volume of blood increases, water is excreted by the kidney in an attempt to maintain the correct concentration of blood. As a result the body tends to become dehydrated, and the circulatory system is deprived of fluid. Ultimately, the correct blood pressure cannot be maintained.

For these reasons, it is critically important that the blood glucose is held within set limits.

Regulation of blood glucose

After the digestion of carbohydrates in the gut, glucose is absorbed across the epithelial cells of the villi (Figure 7.16, page 157) into the hepatic portal vein (Figure 7.20, page 159). The blood carrying the glucose therefore reaches the liver first. If the glucose level is too high then glucose is removed from the blood and stored as glycogen. But, even so, blood circulating in the body after a meal has a raised level of glucose. At the pancreas the presence of an excess of blood glucose is detected by groups of cells within the organ, known as the **islets of Langerhans** (Figure 12.9). These islets are hormone-secreting glands (endocrine glands); they have a rich capillary network, but no ducts that would carry secretions away. Instead, their hormones are transported all over the body by the blood. The islets of Langerhans contain two types of cell, known as α **cells** and β **cells**.

Figure 12.9
An endocrine gland of the pancreas.

TS of pancreatic gland showing an islet of Langerhans

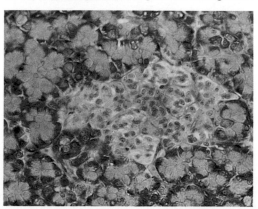

drawing of part of pancreatic gland

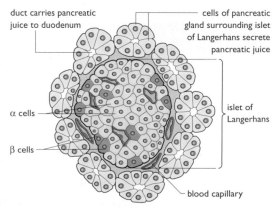

In the presence of a **raised blood glucose level**, the β **cells** are stimulated. They secrete the hormone **insulin** into the capillary network. Insulin stimulates the uptake of glucose into cells all over the body, but especially in cells in the liver and the skeletal muscle fibres (Figure 12.10). It also increases the rate at which glucose is used in respiration, in preference to alternative substances (such as fats). Another effect of insulin is to trigger conversion of glucose to glycogen for storage in cells (**glycogenesis**), and of glucose to fatty acids and fats, and finally the deposition of fat around the body.

As the blood glucose level reverts to normal this is again detected in the islets of Langerhans. The β cells respond by stopping insulin secretion. Meanwhile, the hormone is excreted by the kidney tubules, and the blood insulin level falls.

When the **blood glucose level falls below the normal**, the α **cells** of the pancreas are stimulated. These secrete a hormone called **glucagon**. This hormone activates the enzymes in the liver that convert glycogen and amino acids to glucose (**gluconeogenesis**). Glucagon also reduces the rate of respiration. Low blood glucose also triggers the secretion of other hormones in the body, particularly adrenaline by the adrenal glands (page 292). One effect of adrenaline is to stimulate the conversion of glycogen and amino acids to glucose, which raises the level of blood glucose.

As the blood glucose level reverts to normal, glucagon production and adrenaline production cease, and these hormones in turn are removed from the blood in the kidney tubules.

> **2** What do liver cells receive from blood from the hepatic artery that is not present in blood from the hepatic portal vein?

Figure 12.10
The sites and processes of blood glucose regulation.

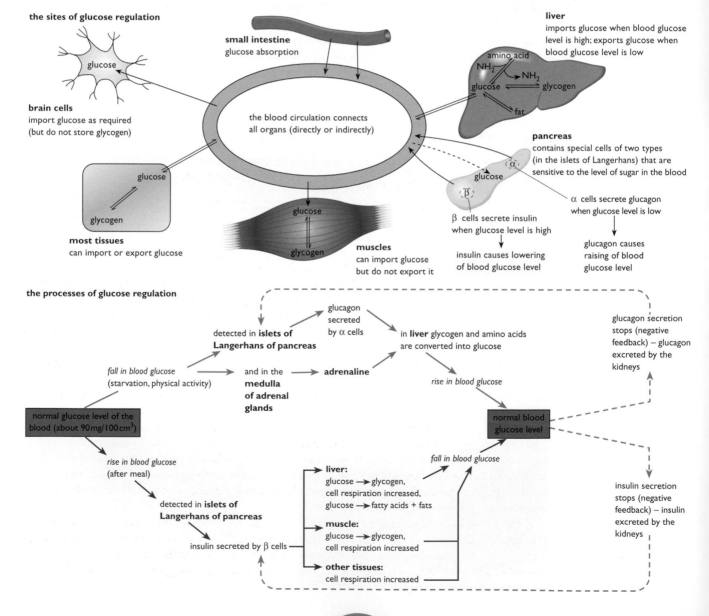

● **Extension** Diabetes

Diabetes is the name for a group of diseases in which the body fails to regulate blood glucose levels. Type I diabetes results from a failure of insulin production by the β cells. Type II is a failure of the insulin receptor proteins on the cell membranes of target cells (Figure 12.11). As a consequence, blood glucose levels are more erratic and, generally, permanently raised. Glucose is also regularly excreted in the urine. If this condition is not diagnosed and treated, it carries an increased risk of circulatory disorders, kidney failure, blindness, strokes and heart attacks.

Figure 12.11
Diabetes, cause and treatment.

type I diabetes,
'early onset diabetes'
affects young people, below the age of 20 years

due to the destruction of the β cells of the islets of Langerhans by the body's own immune system

symptoms:
constant thirst
undiminished hunger
excessive urination

treatment:
injection of insulin into the bloodstream daily
regular measurement of blood glucose level

patient injecting with insulin,
obtained by genetic engineering (page 129)

type II diabetes,
'late onset diabetes'
the common form (90% of all cases of diabetes are of this type)

common in people over 40 years, especially if overweight

symptoms:
mild – sufferers usually have sufficient blood insulin, but insulin receptors on cells have become defective

treatment:
largely by diet alone

● Other roles of the liver in homeostasis

In the liver, blood flows through channels in hexagonal blocks of tissue (Figure 12.12). The channel walls are made up of lines of liver cells. This brings blood in direct contact with the cells of the liver. On entry, blood from both the hepatic portal vein (carrying nutrients absorbed in the villi – see page 157) and the hepatic artery (carrying oxygenated blood) join together. At the centre of each block, a branch of the hepatic vein carries the blood away.

We have seen that the liver helps maintain the required level of blood glucose, but this is only one of several of its functions that contribute to homeostasis. Another important task is the **breakdown of the redundant red blood cells**. Daily, some 2 million red blood cells are destroyed and replaced. Huge numbers of haemoglobin molecules, which are large proteins, need to be dismantled in a way that does not interfere with the smooth running of the rest of the body processes. The breakdown of red blood cells occurs in the liver and spleen. Most of the breakdown products are then stored in the liver for reuse, or are further metabolised there. The role of the liver in haemoglobin breakdown and formation of bile is summarised in Figure 12.13.

In animals, excess proteins and amino acids cannot be stored. Instead they are broken down by a process called **'deamination'** (because the first step is the removal of the amino groups). This process must happen without the release of free ammonia within the tissues. This is important because ammonia is both very toxic and very soluble. To achieve the breakdown safely, cells in the liver convert the amino groups into **urea**, which is a relatively harmless product that can be safely transported in the blood to the kidneys, where it is excreted. The deamination process is summarised in Figure 12.14.

Other roles of the liver include the production of cholesterol and the processing of lipids (combined with protein, known as lipoprotein) for transport in the body. It is also involved in the storage of fat-soluble vitamins (Table 7.3, page 147), the synthesis of blood proteins, and the breakdown of hormones, and also any poisons, toxins and drugs that have been absorbed, prior to excretion in the kidneys.

3 What are the roles of phagocytic cells in the liver?

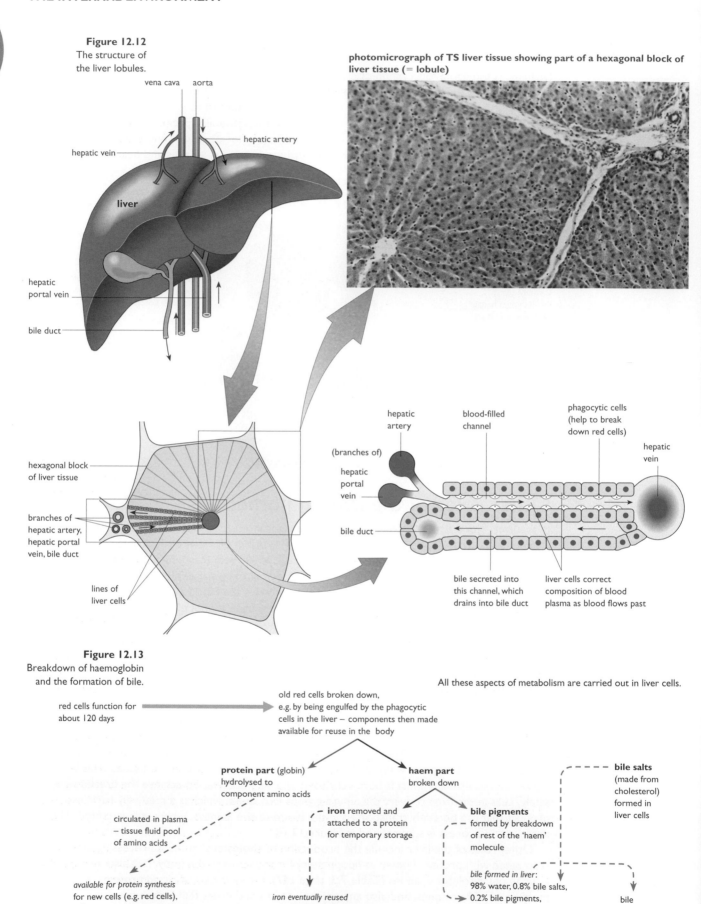

Figure 12.12
The structure of
the liver lobules.

vena cava   aorta

hepatic vein

hepatic artery

liver

hepatic
portal vein

bile duct

**photomicrograph of TS liver tissue showing part of a hexagonal block of
liver tissue (= lobule)**

hexagonal block
of liver tissue

branches of
hepatic artery,
hepatic portal
vein, bile duct

lines of
liver cells

hepatic
artery

(branches of)

hepatic
portal
vein

bile duct

blood-filled
channel

phagocytic cells
(help to break
down red cells)

hepatic
vein

bile secreted into
this channel, which
drains into bile duct

liver cells correct
composition of blood
plasma as blood flows past

Figure 12.13
Breakdown of haemoglobin
and the formation of bile.

All these aspects of metabolism are carried out in liver cells.

red cells function for
about 120 days

old red cells broken down,
e.g. by being engulfed by the phagocytic
cells in the liver – components then made
available for reuse in the body

protein part (globin)
hydrolysed to
component amino acids

haem part
broken down

bile salts
(made from
cholesterol)
formed in
liver cells

circulated in plasma
– tissue fluid pool
of amino acids

iron removed and
attached to a protein
for temporary storage

bile pigments
formed by breakdown
of rest of the 'haem'
molecule

available for protein synthesis
for new cells (e.g. red cells),
cell repair and enzyme formation

iron eventually reused
in red cell formation

bile formed in liver:
98% water, 0.8% bile salts,
0.2% bile pigments,
0.7% ions, 0.6% cholesterol

bile
secreted

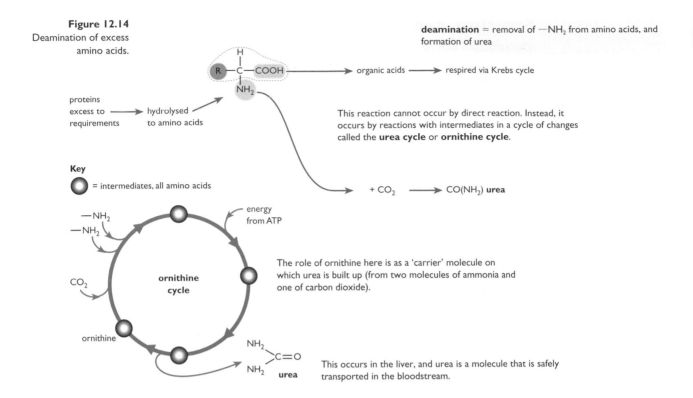

Figure 12.14
Deamination of excess amino acids.

deamination = removal of —NH₂ from amino acids, and formation of urea

proteins excess to requirements → hydrolysed to amino acids

organic acids ⟶ respired via Krebs cycle

This reaction cannot occur by direct reaction. Instead, it occurs by reactions with intermediates in a cycle of changes called the **urea cycle** or **ornithine cycle**.

+ CO_2 ⟶ $CO(NH_2)$ **urea**

Key

⬤ = intermediates, all amino acids

energy from ATP

ornithine cycle

The role of ornithine here is as a 'carrier' molecule on which urea is built up (from two molecules of ammonia and one of carbon dioxide).

ornithine

urea

This occurs in the liver, and urea is a molecule that is safely transported in the bloodstream.

⬤ Extension   Other excretory products

Animals living in water often excrete ammonia rather than urea, e.g. *Amoeba* and bony fish such as trout and herring. Whilst ammonia is toxic, it readily dissolves in the excess water that these animals constantly lose to their environment. The ammonia is thus safely disposed of, and little metabolic energy goes into its formation.

On the other hand, terrestrial insects and birds produce uric acid as their nitrogenous excretion product. This insoluble substance takes up metabolic energy in its formation. However, it is a non-toxic substance, excreted as a paste or solid, so takes up little water in the process.

⬤ Kidneys: the site of excretion and osmoregulation

Figure 12.15
The human urinary system.

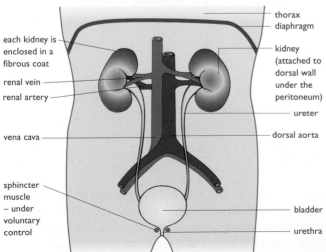

each kidney is enclosed in a fibrous coat

renal vein

renal artery

vena cava

sphincter muscle – under voluntary control

thorax

diaphragm

kidney (attached to dorsal wall under the peritoneum)

ureter

dorsal aorta

bladder

urethra

The kidneys regulate the internal environment by constantly adjusting the blood composition. The reactions of metabolism within the cells produce waste products, some of which would be toxic if allowed to accumulate. **Excretion** is the removal from the body of these waste products of metabolism. They are transported from the cells in the circulating blood and then in turn removed from the blood in the kidneys. The maintenance of the balance of dissolved substances and water in body fluids is called **osmoregulation**. The level of solutes in the blood plasma determines the solute potential (page 64), and therefore the water content, of body fluids. The kidney regulates the concentrations of inorganic ions, such as Na^+ and Cl^-, and of sugars and amino acids (non-electrolytes), along with the water content. It removes any excess solutes and water. The position of the kidneys and the urinary system are shown in Figure 12.15.

Structure and function of the kidneys

The structure and function of the human kidneys and its components are shown in Figure 12.16. Each kidney receives blood down a renal artery and is drained by a renal vein. Urine leaves the kidneys and passes to the bladder down the ureter. When the urine in the bladder reaches a certain level, the bladder sphincter muscle is relaxed and the urine is able to pass down the urethra. Together these structures are known as the urinary system.

Inside a kidney there are two layers: an outer **cortex** and inner **medulla** (Figure 12.16). These contain about a million tiny tubules, called **nephrons**, with an accompanying blood supply that is crucial to their function. A nephron is a thin-walled tubule about 3 cm long. Part of each nephron lies in the cortex and part in the medulla.

Figure 12.16
The structure and function of the nephron.

LS through kidney showing positions of nephrons in cortex and medulla

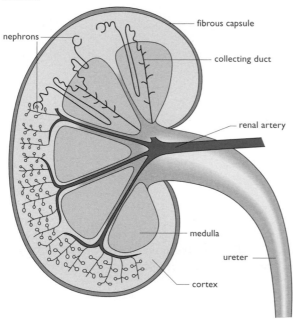

nephron with blood capillaries

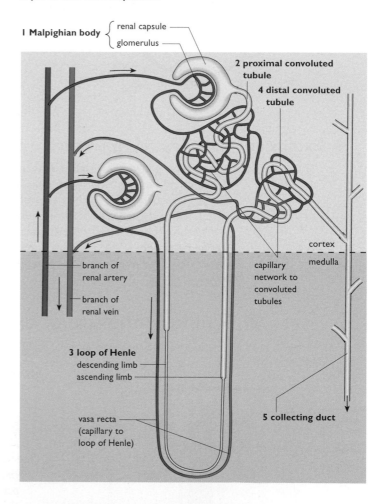

roles of the parts of the nephron:
1 **Malpighian body** = ultrafiltration
2 **proximal convoluted tubule** = selective reabsorption from filtrate
3 **loop of Henle** = water conservation
4 **distal convoluted tubule** = pH adjustment and ion reabsorption
5 **collecting duct** = water reabsorption

The formation of urine

4 What is the source of energy for ultrafiltration in the glomerulus?

In humans, about 1–1.5 litres of urine are formed each day. This amount typically contains about 50 g of solutes, of which urea (30 g) and sodium chloride (15 g) make up the bulk. The nephrons produce urine in a continuous process. However, we can conveniently divide it into five steps, to show how the blood and body fluids composition are so precisely regulated.

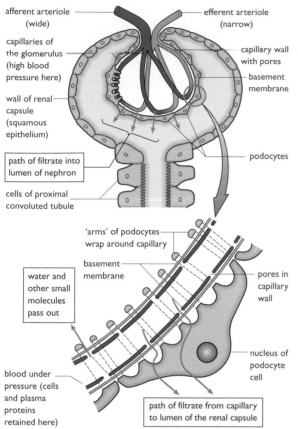

afferent arteriole (wide)

efferent arteriole (narrow)

capillaries of the glomerulus (high blood pressure here)

capillary wall with pores

basement membrane

wall of renal capsule (squamous epithelium)

path of filtrate into lumen of nephron

podocytes

cells of proximal convoluted tubule

'arms' of podocytes wrap around capillary

basement membrane

pores in capillary wall

water and other small molecules pass out

nucleus of podocyte cell

blood under pressure (cells and plasma proteins retained here)

path of filtrate from capillary to lumen of the renal capsule

Figure 12.17
The site of ultrafiltration.

Ultrafiltration in the renal capsule

The first part of the nephron is called the **Malpighian body**; it consists of an outer **renal capsule**, which encloses a blood capillary network, called the **glomerulus** (Figure 12.17). In the glomulerus, water and relatively small molecules within the blood plasma, including useful ions, glucose and amino acids, are forced out of the blood, along with urea, across the capsule and into its inner compartment, called the **lumen**. This passage of solutes and water can occur because of the sieve-like structure of capillary and renal capsule walls. This 'sieve' consists of endothelial cells of the capillary and epithelial cells of the renal capsule (called **podocytes**), both of which have tiny gaps between them. These allow the passage of small particles. Nevertheless, blood cells and the majority of the soluble blood proteins remain in the blood in the capillaries, as they cannot fit through the pores. This is an ultrafiltration process, powered by the pressure exerted by the blood, because the input capillary (the afferent arteriole) is wider than the output capillary (the efferent arteriole).

Selective reabsorption in the proximal convoluted tubule

The **proximal convoluted tubule** is the longest section of the nephron (Figure 12.18). Its walls are one cell thick and are packed with mitochondria (ATP is required for active transport). The cell membrane in contact with the filtrate has a 'brush border' of microvilli (Figure 7.17, page 157). These enormously increase the surface area available for reabsorption. As the filtrate from the renal capsule passes through this tubule, a large part of it is reabsorbed into the capillary network. The individual mechanisms of transport are:

- movement of water by **osmosis**
- **active transport** of glucose and amino acids across membranes
- movement of mineral ions by a combination of **active transport**, **facilitated diffusion** and some exchange of ions
- **diffusion** of urea
- movement of proteins by **pinocytosis**
- active transport of harmful substances (for example, drugs, poisons) from the blood.

5 Cells of the walls of the proximal convoluted tubule have a 'brush border'. What is this and how does it help in tubule function?

Figure 12.18
Reabsorption in the proximal convoluted tubule.

capillary wall cells

water movement by **osmosis**

harmful substances **actively transported** from blood into filtrate

filtrate flow in lumen

proximal convoluted tubule wall cell

glucose + amino acids **actively transported** across membranes

ions (e.g. Na$^+$) filtered by:
- **active transport**
- **facilitated diffusion**
- exchange with H$^+$ ions

the few proteins in filtrate are taken back into blood by **pinocytosis**

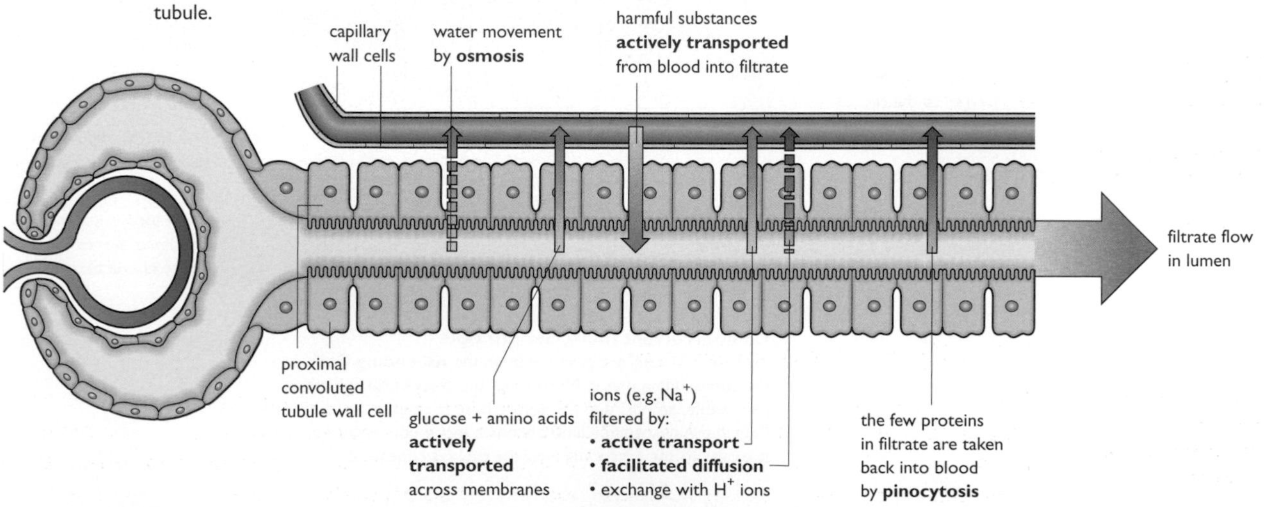

Water conservation in the loop of Henle

Urea is expelled from the body in solution, so water loss in excretion is inevitable. However, mammals (and birds) are able to reduce water loss to a minimum by forming urine that is more concentrated than the blood. They do this in the next section of the nephron: the loop of Henle. This is a U-shaped bend in the tubule that brings the two sections of the tubule, the descending and ascending limbs close together with a parallel blood supply, the **vasa recta**. This arrangement creates and maintains a high concentration of salts in the tissue fluid in the medulla of the kidney. As the high concentration of salts in the tissue of the medulla builds up, it causes water to be reabsorbed from the filtrate in the collecting ducts that run through the medulla.

The role of the vasa recta is to remove carbon dioxide and deliver oxygen to the metabolically active cells of the loop of Henle without removing the accumulated salts from the medulla. This is done by a mechanism called a **countercurrent multiplier**.

Figure 12.19 explains how the countercurrent mechanism works. Look first at the second half of the loop, the ascending limb. Here, sodium and chloride ions are actively pumped out into the surrounding medulla. However, water is retained inside the ascending limb of the tubule. Opposite to this, the descending limb is permeable, so sodium and chloride ions can diffuse in from the medulla. Water passes out in the opposite direction, into the medulla tissue, owing to the high salt concentration in the latter.

As the filtrate flows down the descending limb, this water loss increases the salt concentration in the loop, making the filtrate more concentrated. Consequently, sodium ions and chloride ions diffuse out down their concentration gradient, around the 'hairpin' zone at the base of the descending limb, adding to the concentration of ions in the medulla. How this concentration helps to concentrate the urine in the collecting ducts is explained in the following section.

Figure 12.19 The functioning loop of Henle.

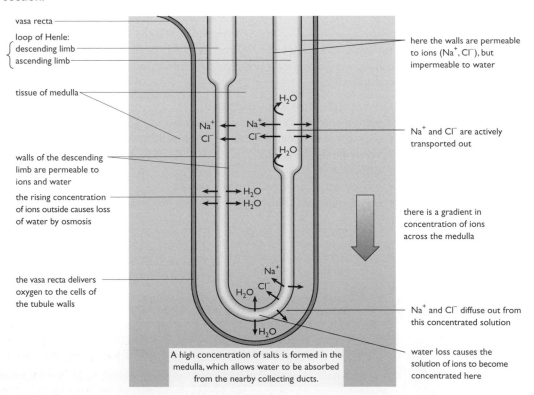

vasa recta

loop of Henle:
descending limb
ascending limb

tissue of medulla

here the walls are permeable to ions (Na$^+$, Cl$^-$), but impermeable to water

H_2O

Na$^+$ Na$^+$
Cl$^-$ Cl$^-$

H_2O

Na$^+$ and Cl$^-$ are actively transported out

walls of the descending limb are permeable to ions and water

the rising concentration of ions outside causes loss of water by osmosis

H_2O
H_2O

there is a gradient in concentration of ions across the medulla

the vasa recta delivers oxygen to the cells of the tubule walls

Na$^+$
Cl$^-$
H_2O

H_2O

Na$^+$ and Cl$^-$ diffuse out from this concentrated solution

A high concentration of salts is formed in the medulla, which allows water to be absorbed from the nearby collecting ducts.

water loss causes the solution of ions to become concentrated here

Countercurrent multiplier principle
Na$^+$ and Cl$^-$ ions are pumped from the **ascending limb** into the surrounding tissue. Meanwhile, the **descending limb** is permeable, so Na$^+$ and Cl$^-$ ions diffuse in (and water out). The fluid in the descending limb becomes more concentrated, and as it passes to the ascending limb the cycle is repeated.

Blood pH and ion concentration regulation in the distal convoluted tubule

The cells in the **distal convoluted tubule** are of the same structure as those in the proximal convoluted tubule, but their role is different: to adjust the composition of the blood, and in particular its acidity (pH). Initially any tendency for the pH of the blood to change is 'buffered' by the blood proteins (page 227). However, if the blood acidity does begin to deviate from pH 7.4, then it is brought back to this level by adjusting the concentration of hydrogen (H^+) ions and hydroxyl (OH^-) ions, along with that of hydrogencarbonate (HCO_3^-) ions.

If the blood pH falls below pH 7.4 then H^+ ions are withdrawn from the blood to the filtrate, and HCO_3^- ions are transported from the filtrate into blood (Figure 12.20). If the pH rises above pH 7.4, then OH^- ions are removed from blood to filtrate, along with HCO_3^- ions. Consequently, blood pH does not vary wider than the limits 7.35–7.45, but the pH of urine varies much more – from pH 4.5 to 8.2.

Also in the distal convoluted tubule, ions that are useful in metabolism are selectively reabsorbed from the filtrate. This process is under the control of the hormone **aldosterone**, which is formed in the cortex of the adrenal glands (Figure 13.20, page 292).

Figure 12.20
pH regulation in the distal convoluted tubule.

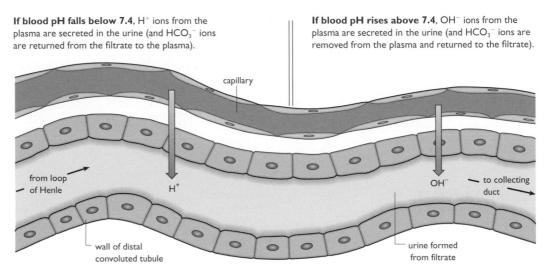

If blood pH falls below 7.4, H^+ ions from the plasma are secreted in the urine (and HCO_3^- ions are returned from the filtrate to the plasma).

If blood pH rises above 7.4, OH^- ions from the plasma are secreted in the urine (and HCO_3^- ions are removed from the plasma and returned to the filtrate).

capillary

from loop of Henle

H^+

OH^-

to collecting duct

wall of distal convoluted tubule

urine formed from filtrate

Water reabsorption in the collecting ducts

The **collecting ducts** are the place where the water content of the blood (and therefore of the whole body) is regulated (Figure 12.21). The body water content is monitored in the hypothalamus. When the water content of the blood is low a hormone, **antidiuretic hormone (ADH)**, is secreted from the posterior pituitary (Figure 13.20, page 292). When it is high, no ADH is secreted.

The presence or absence of ADH affects the permeability of the walls of the collecting ducts to water (a case of facilitated diffusion; see page 62). In the presence of ADH the walls of the collecting ducts are fully permeable. This allows water to be withdrawn from the filtrate of the tubule into the medulla, owing to the high concentration of sodium and chloride ions there (see above). This water is taken up and redistributed in the body by the blood circulation. Meanwhile, the ADH circulating in the blood is removed at the kidneys, so small amounts of concentrated urine are formed.

When no ADH is secreted the walls of the collecting duct become less permeable. The result is that large quantities of very dilute urine are formed.

A summary of osmoregulation by the kidney is given in Figure 12.22.

Figure 12.21
Water reabsorption in
the collecting ducts.

When we have:
• drunk a lot of water
the hypothalamus detects this and stops the posterior pituitary gland
secreting ADH.

When we have:
• taken in little water
• sweated excessively
• eaten salty food
the hypothalamus detects this and directs the posterior pituitary gland to
secrete ADH.

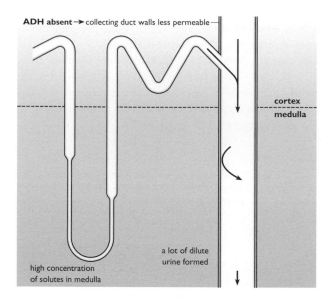

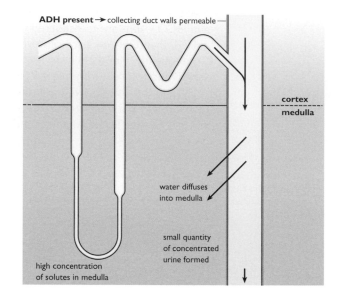

Figure 12.22
Summary: homeostasis
by osmoregulation
in the kidney.

6 In what circumstances
in the body is ADH
released?

7 Distinguish between the
following pairs of terms:

• glucose and glycogen
• hepatic artery and
hepatic portal vein
• ectotherm and
endotherm
• epidermis and dermis
• vasodilation and
vasoconstriction
• cortex and medulla
of a kidney
• glomerulus and renal
capsule
• ultrafiltration and
selective reabsorption
• proximal and distal
convoluted tubule
• loop of Henle and
collecting duct.

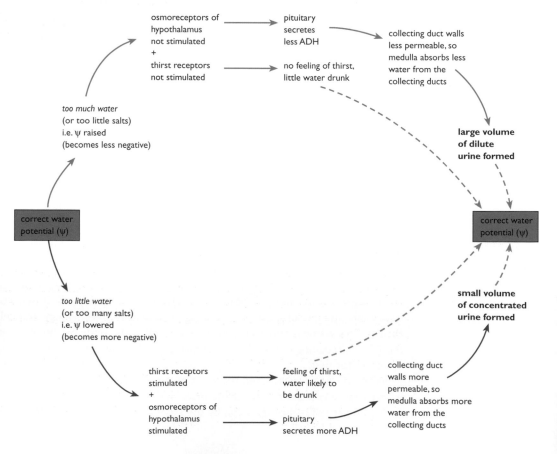

● Extension — Renal failure, dialysis and transplants

Kidney failure may be caused by bacterial infection, by external mechanical damage, or by high blood pressure. In the event of renal failure, urea, water and sodium ions start to accumulate in the blood. In mild cases, a careful diet (to limit intake of fluids, salt and proteins) may be sufficient to minimise the task of the remaining kidney tubules, so the body copes.

In cases where more than 50% of kidney function has been lost, regular haemodialysis may be required every few days, in addition to a strict, prescribed diet. In dialysis, the person's blood circulation is connected to a dialysis machine, as shown in Figure 12.23. The blood is repeatedly circulated outside the body for 6–10 hours, through a fine tube of cellophane (a partially permeable membrane) bathed in dialysate – a fluid with a solute potential and composition the same as that of blood leaving a healthy kidney. This prevents net outward diffusion of the useful components of blood (mainly water, ions, sugars and amino acids) but allows the outward diffusion of urea and toxic substances.

Ideally, acute renal failure can be rectified by the transplantation of a healthy kidney from a donor. However, to be successful the donor's cell type must be sufficiently compatible with that of the recipient; a kidney from a non-compatible donor would generate an overwhelming immunological reaction leading to the patient's body rejecting the new kidney. No match is 'perfect', however, so to avoid rejection at transplantation the antibody-producing cells of the recipient must be suppressed. Subsequently, drugs that will suppress this response (see the immune response, page 337) have to be administered permanently.

Figure 12.23
The principle of dialysis.

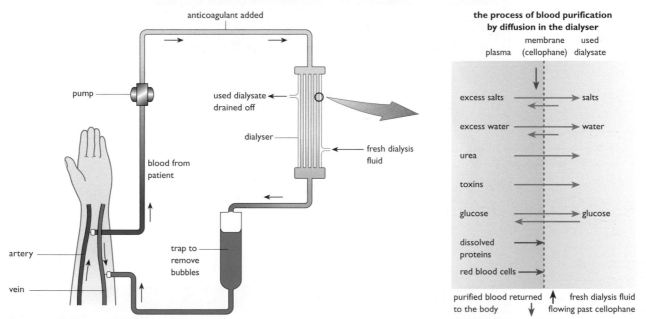

● Extension — The camel – a mammal adapted to desert conditions

Camels are herbivorous mammals adapted to survive in desert regions where daytime temperatures are high, water is scarce, vegetation is mostly fibrous, and often protected by spines, and the land surface is loose sand. The camel does not store water in its body, but instead has adaptations that allow survival despite extreme shortage of water at times, including the following:

• **Tolerance of water shortage:** the camel can go without drinking water for 6–8 days. During this period, loss of up to 25% of the body weight can occur. (By contrast, humans can survive a loss of only 10–12% of body weight for 2–3 days.) Camels achieve this because their red cells are oval shaped and with a strong membrane. They can pass through restricted capillaries when the water content is low.

continued

- **Formation of concentrated urine:** the kidney tubules have long loops of Henle, which allows the formation of very concentrated urine. Camels need much less water to excrete waste nitrogen than do most other mammals.
- **Saving of water vapour during breathing:** moisture in the air breathed out by the lungs is trapped in dried mucus in the nostrils. When the camel breathes in dry air this water evaporates. So the air taken down to the lungs is moist. This 'shunting of moisture' between the lungs and nostrils reduces water loss in breathing to a minimum. It also keeps the muzzle or 'snout' of the animal cooler than the rest of the body.
- **Keeping the brain cool, but allowing body temperature to rise in the day:** the blood cooled in the muzzle is used to cool the blood entering the brain, whilst the temperature of the rest of the body is allowed to rise in the day, if necessary. The additional body heat is then lost by conduction and radiation in the night (without loss of water by evaporation).
- **Adaptations of feet, nostrils, lips and eyelids:** these adaptations allow movement on loose sand, protect the eyes and nostrils in sand storms, and enable selective browsing of generally inaccessible leaves of desert-adapted plants (Figure 12.24).

Figure 12.24
Adaptations of camels to desert environments.

Bactrian camel

fat stored under the skin produces metabolic water (page 210) when respired

body temperature allowed to rise in the heat of the day (rather than being kept lower by evaporation of water)

feet and head of dromedary camel

nostrils are slit like, and can be tightly closed

padded feet adapted for movement on loose sand

lips split and highly mobile, allowing selective browsing

eyes shielded by long dense eye lashes

● **Skills task** The kangaroo rat lives in very hot, dry deserts where water is often not available. Figures for the source of water and the fate of water for this animal in a 4 week period are as follows:

water gain:		water loss:	
food (dry seeds)	6.0 g	breathing	43.9 g
metabolic water	54.0 g	in urine	13.5 g
		defecation	2.6 g
Total	60.0 g		60.0 g

Construct pie charts to illustrate the relative proportions of water gained and lost.
 Find out what is meant by 'metabolic water'.
 Lipids release more water than carbohydrates when oxidised. Why is this so?

SUMMARY

- **Homeostasis** is the maintenance of a **constant internal environment** despite fluctuating external conditions. The ability to do this efficiently has allowed mammals to master life in very diverse habitats.
- **Negative feedback** is the type of control mechanism that operates in homeostasis. When departure from the normal or set value within the organism is detected, responses are set in motion that **restore normal conditions** and switch off the 'disturbance' signal.
- **Temperature regulation** is the process of controlling heat loss and heat gain by the body to maintain a **more or less constant body temperature**. It is advantageous to maintain body temperature at or close to the optimum for the action of **metabolic enzymes**.
- In **ectotherms**, the body temperature is regulated, sometimes quite approximately, by varying the body position and therefore the amount of heat obtained through the skin from outside. When external heat is not available the animal generally becomes sluggish.
- In **endotherms**, the heat source comes from the level of respiratory metabolism in the tissues. The loss of heat from the body is carefully controlled to maintain a high and constant body temperature.
- **Blood glucose regulation** is essential because cells need a more or less constant supply of glucose, especially brain cells. **Too high** a glucose level lowers the water potential of the blood to the point where the blood takes water by osmosis from tissue fluid. This dehydrates cells and tissues. **Too low** a glucose level may lead to loss of consciousness and coma.
- The **liver** plays a key role in maintaining an internal environment that is favourable for metabolism in all the tissues. The liver is an important site of blood glucose regulation and the balance between **glucose** and **stored glycogen**. It is also a main site where the vast numbers of **red cells** that are broken down each day are processed and the products made available for reuse or storage.
- The **liver** is the site of the **deamination** of excess **amino acids** to form **urea**, which is safe to be transported in the blood. Also in the liver, lipids are packaged for safe transport in the blood, fat-soluble vitamins are stored and blood proteins are synthesised.
- The **kidney** is the organ of **excretion** and **osmoregulation**. In excretion the **waste products** of metabolism are removed from the blood and made ready for discharge from the body. In osmoregulation, the balance of **water** and **solutes** in body fluids is maintained at a constant level despite variations in intake.
- The kidney tubule (**nephron**) works by **pressure filtration** of some of the liquid and soluble components of blood, followed by **selective reabsorption** of useful substances from the filtrate, **active secretion** of unwanted substances and **adjustments to water and ion content** according to their relative levels in the body.

Examination questions

I The diagram shows the main blood vessels going to and coming from the liver.

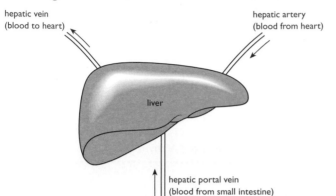

hepatic vein (blood to heart)

hepatic artery (blood from heart)

liver

hepatic portal vein (blood from small intestine)

a In a healthy person the blood glucose level in the hepatic vein fluctuates much less than that in the hepatic portal vein. Explain why this is so. (3)

b Blood sugar level is more or less constant, even if a person has not eaten for several days. How does gluconeogenesis help to maintain this constant blood sugar level? (1)

c Suggest why people suffering from diabetes are advised to eat their carbohydrates in the form of starch rather than as sugars. (2)

NEAB, A level, Paper 1/Sections A & B, June 1997

2 Antidiuretic hormone (ADH) is produced by the hypothalamus, released into the blood and carried all over the body. It affects the concentration of urine produced by the kidneys.

a i State precisely where ADH is released into the blood. (1)

ii Describe how ADH release is controlled. (3)

iii Explain how ADH acts on the kidney to produce a more concentrated urine. (4)

iv Explain why the kidneys do not respond immediately when the release of ADH is stopped. (2)

Diabetes insipidus, a disease characterised by the constant excretion of large volumes of dilute urine, arises when the ADH control system fails to function correctly.

b Suggest **two** ways in which diabetes insipidus might arise due to this failure. (2)

UCLES, A level, 4804, Nov 1997

3 a Explain what is meant by *homeostasis*. (2)

The diagram below shows part of a generalised negative feedback system.

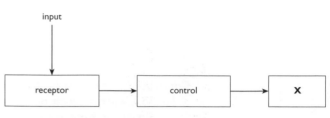

input

receptor → control → **X**

b With reference to the figure
i state what **X** represents (1)
ii on the diagram, draw an arrow to show where negative feedback takes place. (1)

Negative feedback systems often form part of other control systems in the body. The diagram below shows **part** of the control system for temperature regulation in mammals.

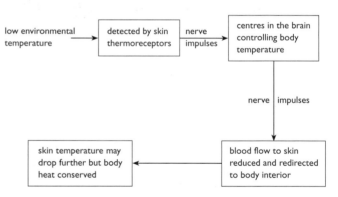

low environmental temperature → detected by skin thermoreceptors → nerve impulses → centres in the brain controlling body temperature

nerve impulses

skin temperature may drop further but body heat conserved ← blood flow to skin reduced and redirected to body interior

c With reference to the diagram, explain why this part of the system does **not** show negative feedback. (3)

Homeostatic mechanisms are responsible for the control of blood carbon dioxide concentration. At high altitudes, an increase in breathing rate occurs which decreases the carbon dioxide concentration of the blood, and leads to an increased urine production.

d Explain the effects of high altitude on urine production. (3)

UCLES, A level, 4804, June 1997

4 In an investigation into kidney function a number of people each drank 1 litre of distilled water. Their urine production over the next five hours was measured. The bar chart shows the mean volume of urine collected at one-hour intervals.

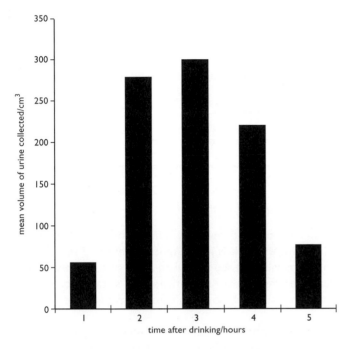

a Explain how drinking distilled water results in the increase in volume of urine in the first three hours. (4)

b Explain why the volume of urine starts to decrease after three hours. (1)

c Suggest **one** reason why it was important for the subjects to remain at rest during the investigation. (1)

AQA(NEAB), AS/A level, Module BY03, Mar 1999

5 The graph shows the blood glucose and glucagon concentrations in a healthy person during and after eating a meal.

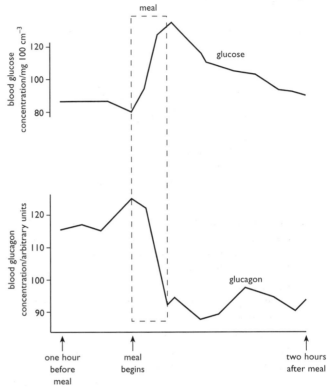

a i From where is glucagon secreted? (1)

ii Explain the changes that occur in the glucagon concentration over the period on the graph. (2)

b Explain how the information shown in the graph provides an example of negative feedback. (2)

AQA(AEB), AS/A level, Module 1, June 1999

Control and communication

STARTING POINTS ● Organisms detect changes in their environment and respond to them – a characteristic known as **sensitivity**.
● Changes detected in cells and organisms that bring about responses are called **stimuli**.
● Organisms have mechanisms of **internal communication** that bring about responses to appropriate stimuli.
● In **animals**, communication involves both the **nervous system** and **hormones** from endocrine glands.
● In **plants**, communication is via plant **growth regulator substances**.

● Detecting and responding to change

Living things are able to detect changes and respond appropriately. This characteristic, known as **sensitivity**, is essential for the survival of living things. It is just as much a feature of single-celled organisms as it is of flowering plants and mammals. We see this when a cell such as a phagocytic white cell (Figure 15.17, page 336) or an organism such as *Amoeba* detects a suitable 'food' organism immediately outside its plasma membrane and moves to take it into a vacuole by phagocytosis.

Changes that bring about responses are called **stimuli**. The stimulus is detected by a **receptor**, and an **effector** brings about a response. Since in a multicellular organism the receptor and effector are often widely separated, mechanisms of **internal communication** are essential. In **animals**, internal communication involves both the **nervous system** and **endocrine (hormone-producing) system**. In **plants**, internal communication is via plant **growth regulator substances**, which are similar to animal hormones, but are not identical.

● Nervous communication

Neurones and their fibres

The nervous system is built from specialised cells called **neurones**. Each neurone has a **cell body**. This contains the nucleus and the bulk of the cytoplasm from which fine cytoplasmic **nerve fibres** run. Most fibres are very long. These fibres are specialised for the transmission of information. They pass messages in the form of **impulses**. In mammals, impulses are transmitted along them at speeds between 30 and 120 metres per second, so nervous coordination is extremely fast, and responses are virtually immediate.

The three types of neurones are shown in Figure 13.1.

- **Motor neurones** have many fine **dendrites**, which carry impulses *towards* the cell body, and a single long **axon**, which carries impulses *away* from the cell body.
- **Interneurones** (also known as relay neurones) have numerous, short fibres.
- **Sensory neurones** have a single long **dendron**, which brings impulses *towards* the cell body, and a single long **axon**, which carries impulses *away*.

Surrounding the neurones there are different types of supporting cells, called **neuroglia cells**. One type of neuroglia cell is called a **Schwann cell**. Many of the long fibres (dendrons and axons) are protected by Schwann cells. These wrap themselves around the fibres, forming a structure called a **myelin sheath**. Between each pair of Schwann cells is a junction in the myelin sheath, called a **node of Ranvier** (Figure 13.1). The myelin sheath and its junctions help increase the speed at which impulses are conducted (see Figure 13.7, page 279).

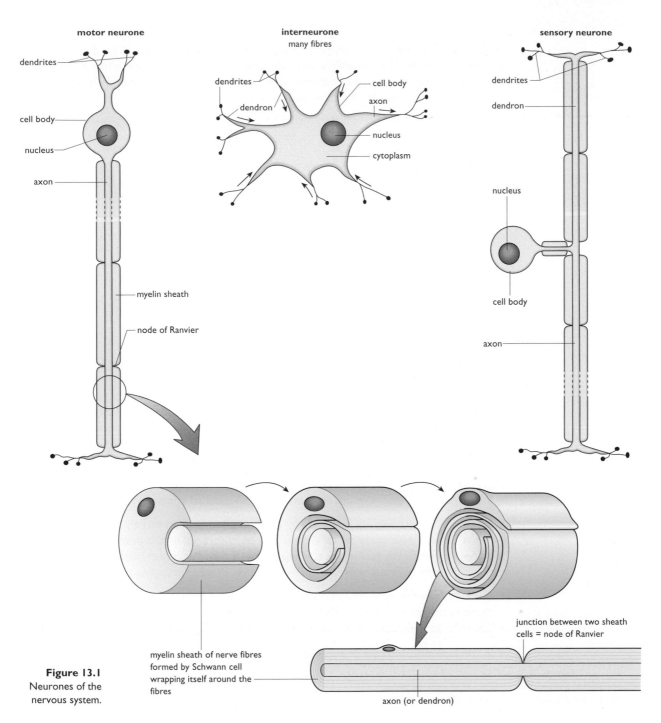

Figure 13.1
Neurones of the nervous system.

Reflex arcs and reflex action

The neurones within the nervous system transmit impulses along pathways called **reflex arcs**. A generalised reflex arc is shown in Figure 13.2. The reflex arc connects a **sense organ** (receptor) with a **muscle** or **gland** (effector), via the neurones, as follows. Firstly, the sense organ detects a stimulus, which is a form of energy such as sound, light, or mechanical pressure. This is converted into an impulse in the nerve fibre of a neurone that serves the sense cell. Some receptors are elaborate organs, like the eye of mammals. Others are single cells or even merely sensitive nerve fibre endings. Once generated, the impulse is transmitted along the fibres of a sequence of neurones of the reflex arc to an effector organ. When it arrives at the effector, the impulse causes a **response** – for example, it may cause a muscle to contract or a gland to secrete.

The simplest form of response in the nervous system is called a **reflex action**. This is a rapid, automatic but short-lived response to a stimulus. It is an involuntary response, as it is not generally controlled by the brain's decision-making centres. In a reflex action a particular stimulus produces the same automatic response, every time. In humans, an example is when you react by jerking your hand away from scalding hot water.

Figure 13.2
The layout of a reflex arc. This is the structural basis of reflex action.

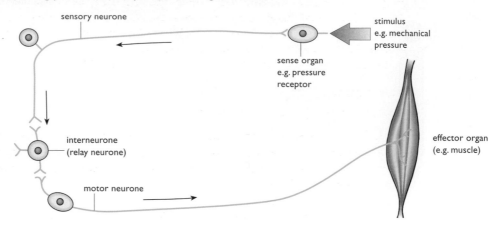

Reflex arcs and the nervous system

In vertebrates, and particularly in mammals, there is a complex nervous system, and we will return to its structure later in the chapter (Figure 13.16, page 288). Within the nervous system are very many reflex arcs, of course. In addition, many neurones connect reflex arcs with a control centre, the **brain**. The brain contains a highly organised mass of interneurones, connected to the rest of the nervous system by motor and sensory neurones. With a nervous system of this type, complex patterns of behaviour are common, in addition to reflex actions. This is because:

* impulses that originate in a reflex arc also travel to the brain
* impulses may originate in the brain and be conducted to effector organs.

Consequently much activity is *initiated* by the brain, rather than merely being a response to external stimuli. Also many reflex actions may be overruled by the brain, and the response modified (as when we decide not to drop an extremely hot object because of its value). So, we can see that the nervous system of animals such as the mammals has two roles:

* quick and precise communication between the sense organs that detect stimuli and the muscles or glands that respond with changes
* coordination and control of the body's responses by the brain (Figure 13.3).

We will look into the role of quick communication first of all.

Figure 13.3
Coordination and control by the nervous system.

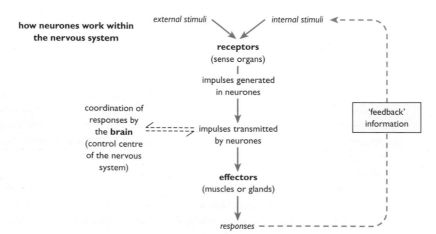

Transmission of an impulse

Am impulse is transmitted along nerve fibres, but it is *not* an electrical current that flows along the 'wires' of the nerves. Rather, the impulse is a momentary reversal in the electrical potential difference in the membrane of the fibres. That is, it is a change in the **position of positive and negative charged ions between the inside and outside of the membrane** (see Figure 13.5). This reversal travels from one end of the neurone to the other in a fraction of a second. Between impulses the neurone is said to be 'resting'. Actually, though, this is far from the case. During the 'resting' interval between impulses the membrane of a neurone actively creates and maintains an electrical potential difference between its inside and outside. How is this done?

The resting potential

Two processes together create the resting potential difference across the neurone membrane.

- There is **active transport** of potassium (K⁺) ions into the cell and sodium (Na⁺) ions out of the cell across the membrane. The ions are transported by a K⁺/Na⁺ pump, which uses energy from ATP (Figure 3.26, page 71). So potassium and sodium ions gradually concentrate on opposite sides of the membrane. However, this in itself makes *no change* to the potential difference across the membrane.
- There is also **facilitated diffusion** of K⁺ ions out and Na⁺ ions back in (see Figure 3.14, page 62). The important point here is that the membrane is *far more permeable* to K⁺ ions flowing out than to Na⁺ ions returning. This causes the tissue fluid outside the neurone to contain many more positive ions than the cytoplasm inside. As a result, the inside becomes more and more negatively charged compared with the outside; the resting neurone is said to be **polarised**. The difference in charge, or potential difference, is about −70 mV. This is known as the **resting potential**. Figure 13.4 shows how it is set up.

Figure 13.4
The establishment of the resting potential.

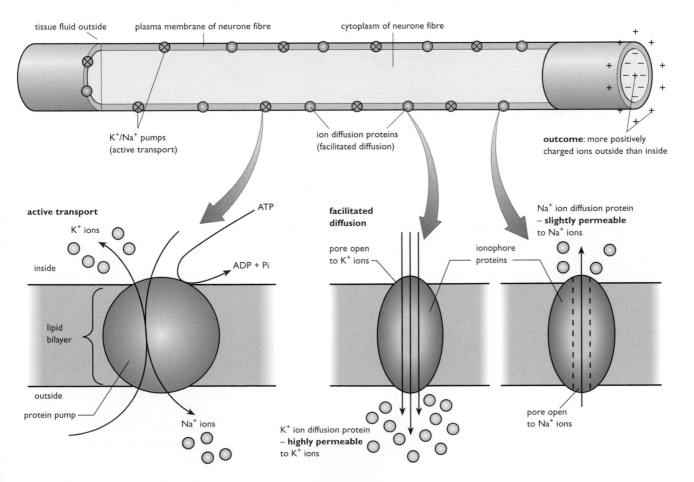

tissue fluid outside   plasma membrane of neurone fibre   cytoplasm of neurone fibre

outcome: more positively charged ions outside than inside

K⁺/Na⁺ pumps (active transport)

ion diffusion proteins (facilitated diffusion)

active transport

K⁺ ions

inside

ATP

ADP + Pi

lipid bilayer

outside

protein pump

Na⁺ ions

facilitated diffusion

pore open to K⁺ ions

ionophore proteins

K⁺ ion diffusion protein – **highly permeable** to K⁺ ions

Na⁺ ion diffusion protein – **slightly permeable** to Na⁺ ions

pore open to Na⁺ ions

The action potential

The next event, sooner or later, is the passage of an impulse. An impulse or **action potential** (Figure 13.5) is triggered by a stimulus arriving at a receptor cell or sensitive nerve ending. The energy of this stimulus causes a temporary and local reversal of the resting potential. The result is the membrane is briefly **depolarised** at this point. How does this happen?

The change in potential across the membrane happens through pores in the membrane. They are called **ion channels** because they can allow ions to pass through. One type of channel is permeable to sodium ions, and another to potassium ions. These channels are globular proteins that span the entire width of the membrane. They have a central pore, with a '**gate**' that can open and close. During a resting potential these channels are all closed.

The energy of the stimulus first opens the gates of the **sodium channels** in the plasma membrane. This allows sodium ions to diffuse in, down their electrochemical gradient. So the cytoplasm inside the neurone fibre quickly becomes progressively more positive with respect to the outside. This charge reversal continues until the potential difference has altered from -70 mV to $+40$ mV. At this point, an action potential is created in the neurone fibre.

The action potential then travels along the whole length of the neurone fibre. At any one point of the fibre it exists for only two-thousandths of a second (2 milliseconds), before the membrane starts to re-establish the resting potential. So action potential transmission is exceedingly brief.

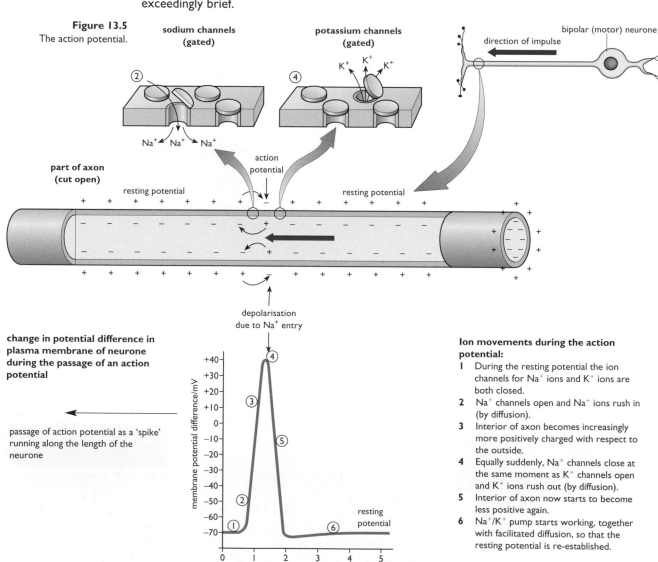

Figure 13.5
The action potential.

Ion movements during the action potential:
1 During the resting potential the ion channels for Na^+ ions and K^+ ions are both closed.
2 Na^+ channels open and Na^+ ions rush in (by diffusion).
3 Interior of axon becomes increasingly more positively charged with respect to the outside.
4 Equally suddenly, Na^+ channels close at the same moment as K^+ channels open and K^+ ions rush out (by diffusion).
5 Interior of axon now starts to become less positive again.
6 Na^+/K^+ pump starts working, together with facilitated diffusion, so that the resting potential is re-established.

I What is the source of energy used to:
a establish the resting potential, and
b power an action potential?

Almost immediately after an action potential has passed, the sodium channels close and the **potassium channels** open. So potassium ions can exit the cell, again down their electrochemical gradient, into the tissue fluid outside. This causes the interior of the neurone fibres to become less positive again. Then the potassium channels also close. Finally, the resting potential of -70 mV is re-established by the action of the sodium/potassium pump and the process of facilitated diffusion.

The refractory period

For a brief period after the passage of an action potential, the neurone fibre is no longer excitable. This is called the **refractory period**. It lasts only 5–10 milliseconds in total. During this time, firstly there is a large excess of Na^+ ions inside the neurone fibre and it is impossible for any more to enter. As the resting potential is progressively restored, however, it becomes increasingly possible for an action potential to be generated again. Because of the refractory period, the maximum frequency of impulses is 500–1000 per second.

The 'all or nothing' principle

Obviously the energy carried by various stimuli may be widely different – think of the difference between a light touch and the pain of a finger hit by a hammer! A stimulus must be at or above a minimum intensity, known as the **threshold of stimulation**, in order to initiate an action potential. Either a stimulus depolarises the membrane sufficiently to reverse the potential difference in the cytoplasm fully (that is, from -70 mV to $+40$ mV), or it does not. If not, no action potential at all arises and no message is sent along the fibre. With all subthreshold stimuli, the influx of sodium ions is quickly reversed, and the resting potential is re-established.

However, as the intensity of the stimulus increases, the frequency at which the action potentials pass along the fibre increases (the individual action potentials are all of standard strength). For example, with a very persistent stimulus, action potentials pass along a fibre at an accelerated rate, up to the maximum possible permitted by the refractory period. This means the effector (or the brain) recognises the intensity of a stimulus from the **frequency** of action potentials. This is shown in Figure 13.6.

Figure 13.6
Weak and strong stimuli and the threshold value.

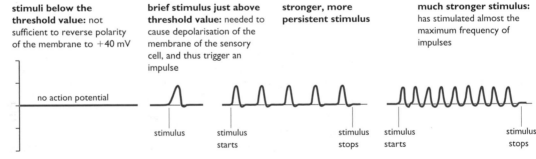

Figure 13.7
Saltatory conduction. The action potential is transmitted at up to 100 m s^{-1}.

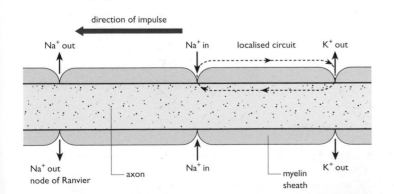

Speed of conduction of the action potential

The presence of a myelin sheath affects the speed of transmission of the action potential. The junctions in the sheath (the nodes of Ranvier) are spaced at intervals of 1–2 mm. Only at these nodes is the axon membrane exposed. Elsewhere along the fibre, the electrical resistance of the myelin sheath prevents depolarisations. So, the action potentials are forced to jump from node to node (called **saltatory conduction** = 'to leap') (Figure 13.7). This is an advantage, as it greatly increases the rate of transmission.

2 Why do myelinated nerve fibres conduct impulses faster than non-myelinated fibres of the same size?

Not all neurones have myelinated fibres, however. Non-myelinated dendrons and axons are common in non-vertebrate animals. Here, transmission is much slower, because the action potential has to proceed step by step along every part of the fibres. However, even with non-myelinated fibres it is possible to speed up the passage of the action potential. Large diameter axons transmit action potentials much more speedily than do narrow ones. Certain non-vertebrates like the squid and the earthworm have giant fibres, which allow fast transmission of action potentials (but not as fast as in myelinated fibres). Experimental investigation of action potentials has been carried out on giant fibres from these animals.

Junctions between neurones

The **synapse** is the point where the ends of two neurones meet. It consists of the swollen tip (**synaptic knob**) of the axon of one neurone (**presynaptic neurone**) and the dendrite or cell body of the next neurone (**postsynaptic neurone**) (Figure 13.8). At the synapse, the neurones are extremely close, but they are not in direct contact. Between them there is a tiny gap, called the **synaptic cleft**, about 20 nm wide.

Because there is a gap here the action potential cannot cross it. Here, another form of transmission must carry the impulse. Transmission across the synaptic cleft is not electrical, but chemical. The impulse is carried from one side of the gap to the other by specific chemicals, known as **transmitter substances**. These substances are all relatively small, diffusable molecules. They are produced in the Golgi apparatus in the synaptic knob, and held in tiny vesicles prior to use.

Acetylcholine is a commonly occurring transmitter substance; the neurones that release acetylcholine are known as **cholinergic neurones**. Another common transmitter substance is **noradrenaline** (released by **adrenergic neurones**). The brain uses the transmitters **glutamic acid** and **dopamine**, among others.

Figure 13.8
A synapse in section.

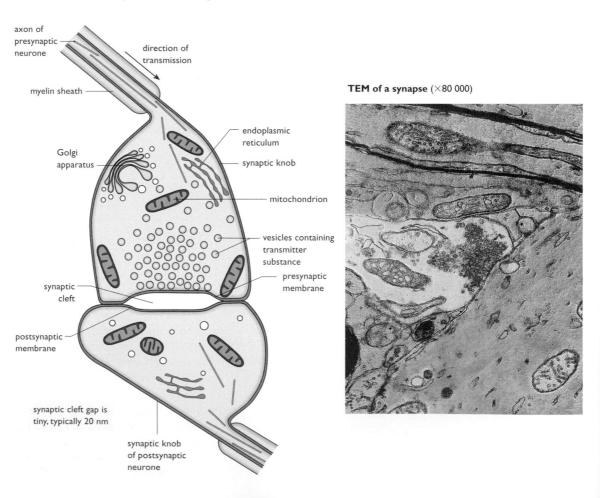

TEM of a synapse (×80 000)

Steps to synapse transmission

The arrival of an action potential at the synaptic knob opens **calcium ion channels** in the presynaptic membrane, and calcium ions enter from the synaptic cleft (Figure 13.9). The calcium ions cause **vesicles (packets) of transmitter substance** to fuse with the presynaptic membrane. As they do so they release the transmitter substance into the synaptic cleft.

The transmitter substance diffuses across the synaptic cleft. In the postsynaptic membrane there are specific **receptor sites** containing a receptor protein for each transmitter substance. Each of these receptors also acts as a channel in the membrane for a specific ion (for example, Na^+, or Cl^- or some other ion). As a transmitter molecule binds to its receptor protein this instantly **opens the ion channel**, allowing the specific ion to pass through.

For instance, when a molecule of acetylcholine attaches to its receptor site a Na^+ channel opens. As the sodium ions rush into the cytoplasm of the postsynaptic neurone, depolarisation of the postsynaptic membrane occurs. As more and more molecules of acetylcholine bind to their receptors it becomes increasingly likely that this depolarisation will reach the threshold level. When it does, an action potential is generated in the postsynaptic neurone. This process of build-up to an action potential in postsynaptic membranes is called **facilitation**.

3 What are the roles of:
  a the Golgi apparatus, and
  b mitochondria in the synaptic knob?

Figure 13.9
Chemical transmission by acetylcholine.

how a cholinergic synapse works

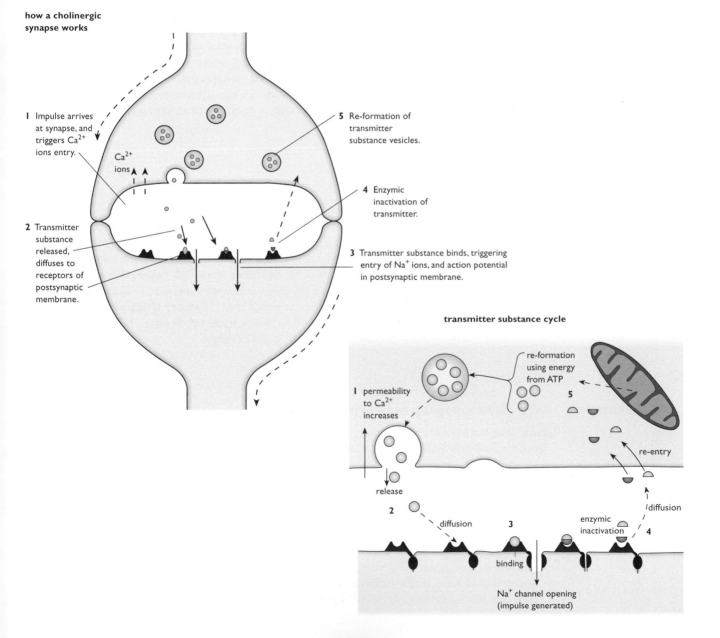

1 Impulse arrives at synapse, and triggers Ca^{2+} ions entry.

Ca^{2+} ions

5 Re-formation of transmitter substance vesicles.

4 Enzymic inactivation of transmitter.

2 Transmitter substance released, diffuses to receptors of postsynaptic membrane.

3 Transmitter substance binds, triggering entry of Na^+ ions, and action potential in postsynaptic membrane.

transmitter substance cycle

re-formation using energy from ATP

1 permeability to Ca^{2+} increases

5

re-entry

release

2

diffusion

3

binding

enzymic inactivation

4

diffusion

Na^+ channel opening (impulse generated)

Meanwhile, the transmitter substance on the receptors is immediately inactivated by enzyme action. This causes the ion channel of the receptor protein to close again. The resting potential in the postsynaptic neurone can then be re-established. Meanwhile, the inactivated form of the transmitter diffuses back across the gap, re-enters the presynaptic knob, is resynthesised into transmitter substance, and packaged for reuse (Figure 13.9).

● Extension   Excitatory synapses, facilitation and summation

In the cholinergic synapse described above, the effect of the transmitter substance, acetylcholine, was to open sodium channels in the postsynaptic neurone and thereby cause transfer of an action potential from one neurone to the next. Consequently, this type of synapse is described as an **excitatory synapse**.

The arrival of the contents of a single vesicle of acetylcholine may not be quite sufficient to reach the threshold of depolarisation needed to cause an action potential in the postsynaptic membrane on its own. Even so, it may increase the likelihood of an action potential being initiated when more of the transmitter substance arrives (it has facilitated it). The combined effect of two or more depolarisation events is known as **summation**. They may be depolarisations arriving in rapid succession from the *same* presynaptic membrane (**temporal summation**, separated in time); that is, there may be repeated stimulation from one presynaptic neurone. Alternatively, the depolarisations may arrive at the same time but come from *different* sources (**spatial separation**); that is, the postsynaptic neurone may have more than one presynaptic neurone forming a synapse with it. Here, simultaneous but subthreshold stimulations from several presynaptic neurones add up to produce an action potential in the postsynaptic neurone.

● Extension   Inhibitory synapses

At some synapses the arrival of the transmitter at the postsynaptic membrane causes the entry of chloride ions (and the release of potassium ions). As a result, the interior of the postsynaptic neurone becomes even *more* negative (it is said to be **hyperpolarised**), and the passage of an action potential is inhibited. This type of synapse is known as an **inhibitory synapse**.

Neurones may have synapses with many other neurones, some excitatory, others inhibitory. These will respond to impulses according to the balance between the two. In this case, only if there are sufficiently more excitatory synapses activated than inhibitory synapses will the postsynaptic neurone be depolarised, setting off an action potential. In effect, the neurone is summing up and integrating the different impulses it has received.

● Extension   Why have synapses between neurones?

Since synapses have the disadvantage of very slightly slowing down the transmission of action potentials, we may assume that this disadvantage must be outweighed by distinct advantages they bring to the operation of nervous communication in organisms. These may include:

• the filtering out of low level stimuli of limited importance
• the protection of the effectors (muscles and glands) from overstimulation, since continuous transmission of action potentials would eventually exhaust, at least temporarily, the supply of transmitter substances (that is, synapse fatigue)
• allowing 'convergence', since the postsynaptic neurone may receive action potentials from both excitatory presynaptic neurones and inhibitory presynaptic neurones. The postsynaptic neurone summates all the action potentials, thereby integrating action potentials from more than one source neurone or sense organ, for example.

● **Extension** Drugs and poisons that affect neurones

The performance of synapses may be altered by drugs, sometimes with dangerous or tragic consequences.

- Some drugs *amplify the processes of synaptic transmission:* amphetamines cause increased release of noradrenaline leading to enhanced activation of neurones in the brain. This may cause a high state of mental activity. Cocaine causes noradrenaline to persist in the synaptic cleft, with similar consequences.

  Nicotine is similar in chemical structure to the active part of the acetylcholine molecule, and it fits on to acetylcholine acceptor molecules on postsynaptic membranes. However, it is not broken down by the enzyme that inactivates acetylcholine. So it remains on the receptors, prolonging the cholinergic effects.

- Other drugs *inhibit the processes of synaptic transmission:* atropine inhibits acetylcholine, preventing an action potential being generated. Curare, a poison obtained from certain plants of South America, similarly blocks nerve/muscle junctions. Both these drugs have applications in medicine.

- Some substances have been found to *inhibit the enzymic breakdown of transmitter substance* on the receptor sites of the postsynaptic membranes: this is the action of the insecticide malathion and the nerve gas sarin.

Receptors – the sensory system

Receptors may be sense organs containing specialised cells, or sensitive nerve endings. In response to stimuli, they can initiate action potentials in sensory nerve fibres connected to them. Receptors are typically sensitive to one type of stimulation only – for example, differences in temperature, light, touch or presence of chemicals. Receptors consisting of a sensitive nerve ending include the Pacinian corpuscle, a pressure receptor. These are found below the skin and at joints in the body (Figure 13.10). Others consist of an individual cell or small groups of cells. Still others are complex organs like the eye, containing elaborate receptor cells within a complex supporting structure (see Figure 13.11).

Figure 13.10
The Pacinian corpuscle: structure and function.

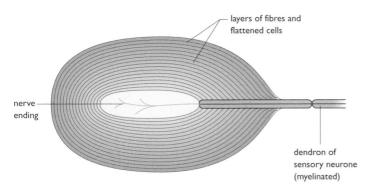

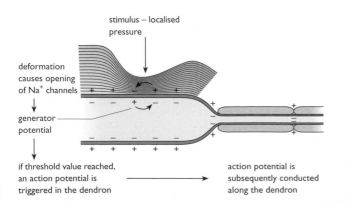

The generation of an action potential in a Pacinian corpuscle

At rest, the nerve ending within the Pacinian corpuscle maintains the resting potential of −70 mV that is typical of the membrane of a neurone. When strong, localised pressure is applied to a Pacinian corpuscle it causes the layers of collagen of the corpuscle to be deformed. This creates a temporary change in the permeability of the membrane at the nerve ending. Sodium ions flow in, the membrane is depolarised, and the interior starts to become less negative. This early, localised depolarisation is called a **generator potential** (Figure 13.10). The size of the generator potential depends on the intensity of the stimulus: the stronger the stimulus, the greater is the generator potential. If the generator potential reaches (or exceeds) a threshold value it triggers an action potential in the sensory neurone that serves the sense cell.

The sensitivity of a sense organ

We have seen that in neurones the intensity of a stimulus determines the frequency of the action potentials (Figure 13.6, page 279): as a stimulus becomes stronger, action potentials flow more frequently along the fibre. This is the situation in sense cells, too, at least initially. However, in this case, if a stimulus is *maintained* at a high level, then sooner or later the permeability of the membrane of the sense cell to Na$^+$ ions decreases. As a result, the frequency of action potentials slows and may eventually stop. The sense organ is said to have **adapted**.

Sense organs adapt to varying degrees. Fine-touch receptors in the skin adapt quickly; after dressing we soon cease to notice the touch of clothing on skin. Conversely, pain receptors all over our bodies, and stretch receptors in our muscles, hardly adapt at all.

The sense of sight

4 What is the difference in structure between the fovea and the blind spot?

The eyes of mammals are protected in deep, bony sockets called **orbits**. The eyes supply information from which the brain perceives the size, shape, movement and (sometimes) the colour of objects in the environment, and about the direction and intensity of light. In those mammals which have their eyes directed forwards so that the visual field of each eye overlaps (for example, as in all primates), the brain also resolves the slightly different information from the two retinas into a three-dimensional image, known as stereoscopic vision. The structure of the eye is illustrated in Figure 13.11 and the focusing of an image on the retina in Figure 13.12.

Figure 13.11
The structure of the eye.

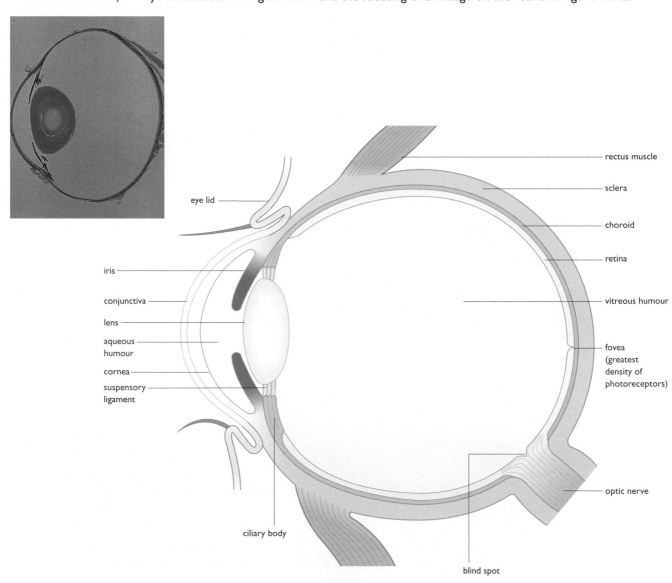

eye lid

rectus muscle

sclera

choroid

retina

vitreous humour

iris

conjunctiva

lens

aqueous humour

cornea

suspensory ligament

fovea (greatest density of photoreceptors)

ciliary body

optic nerve

blind spot

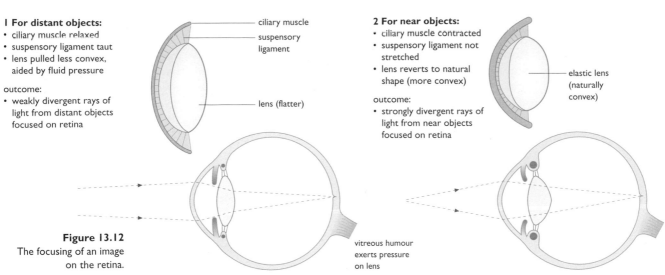

1 For distant objects:
- ciliary muscle relaxed
- suspensory ligament taut
- lens pulled less convex, aided by fluid pressure

outcome:
- weakly divergent rays of light from distant objects focused on retina

ciliary muscle

suspensory ligament

lens (flatter)

2 For near objects:
- ciliary muscle contracted
- suspensory ligament not stretched
- lens reverts to natural shape (more convex)

outcome:
- strongly divergent rays of light from near objects focused on retina

elastic lens (naturally convex)

vitreous humour exerts pressure on lens

Figure 13.12
The focusing of an image on the retina.

The working retina

The **retina** of the eye is sensitive to light of wavelengths in the range 380–760 nm – that is, the visible part of the electromagnetic spectrum (the radiation from the Sun). The retina has two types of light-sensitive cell, called **rods** and **cones**, shown in Figure 13.13. They are very elongated cells with an outer part called the **outer segment**. This consists of flattened membranous vesicles housing a light-sensitive pigment. An **inner segment** contains many mitochondria for ATP production. Rods are far more numerous than cones: the human retina contains about 120 million rods compared with 6 million cones. Rods are distributed evenly throughout the retina, whereas cones are concentrated in and around a region called the **fovea**. This is the area where vision is most accurate, since it contains the greatest density of photoreceptors (see Figure 13.11). (Note that light passes through the neurones synapsing with the rod and cone cells *before* reaching the outer segments, so we can say that the retina is 'inverted' (Figure 13.13).)

Figure 13.13
The structure of the retina.

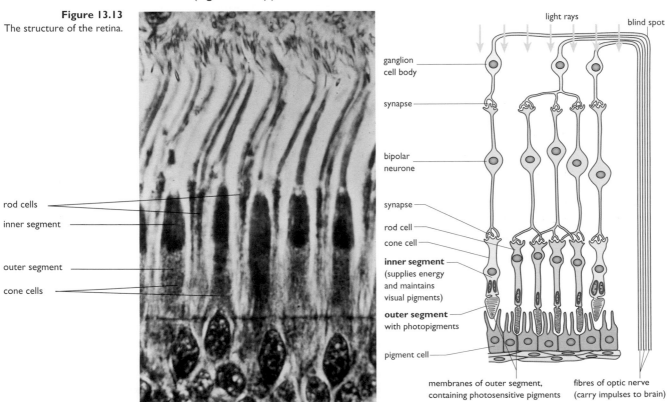

rod cells

inner segment

outer segment

cone cells

light rays

blind spot

ganglion cell body

synapse

bipolar neurone

synapse

rod cell

cone cell

inner segment (supplies energy and maintains visual pigments)

outer segment with photopigments

pigment cell

membranes of outer segment, containing photosensitive pigments

fibres of optic nerve (carry impulses to brain)

● Extension Rod cells

Rod cells are extremely sensitive to light, much more sensitive than the cones, but rod cells do not discriminate colours. Since they respond to lower light intensities than cones, they are principally used in dim light and night vision. The type of visual pigment housed in the rods is called 'visual purple' or **rhodopsin**. This molecule is a combination of a protein, opsin and a light-absorbing compound derived from vitamin A, called retinal. (Remember, a diet deficient in vitamin A causes 'night blindness' – see Table 7.3, page 147.)

Figure 13.14
The working rod cell.

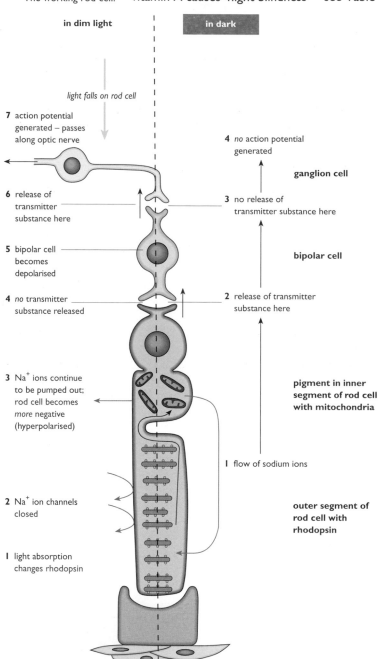

Light falling on the retina causes a reversible structural change in the rhodopsin molecule (called 'bleaching'). This immediately affects the permeability of the cell surface of the outer segment where rhodopsin is embedded; hence the pattern of ion movements in the rod cell is changed. This *blocks* the production of a special transmitter substance by the rod cell. The inhibition of this first neurotransmitter causes the next cell (called a **bipolar cell**) to become depolarised. This in turn causes the *release* of a second type of neurotransmitter, which finally generates an action potential in a neurone of the optic nerves serving the rod cell. The action potential transmitted eventually arrives in the visual cortex of the brain. Meanwhile, the structure of rhodopsin is rebuilt, using energy from ATP. This complex sequence of events in a rod cell is summarised in Figure 13.14.

Temporary blindness in very bright light
In very bright light, all the rhodopsin becomes bleached. It takes time for sufficient reversal of bleaching to occur. In these conditions the cone cells are responding, so the state of the visual pigment in the rod cells is not of immediate consequence. However, if we move quickly from bright to very dim light we become temporarily blinded since the cone cells are insufficiently sensitive to dim light and the rod cells are not yet able to respond. We say our eyes are 'adapting to the dark'.

Mammals and colour vision

Mammals with **cone cells** in their retinas are able to distinguish colours. Although cones occur throughout the retina they are concentrated in the fovea, where most light rays are focused. Cone cells operate on the same principle as the rod cells, but use a different pigment, called **iodopsin**. This is less readily broken down; it needs more light energy. This is why cones work only in high light intensities, and we cannot see colours in dim light.

According to the **trichromatic theory of colour vision**, there are three types of cone cell present in the retina, each with a different form of iodopsin. Each of the three absorbs a different wavelength of light – in the blue, green and red regions of the spectrum. White light stimulates all three types of cone equally, but we perceive different colours according to the relative amount of stimulation of each of the three types of cone.

Resolution (**visual acuity**) describes how much detail we can see. Cone cells are tightly packed together in the retina, and each cone may synapse with a single bipolar neurone. This bipolar neurone in turn may synapse with only a single ganglion cell. This gives a 1 : 1 relationship, so each part of an image is detected by a separate cell. Such an arrangement produces a high degree of resolution.

On the other hand, very many rod cells synapse with a single bipolar cell, which is called '**convergence**'. Convergence results in poor resolution. However, sensitivity at low light intensity increases with convergence since the impulses from many rods are pooled to generate an action potential. We can still 'see' at very low light intensities because of this.

We 'see' in our brain, and the seeing process, known as **perception**, is complex. Neurones of the optic nerve carry action potentials that end up in the visual cortex area at the back of the brain (see Figure 13.17). Here the brain receives action potentials from the left and right eyes separately, and these two sets of information are combined to produce a single impression: our 'sight'. In addition, sensory information from the retina is 'interpreted' according to past experiences and expectations. (How complex human vision is, and how research scientists have investigated perception, are introduced in the *New Scientist* Inside Science Number 99, 'Before your very eyes', which is well worth reading.)

Nerves in control and integration of behaviour

Figure 13.16 shows how the nervous system of a mammal is organised. Neurones are grouped together to form the **central nervous system** (**CNS**), which is made up of the **brain** and **spinal cord**.

To and from the CNS run nerves of the **peripheral nervous system**. Communication between the CNS and all parts of the body occurs by these nerves. Nerves consist of nerve fibres (axons and dendrons) arranged in bundles, protected by a connective tissue sheath. Some nerves contain sensory neurone fibres only and convey impulses towards the CNS (e.g. the optic nerve) – these are **sensory nerves**. Others contain motor neurone fibres only and they convey impulses to effector organs, such as muscles – these are **motor nerves**. **Mixed nerves** have fibres of both motor and sensory neurones and carry impulses in both directions – the spinal nerves are all mixed nerves (Figure 13.15).

The peripheral nervous system can be divided into parts that are under our voluntary control, and the **autonomic nervous system** (**ANS**), which operates largely automatically (that is, involuntarily, or without conscious thought) (see Table 13.1, page 291). These divisions are summarised in Figure 13.16.

Figure 13.15
A peripheral nerve in TS (×600). The vagus nerve is mixed, containing axons of motor neurones, and dendrons and axons of sensory neurones, each surrounded by a myelin sheath (dark).

connective tissue around the bundles of nerve fibres

lipid of the myelin sheaths stained black with osmium tetroxide stain

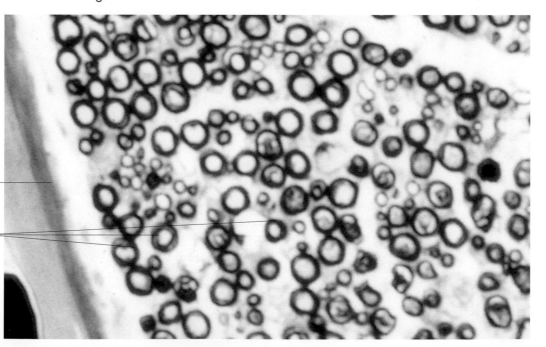

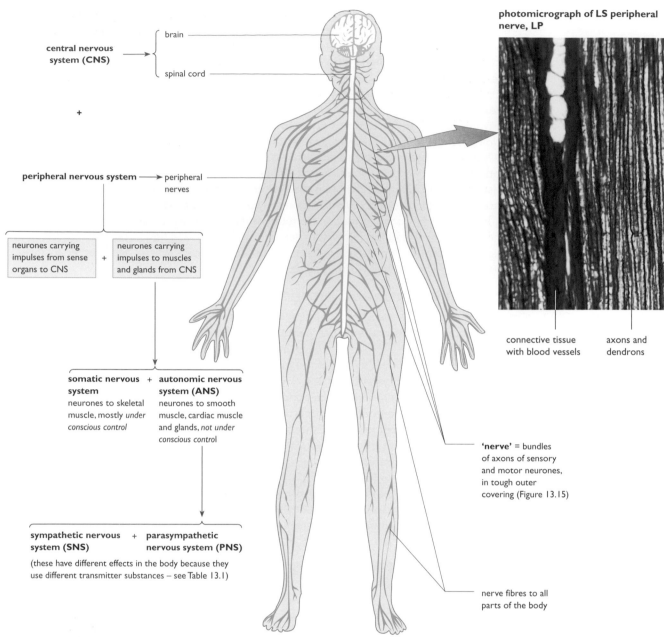

photomicrograph of LS peripheral nerve, LP

central nervous system (CNS)
- brain
- spinal cord

+

peripheral nervous system → peripheral nerves

neurones carrying impulses from sense organs to CNS

+

neurones carrying impulses to muscles and glands from CNS

somatic nervous system
neurones to skeletal muscle, mostly *under conscious control*

+

autonomic nervous system (ANS)
neurones to smooth muscle, cardiac muscle and glands, *not under conscious control*

sympathetic nervous system (SNS)

+

parasympathetic nervous system (PNS)

(these have different effects in the body because they use different transmitter substances – see Table 13.1)

connective tissue with blood vessels

axons and dendrons

'nerve' = bundles of axons of sensory and motor neurones, in tough outer covering (Figure 13.15)

nerve fibres to all parts of the body

Figure 13.16
The organisation of the mammalian nervous system.

Central nervous system

The brain

The vertebrate brain develops in the embryo from the anterior end of a simple tube, the **neural tube**. This tube enlarges to form three primary structures, known as the **forebrain**, **midbrain** and **hindbrain** (Figure 13.17). The various parts of the mature brain develop from these by selective thickening and folding of the walls and the roof.

These enlargement processes are most pronounced in mammals, and a striking feature is the enormous development of the **cerebral hemispheres** (Figure 13.17), which are an outgrowth of the forebrain. The human brain contains about 10^{11}–10^{12} relay neurones and about the same number of neuroglia cells. The majority of these neurones occur in the cerebral hemispheres. There, it is estimated, each relay neurone forms synapses with a thousand other neurones. Mammals are the most intelligent of all animals, and their long memory, complexity of behaviour and subtlety of body control are also linked to this development.

When tissue inside the CNS is examined, the parts where cell bodies are grouped together appear grey, so are known as '**grey matter**' (see Figure 13.18). Areas where myelinated nerve fibres occur together appear whiter, so are called **white matter**. White and grey matter are present both in the brain and in the spinal cord. Grey matter makes up the interior of the brain, and white the exterior. However, in the cerebral hemispheres and cerebellum (see below) there are additional layers of grey matter (that is, extra neurones).

Figure 13.17
The human brain.

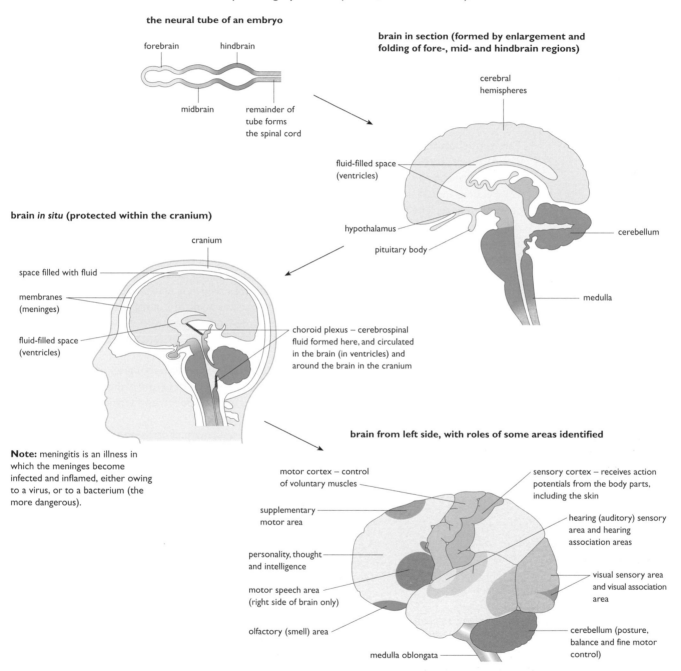

the neural tube of an embryo

forebrain   hindbrain

midbrain   remainder of
tube forms
the spinal cord

brain in section (formed by enlargement and
folding of fore-, mid- and hindbrain regions)

cerebral
hemispheres

fluid-filled space
(ventricles)

hypothalamus

pituitary body

cerebellum

medulla

brain *in situ* (protected within the cranium)

cranium

space filled with fluid

membranes
(meninges)

fluid-filled space
(ventricles)

choroid plexus – cerebrospinal
fluid formed here, and circulated
in the brain (in ventricles) and
around the brain in the cranium

Note: meningitis is an illness in which the meninges become infected and inflamed, either owing to a virus, or to a bacterium (the more dangerous).

brain from left side, with roles of some areas identified

motor cortex – control
of voluntary muscles

supplementary
motor area

personality, thought
and intelligence

motor speech area
(right side of brain only)

olfactory (smell) area

medulla oblongata

sensory cortex – receives action
potentials from the body parts,
including the skin

hearing (auditory) sensory
area and hearing
association areas

visual sensory area
and visual association
area

cerebellum (posture,
balance and fine motor
control)

Blood capillaries are also present throughout the nervous tissue. However, in the brain the capillary walls form a barrier against many of the dissolved substances in the blood. This means that only essential substances, such as oxygen and glucose, can cross into the brain. This is called the **blood/brain barrier**. Other substances dissolved in the plasma that might affect the brain's activity are excluded. For instance, some amino acids present in the blood also act as neurotransmitters in brain synapses. This barrier is therefore important for maintenance of normal brain function.

5 Where is the control centre of the autonomic nervous system?

Brain function

The human brain controls all body functions, apart from those under the control of simple spinal reflexes mentioned earlier. According to current understanding of brain function, it achieves this by:

• receiving impulses from sensory receptors
• integrating and correlating incoming information in association centres
• sending impulses to effector organs (muscles and glands) causing bodily responses
• storing information and building up an accessible memory bank
• initiating impulses from its own self-contained activities (for the brain is also the seat of 'personality' and emotions, and enables us to imagine, create, plan, calculate, predict and abstractly reason).

Within the brain as a whole, certain tasks and roles are localised (see Figure 13.17). For example:

• The **hypothalamus**, part of the floor of the forebrain, and exceptionally well supplied with blood vessels, is the control centre for the ANS. Here the body monitors and controls body temperature and the levels of sugars, amino acids and ions (that is, homeostasis, see Chapter 12). Feeding and drinking reflexes, and aggressive and reproductive behaviour, are also controlled here. The hypothalamus works with a 'master gland' called the **pituitary gland**, to which is attached, monitoring hormones in the blood, and controlling the release of hormones. So the hypothalamus is the main link between the nervous and endocrine systems.
• The **cerebral hemispheres**, an extension of the forebrain, form the bulk of the human brain. Here the body's voluntary activities are coordinated, together with many involuntary ones. These hemispheres have a vastly extended surface area, which is achieved by extensive folding of the surface so that it forms deep grooves. The surface layer, the **cerebral cortex**, is covered by grey matter to a depth of 3 mm, and is densely packed with non-myelinated neurones. The areas of the cortex with special sensory and motor functions have now been mapped out.
• The **cerebellum**, part of the hindbrain, has an external surface layer of grey matter. It is concerned with the control of involuntary muscle movements of posture and balance. Here precise, voluntary manipulations including hand movements, speech and writing are coordinated (rather than initiated).
• The **medulla**, the base of the hindbrain, houses the regulatory centres concerned with maintaining the correct heart rate, ventilation of the lungs and temperature. In the medulla the ascending and descending pathways of nerve fibres connecting the spinal column and brain cross over. As a consequence, the left side of our body is controlled by the right side of the brain, and vice versa.

Figure 13.18
Transverse section through a spinal cord (photomicrograph, LP).

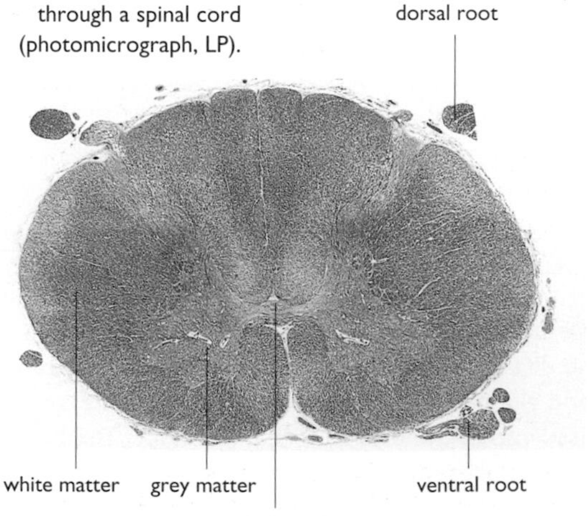

white matter   grey matter   central canal   dorsal root   ventral root

The spinal cord

The **spinal cord** is a cylindrical structure with a tiny central canal (Figure 13.18). The canal contains cerebrospinal fluid and is continuous with the fluid-filled spaces (ventricles) in the centre of the brain (see Figure 13.17). The cord consists of an inner area of grey matter (cell bodies and synapses) surrounded by white matter (myelinated nerve fibres). The spinal cord is surrounded and protected by the vertebrae of the backbone. In the junction between each pair of vertebrae two **spinal nerves** leave the cord, one to each side of the body. The role of the spinal cord is to relay action potentials between sensory organs and effector organs of the body (in a reflex action), and also between them and the brain, so that the reflex action may be overridden. For example, in the reflex action illustrated in Figure 13.19, impulses sent to the brain may cause the hot object to be tolerated in a dangerous situation or as a test of 'will-power'.

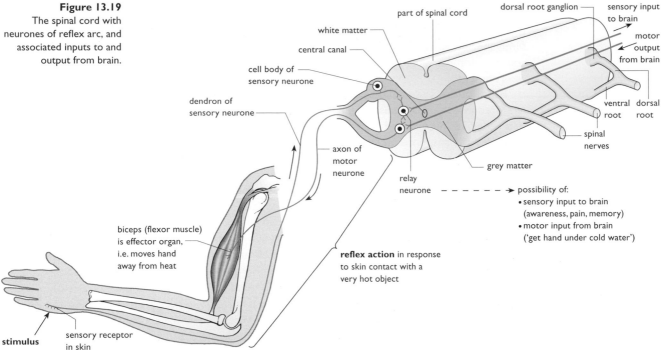

Figure 13.19
The spinal cord with neurones of reflex arc, and associated inputs to and output from brain.

Peripheral nervous system: motor nerves to the body

The peripheral nerves (see Figure 13.17) consist of sensory neurones carrying impulses to the CNS, as discussed above, and motor neurones carrying impulses to muscles and glands. Many of the motor neurones are to muscles we use in conscious actions to produce voluntary movements, and they form the **somatic system**. (The working of the somatic system in muscle contraction is discussed in Chapter 14.)

The **autonomic nervous system** controls activities inside the body that are mostly under unconscious (involuntary) control. It consists of motor neurones running to the smooth muscle of the internal organs and to various glands. The autonomic nervous system acts to keep the body's internal environment constant (autonomic means 'self-governing'). It is divided into two parts: the **sympathetic nervous system** (**SNS**) and the **parasympathetic nervous system** (**PNS**). Table 13.1 illustrates the key differences between these systems. Note that:

- In some of the functions the two systems are antagonistic in their effects (for example, the SNS causes the heart rate to increase and the PNS causes it to decrease. However, in other cases they may have the same effect on a gland or muscle.
- The ANS is largely coordinated by unconscious regions of the brain (medulla and the hypothalamus). However, some of its activities are regulated by conscious areas of the brain, including control over the sphincter muscles of the bladder and anus.

Table 13.1
The components of the autonomic nervous system.

Sympathetic nervous system	Parasympathetic nervous system
more active in times of stress to produce 'flight or fight' responses	concerned in conservation of energy and the replacement of body reserves
at its junctions with effector tissues (muscles or glands) the neurones release noradrenaline	at its junctions with effector tissues the neurones release acetylcholine
Some of the responses of the two systems: causes widening (dilation) of the pupils	causes narrowing (constriction) of the pupils
has no effect on the tear glands	causes the secretion of tears
has no effect on salivary glands	causes secretion of saliva from salivary glands
constricts bladder sphincter muscles	causes relaxation of the sphincter muscle of the bladder and contraction of the muscular wall of bladder (under overall control of conscious part of brain)

Behaviour

Behaviour is the way organisms respond to the environment, including other members of the same species. Behaviour is based on a 'feedback' mechanism, routed through the control and coordination machinery of the body. It enables animals to survive and to seek out favourable environments.

'Behaviour' is sometimes said to be either **innate** (or instinctive – that is, automatically triggered in certain circumstances) or **learned**. Innate behaviour includes behaviour that is due to a reflex action. Learned behaviour occurs when a memory of experiences is retained and used to modify the response on future occasions. However, in the natural world, the differences between 'innate' and 'learned' behaviour are not clear cut. Rather, many animals display a range of behaviours, some of which are innate, and some of which are clearly learned, at least in part. In vertebrates, and especially in mammals, very complex patterns of behaviour are common. The study of behaviour at this level is outside the scope of this book.

Orientation behaviour is a relatively simple response to stimuli, used by simple motile organisms (and motile gametes – page 412). It enables the individual to seek out and remain within a favourable environment. Many non-vertebrate animals have very simple patterns of this kind of behaviour, where their direction or rate of movement is altered in response to a stimulus. Their actions appear to be largely determined by reflexes. Two broad types of orientation behaviour can be demonstrated in the laboratory, where a single stimulus can be applied under controlled conditions. The following types of orientation behaviour may be investigated in simple laboratory experiments, using a choice chamber (page 301), for example.

Kinetic movements or **kineses** are random movements in which the rate of movement is related to the *intensity* of the stimulus (but not its direction). An example is seen in woodlice, which move randomly and quickly in dry conditions, but slow and stop when their movements bring them into a humid area.

Tactic movements or **taxes** occur when the *direction* of the stimulus determines the direction of the response. This is also seen in woodlice, which move directly away from a bright light source.

Hormonal control in animals

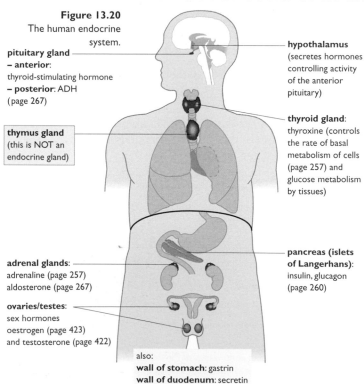

Figure 13.20
The human endocrine system.

pituitary gland
– anterior:
thyroid-stimulating hormone
– posterior: ADH
(page 267)

thymus gland
(this is NOT an
endocrine gland)

adrenal glands:
adrenaline (page 257)
aldosterone (page 267)

ovaries/testes:
sex hormones
oestrogen (page 423)
and testosterone (page 422)

hypothalamus
(secretes hormones
controlling activity
of the anterior
pituitary)

thyroid gland:
thyroxine (controls
the rate of basal
metabolism of cells
(page 257) and
glucose metabolism
by tissues)

**pancreas (islets
of Langerhans)**:
insulin, glucagon
(page 260)

also:
wall of stomach: gastrin
wall of duodenum: secretin

Hormones are 'chemical messengers' produced and secreted from the cells of ductless or **endocrine glands**. They are transported generally in the bloodstream, but *act* only at specific sites, called **target organs**. Although present in small quantities, hormones are extremely effective messengers, helping to control and coordinate many body activities. They typically cause specific changes in metabolism in their target organs. Hormones circulate in the bloodstream only briefly as they are broken down in the liver and their breakdown products are excreted in the kidneys. So, to be long acting, hormones must be secreted continuously.

Examples of hormones already discussed include insulin, released from the islets of Langerhans in the pancreas. Insulin regulates blood glucose (page 260). Also, there is antidiuretic hormone (ADH), which controls water reabsorption in the collecting ducts of the kidneys (page 267). The positions of endocrine glands of the body are shown in Figure 13.20, where the hormones they produce are also listed.

The endocrine system and the nervous system work in distinctive and different ways in the control and coordination of body activities (Table 13.2). However, the activities of the two systems are coordinated by the pituitary gland, the master gland of the endocrine system working in tandem with the hypothalamus of the brain. The hypothalamus secretes hormones that regulate the functioning of the pituitary. The hypothalamus also monitors the level of hormones in the blood and regulates secretion by negative feedback control.

Table 13.2
Endocrine and nervous
systems compared.

Endocrine system	Nervous system
communications by chemical messengers transmitted in the bloodstream	communications by electrochemical action potentials (impulses) transmitted via nerve fibres
hormones 'broadcast' all over the body but influence target cells and tissues only	action potentials are targeted on specific cells
cause changes in metabolic activity	cause muscles to contract or glands to secrete
have their effects over many minutes, several hours or longer	produce their effects within milliseconds
effects tend to be long lasting	effects tend to be short lived and reversible

● **Extension**   The two modes of actions of hormones

Chemical analysis of animal hormones shows that they fall into two groups of compounds. Some hormones are **steroids**; examples are the sex hormones oestrogen and testosterone. Other hormones are either **amides** or **peptides** (small proteins); examples of these are ADH and insulin (see Chapter 12).

Figure 13.21
How the two groups
of hormones influence
target cells.

These two groups of hormones have different mechanisms of action within target cells, depending on what happens when the hormone makes initial contact with the plasma membrane of the target cells (Figure 13.21). Steroid hormones move through the membrane to activate specific genes, causing protein synthesis, whereas amide and peptide hormones bind to membrane receptors, activating existing proteins in the cytoplasm.

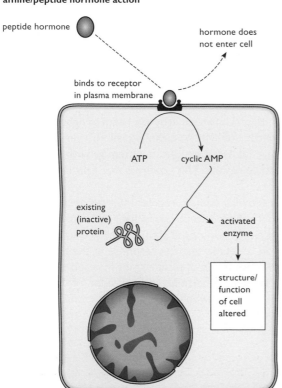
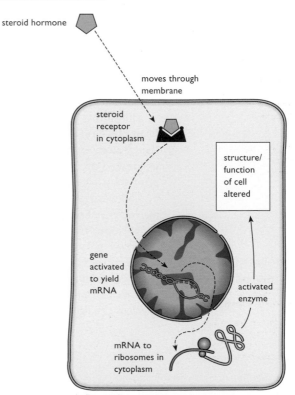

Plant sensitivity and responses

Sensitivity is a characteristic of all living things, but the responses of organisms can be very different. In contrast to the responses of animals, plant responses are mostly **growth movements**. For example, young stems grow towards the light, whereas the main roots of plants grow towards gravity. These responses, although quite slow and unspectacular, are essential to plant growth, development and nutrition. We shall see that they are also quite precise and carefully regulated. The investigation of plant responses to light as an external stimulus led to the discovery of plant 'hormones', better known as growth regulators. The list of plant growth regulators now includes five groups of substances, all chemically very different, which we will look at in turn. They are the **auxins**, **gibberellins**, **cytokinins**, **abscisic acid** and **ethene**. They are more correctly called growth regulators rather than hormones because they bear little resemblance to the hormones of animals, for the reasons listed in Table 13.3.

Table 13.3
The differences between plant growth regulators and animal hormones.

Plant growth regulators	Animal hormones
produced in a region of plant structure, e.g. stem or root tips, in unspecialised cells	produced in specific glands in specialised cells, e.g. islets of Langerhans in the pancreas
not necessarily transported widely or at all, and some are active at sites of production	transported to all parts of the body by the bloodstream
not particularly specific – tend to influence different tissues and organs, sometimes in contrasting ways	effects are mostly highly specific to a particular tissue or organ, and without effects in other parts or on different processes

Plant stems and light

The response of green plants to light is shown in Figure 13.22. The photograph shows that the relationship between the growth of a green plant shoot and light is complex and very interesting. In the dark, plant stems grow thin and weak, and they bear tiny, undeveloped leaves, yellow in colour. The shoots of plants grown in the dark are said to be **etiolated**.

By contrast, shoots grown in full light are short, with sturdy stems. The leaves are fully expanded and dark green in colour.

We already know that sunlight is essential for photosynthesis, to sustain plant nutrition. But we cannot also say that light is essential for plant growth in terms of length. Quite the contrary in fact: light *inhibits* plant stem growth, but light *is* essential for chlorophyll formation and leaf expansion.

The shoots grown in unilateral light confirm this. (Unilateral light is a beam of light coming from one direction.) Here the stems grow towards the light. We can explain this on the basis that growth on the illuminated side of the stem is inhibited by light, but stem growth is unchecked on the dark side, so a growth curvature results. This confirms that light *does* inhibit plant stem growth in length.

To investigate this response, we can mark a growing stem at regular intervals, using a felt-tip marker pen. Some of the marked stems are then exposed to unilateral light and others to normal illumination. This reveals that the region where elongation of the stem occurs is also the region of growth curvature in unilateral light. So we can conclude that the response of the plant stem to unilateral light is a **growth response**. Growth movements of plant organs in response to an external stimulus in which the direction of the stimulus determines the direction of the response are called tropic movements, or **tropisms**. For example, when the stem tip responds by growing towards the light, it is called **positively phototropic**.

6 Make a list of the various effects of light on plant growth and development.

Figure 13.22
Seedling growth and light.

Figure 13.22 **the effects of light on plant growth**

seedlings grown in total darkness; long weak stems and small, yellow leaves

pea seedlings in unilateral light; the stems have grown towards the light = positive phototropism

seedlings grown in even illumination; short, strong stems and large, green leaves

the region of stem growth

stems of seedlings marked at 2 mm intervals

batch of seedlings grown in the dark

batch of seedlings grown in unilateral light

48 hours later

region of elongation of stem

region of growth curvature

light

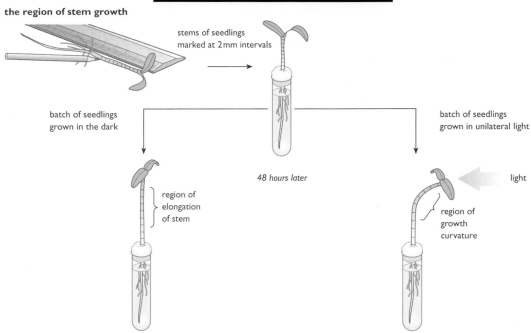

the phototropic response of the stem is a growth response

Using coleoptiles to investigate phototropism

The **coleoptile** is a sheath of tissue, unique to the grass family, that encloses the shoot of a germinating grass seedling, as it grows up through the soil. The coleoptile grows rather like a stem does, but since it is uncluttered by leaves or buds its growth is more easily observed. Experiments have been conducted with oat seedling coleoptiles, the plant organ first used to investigate phototropism (Figure 13.23). In fact, experiments on the responses of oat coleoptiles to unilateral light led to the discovery of the plant growth substance named 'auxin', which was later shown to be a substance called **indoleacetic acid** (**IAA** – see Figure 13.27, page 299).

Auxin is manufactured by cells undergoing repeated cell division, such as those found at the stem (see Figure 11.19, page 240) and root tips (and at the tip of coleoptiles). Consequently, the concentration of auxin is highest there. Auxin is then transported to the region of growth behind the tip where it causes cells to elongate. In the process the auxin is used up and inactivated.

In one experiment the tip of the stem or coleoptile was cut off and stood on a gelatin block for a short while. Then the gelatin block was placed on a cut stump of stem or coleoptile. Growth in length was found to continue. The explanation for this result was that auxin passed into the gelatin block, so when the gelatin was placed on the stump the auxin passed down into the tissue and stimulated elongation of the cells. This technique has been used to investigate auxin actions further, as follows.

Figure 13.23
The coleoptile as an experimental organ, and the discovery of auxin.

the coleoptile as an experimental organ

LS through oat seedling (cultivated grass)

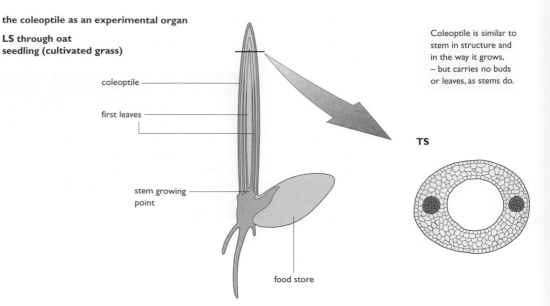

Coleoptile is similar to stem in structure and in the way it grows, – but carries no buds or leaves, as stems do.

- coleoptile
- first leaves
- stem growing point
- food store

steps in the discovery of auxin (experiments are conducted with batches of similar coleoptiles)

1 Light is a stimulus perceived at the stem tip.

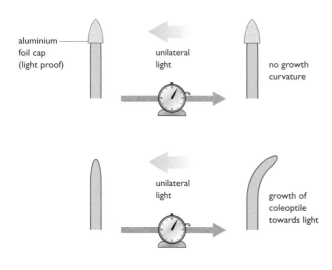

2 A growth-promoting substance, formed in the stem tip, passes to cells below where the growth response occurs.

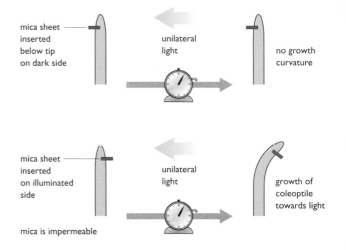

3 The growth-promoting substance can pass through gelatin.

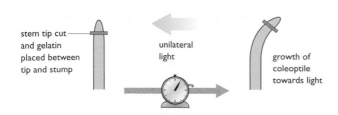

4 An asymmetrically replaced source of growth-promoting substance has the same effect on growth as unilateral light.

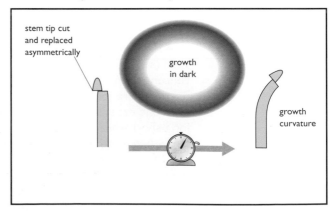

The effect of light on auxin distribution

In stems and coleoptiles exposed to unilateral light, the auxin passing down the stem is redistributed and accumulates on the darkened side. This causes differential growth and the curvature of the stem. The degree of curvature is proportional to the amount of auxin present, up to a certain concentration. Above this concentration, additional auxin inhibits growth.

This discovery was used in tests to estimate the concentration of auxin in samples from plant tissues. A cut tip of a coleoptile or a gelatin block with auxin was placed asymmetrically on a freshly decapitated oat seedling coleoptile, and the resulting curvature was found to be proportional to the amount of auxin present. Consequently, the degree of curvature caused by an unknown sample can be measured and compared with the curvature produced by samples of known concentration of IAA. This is an example of a biological measurement, called a **bioassay** (Figure 13.24).

An explanation of how auxin affects coleoptile growth is shown in Figure 13.25.

Figure 13.24
The oat coleoptile curvature test.

tip then discarded

coleoptile tip stood on gelatin block for 2 hours

tip discarded

fresh coleoptile stump (tip removed)

2 hours

curvature due to asymmetric growth of coleoptile

measurement of the angle of curvature taken from a photograph of curved coleoptile

angle of curvature

Degree of curvature was found to be proportional to the number of coleoptile tips stood on the gelatin block.

degree of curvature

increasing number of coleoptile tips

After auxin was found to be IAA, the curvature test was repeated with IAA in gelatin, at a range of concentrations.

degree of curvature

higher concentrations of IAA inhibit growth

IAA concentration in gelatin block/mg dm^{-3}

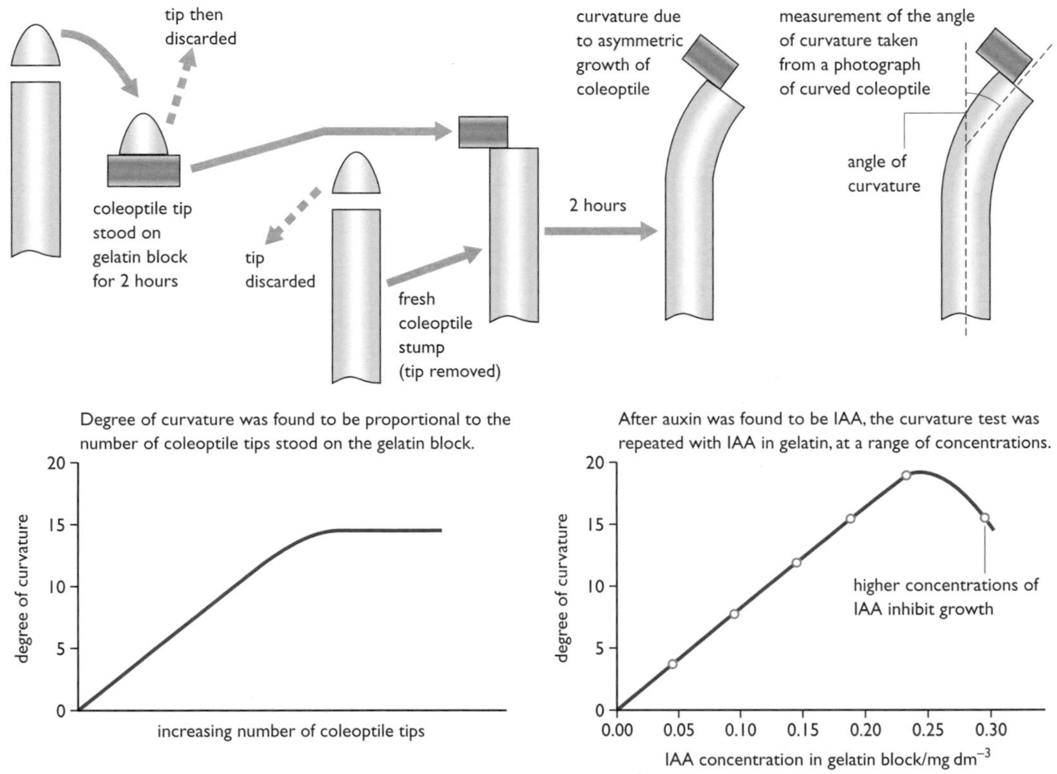

Figure 13.25
Auxin and positive phototropism in coleoptiles.

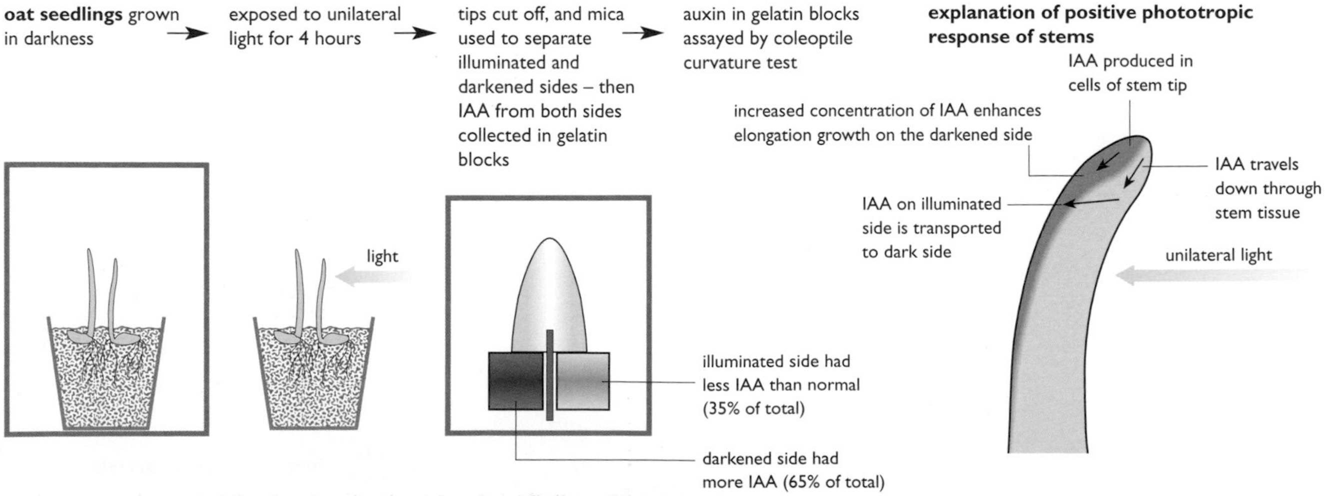

oat seedlings grown in darkness → exposed to unilateral light for 4 hours → tips cut off, and mica used to separate illuminated and darkened sides – then IAA from both sides collected in gelatin blocks → auxin in gelatin blocks assayed by coleoptile curvature test

explanation of positive phototropic response of stems

IAA produced in cells of stem tip

increased concentration of IAA enhances elongation growth on the darkened side

IAA on illuminated side is transported to dark side

IAA travels down through stem tissue

unilateral light

light

illuminated side had less IAA than normal (35% of total)

darkened side had more IAA (65% of total)

The response to gravity – geotropism

Both stem and root tips are sensitive to gravity. Seedlings are used to demonstrate this response because of their high growth rate and, therefore, rapid responses. If placed horizontally, their stem tips grow up and the main root tip down (Figure 13.26). The value of this response is that if seedlings are accidentally planted at an angle their growth is rapidly adjusted.

The auxin in stems and roots exposed to gravity in this way has been measured. It is shown to collect on the lower surfaces of stem and root. However, in the presence of a raised concentration of auxin on the lower sides, stem tips grow up but root tips grow down. How can it be that the responses of these two organs are completely opposite to one another? The answer appears to be that concentrations of auxin that stimulate stem growth actually inhibit root growth. Root extension growth is promoted by a much lower concentration of auxin than is active in the stem.

It is not known how the unilateral stimulus of gravity is detected in plant stems and roots and leads to a redistribution of auxin. The movements of auxin and other growth regulators in plant tissues are not *directly* influenced by gravity. The presence of large mobile starch grains in cells at the root tip has been observed, however. Perhaps movements of these grains in response to the pull of gravity could lead to the observed redistribution of auxin. If so, the chain of events is not known at this time.

Other roles of IAA

Natural auxins occur widely, and are responsible for several aspects of plant growth. These are summarised in Figure 13.27.

The structure of auxin is shown in Figure 13.28. Synthetic compounds that simulate some of the effects of auxin at low concentrations are used as growth stimulants in the rooting of cuttings in horticulture (hormone rooting powders). These artificial hormones are often toxic to plants at higher concentration, and are also widely used in herbicides in agriculture.

Figure 13.26
The role of auxin in the geotropic response.

In a horizontal seedling auxin is redistributed – a higher concentration collects on the lower surface.

The response from the plant: stem tip grows up, the root tip grows down.

explanation:
• root growth inhibited by (higher) auxin concentrations that enhance growth in stems (and coleoptiles)
• shown by collecting auxin in gelatin blocks in contact with upper and lower halves

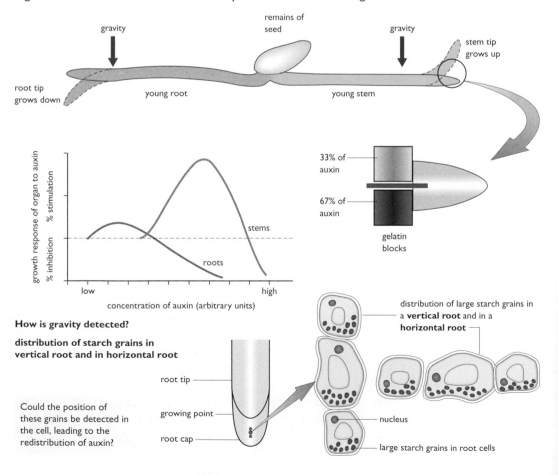

Figure 13.27
The roles of auxin in plant growth and development: a summary.

Figure 13.28
The structure of natural auxin, and synthetic alternatives.

Auxin has been shown to be indoleacetic acid (IAA).

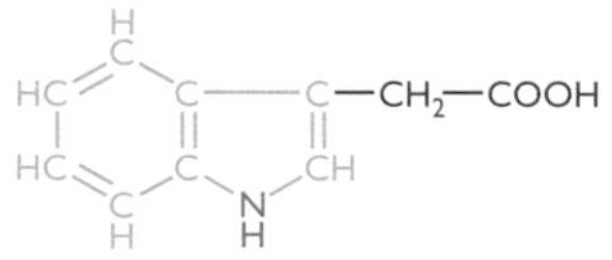

skeletal formula

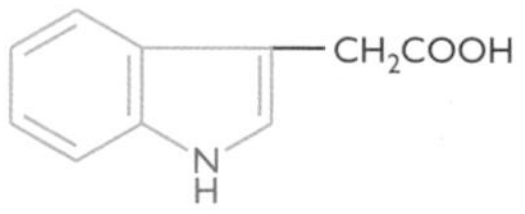

Some synthetic compounds with the properties of auxin are used in hormone rooting powder for plant cuttings and as herbicides, to kill weeds (at different concentrations).

α-naphthalenacetic acid

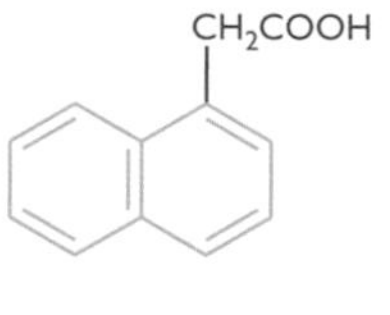

indolebutyric acid

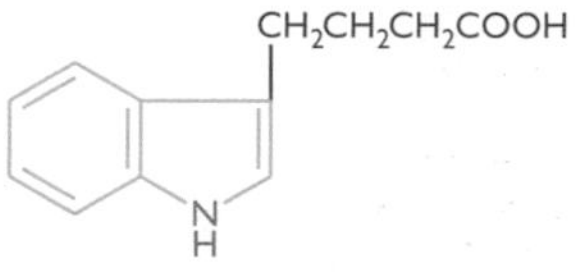

A review of other plant growth regulators

Gibberellins

Gibberellins (GA) are plant growth regulators that promote stem elongation and germination. They are formed in seeds, and in young leaves. Their known effects include:

- when applied to dwarf varieties of plants (that is, with short stems) they cause the plants to grow rapidly to the height of tall varieties
- they stimulate leaf growth
- they interact with IAA (from the stem apex) to increase growth in stem length
- during germination of seeds, GA produced by the embryo pass into the food store and activate the formation of the hydrolytic enzymes that mobilise food reserves to aid germination (Figure 13.29).

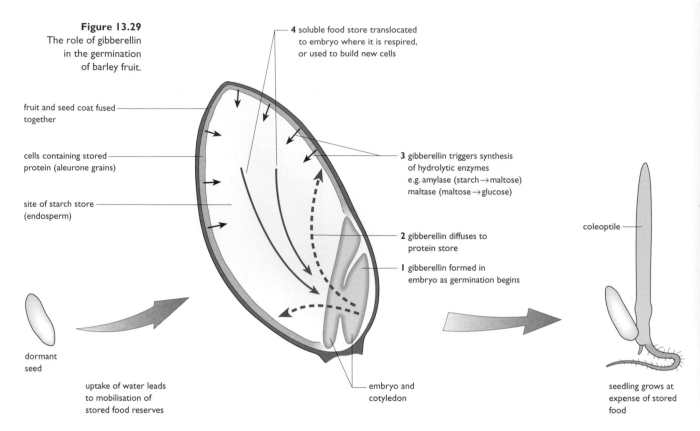

Figure 13.29
The role of gibberellin in the germination of barley fruit.

4 soluble food store translocated to embryo where it is respired, or used to build new cells

fruit and seed coat fused together

cells containing stored protein (aleurone grains)

site of starch store (endosperm)

3 gibberellin triggers synthesis of hydrolytic enzymes e.g. amylase (starch→maltose) maltase (maltose→glucose)

2 gibberellin diffuses to protein store

1 gibberellin formed in embryo as germination begins

coleoptile

dormant seed

uptake of water leads to mobilisation of stored food reserves

embryo and cotyledon

seedling grows at expense of stored food

Cytokinins

Cytokinins are chemically very similar to the nucleic acid base, adenine (page 45). They are produced in dividing cells, and they promote cell division. The known effects of cytokinins include the following.

- Mature plant cells tend not to divide and grow further. However, when cytokinin is applied to blocks of mature plant tissue placed on agar jelly that also contain auxin (in the technique of laboratory cell culture) the cells divide in an uncontrolled way, producing a lump of tissue known as **callus**. This is exploited in plant tissue culture, for example in the genetic engineering of new varieties (page 120).
- In young leaves they promote growth, and combat ageing and senescence (yellowing due to loss of proteins) in older leaves.
- In normal plant growth they enhance cell division at stem and root tip, and in lateral buds.

Abscisic acid

Abscisic acid (ABA) is a plant growth regulator made in stems, leaves and fruits. In some cases it may inhibit plant growth or development. ABA was once thought to be widely involved in leaf fall, but this is the case in only a few plant species. Its known effects include the following.

- It interacts with other substances to prevent immediate germination in mature seeds with a fully formed embryo and food store.
- It assists the plant to survive times of physiological stress, such as prolonged drought. In these conditions ABA keeps the stomata closed, reducing water loss.

Ethene

Ethene is a plant growth regulator that is a relatively simple molecule. It is a gas with the formula $CH_2{=}CH_2$. It is produced in fruits as they ripen, and speeds up the ripening process. So it is used by commercial fruit growers. For instance, fruits such as bananas can be picked unripe for safe transport, and then ripened by external application of ethene just before being marketed.

7 Distinguish between the following pairs:

- receptors and effectors
- reflex arc and reflex action
- action potential and resting potential
- neurones and neuroglia cells
- presynaptic and postsynaptic neurones
- grey matter and white matter
- motor and sensory neurones
- cerebral hemispheres and cerebellum
- phototropism and geotropism
- gibberellins and cytokinins.

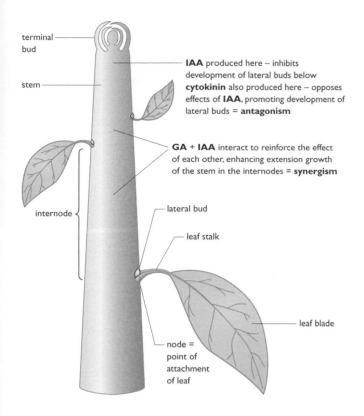

terminal bud

stem

IAA produced here – inhibits development of lateral buds below
cytokinin also produced here – opposes effects of **IAA**, promoting development of lateral buds = **antagonism**

GA + IAA interact to reinforce the effect of each other, enhancing extension growth of the stem in the internodes = **synergism**

internode

lateral bud

leaf stalk

leaf blade

node = point of attachment of leaf

Interactions of plant growth regulators

Sometimes these plant growth regulators produce effects entirely on their own; in other situations they interact (Figure 13.30). When one substance enhances the effects of another, this is known as **synergism**. For instance, GA and IAA work in synergism in stem extension growth.

Alternatively, a growth regulator may reduce the effects of another. This situation is known as **antagonism**. For example, IAA and cytokinins work antagonistically in lateral bud dormancy.

Figure 13.30
Interaction of growth regulators.

● Skills task

The response of organisms to particular environmental conditions is sometimes investigated by means of a choice chamber experiment. For example, the response of woodlice to a gradient in humidity can be investigated in a simple choice chamber made from a plastic Petri dish, similar to that shown in Figure 13.31. The woodlice are free to move about on the perforated platform in the upper half. Below, on one side is moist filter paper from which water evaporates. On the other side is dried silica gel, which strongly absorbs water vapour. As a consequence, the atmosphere of one half of the dish is very humid and that of the other half very dry. The experiment may be conducted at low light intensity. At the start of the experiment, woodlice are introduced at the entry hole arranged on the midline. The number found in each half of the dish is subsequently recorded at 10 minute intervals.

Figure 13.31
A simple choice chamber constructed from a plastic Petri dish.

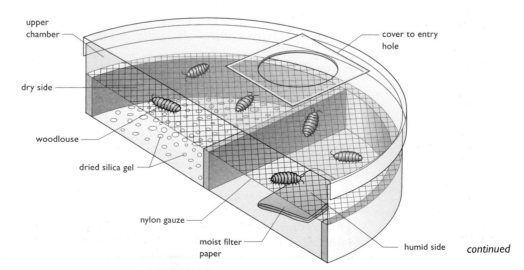

upper chamber

cover to entry hole

dry side

woodlouse

dried silica gel

nylon gauze

moist filter paper

humid side

continued

In the experiment reported here, samples of the woodlice used were held for 30 minutes in (A) a dry environment, or (B) a humid environment, prior to the investigation. The results of the experiment were as follows:

(A) using woodlice pre-treated in a dry environment

Time/min	Numbers found in humid side	Numbers found in dry side
10	16	4
20	17	3
30	16	4
40	19	1
50	20	0
60	20	0

(B) using woodlice pre-treated in a humid environment

Time/min	Numbers found in humid side	Numbers found in dry side
10	9	11
20	11	9
30	12	8
40	14	6
50	15	5
60	16	4

1. Plot a graph showing the percentage of (A) dry pre-treated, and (B) humid pre-treated, woodlice in the humid half of the choice chamber at 10 minute intervals throughout the experiment

2. Suggest reasons why the dry pre-treated woodlice showed a greater preference for the moist half of the chamber initially.

3. Are the responses of woodlice shown here best described as a kinesis or a taxis (see page 292)? Explain why.

SUMMARY

- **Neurones** are the basic units of the nervous system. The **nerve fibres** of neurones, the **dendron** and **axon**, are typically protected by a **myelin sheath**, which also speeds conduction of the impulse.
- The nervous system contains **receptors** (e.g. sense organs) linked to **effectors** (muscles or glands) by pathways of neurones, known collectively as **reflex arcs**. In higher animals the reflex arcs are connected to the brain.
- An impulse or **action potential** is a temporary reversal of the electrical potential difference that is maintained across the membrane of the nerve fibres. Conduction is extremely fast, and after an action potential there is a brief period when the fibre is no longer excitable (**refractory period**).
- Action potentials are transmitted between neurones across tiny gaps at **synapses**. Transmission here is chemical, involving diffusion of a specific **transmitter substance**.
- Receptors contain cells that respond to **stimuli** such as changes in light, differences in temperature, touch or chemicals. They respond by producing action potentials.
- The **brain** receives and integrates incoming information from sensory receptors, sends impulses to effectors, stores information as a memory bank, and initiates activities in its own right.
- **Behaviour**, the way organisms respond to the environment, is based on feedback, using the control and coordination mechanisms of the body. Some behaviour is instinctive (innate) and some is learned, but the division between these is not clear cut.
- **Hormones** work with the animal's nervous system in the control and coordination of the body. They are produced in **endocrine glands**, transported all over the body in the blood, and affect specific target organs.
- Plant responses are mainly **growth responses**. For example, the tips of plant stems grow towards the light (**positive phototropism**), and plant stems and root tips respond differently to gravity (**geotropism**) such that the aerial shoot grows up and the roots down.
- Plant sensitivity and coordination are mediated by **growth regulators** (auxin, **gibberellins**, **cytokinins**, **abscisic acid** and **ethene**), which are different from animal hormones.

Examination questions

1 The diagram below shows a rod cell from the retina of a mammal.

a Name the regions labelled A and B. (2)
b State the location of most of the rod cells in the human retina. (1)
c i Give the name of the light sensitive pigment contained in the rod cells. (1)
ii Use the letter P to label on the diagram the region of the rod cell in which this pigment is located. (1)

London, A level, Module B3, Jan 1996

2 The diagram below shows a human brain seen from the right side.

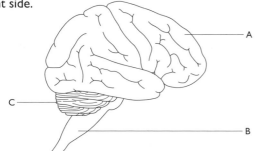

a Name the parts labelled A, B and C. (3)
b Give **two** functions of the part labelled B. (2)

London, A level, Module B3, June 1997

3 a Describe the sequence of events that takes place when a nerve impulse arrives at a synapse. (4)
b The diagram below shows the changes in membrane potential in a presynaptic neurone and postsynaptic neurone when an impulse passes across a synapse.

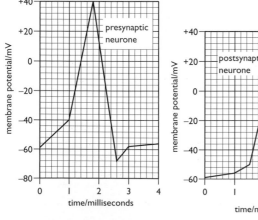

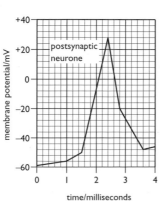

i Explain how depolarisation occurs in the presynaptic neurone. (3)
ii The maximum depolarisation in the presynaptic neurone is +40 mV. What is the maximum depolarisation in the postsynaptic neurone? (1)
iii How long is the delay between the maximum depolarisation in the presynaptic and postsynaptic neurones? (1)
iv What is the cause of this delay? (1)
c Describe how nicotine affects synaptic transmission. (2)

London, A level, Module B3, June 1996

4 a Explain what is meant by dormancy in seeds. (1)
b Give **two** advantages of dormancy in seeds. (2)

AQA(NEAB), A level, Paper 1/Sections A & B, June 1999

5 The diagram shows how the movement of auxin through plant shoots was investigated. Shoots were removed from young plants and each was placed on a block of agar. A second block of agar was placed in the side of each shoot where a portion of its tissue had been cut away. Samples of shoots treated in this way were left for several hours. Half the shoots were left in darkness and half were left with a light source from one side.

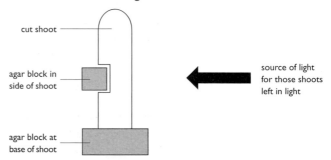

The concentration of auxin collected in the two blocks of agar from each shoot was measured. The table shows the mean percentage of auxin found in the two blocks of agar from each shoot.

	Mean percentage of auxin collected in the two agar blocks from each shoot	
Location of block	Shoot in dark	Shoot lit from side
side of shoot	27	35
base of shoot	73	65
both blocks	100	100

a What do the results of this investigation show about the movement of auxin? (2)
b Explain how the movement of auxin shown in this experiment enables intact plants to photosynthesise efficiently. (3)

AQA(AEB), A level, Module 4, June 1999

14 Support and movement

STARTING POINTS ● Organisms **support** themselves and maintain **positions** to carry out the essential processes of life, including movement.
● Support systems maintain **body shape**, resist **stress forces** and are specially important to land organisms.

● The roles of support systems

Living things maintain their characteristic shape, and support their bodies in positions favourable for the essential processes of life. For example, plant leaves are held aloft to trap light, flowers are supported for pollination, and fruits are supported prior to seed dispersal. In most animals, support systems are adapted to allow locomotion, which is essential for nutrition and most other activities.

In the process of maintaining themselves, mechanical forces act on plants and animals, generating **stress**. In particular, stress comes from:

- supporting the **weight of the body**; this is much greater on land than in water, which, by comparison, is a very supportive medium
- resisting **environmental forces**, such as the wind, or the waves and currents in water
- forces generated by **movement** of the body.

Stress forces take three forms. **Compression** is the stress of objects or their parts pushing together, **tension** that when they try to pull apart, and **shear** that when they attempt to slide past each other (Figure 14.1). The bodies of living things have to resist these stresses, but using strengthening materials in ways that will not interfere with the body's activities. As animals and plants increase in size the need for support increases. Supporting structures are known as **skeletons**. The skeletal systems of organisms take many different forms.

Figure 14.1
Mechanical stress the body needs to resist.

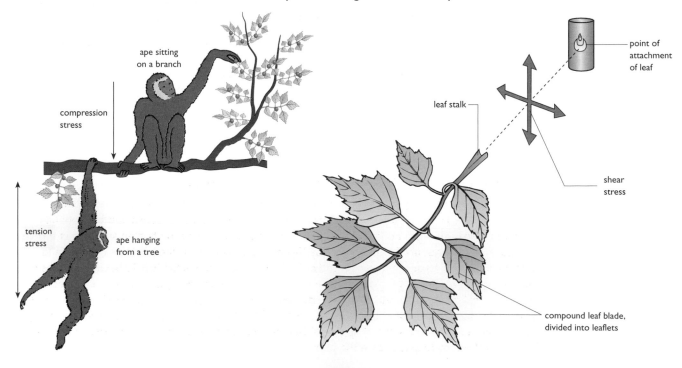

ape sitting on a branch

compression stress

tension stress

ape hanging from a tree

leaf stalk

point of attachment of leaf

shear stress

compound leaf blade, divided into leaflets

Skeletons for support, movement and locomotion

The **support system of plants** brings and maintains their leaves, flowers and fruits into the best positions to carry out their functions. Support in a plant is provided, firstly, by the **turgidity** of living cells. The contents of cells press hard against their inelastic cellulose cell walls. This turgidity provides support for all the soft parts of the plant's structure, particularly the leaves. Secondly, there is added strength from the **lignified walls of fibres** and xylem **vessels**, which are found in and around the vascular tissue. These add support to the stem, leaves and roots. The interconnected system of **vascular bundles** of flowering plants has a skeletal role (although it has an equally important function in internal transport – see Chapter 11, page 240).

The **support systems of animals** are skeletons. These help maintain the distinctive form of the animal, by which it is recognised. The skeleton of many (but not all) animals is a quite rigid structure that also provides some protection to certain internal tissues and organs. Most typically, the animal skeleton also allows locomotion. For example, mammals and other vertebrates have an internal skeleton (an **endoskeleton**) of many component parts, which are mostly made of bone. Attached to the bones are muscles, and between the bones are joints. Muscles, bones and movable joints work together to act as a system of levers. This system allows an animal to push parts of its body against external surfaces (the ground, water, or air). These act as a resistance force to propel the animal's body forward, and bring about locomotion.

The endoskeleton of mammals contrasts with the skeleton of insects, which is formed around the outside of the body (an **exoskeleton**), and the fluid-filled compartments of the earthworm (a **hydrostatic skeleton**). In this chapter, the functioning of these three types of animal skeleton is considered by examining support and movement in humans, insects and the earthworm in turn. Finally, the plant stem will be considered as a support structure.

Movement and locomotion

Movement is a characteristic of all living things, and occurs within cells (for example, cytoplasmic streaming), within organisms (for example, the pumping action of the heart) and as movement of whole organisms, known as **locomotion**.

Although plants are stationary organisms, most animals support themselves in a way that permits locomotion in the search for food, to avoid predators and for reproduction, for example. However, a few animals remain attached to one place (called **sessile** organisms – for example, sponges and sea anemones). For the majority of animals, which are on the move, there are just **three basic mechanisms of locomotion** available to them in the living world:

- **amoeboid movement**, seen in some unicellular organisms such as *Amoeba* (page 350) and in white blood cells (page 336)
- **movement by cilia and flagella**, whip-like organelles that project from the surface of certain cells (page 16)
- **muscular locomotion**, which is examined in this chapter.

Support and movement in mammals

An endoskeleton is a rigid internal framework of many component bones. In mammals the endoskeleton consists of the axial skeleton (**skull** and **vertebral column**) and the appendicular skeleton (**limb girdles** and **limbs**). The arrangement of bones of the human skeleton is shown in Figure 14.2. Bones are held together by **ligaments**, made from the proteins collagen and elastin, which is a strong, but very slightly elastic material. Immovable **joints** between bones can be seen in the bones of the cranium. However, in most joints the ligaments permit controlled movements. For example, the limbs are attached to the limb girdles by **ball and socket joints**, and there are **hinge joints** at elbows and knees. Other joints in the limbs are gliding or sliding joints. These are all examples of **synovial joints** because they contain a thick viscous fluid, the **synovial fluid**, to help lubricate the joint.

305

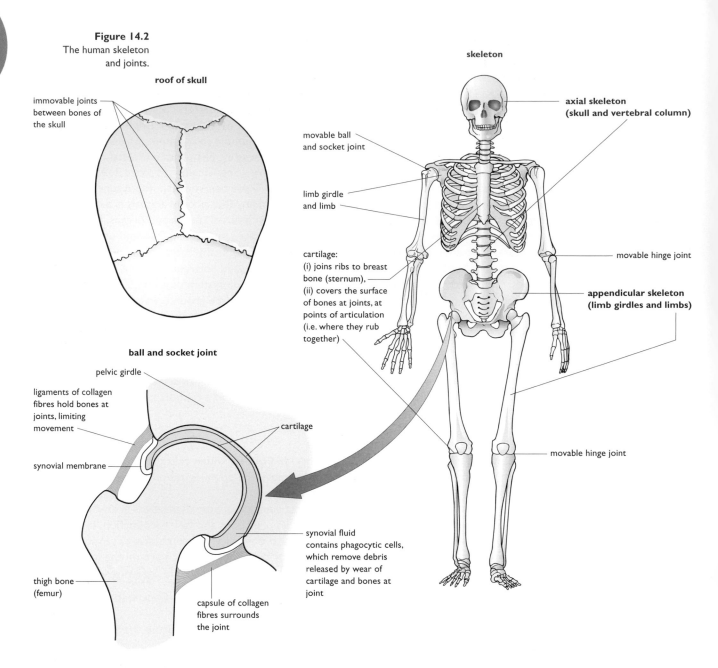

Figure 14.2
The human skeleton and joints.

roof of skull

immovable joints between bones of the skull

skeleton

axial skeleton (skull and vertebral column)

movable ball and socket joint

limb girdle and limb

movable hinge joint

cartilage:
(i) joins ribs to breast bone (sternum),
(ii) covers the surface of bones at joints, at points of articulation (i.e. where they rub together)

appendicular skeleton (limb girdles and limbs)

ball and socket joint

pelvic girdle

ligaments of collagen fibres hold bones at joints, limiting movement

cartilage

synovial membrane

movable hinge joint

thigh bone (femur)

synovial fluid contains phagocytic cells, which remove debris released by wear of cartilage and bones at joint

capsule of collagen fibres surrounds the joint

● **Extension**   Arthritis and osteoporosis

Arthritis is a disease of the joints, which makes them painful and stiff. There are three forms of this disease:

1 **osteoarthritis** – due to the wearing away of cartilage on the articulating surfaces, and the deposition of some new bone. This leads to restricted movement
2 **rheumatoid arthritis** – due to the body's immune system mistakenly recognising the synovial membrane and articulating cartilage as foreign tissue and destroying them
3 **gouty arthritis** – due to uric acid, which has unusually built up in the blood, being deposited as hard crystals of sodium urate in the cartilage at the joints.

Osteoporosis is an age-related disorder of bones. As people age, the density of the bone decreases and it is therefore more likely to fracture. Our sex hormones stimulate osteocytes to form new bone – as levels of these hormones decrease in old age in both men and women, especially after the menopause in women, the likelihood of osteoporosis increases.

The structure of bone and cartilage

Bone is a living tissue. The specialised bone cells, called **osteocytes**, are surrounded by a hard substance, or matrix. The bone cells are in tiny cavities (called lacunae) in the matrix, with connections to the cytoplasm through tiny tubes. Chemically, bone is approximately 70% mineral matter (a form of **calcium phosphate**) and 30% organic matter (mainly protein **collagen fibres**). Bone cells both form the matrix (by secretion) and maintain (or repair) it. Although the matrix is impervious to tissue fluid, blood vessels run into the bone and so blood delivers essential nutrients and removes waste products. Bone is a very strong tissue. It is especially able to resist compression. There are two types of bone tissue: compact bone and spongy bone.

Compact bone makes up the greater part of the bones of the body. It has osteocytes arranged in concentric rings around a central canal, known as a Haversian system (Figure 14.3). The spaces within **spongy bone** contain a tissue known as bone marrow.

Figure 14.3
The structure of bone.

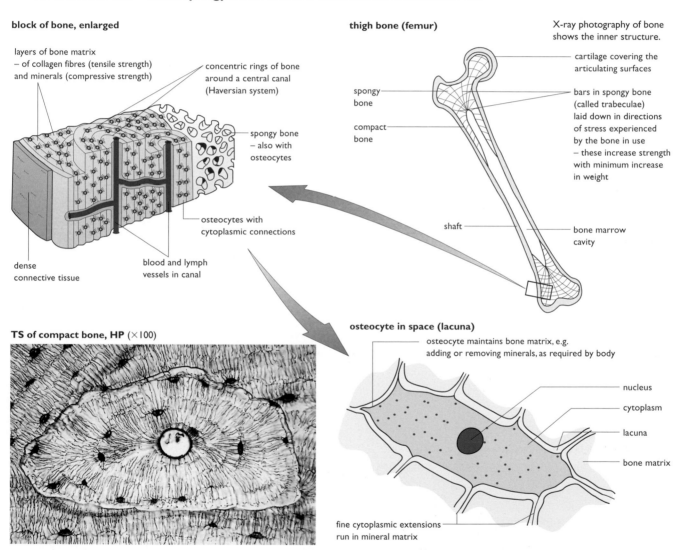

block of bone, enlarged

layers of bone matrix
– of collagen fibres (tensile strength)
and minerals (compressive strength)

concentric rings of bone
around a central canal
(Haversian system)

spongy bone
– also with
osteocytes

osteocytes with
cytoplasmic connections

dense
connective tissue

blood and lymph
vessels in canal

thigh bone (femur)

X-ray photography of bone
shows the inner structure.

cartilage covering the
articulating surfaces

spongy
bone

compact
bone

bars in spongy bone
(called trabeculae)
laid down in directions
of stress experienced
by the bone in use
– these increase strength
with minimum increase
in weight

shaft

bone marrow
cavity

TS of compact bone, HP (×100)

osteocyte in space (lacuna)

osteocyte maintains bone matrix, e.g.
adding or removing minerals, as required by body

nucleus

cytoplasm

lacuna

bone matrix

fine cytoplasmic extensions
run in mineral matrix

Cartilage is a firm, flexible, elastic material. Unlike bone, it is not hardened by calcium salts. There are living cells embedded in its matrix. At joints it forms the 'slippery' covering on the surfaces of bones. Cartilage also forms the flexible connections between the ribs and sternum, the incomplete rings that hold open the trachea and bronchi, and the 'skeleton' of outer ears, tip of the nose and the epiglottis.

Special fibre-reinforced cartilage pads make up the intervertebral discs of the spinal cord. Under exceptional stress these discs can rupture, and as a result the cartilage squeezes the spinal cord or spinal nerve. We call this a 'slipped disc'.

1 What functions does the skeleton of a mammal have?

Muscles and movement

The muscles that cause locomotion, the **voluntary (skeletal) muscles**, are attached across the joint to the movable parts of the skeleton. Contraction of the muscles allows the joints and bones to act as a system of levers. Most skeletal movement is controlled by muscles working in **antagonistic pairs**, as shown in Figure 14.4. Muscles are attached to bones by **tendons**. Tendons, like ligaments, contain collagen, but their fibres are less elastic.

Voluntary muscle consists of bundles of muscle fibres (Figure 14.5). A fibre is a long cell with many nuclei. Fibres are able to shorten to half or even a third of their 'resting' length. They appear striped under the light microscope, and so voluntary muscle is also known as **striped** or **striated muscle**. Each fibre is itself composed of a mass of **myofibrils**, but we need the electron microscope to see them.

Figure 14.4
Muscles operate in antagonistic pairs.

The lower arm is extended by contraction of the triceps muscle, accompanied by relaxation of the biceps muscle.

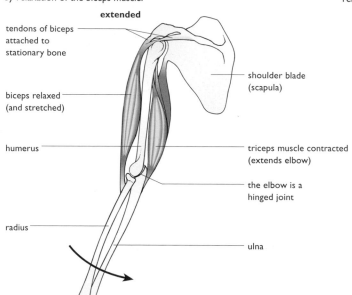

extended

tendons of biceps attached to stationary bone

biceps relaxed (and stretched)

humerus

radius

shoulder blade (scapula)

triceps muscle contracted (extends elbow)

the elbow is a hinged joint

ulna

The lower arm is flexed by contraction of the biceps muscle, accompanied by relaxation of the triceps muscle.

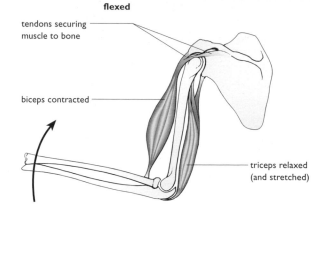

flexed

tendons securing muscle to bone

biceps contracted

triceps relaxed (and stretched)

Figure 14.5
The structure of voluntary muscle.

photomicrograph of LS voluntary muscle fibres, HP (×1500)

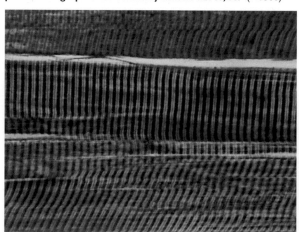

Voluntary muscle is also known as skeletal, striped or striated muscle.

voluntary muscle cut to show the bundle of fibres

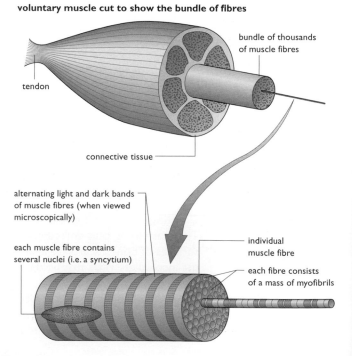

tendon

bundle of thousands of muscle fibres

connective tissue

alternating light and dark bands of muscle fibres (when viewed microscopically)

each muscle fibre contains several nuclei (i.e. a syncytium)

individual muscle fibre

each fibre consists of a mass of myofibrils

The ultrastructure of striped muscle

A muscle fibre consists of numerous parallel myofibrils within a plasma membrane, called the **sarcolemma**, together with cytoplasm, called the **sarcoplasm**. The sarcoplasm contains many mitochondria packed between the myofibrils. Infolding of the sarcolemma forms a system of transverse tubular endoplasmic reticulum, known as **sarcoplasmic reticulum**. This reticulum forms a network around the individual myofibrils. The positions of the myofibrils, sarcoplasm, sarcolemma and mitochondria, surrounded by the sarcoplasmic membrane, are shown in Figure 14.6.

Figure 14.6
The ultrastructure of a muscle fibre.

The 'stripy' appearance of voluntary muscle is due to the interlocking arrangement of two types of protein filaments that make up the myofibrils, and the alignment of all the muscle fibres.

electron micrograph of TS through a single muscle fibre, HP (×11 000)

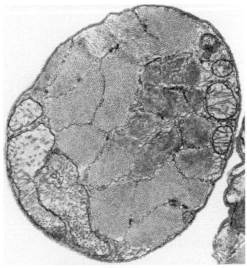

Figure 14.7
The ultrastructure of a myofibril.

stereogram of part of a single muscle fibre

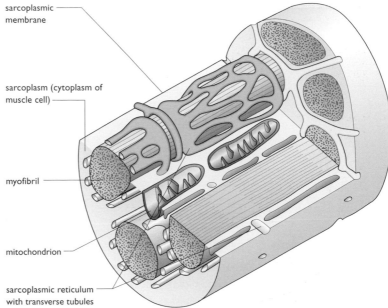

- sarcoplasmic membrane
- sarcoplasm (cytoplasm of muscle cell)
- myofibril
- mitochondrion
- sarcoplasmic reticulum with transverse tubules

electron micrograph LS part of voluntary muscle fibre, HP (×36 000)

sarcomere

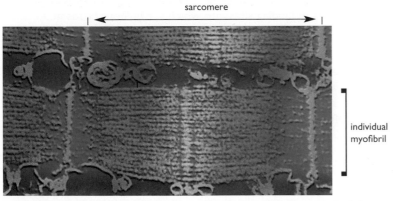

individual myofibril

interpretive drawing of the thick filaments (myosin) and thin filaments (actin)

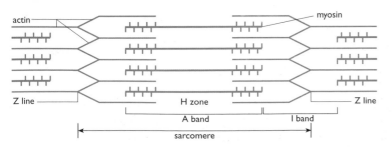

actin — myosin

Z line — H zone — Z line

A band — I band

sarcomere

They are shown in the electron micrograph and diagram in Figure 14.7. The muscle comprises, firstly, **thick filaments** made of the protein **myosin**; these are about 15 nm in diameter, and short in length. There are also **thin filaments**, made of **actin**, which are about 7 nm in diameter and of greater length. These thin filaments are held together by transverse bands, called **Z-bands**. Each repeating unit of the myofibril, for convenience, is measured from Z-line to Z-line (see Figure 14.7), and referred to as a **sarcomere**. The thick filaments lie in the central part of each sarcomere, sandwiched between the thin filaments.

When voluntary muscle contracts in response to nervous stimulation, the actin and myosin filaments slide past each other. The result is that each sarcomere shortens (Figure 14.8). A great deal of ATP is used in this contraction.

Figure 14.8
Muscle contraction.

change in a single sarcomere in relaxed, and contracted myofibril

muscles contract as the actin and myosin filaments
slide between each other, shortening each sarcomere

relaxed   **contracted**

thin filament = actin   thick filament = myosin   Z line

electron micrographs of muscle fibres, relaxed (left) and contracted (right)

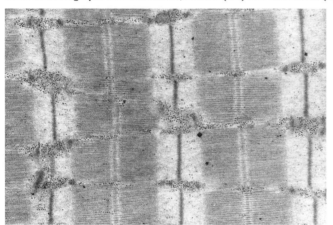
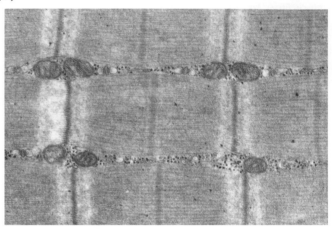

● **Extension**   The sliding-filament hypothesis of muscle contraction

Shortening of each sarcomere is brought about by actin (thin filaments) and myosin (thick filaments) sliding past each other in response to nervous stimulation. This occurs in a series of steps described as a **'ratchet mechanism'**.

Thick filaments are composed of many myosin molecules, each ending in a **bulbous head**. These bulbous heads protrude from the length of the myosin filament (Figure 14.9). Along the surface of the actin filament are a series of binding sites into which the bulbous heads fit. In muscle fibres at rest the binding sites carry **blocking molecules**. The sequence of events is as follows:

1 The myofibril is stimulated to contract by the arrival of an action potential. This triggers release of Ca^{2+} ions around the actin molecules, and the Ca^{2+} ions react with the blocking molecules, exposing the binding sites.
2 Each bulbous head to which ADP and a phosphate group (P_i) is attached (called a *charged* bulbous head) reacts with a binding site on the actin molecule beside it. The P_i group is shed at this moment.
3 Then the ADP molecule is released from the bulbous head, and this is the trigger for the 'rowing movement' of the head, which tilts by an angle of about 45°, pushing the actin filament along. At this step, the 'power stroke', the myofibril has been shortened slightly (**contraction**).
4 Finally, a fresh molecule of ATP binds to the bulbous head. The protein of the bulbous head includes the enzyme ATPase, which catalyses the hydrolysis of ATP. When this reaction occurs, the ADP and P_i formed remain attached, and the bulbous head is now 'charged'. The charged head detaches from the binding site and straightens.

2 What is the relationship to a muscle of:
a a muscle fibre,
b a myofibril, and
c a myosin filament?

This cycle of movements is shown in Figure 14.9. The cycle is repeated many times per second, with thousands of bulbous heads working along each myofibril. ATP is rapidly used up. The muscle may shorten by about 50% of its relaxed length.

continued

Figure 14.9
The sliding-filament
hypothesis.

Arrival of action potential at myofibril releases Ca^{2+} ions from sarcoplasmic reticulum.

Ca^{2+} ions bind to blocking molecules, exposing binding sites on actin molecules.

Each myosin molecule has a 'head' that reacts with ATP → ADP + P$_i$, which remain bound.

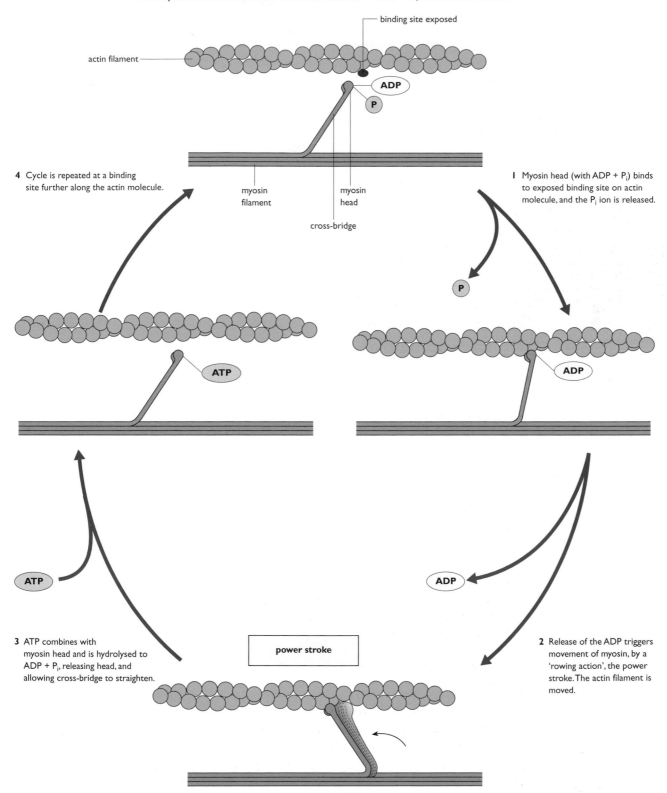

binding site exposed

actin filament

ADP

P

4 Cycle is repeated at a binding
site further along the actin molecule.

myosin
filament

myosin
head

cross-bridge

1 Myosin head (with ADP + P$_i$) binds
to exposed binding site on actin
molecule, and the P$_i$ ion is released.

P

ATP

ADP

ATP

ADP

3 ATP combines with
myosin head and is hydrolysed to
ADP + P$_i$, releasing head, and
allowing cross-bridge to straighten.

power stroke

2 Release of the ADP triggers
movement of myosin, by a
'rowing action', the power
stroke. The actin filament is
moved.

When action potential ceases, Ca^{2+} ions return to sarcoplasmic reticulum, and binding sites become blocked again.

How the motor nerve ending makes connection with a muscle fibre

Muscle fibres are innervated by a motor neurone nerve ending, at a structure known as a **motor end plate** (Figure 14.10). A motor end plate is a special type of synapse, but the transmitter substance is the familiar acetylcholine (page 280).

On arrival of an action potential at the motor end plate, vesicles (packets) of acetylcholine are released. These neurotransmitter molecules bind to receptors on the sarcoplasm (that is, the plasma membrane of the muscle fibre). This binding triggers the release of Ca^{2+} ions, from the sarcoplasmic reticulum into the cytoplasm around the myofibrils. The Ca^{2+} ions remove the blocking molecules on the binding sites of the actin filaments. In the absence of the blocking molecules, the contraction process begins. When action potentials stop arriving at the muscle fibres, Ca^{2+} ions return to the sarcoplasmic reticulum, and the binding sites are again covered by blocking molecules.

Figure 14.10
The motor end plate.

The motor end plate is a type of synapse
(formed between a motor neurone and a muscle fibre).

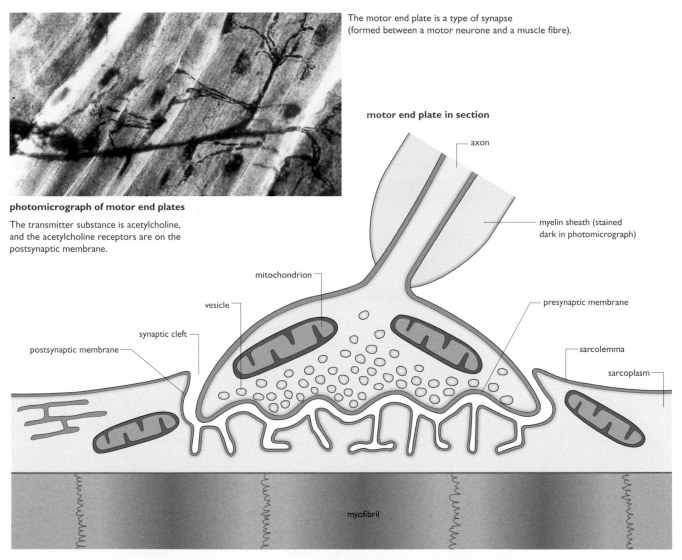

photomicrograph of motor end plates

The transmitter substance is acetylcholine, and the acetylcholine receptors are on the postsynaptic membrane.

The supply of resources for contraction: a summary

The blood supply to the muscle supplies glucose, fatty acids and oxygen. These are used to power contraction. Glycogen is held in reserve in muscle fibres, and is available for hydrolysis to glucose when required. The energy for muscle contraction comes from the aerobic respiration of glucose or fatty acids to produce ATP. In repeated contraction, when oxygen, glucose and fatty acids are consumed faster than they can be delivered, muscles have alternative reserve stores that they can use.

Reserves of **oxygen** are held as **oxymyoglobin** (page 239). Under very low partial pressures of oxygen (that is, muscle is almost without oxygen), oxymyoglobin breaks down to release molecular oxygen for respiration. In muscles that are at rest and relaxed, oxymyoglobin reserves are re-formed.

Reserves of **ATP** are held in the form of molecules of **creatine phosphate**. When most of the ATP available has been hydrolysed to ADP, creatine phosphate reacts with ADP to form ATP and creatine. Creatine phosphate is re-formed from fresh ATP when muscle is at rest and relaxed.

If muscle continues to be active, for example in prolonged heavy work, then all these reserves may become exhausted, too. In this case, voluntary muscle can continue to obtain ATP by **lactic acid fermentation** (anaerobic respiration, page 200). This is wasteful of glucose, however, and the accumulating lactic acid may be harmful to the tissues. As lactic acid builds up in the muscle, it causes tiredness and pain. The muscle becomes fatigued. (The body tolerates only limited accumulation of lactic acid since its presence in the blood lowers its pH.) Lactic acid is removed from the bloodstream in the liver and converted back to glucose, a process that also requires energy from respiration. After lactic acid fermentation by muscles an **oxygen debt** builds up in the body, as the body requires additional oxygen to rebuild its oxymyoglobin reserves in muscles and to meet the increased respiration of the liver cells.

> **3** What are the roles of:
> **a** myoglobin, and
> **b** creatine phosphate in muscle tissue?

Contractions for locomotion and posture

Animals use muscles both to move about (locomotion) and to maintain their posture. This dual role of muscles explains the presence of two types of muscle fibre. Fast muscle fibres are used for locomotion, whereas slow muscle fibres maintain posture. ('Fast' and 'slow' refer to how quickly the cross-bridges form in the sliding-filament mechanism of muscle contraction.) In humans, both types of fibre occur in all muscles: fast fibres mostly at the surface of muscles, slow fibres occur deep in the muscles.

Fast fibres contract immediately there is a need for movement, and normally well before the circulation of blood to muscles has been adjusted in order to cope with the increased muscle activity. They:

- are fast at contraction but fatigue quite quickly
- use glycogen as the respiratory substrate
- have few mitochondria and little myoglobin, and depend on anaerobic respiration of glycogen for their ATP supply, once available oxygen has been used up.

Slow fibres enable the sustained muscle contraction required in maintaining body posture. They:

- are slow at contraction but maintain their contraction for a long time
- use glucose or fatty acids from the blood circulation, and respire them aerobically
- are well supplied with mitochondria and myoglobin.

Three types of muscle in mammals

There are three types of muscle tissue found in mammals. Voluntary (striped or striated) muscle, described above, is used for quick and powerful contractions and to maintain body posture.

The other types of muscle are:

- **cardiac muscle**, which occurs only in the walls of the four chambers of the heart (page 230)
- **involuntary muscle**, which occurs as sheets or bundles in the walls of the gut, in the tubes and ducts of the respiratory, urinary and genital systems, and in the walls of blood vessels.

This tissue is under control of the autonomic nervous system (Figure 13.16, page 288), and is capable of sustained and rhythmical contractions without noticeable fatigue. The muscle fibres are shorter than those of striped muscle fibres, and they are unstriped.

Support and movement in insects

The insects are non-vertebrate animals with a distinctive organisation of the body (page 361). Their segmented bodies are divided into a head, thorax and abdomen. The thorax, which is built from three body segments, has three pairs of jointed legs and two pairs of wings attached.

The body and limbs are covered by a tough external skeleton or exoskeleton. This is made of **chitin**, and is a non-living layer secreted by the outermost layer of body cells. The exoskeleton has joints of flexible membrane between the body segments, and in the joints of the limbs.

The insects are the most successful group of animals in terms of their numbers, although they are mostly small, typically no more than a few centimetres in length at most. The exoskeleton protects the insect's body, at least from smaller predators. An exoskeleton is efficient provided the animal remains small. Using skeletal material as an external cylinder is efficient in a small organism, but as an animal increases in size a sufficiently strong external skeleton becomes cumbersome and unwieldy.

In addition to limiting the overall size, the exoskeleton also interrupts the animal's growth. During development, insects periodically have to shed their exoskeleton and re-form a new one, larger than the last, into which they then grow. This process, called **ecdysis**, occurs several times before the juvenile stage becomes a fully grown adult. Each ecdysis is an especially vulnerable time in an insect's life cycle.

The chitin of the exoskeleton has an external layer of wax, which reduces water loss from the body surface to a minimum. Insects excrete nitrogenous waste as a solid paste of uric acid, so they lose very little water during excretion. Oxygen is delivered to the tissues including all the muscles, by diffusion through internal air tubes (page 215). Diffusion is an extremely efficient mechanism, but only over short distances. So this method of delivering oxygen is another reason why there are no large insects.

The muscles for movement are attached to the inside of the skeleton. The way muscles move the wings in flight in the dragonfly is shown in Figure 14.11. They also compress the body cavity, which incidentally helps in the delivery of oxygen to the muscles. As well as for flight, insects use their limbs for movement over surfaces. The insect's legs are a series of hollow cylinders held together by joints. Muscles are attached across the joints in antagonistic pairs.

Figure 14.11
The exoskeleton of an insect, and methods of locomotion.

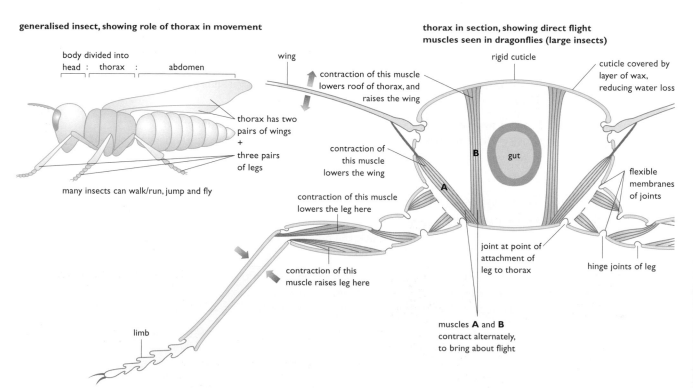

generalised insect, showing role of thorax in movement

body divided into
head : thorax : abdomen

wing

thorax has two pairs of wings + three pairs of legs

many insects can walk/run, jump and fly

contraction of this muscle lowers the leg here

contraction of this muscle raises leg here

limb

thorax in section, showing direct flight muscles seen in dragonflies (large insects)

rigid cuticle

cuticle covered by layer of wax, reducing water loss

contraction of this muscle lowers roof of thorax, and raises the wing

contraction of this muscle lowers the wing

B gut

A

flexible membranes of joints

joint at point of attachment of leg to thorax

hinge joints of leg

muscles **A** and **B** contract alternately, to bring about flight

Support and movement in the earthworm

A **hydrostatic skeleton** is a fluid-filled space surrounded by a flexible, muscular wall (Figure 14.12). Hydrostatic skeletons exploit the fact that a fluid under pressure cannot be compressed. This type of skeleton is found in several groups of non-vertebrate animals, including the molluscs (page 359) and the segmented worms or annelids (page 360). The hydrostatic skeleton allows extremely flexible movement, but provides none of the protection to soft body parts that an exoskeleton does.

The common earthworm, *Lumbricus*, is a segmented worm. Observation of the earthworm's movement shows the way that the muscles (making up the bulk of the body wall) bring about locomotion (Figure 14.12).

To do this, the circular muscles of each segment and the longitudinal muscles running the length of the body act antagonistically. The fluid-filled body cavity (called a **coelom**), which the muscles surround, is divided into compartments by cross-walls called **septa** (*singular*, **septum**). Because the fluid of the coelom is divided into compartments (and their volume is not reduced under pressure), when the circular muscles around a segment contract then its diameter is reduced but its length increases. This stretches the longitudinal muscles and pushes the body compartment forwards. Conversely, when the longitudinal muscles contract the diameter of a body segment is increased and the circular muscles are stretched. However, the length of segment is shortened, and that part of the body is pulled forward. These contractions and extensions of each segment are coordinated with the extension and retraction of sets of tiny bristles in the body wall of each segment, called **chaetae**. When extended, these anchor the body to the surrounding soil.

The sequence of contractions, first of circular muscles and then of longitudinal muscles, passes as waves down the body (Figure 14.12). These contractions are coordinated by reflexes between the segments that are triggered by sensory stretch receptors in the muscles. The reflex arc linking the segments passes through the sensory and motor neurones in the ventral spinal cord. There are also some giant nerve fibres, which run the entire length of the body. These provide fast communication between the longitudinal muscles in all segments. Impulses down these giant fibres can bring about instantaneous contraction of all the longitudinal muscles together. The result is that the worm can shorten itself abruptly. The worm uses this movement to pull itself back into its burrow in the soil in the presence of external danger.

Figure 14.12
The hydrostatic skeleton and musculature of the earthworm, bringing about movement.

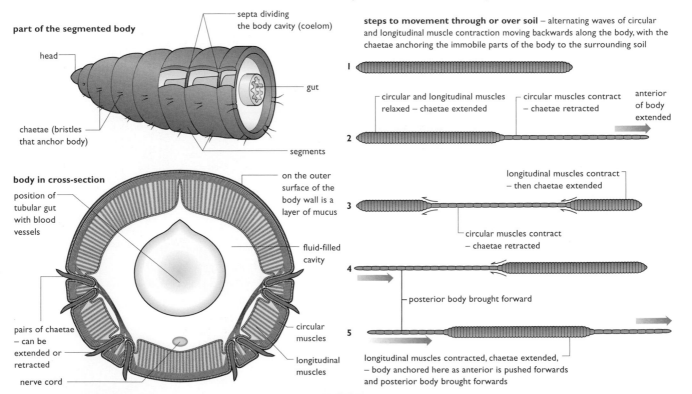

part of the segmented body

- head
- chaetae (bristles that anchor body)
- septa dividing the body cavity (coelom)
- gut
- segments

body in cross-section

- position of tubular gut with blood vessels
- on the outer surface of the body wall is a layer of mucus
- fluid-filled cavity
- pairs of chaetae – can be extended or retracted
- nerve cord
- circular muscles
- longitudinal muscles

steps to movement through or over soil – alternating waves of circular and longitudinal muscle contraction moving backwards along the body, with the chaetae anchoring the immobile parts of the body to the surrounding soil

1

circular and longitudinal muscles relaxed – chaetae extended · circular muscles contract – chaetae retracted · anterior of body extended

2

longitudinal muscles contract – then chaetae extended

3

circular muscles contract – chaetae retracted

4

posterior body brought forward

5

longitudinal muscles contracted, chaetae extended, – body anchored here as anterior is pushed forwards and posterior body brought forwards

Support and movement in plants

4 Distinguish between
the following pairs:

- compression and
  tension
- endoskeleton and
  exoskeleton
- circular and
  longitudinal muscles
- chaetae and septa
- hinge joint and ball
  and socket joint
- sarcomere and
  myofibril
- actin and myosin
- haemoglobin and
  myoglobin
- parenchyma and
  collenchyma
- xylem and
  sclerenchyma
  (fibres).

Support in the herbaceous plant comes from the **turgidity** of all the cells of the packing tissue, known as **parenchyma**. These cells are normally turgid, so the cell contents are pushed hard against the walls (Figure 3.21, page 67) and the walls press against each other. Parenchyma cells are contained within the thin but tough **epidermis** (Figure 14.13). The epidermis, therefore, contributes to mechanical support, as well as giving protection against entry of pathogenic organisms – fungi, for example. Immediately below the epidermis is often found **collenchyma** tissue. Collenchyma cells, similar to parenchyma, have additional layers of cellulose at their angles. Collenchyma tissue consists of flexible supporting cells, and typically occurs in leaves as well as at the margin and around or above leaf veins. Parenchyma and collenchyma are living tissues. Starch grains are typically stored here, for example. The importance of the turgidity of parenchyma in support of stem and leaves can be demonstrated. When a herbaceous plant is deprived of water it eventually wilts (Figure 3.22, page 67).

In addition to support from the turgid living cells, the stem is also supported by its ring of **vascular bundles** (Figure 14.13) and the network of leaf-trace bundles, which run along the leaf stalks into the leaf blades. The vascular bundles contain **xylem vessels** (Figure 14.14; also see Figure 11.26, page 245), which have thickened walls. Here the cellulose is impregnated with **lignin**. Lignified cell walls have great tensile strength. Alongside the xylem, and forming a cap to the vascular bundles, are **fibres** (**sclerenchyma**). These are dead, empty cells with tapering, interlocking walls. Their walls are also thickened and impregnated with lignin.

The plant stem can be likened to a modern high-rise ferroconcrete building, in which hard steel girders that resist extension (vascular bundles) are surrounded by softer concrete that resists compression (parenchyma). Of course, unlike the building the stem has significant flexibility, allowing it to bend in the wind, which lessens the chance of it snapping.

Figure 14.13
Support in the herbaceous
plant stem.

the stem is a structure that resists mechanical stress

the leaf traces branch from the vascular bundles, to the leaves

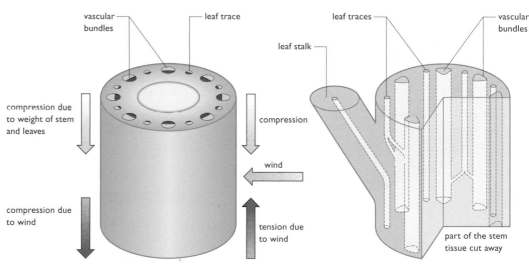

photomicrograph of TS of part of stem of sunflower (*Helianthus*)

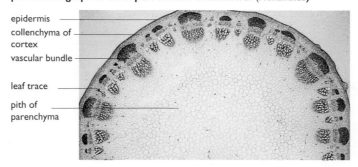

in a mature stem the
pith often breaks down
and becomes hollow

Figure 14.14
A vascular bundle and cell types in the herbaceous plant stem.

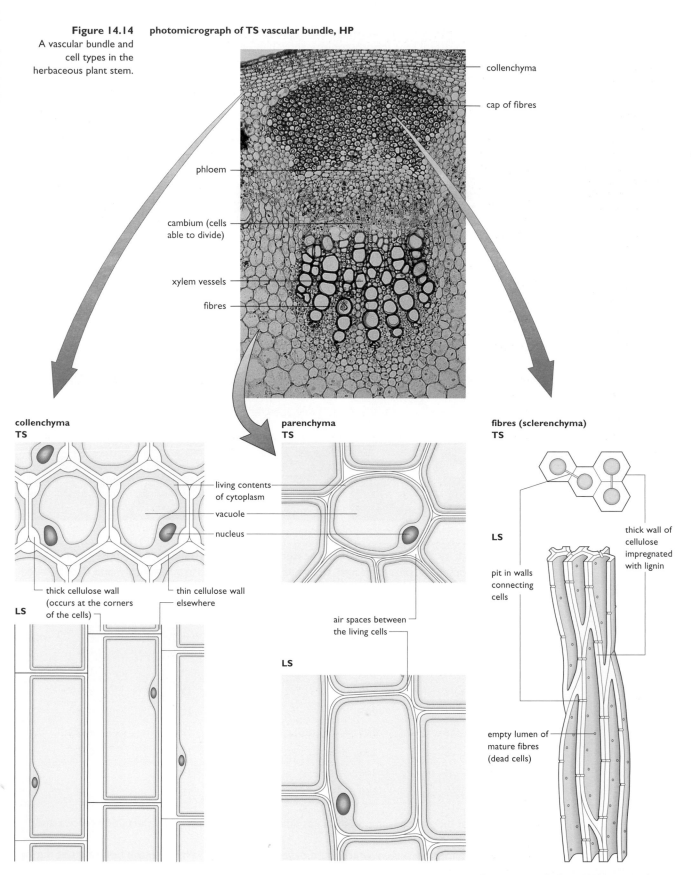

photomicrograph of TS vascular bundle, HP

collenchyma

cap of fibres

phloem

cambium (cells able to divide)

xylem vessels

fibres

collenchyma
TS

LS

thick cellulose wall (occurs at the corners of the cells)

thin cellulose wall elsewhere

parenchyma
TS

living contents of cytoplasm

vacuole

nucleus

air spaces between the living cells

LS

fibres (sclerenchyma)
TS

LS

pit in walls connecting cells

thick wall of cellulose impregnated with lignin

empty lumen of mature fibres (dead cells)

the structures of xylem and phloem vessels are shown on pages 245 and 248 respectively

Movements in plants are slow, growth movements (Figure 14.15), and include the stem's response to unilateral light (phototropism, see Chapter 13, page 294). Some plants, however, are able to make speedy movements of their leaves. The retraction of the leaves in response to the stimulus of touch in the sensitive plant, *Mimosa*, is a rare example (Figure 14.15).

Figure 14.15
Movement in plants.

time-lapse photography of the germination of a sunflower seedling

plant growth movements are mostly too slow to register

the compound leaf (blade divided into leaflets) of *Mimosa*, before and after a response to touch

● **Skills task**   Oxygen uptake by a healthy person was measured (in dm³ min⁻¹) during 15 minutes of an experiment. Firstly the person rested, then was made to exercise strenuously, and then allowed to recover (rest). The data obtained were as follows:

	Time/min	Oxygen uptake/ dm³ min⁻¹		Time/min	Oxygen uptake/ dm³ min⁻¹
at rest	0	0.32	**at rest**	8	1.77
	1	0.32		9	1.19
exercise	2	1.18		10	0.81
	3	2.35		11	0.58
	4	2.65		12	0.42
	5	2.85		13	0.35
	6	2.96		14	0.33
	7	3.00		15	0.32

Plot a graph of oxygen consumption against time, labelled to show the effects of exercise and 'recovery' on oxygen uptake.

Outline the mechanisms by which *more* oxygen was made available to the body tissues during exercise.

What uses were made by body tissues of the oxygen taken up during recovery?

● Examination questions

1 The diagram below shows a sarcomere from a myofibril of a striated muscle fibre.

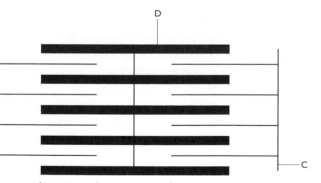

a i Name the regions labelled A, B and C. (3)
ii Name the material which makes up part D. (1)
b State the change in appearance of B when the muscle fibre contracts. (1)

London, A level, Module B3, June 1996

2 The diagram shows the main muscles in a human leg.

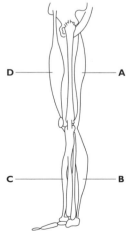

Which of muscles **A** to **D** on the diagram:
a must contract to raise the heel from the ground
b is antagonistic to this muscle? (2)

NEAB, A level, Paper 1/Sections A & B, June 1996

3 a What is the role of phosphocreatine in providing energy for muscle contraction? (1)

b The table shows some differences between slow and fast muscle fibres.

Slow muscle fibres	Fast muscle fibres
enable sustained muscle contraction to take place	allow immediate, rapid muscle contractions to take place
many mitochondria present	few mitochondria present
depend mainly on aerobic respiration for the production of ATP	depend mainly on glycolysis for the production of ATP
small amounts of glycogen present	large amounts of glycogen present

i Explain the advantage of having large amounts of glycogen in fast muscle fibres. (2)

ii Slow muscle fibres have capillaries in close contact. Explain the advantage of this arrangement. (2)

AQA(AEB), AS/A level, Module 5, June 1999

4 Muscles contract when some of their cells become shorter in length. This shortening is brought about when myosin and actin filaments in the cytoplasm of muscle cells slide over each other.

a Explain how ATP and calcium ions (Ca^{2+}) help the myosin and actin filaments to slide over each other during the shortening of a muscle cell. (4)

b Very active muscle cells produce large amounts of lactate. Explain why lactate is produced in these muscle cells. (2)

AQA(AEB), A level, 0607/1, June 1999

5 The drawing has been made from an electron micrograph of a neuromuscular junction in a motor end plate.

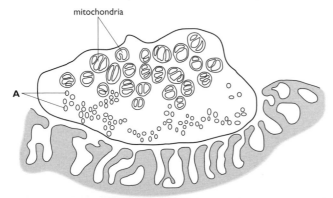

mitochondria

A

a i Describe the part played by the structures labelled **A** in transmission across this neuromuscular junction. (2)

ii During and after a period of repeated muscle activity, the number of the structures labelled **A** changes. Describe how you would expect the number to change. Give a reason for your answer. (2)

b i Mitochondria are often described as elongated organelles. Suggest why they appear roughly circular in shape in this drawing. (1)

ii Suggest an explanation for the large number of mitochondria shown in this drawing. (1)

AQA(AEB), A level, 0607/1, June 1999

6 The table below refers to the structure and functions of xylem vessels and phloem sieve tubes in plants.

If the statement is correct, place a tick (✓) in the appropriate row and if the statement is incorrect, place a cross (✗) in the appropriate row. (4)

Statement	Xylem vessels	Phloem sieve tubes
possess living contents		
provide support		
composed of cells fused together end to end		
walls contain lignin		

London, A level, Module B3, June 1996

7 The diagrams below show two supporting tissues present in flowering plants.

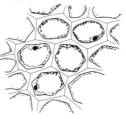

collenchyma   sclerenchyma

a Give **two** structural features shown in the diagram which are characteristic of collenchyma. (2)

b i Give **two** ways in which sclerenchyma differs from collenchyma. (2)

ii Collenchyma is often present in the petiole and midrib of leaves. Suggest **two** reasons why collenchyma is more suitable than sclerenchyma for support in these locations. (2)

c Both tissues are shown in transverse section. Make a drawing of a sclerenchyma cell as it would appear in longitudinal section. (2)

London, A level, Module B6, Jan 1997

15 Health and disease

● What are health and disease?

Disease is defined as 'an unhealthy condition of the body'. This may be infectious or **communicable disease**, caused by invading organisms that live parasitically on or in the body. The disease-causing organisms include viruses, some bacteria and certain other organisms that may be passed from organism to organism, such as the protoctistan *Plasmodium* that causes malaria, or a multicellular animal like the tapeworm. The diseases these organisms cause are alternatively referred to as contagious or infectious, and the organisms that cause them are **pathogens**.

However, good health is more than the absence of harmful effects of disease-causing organisms. Ill-health may also be caused by unfavourable environmental conditions. Disorders of this type are non-infectious or **non-communicable**, and they include conditions such as cardiovascular disease, malnutrition and respiratory disease. Genetic disorders might be included here, although a genetic defect present at birth has been transmitted between organisms – in this case from parent to offspring.

Not included in any of the above types of ill-health is damage due to **accidents**, such as broken bones. A bone fracture is not a disease, but it is certainly an unhealthy condition of the body that takes time to repair. Clearly, there is a borderline between health and disease that is not easy to define. The broad range of disease conditions is summarised in Figure 15.1. In this chapter a range of human diseases is examined.

Figure 15.1
Issues in health and disease.

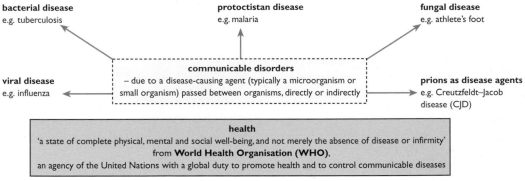

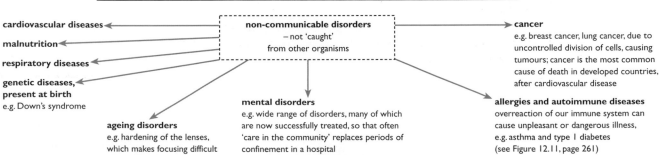

Non-communicable disorders

Malnutrition

Malnutrition is a condition that occurs when a balanced diet (page 145) is not available or is not consumed. Malnutrition is just as likely to arise from overeating as from undereating, or from a lack of small quantities of a particular nutrient such as a vitamin. However, there are many more undernourished humans than obese ones, although both tend to die prematurely.

Malnutrition in less-developed countries

A subsistence diet (eating only enough food to survive), or less, is the daily lot of about two-thirds of the world-wide human population (Figure 15.2). However, the hungry rarely die of their undernourishment. Instead they succumb to common and curable diseases, like measles. This is because, in the persistently undernourished body, the fully functioning immune system (page 337) is an early casualty. Without a working immune system, people are susceptible to many diseases.

When the body is deprived of a sufficient supply of energy, any reserves of glycogen in the liver and other tissues are used up before fat stores around the body are mobilised. Fats are broken down to fatty acids in the liver. Muscles respire fatty acids as an energy source. An excess of fatty acids being transported around the body tends to make the blood acidic, a condition that the kidneys work to correct (page 267). However, with continuing starvation and the absence of remaining fat reserves, muscle protein starts to be used as a source of energy. This is the final phase of starvation.

Protein deficiency is a special form of malnutrition. It may arise as described above. Alternatively, the diet may contain enough energy but not enough protein. This happens when starchy foods like maize, yam or cassava are all that is eaten – for example, because protein-rich seeds of legumes (including peas, beans, soya beans and chick peas), or cereals like wheat, or meat protein, are not available. This condition is known as **protein energy malnutrition**.

Figure 15.2
Malnutrition in the developing world.

1 **On a world scale, food production is successful**, but there is an uneven distribution of population and food excess. There are both cultural and economic barriers to a solution to world hunger, apparently.

2 **Protein energy malnutrition** takes different forms. Both show stunted growth, specific vitamin deficiencies and generally reduced resistance to infection.

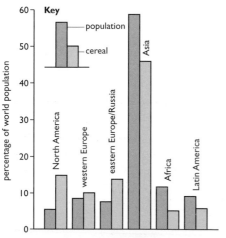

distribution of world population and shares of cereal production

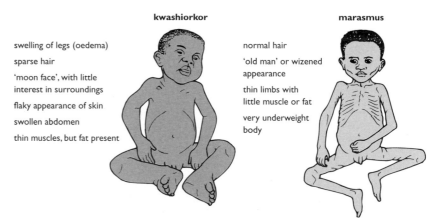

Malnutrition in developed countries

Obesity is most prevalent in people of the developed countries, where it is a recognised public health problem for all age groups. Overweight people have increased risks of coronary heart disease, gall bladder disease, high blood pressure and diabetes. Most people who become overweight do so because of persistent consumption of too many energy-rich items in their diet in relation to their energy requirements. We define the terms 'overweight' and 'obesity' using the concept of the '**body mass index**' (BMI). This is calculated as:

$$\frac{body\ mass\ in\ kg}{height\ (in\ m)^2}$$

A BMI of less than 20 indicates someone who is underweight, 20–25 is ideal, 25+ indicates overweight, and 30+ indicates obesity.

Not all 'weight problems' are due to people being overweight – quite the reverse, in fact. The conditions known as **anorexia nervosa** and **bulimia nervosa** are examples. They are thought to be on the increase, particularly among young Caucasian females from the middle or upper social classes. In anorexia, deliberate dieting, and sometimes deliberate vomiting, lead to serious weight loss and even the loss of consecutive menstrual cycles. Patients have an obsessive fear of gaining weight or becoming fat; they see themselves as being much fatter than they actually are.

In bulimia, periods of excessive eating ('binge eating') are followed by self-induced vomiting and use of laxatives to achieve weight control. Here, patients do not necessarily lose a great deal of weight and their menstrual cycles remain normal.

In many cases, these two conditions are believed to have more to do with anxiety about maturation and sexuality than with diet (Figure 15.3).

Figure 15.3
'Girls gripped by worry over looks'; *The Guardian* 16/11/98.

Many teenage girls worry about their appearance more than anything else in their lives. Weight and appearance are by far the main concerns for girls, eclipsing family problems, difficulties with friends, health, careers and school, according to an **Exeter University survey**.

'The overwhelming majority of those who say they wish to lose weight have no medical weight problem at all, and some are underweight' said researcher John Balding.

Researchers from the Schools Health Education unit questioned 37500 young people aged 12–15 years, and concluded that girls were much more worried about their appearance than boys.

The study concluded that, to help counter the problem, a greater diversity of body shapes among actresses and models needed to be seen on television and in newspapers.

by journalist Helen Carter
First published in *The Guardian*, 16/11/98

Cardiovascular diseases

Diseases of the blood vessels are the cause of more premature death in the developed world than any other single cause. Most of these are due to **atherosclerosis**: the progressive degeneration of the artery walls (Figure 15.4).

Healthy arteries have pale, smooth linings, but in unhealthy arteries the walls have strands of yellow fat deposited under the endothelium (Figure 11.4, page 228). This fat builds up from cholesterol circulating in the blood in a form called low density lipoproteins (page 261). Fibrous tissue is also laid down together with the fatty streaks. These deposits start to impede the blood flow and, as the diameter of the blood vessel is decreased, the blood inside comes under greater pressure. Progressive reduction of the blood flow to the heart muscle also impairs oxygenation to the organ. This leads to chest pains, known as **angina**, which are usually brought on by physical exertion.

At places where the smooth lining actually breaks down, the blood itself is exposed to these fatty, fibrous deposits. Blood platelets then attempt to repair the break. They collect at the exposed roughened surface, releasing factors that trigger blood clotting (Figure 15.18, page 337). A blood clot may form *within* the vessel. It is known as a **thrombus**, at least until it breaks free and is circulated in the bloodstream, where it becomes known as an **embolus**.

An embolus may then be swept into a small artery or arteriole that is narrower than the diameter of the clot, causing a complete blockage of the vessel. Immediately, the blood supply to the tissue downstream of the block is deprived of oxygen. Without oxygen, the tissue dies. The arteries supplying the heart (the coronary arteries) are especially vulnerable to this process,

1 How do conditions in an artery damaged by atherosclerosis favour the formation of a blood clot?

Figure 15.4
Atherosclerosis, leading to a thrombus.

particularly those to the left ventricle. When heart muscle dies in this way the heart may cease to be an effective pump. We say a **heart attack** has occurred (known as a **myocardial infarction**). Coronary arteries that have been damaged can be surgically by-passed (Figure 15.5).

artery in LS

photomicrograph of human diseased artery in TS

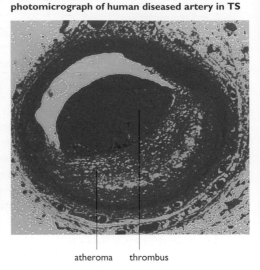

healthy

endothelium

flow of blood

diseased

blood clot = thrombus formed where atheroma has broken through the endothelium

lipid + fibre deposit = atheroma

atheroma   thrombus

Figure 15.5
A 'heart by-pass'.

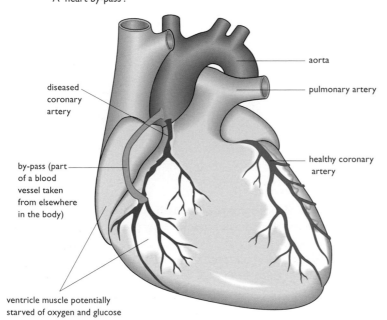

diseased coronary artery

by-pass (part of a blood vessel taken from elsewhere in the body)

ventricle muscle potentially starved of oxygen and glucose

aorta

pulmonary artery

healthy coronary artery

When an embolus blocks an artery in the brain a **'stroke'** occurs. Neurones in the brain depend on a continuous supply of blood for oxygen and glucose. Within a few minutes of the blood supply being lost the neurones die. These cannot be replaced, so the result is a degree of loss of the functions controlled by that region of the brain.

In arteries where the wall has been weakened by atherosclerosis, the remaining layers may be stretched and bulge into a 'balloon' under the pressure of the blood. This is called an **aneurysm**. An aneurysm may burst at any time.

Respiratory diseases

Asthma

In an asthma attack, the airways in the lungs become narrow owing to contraction of the smooth muscle in the walls of the trachea, bronchi and bronchioles. Breathing becomes difficult. Extra mucus, which is produced as part of the asthmatic condition, exaggerates the symptoms. Asthma is in fact a disease involving the immune system (as are hay fever and eczema). It is the immune response – an acute inflammatory response (page 335) – that causes the breathing difficulties. Part of the response is release of histamine, which causes many of the symptoms including narrowing of the airways and attraction of phagocytic cells. A chronic long term effect of asthma is the build-up of fibrous tissue – replacing the normal epithelium of the alveoli (Figure 10.14, page 219). This reduces the gas exchange surface.

Asthma is increasing in incidence. Some argue this is because we are underexposed to disease-causing organisms as affluence alters our lifestyles. Perhaps when the immune system is underchallenged in early life it becomes hypersensitive and overreacts to certain irritative conditions we may experience in our lungs? This is just one hypothesis.

Asthma attacks are triggered by irritants like pollen, dust from pets, droppings from house dust mites, certain viruses, or oxides of nitrogen present in vehicle exhaust fumes. People diagnosed as susceptible to an asthma attack carry an inhaler to treat themselves (Figure 15.6).

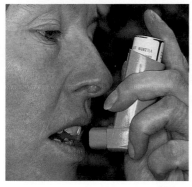

Figure 15.6
Asthma patient using an inhaler. The vapour inhaled includes drugs that cause the smooth (involuntary) muscle of the bronchi and bronchioles to relax, allowing easy breathing.

Smoking and health

Tobacco has been smoked for centuries, but cigarette smoking became popular only with the development of machinery for the mass manufacture of cigarettes, about 150 years ago. Subsequently, specific health problems became common among smokers. One of the effects of cigarette smoke is to reduce the activity of the cilia lining the airways (see Figure 10.17, page 221). These, when functioning normally, beat to move mucus towards the pharynx. Coupled with the production of more viscous mucus, this reduced activity causes an accumulation of mucus in which is trapped dust and carcinogenic chemicals present in the smoke. Nicotine, which is also present, constricts blood vessels and thus increases blood pressure and the heart rate.

For many years now it has been appreciated that smoking is harmful to health, but only recently has it become clear how harmful. A statistical study of the lives of 40 000 people, their smoking habits, and the ultimate cause of their death, leaves no doubts (Table 15.1).

Table 15.1
The incidence of certain fatal diseases in a sample of 40 000 people.

Cause of death	Annual death rate/million		
	Non-smokers	Continuing pipe smokers	Continuing cigarette smokers (25+ per day)
heart disease	606	690	1184
vascular system disease	282	325	583
chronic bronchitis	9	42	209
lung cancer	3	13	80
other cancers	33	57	170
total	**943**	**1194**	**2149**

In developed countries today, life expectancy is so improved that deaths under 70 years of age should now be regarded as premature. The recent reduction in premature deaths, which is largely due to improved control of infection through the use of antibiotics, has unfortunately been countered by an increased mortality from tobacco. More than 30% of men who survive to 35 years in developed countries die before they are 70. Many of these premature deaths may be attributed to tobacco. The number of women smoking has increased and, as a consequence, mortality due to smoking-related diseases in women is also increasing.

There are also **moral and ethical issues** associated with smoking. Today the risks are well established, and there is the added possibility of causing harm to people nearby who may have to breathe in smoke-polluted air. If a smoker succumbs to a major disease, treatment may divert funds from the cure of other diseases: smoking-related diseases may cause a drain on health services. The taxation that smokers pay (in the purchase of the cigarettes) and the publicity about health risks has not deterred as many smokers as was hoped, probably because of the habit-forming nature of the drug nicotine.

With the encouragement of those who stand to gain, the habit of smoking is spreading throughout the world. In many less-developed countries, more than 50% of the male population now smokes cigarettes. Of the approximately 2.3 billion children and teenagers in the world now, about 30–40% will be smokers in early adult life. Up to half of them could be killed by smoking. This need not happen.

2 What is the role of the mucus secreted by the epithelial lining of the lungs?

Emphysema – an example of a smokers' disease

In emphysema the walls of the alveoli lose their elasticity and can no longer recoil elastically as they should during expiration. The lung tissue also breaks down and several alveoli merge to form larger air sacs (Figure 15.7). The walls of the expanded sacs become thickened with fibrous

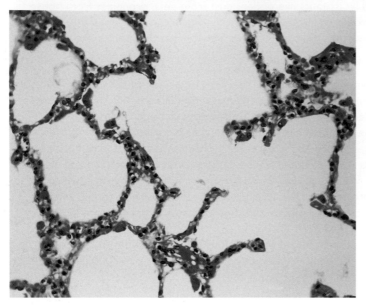

connective tissue. Gaseous exchange therefore becomes exceedingly inefficient. The sufferer over the course of time progressively deteriorates from merely being breathless to being a complete invalid.

Emphysema is caused by chemicals in cigarette smoke, air pollution and industrial dust. These chemicals harm the cells that regulate the structure and condition of the elastic fibres in the lung connective tissue. Naturally occurring enzymes that break down elastic material of the alveoli walls are not checked by natural inhibitors, and emphysema develops. The elastic properties of the tissue are destroyed. If the person stops smoking then this destruction of lung elasticity stops, but existing damage cannot be reversed.

Figure 15.7
Photomicrograph of lung tissue damaged by advanced emphysema (x 200). (Compare the appearance with the normal alveoli in Figure 10.14, page 219.)

Communicable diseases

Communicable diseases are passed on to other people from someone already infected. Some such diseases occur quite infrequently and to few people. However, an **epidemic** occurs when a disease becomes widespread in a community. A **pandemic** exists if the disease spreads across several countries around the world, as AIDS has. An **endemic** disease regularly occurs in a country or region and has not yet been eradicated, such as malaria in many tropical regions. We will look into some of these diseases and the organisms causing them.

Viral diseases

Viruses are not living as biologists use the term; that is, they are not cellular in organisation. As viruses are 20–300 nm in size, they are far too small to be seen by light microscopy. We know about their structure only because of the electron microscope. A virus consists of a strand of nucleic acid (either DNA or RNA), wrapped up in a protein coat (known as a **capsid**). Some also have an external envelope, made of lipid and protein with a glycocalyx (glycolipid and glycoprotein) attached. This envelope is derived from the cell membrane of the host cell in which the virus copied itself (replicated).

Viruses can reproduce themselves only inside a host cell, so the virus's 'existence' is essentially parasitic. They are highly specific in their choice of host, some being parasites of a particular plant species, others of a particular animal species, and others (known as **bacteriophages**) of a particular bacterial species. Examples of viral diseases in humans are listed in Table 15.2 and the structure of two viruses is shown in Figure 15.8. The common cold virus is without an external envelope. The HIV virus does have an envelope, and contains reverse transcriptase enzyme. In both, the nucleic acid is RNA.

In reproduction, the virus takes over the enzymic machinery of production of the host cell, switching it over to the exclusive production of virus particles. Either the virus brings with it the enzymes it needs to assemble the parts of itself that are made by the host cell's machinery, or its nucleic acid merely codes for these essential enzymes but they are actually synthesised by the host's ribosomes. The way viruses replicate in their host cells (incidentally causing the symptoms of the viral disease) is shown in Figure 15.9. (Remember, virus diseases cannot be treated with antibiotics; these work only against bacterial infections.)

Table 15.2
Table of common viral diseases.

Disease spread by and caused by	Symptoms	Prevention
1 *Droplet infection* influenza due to a DNA virus (different strains)	fever with headaches, sore throat, and muscular aches, attacks epithelia of trachea and bronchi, recovery takes about a week	vaccine of killed virus – must be of the correct strain
Smallpox due to a DNA virus	WHO campaign 1956–1977 **eradicated** this virus (there were previously 15 million cases annually) by vaccination, and by surveillance of patients and contacts	
2 *Droplet infection or human faeces* poliomyelitis due to an RNA virus (different strains)	headaches, stiffness of neck muscles, followed by destruction of nerve cells causing paralysis and muscle wasting	vaccine of living attenuated virus
3 *Blood/sexual intercourse* AIDS due to an RNA retrovirus (HIV)	blood develops antibodies to the virus, but only some patients develop symptoms of AIDs – range of infections and health problems due to breakdown of immune system	no vaccine available

Figure 15.8
The structure of viruses.

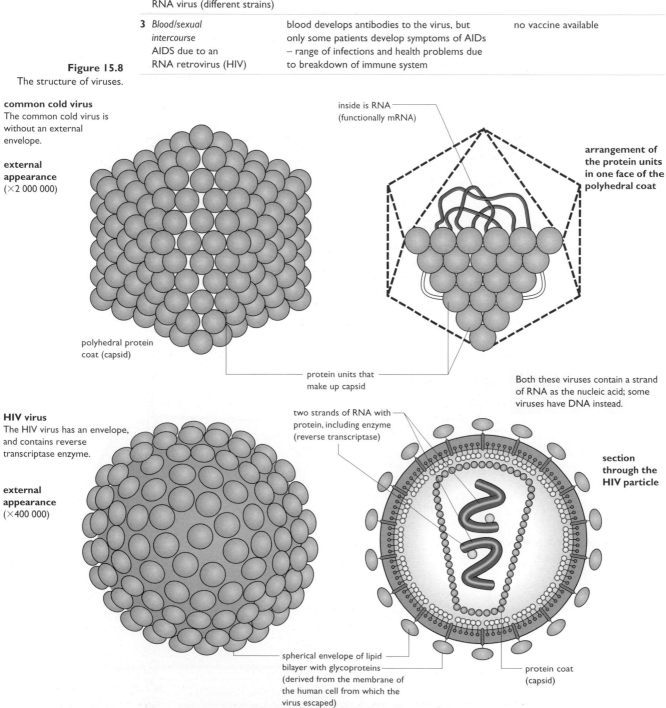

common cold virus
The common cold virus is without an external envelope.

external appearance (×2 000 000)

polyhedral protein coat (capsid)

protein units that make up capsid

inside is RNA (functionally mRNA)

arrangement of the protein units in one face of the polyhedral coat

Both these viruses contain a strand of RNA as the nucleic acid; some viruses have DNA instead.

HIV virus
The HIV virus has an envelope, and contains reverse transcriptase enzyme.

external appearance (×400 000)

two strands of RNA with protein, including enzyme (reverse transcriptase)

section through the HIV particle

spherical envelope of lipid bilayer with glycoproteins (derived from the membrane of the human cell from which the virus escaped)

protein coat (capsid)

Figure 15.9
Reproduction of viruses.

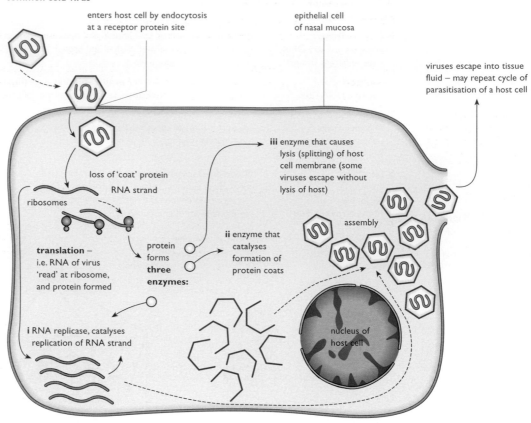

common cold virus

enters host cell by endocytosis
at a receptor protein site

epithelial cell
of nasal mucosa

viruses escape into tissue
fluid – may repeat cycle of
parasitisation of a host cell

loss of 'coat' protein
RNA strand

ribosomes

iii enzyme that causes
lysis (splitting) of host
cell membrane (some
viruses escape without
lysis of host)

assembly

translation –
i.e. RNA of virus
'read' at ribosome,
and protein formed

protein
forms
**three
enzymes:**

ii enzyme that
catalyses
formation of
protein coats

i RNA replicase, catalyses
replication of RNA strand

nucleus of
host cell

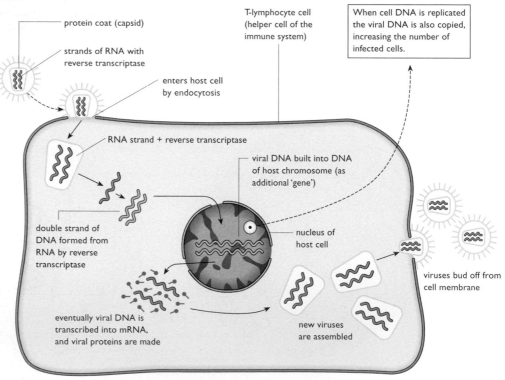

HIV virus

protein coat (capsid)

strands of RNA with
reverse transcriptase

enters host cell
by endocytosis

T-lymphocyte cell
(helper cell of the
immune system)

When cell DNA is replicated
the viral DNA is also copied,
increasing the number of
infected cells.

RNA strand + reverse transcriptase

viral DNA built into DNA
of host chromosome (as
additional 'gene')

double strand of
DNA formed from
RNA by reverse
transcriptase

nucleus of
host cell

viruses bud off from
cell membrane

eventually viral DNA is
transcribed into mRNA,
and viral proteins are made

new viruses
are assembled

Period that virus DNA is inactive in host chromosome
is known as the latency period, and may be up to 5 years.

Bacterial diseases

Bacteria are unicellular, prokaryotic organisms. They occur in vast numbers in air, soil and water, and contaminate every surface of the places where we live and work. They are present on the surface and inside our bodies and those of other organisms. Bacteria are often associated in people's minds with disease. However, whilst some are parasitic and cause disease (that is, they are **pathogenic**), the vast majority are not. On the contrary, most are saprotrophic (Figure 7.2, page 141), and play key roles in the cycling of mineral ions and other nutrients, for example (Chapter 17, page 370).

The structure of a typical bacterial cell is shown in Figure 1.23 (page 21), and the range of bacteria is outlined in Chapter 16, page 349. A selection of the common diseases of humans that are caused by bacteria is listed in Table 15.3.

3 Tabulate the differences in structure between a bacterial cell and a virus.

Table 15.3 Some common bacterial diseases of humans.

Disease spread by and caused by	Symptoms	Prevention/treatment
1 *Droplet infection (coughs and sneezes) or milk from infected cows* tuberculosis (TB) due to *Mycobacterium tuberculosis*	may infect many organs of the body, but typically the lungs, causing general weight loss, cough; one of the world's great killer diseases, still a problem because of growing resistance to drugs/antibiotics	BCG (living, attenuated = reduced virulence) bacteria, but only after test to see if patient is already immune/antibiotics
2 *Wound infection* tenanus due to *Clostridium tetani*	muscular spasms in the region of mouth and neck, then extending through rest of body (Figure 9.12, page 201); interference with breathing may cause death; contamination of deep wounds, e.g. by soil or dung	toxoid (inactivated toxin, still able to induce formation of antibodies)/antibiotics
3 *Water supply faeces contaminated by* cholera due to *Vibrio cholerae*	inflammation of the gut, leading to severe diarrhoea, fluid loss and loss of minerals causes dehydration, possibly leading to death	killed vaccine/antibiotics
4 *Food poisoning* gastroenteritis due to *Salmonella* spp.	pain in the gut, diarrhoea and vomiting, leading to dehydration	no vaccine commonly used/antibiotic not normally needed

● **Extension**

Which bacterium caused the disease?

Because bacteria are so common it may be difficult to know which organism among those present in a patient has actually caused the disease. This problem was solved by a bacteriologist (Koch), and the procedure he proposed is named after him. It is as follows:

• the same bacterium must be found in all cases of the disease
• the pathogen must be isolated and grown in pure culture from the infected host
• bacteria of the pure culture must be shown to cause the disease in a healthy host
• the bacterium must be isolated from the experimentally infected host.

Antibiotics

Many bacterial diseases of humans and other animals can be successfully treated with **antibiotics**. Antibiotics are naturally occurring substances (Figure 15.10) that slow up or kill microorganisms. They are obtained mainly from fungi or bacteria that these organisms manufacture in their natural habitats. An antibiotic, when present in low concentrations, may inhibit the growth of other microorganisms. Since their original discovery, over four thousand different antibiotics have been isolated, but only about fifty have proved to be safe to use as drugs. The antibiotics that are effective over a wide range of pathogenic organisms are called **'broad spectrum antibiotics'**. Others are effective against just a few pathogens. Many antibiotics in use today are not naturally occurring and have been synthesised by biochemists.

Resistance to antibiotics

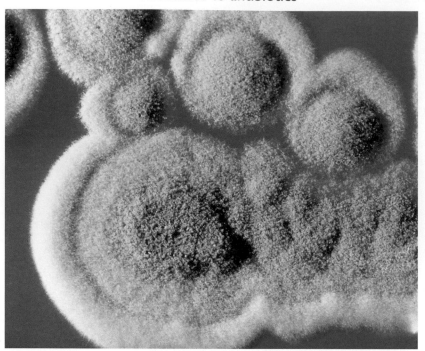

Most antibiotics are so extremely effective at disrupting metabolism or the cell structure of a bacterium that whole populations are quickly suppressed. All, that is, except for the occasional individual bacterium in the population that possesses a gene giving some resistance to the effect of the antibiotic. This naturally resistant individual is left with very little competition for resources as the action of the antibiotic has killed the rest of the population, so a new population grows from the resistant bacterium even more quickly. All or most of these bacteria have the resistance gene. Many disease-causing bacteria now show resistance to particular antibiotics. In bacteria resistance develops relatively quickly because of the fast rate at which they reproduce. The pharmaceutical industry has a problem producing new antibiotics faster than bacteria can evolve resistance to them.

Figure 15.10
Petri dish with nutrient medium, supporting the growth of the fungus *Penicillium*, which produces and releases the antibiotic penicillin.

Resistance in a bacterium develops either by a spontaneous mutation of a gene, giving the offspring new abilities, or by transfer of a gene between bacteria by conjugation (a form of sexual reproduction). A resistant bacterium can survive and prosper despite the presence of an antibiotic. Resistance may be due to a change in the wall or membrane chemistry of the bacterium, which prevents the antibiotic from entering the cell. Alternatively, the resistant bacterium may have developed new enzymes that turn the antibiotic into a harmless substance on arrival, or the antibiotic may be 'pumped out' as fast as it enters the bacterium.

Antibiotics are used very widely indeed, possibly too widely. If used appropriately when a disease has been diagnosed (that is, used *therapeutically*), then the infection may be eradicated. However, the patient must complete the whole course of antibiotic. Sometimes patients stop taking the antibiotic as soon as they feel well. Doing this aids the development of resistance, as some of the bacteria may still be alive at this point, and these are going to be the very ones that are most resistant to the drug's effects.

Antibiotics are also used widely in farming to prevent infection (*prophylactically*). For example, farmers may add broad spectrum antibiotics to the feed of intensively reared farm animals. This leads to animals that grow faster because they do not succumb to disease, so they reach marketable weight more quickly. However, when antibiotics are used on this scale, more and more species of bacteria are exposed to them, increasing the chances of resistance developing.

Production of antibiotics – fermenter technology

Fermenters are vessels used for the growth of microorganisms in liquid media, normally under aerobic conditions. **Open fermenter tanks** are non-sterile systems, open to the atmosphere. These include the brewing vats used in alcoholic fermentation, and the activated sludge aeration tanks of sewage works (Figure 18.17, page 403).

In **closed fermentation systems** a specific type of microorganism is used, uncontaminated by others. This requires an enclosed, sterilised vessel (Figure 15.11). In **batch culture**, an initial, fixed volume of culture medium and microorganisms is processed in the fermenter, with few additions, until the maximum product has accumulated. In **continuous culture**, the fermenter is run for an extended period, then fresh nutrients are added, and the product is harvested steadily.

The first step in antibiotic production may be the finding of a new antibiotic-producing organism. The microbiologist screens soil samples and other sources for different strains of organisms capable of manufacturing a particular antibiotic. When a suitable microorganism has been found, it has to be cultured in laboratory conditions on agar plates to find the nutrient requirements and environmental conditions that favour formation and secretion of the antibiotic. Once the laboratory process has been refined, the production then has to be developed on increasingly larger scales to test that it would proceed successfully in an aseptic closed fermenter vessel under industrial conditions (called **scale-up**). Conditions often require some adaptation to deliver a result similar to that achieved on the laboratory bench.

Figure 15.11
The large scale production of an antibiotic, such as penicillin.

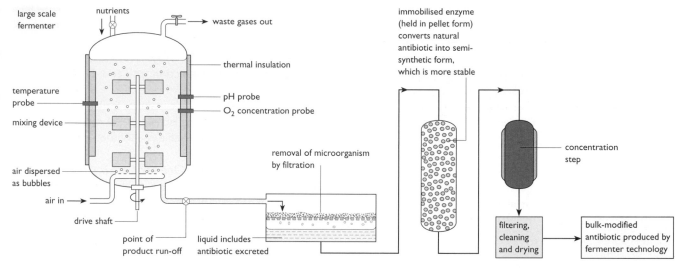

An industrial fermenter has a capacity of thousands of litres, and its internal environment, e.g. pH, oxygen, temperature and concentration of substrate, is continuously monitored. Automatic valves regulate the input of fresh medium, and the sampling or harvesting of products. The contents are continuously stirred to achieve uniform conditions.

After harvesting, the production of the antibiotic (called **downstream processing**) may involve more than just purification of the product. Sometimes it is also necessary to modify and improve the antibiotic, perhaps using enzyme technology (page 90).

'Model' fermenter systems are marketed for schools and colleges. These are expensive, though realistic, models. It is, however, easy to make and test a fermenter made from a clear plastic fizzy-drink bottle, in which the mixture is stirred by an aeration system, as used for a fish tank (Figure 15.12). The simple apparatus may include some way of monitoring the growth of the bacterial culture (and possibly of one or more of the physical conditions within the fermenter). A simple fermenter such as the one illustrated provides ideal conditions in which, for example, the microorganism yeast can be safely grown with reasonable precautions, and so it is possible to mimic a biotechnological industrial process. Yeast is actually one of the microorganisms often used in industry, possibly after being genetically modified (page 129), in order to produce valuable organic chemicals.

Figure 15.12
A laboratory-built fermenter.

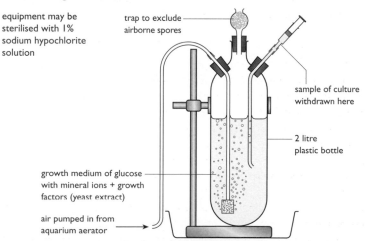

equipment may be sterilised with 1% sodium hypochlorite solution

trap to exclude airborne spores

sample of culture withdrawn here

2 litre plastic bottle

growth medium of glucose with mineral ions + growth factors (yeast extract)

air pumped in from aquarium aerator

monitoring yeast growth either by use of a colorimeter (change in optical density as numbers of cells increase), or direct counting of cells in a haemocytometer

checking that yeast cells are viable with a drop of methylene blue, live yeast cells decolorise the stain, but dead cells will stain blue

collecting data on:
- changing sugar concentration (using Clinistix)
- pH of the medium

A disease caused by a protoctistan

Malaria is a major disease, one of the most destructive to humans. It is caused by certain species of a protoctistan (page 350) called *Plasmodium*, of which two, namely *P. falciparum* and *P. vivax*, cause the more debilitating forms of malaria. The life cycle of *Plasmodium* involves several stages and a secondary host: the female blood-sucking mosquito *Anopheles* (Figure 15.13). The mosquito is also described as a **vector**, because it transports the parasite between human hosts.

In humans, the parasite feeds, grows and reproduces into merozoites (a stage in its life cycle), initially in liver cells, and subsequently in red cells. In both types of cell it is protected from attack by the host's immune system. Each time, vast numbers of merozoites are released. So too are toxins. Release of toxins triggers fever (temperatures of 40–41.5 °C), generalised aches and nausea. These symptoms typically occur 7 days after the initial infection, and at 3 day intervals subsequently.

The WHO (Figure 15.1, page 321) has a programme to eradicate malaria. It may be possible to overcome this pathogen indirectly, either by attacking the larval stages of the mosquito, or by killing with insecticides the adult mosquitoes that enter human dwellings. Another important approach is the search for an effective vaccine.

However, complete eradication of malaria is a long way away. One problem is that there are 'reservoirs' of the parasite in monkeys, birds, rodents and reptiles. Also, periods of political instability and civil warfare regularly disrupt national programmes in some of the countries where malaria is regularly found. This often hinders progress in neighbouring countries also.

Figure 15.13
The life cycle of the malarial parasite (*Plasmodium*).

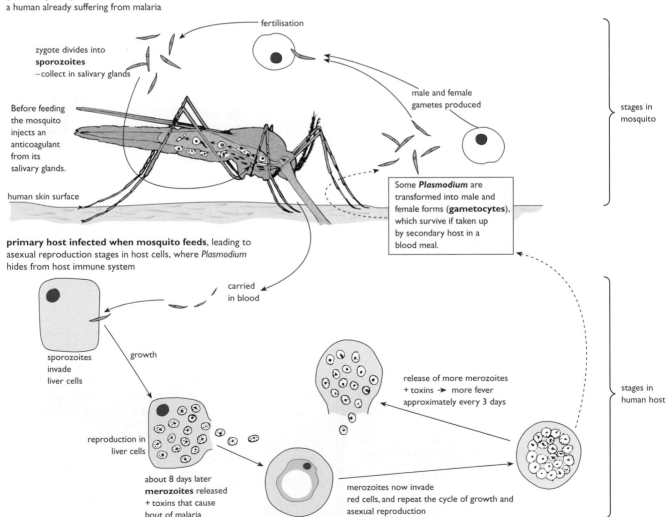

stages of the life cycle in the female mosquito
(secondary host), infected when she takes a blood meal from a human already suffering from malaria

fertilisation

zygote divides into **sporozoites** –collect in salivary glands

Before feeding the mosquito injects an anticoagulant from its salivary glands.

human skin surface

male and female gametes produced

stages in mosquito

Some *Plasmodium* are transformed into male and female forms (**gametocytes**), which survive if taken up by secondary host in a blood meal.

primary host infected when mosquito feeds, leading to asexual reproduction stages in host cells, where *Plasmodium* hides from host immune system

carried in blood

sporozoites invade liver cells

growth

release of more merozoites + toxins ➤ more fever approximately every 3 days

stages in human host

reproduction in liver cells

about 8 days later **merozoites** released + toxins that cause bout of malaria

merozoites now invade red cells, and repeat the cycle of growth and asexual reproduction

Diseases caused by flatworms

Tapeworms are intestinal parasites. They are flatworms, members of the Phylum Platyhelminthes. The adult human tapeworm (Figure 15.14) grows up to 10 metres long. Its body consists of a long chain of flattened units called **proglottids**. At the anterior end is a 'head', adapted for anchorage in the gut wall; it effectively resists dislodgement by the waves of peristalsis. Below the head region, new proglottids are formed. At the other end of the tapeworm, the proglottids fall off and are excreted in the faeces. The tapeworm defends itself from digestion by the host's intestinal enzymes – principally by secreting large volumes of mucus all over the proglottid walls.

Proglottids absorb their host's digested food through their body wall; the parasite itself contains no digestive organs. In fact, the function of the proglottid is reproduction. Sexual reproduction occurs by self-fertilisation, and the eggs develop into embryos with hooks. When the proglottids eventually fall off the gut wall and leave the body with the faeces they contain a sack of these embryos in individual capsules.

The pig is the secondary host and vector of *Taenia solium*. If the food it eats contains proglottids then the capsules are digested and their embryos are released. These develop into larvae that eventually burrow into the pig's skeletal muscle. There they form into 'bladderworms', which await the chance of transfer to humans in uncooked or undercooked meat.

Figure 15.14
The life cycle of the human tapeworm.

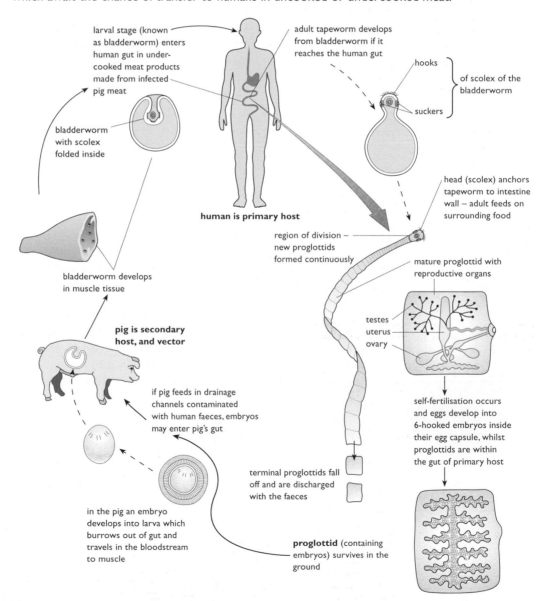

● **Extension** The blood fluke *Schistosoma*

Schistomiasis is an infection that harms millions of people and kills many thousands of children in tropical and subtropical regions of the world each year. The disease is caused by male and female flukes that live in blood vessels in the abdomen and pelvic region. Fertilised eggs are produced, of which some attack the liver, but others bore into the large intestine or bladder and are discharged from the body. If deposited in ponds the eggs hatch into larvae and enter into aquatic snails (the secondary host). Here they multiply and become motile larvae – that is, able to swim in the water in search of the primary host, the human. If the snail makes contact with the skin surface of a human, they bore into it and reach the bloodstream. There they mature into adult flukes, and so their life cycle is completed.

Fungal diseases

Very many of the fungi are saprotrophs, feeding on dead organic matter (Figure 7.2, page 141). Of those that are parasitic, most cause diseases of plants. However, the parasitic fungi include some human pathogens (Figure 15.15).

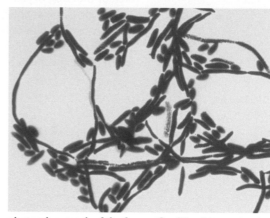

photomicrograph of the fungus *Candida albicans*, showing cells and thick-walled spores

Figure 15.15 Some fungal diseases of importance.

Fungi-causing diseases in plants include potato blight (*Phytophthora*) and rust of wheat (*Puccinia*). Fungal parasites of animals are much less numerous. Common examples include athlete's foot (*Tinea pedis*), and vaginal thrush (*Candida albicans*).

● **Extension** Prions as disease agents

Proteins called **prions** are believed to be the agents that cause diseases known as 'encephalopathies' – diseases in which the brain tissue becomes spongy and forms holes where once there were groups of neurones. The afflicted organism, which may be human (with Creutzfeldt–Jacob disease, or CJD), sheep (with scrapie), or cattle (with bovine spongiform encephalopathy, BSE) loses physical coordination (Figure 15.16). In humans the memory is lost, as well as body control, prior to death.

Prions are proteins that are normal components of brain cells. However, in cases of infection they show subtle shape changes. How they cause loss of brain tissue is not known. The first 'prion' disease to be understood was called **kuru**. It occurred among people of a tribe in Papua New Guinea, whose custom was to honour their dead by eating them. Men ate the muscle tissue, but women and children received the brain tissue. It was only the latter group that developed kuru – from an ancestor that had died with the condition initially.

Other prion diseases, for example scrapie in sheep, also have a long history. Until recently, however, none had appeared to 'jump' between species. Today, it appears that the agent responsible may be able to cross the so-called 'species barrier', particularly if nerve tissue is eaten. Recent farming practices of using offal from sheep or cows to supplement manufactured animal feeds may have spread BSE among cattle, with fatal consequences for cattle and humans, and possibly other animals. It is also likely that pituitary extracts prepared by vets for injection into cattle may have been a source of prions.

Figure 15.16 Photograph of cow with advanced BSE.

● **Extension**   Parasitic existence

The disease-causing organisms discussed earlier are parasites. That is, they live for all or most of their life cycle either on (**ectoparasites**) or in (**endoparasites**) host organisms, on which they also feed. Parasitism is a distinctive lifestyle and form of nutrition, and is shown by a diverse range of organisms among the protoctistans, animals, plants and fungi. Also, all viruses are parasites, once they are within a host cell. There are distinctive features associated with parasitism. Many if not all are shown by most parasites. These include the modifications shown in Table 15.4.

Table 15.4
Features of successful parasitism.

Structural features:	simplified, degenerate or absent feeding organs, especially where food is freely available once in or on host degenerate or absent locomotory organs pronounced attachment structures securing parasite on or in host external defences to resist enzymes or antibodies of host
Physiological features:	enzymes to digest surrounding host tissues ability to detect favourable location in or on body of host anaerobic respiration, in gut-living parasites
Reproductive:	hermaphrodite, allowing self-fertilisation where parasite is alone in host vast numbers of eggs or spores, aiding chances of reaching new hosts protective wall to eggs or larvae for transit period presence of secondary host with a relationship to primary host, as vector

● Defence against disease

A barrier against entry

Mostly, pathogens do not gain easy entry to the body through the intact skin (Figure 12.7, page 257). Externally, the keratinised protein of the dead cells of the epidermis is tough and impervious unless broken, cut or deeply scratched. However, folds or creases in skin areas that are permanently moist can harbour microorganisms that breach the barrier and cause infection, as in athlete's foot.

Internal surfaces – for example, the trachea, bronchi and the bronchioles of the breathing apparatus, and the gut – are all lined by moist epithelium. These internal barriers are protected by mucus, by the actions of cilia removing the mucus, and some by digestive enzymes or strong acid (as in the stomach). However, these barriers are also sometimes crossed by certain pathogens. Consequently it is fortunate there are internal 'lines of defence' too. The body responds to localised damage (cuts and abrasions, for example) by **inflammation**. If a blood vessel is ruptured, then the **blood-clotting** mechanism is activated. In the blood and tissue fluid, the **immune system** is triggered.

Inflammation

Inflammation is the initial, rapid, localised response the tissues make to damage, whether it is to a cut, scratch, bruising or a deep wound. We are quickly aware the site has become swollen, warm and painful. Inflammation is triggered by the damaged cells themselves, which release 'alarm' chemicals, including histamine (Figure 15.17). As a result, the volume of blood in the damaged area is increased, and white cells and plasma accumulate outside the enlarged capillaries.

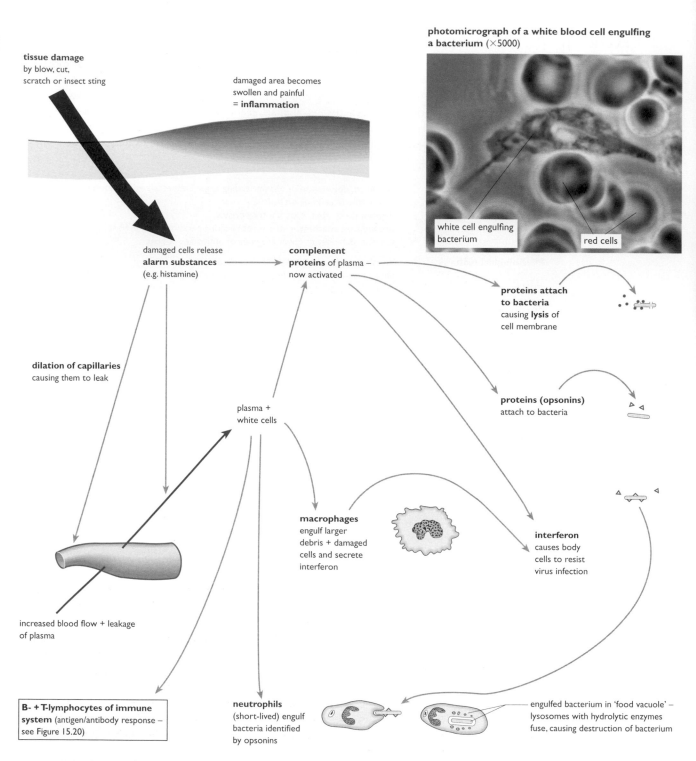

tissue damage
by blow, cut,
scratch or insect sting

damaged area becomes
swollen and painful
= **inflammation**

**photomicrograph of a white blood cell engulfing
a bacterium** (×5000)

white cell engulfing
bacterium

red cells

damaged cells release
alarm substances
(e.g. histamine)

**complement
proteins** of plasma –
now activated

**proteins attach
to bacteria**
causing **lysis** of
cell membrane

dilation of capillaries
causing them to leak

plasma +
white cells

proteins (opsonins)
attach to bacteria

macrophages
engulf larger
debris + damaged
cells and secrete
interferon

interferon
causes body
cells to resist
virus infection

increased blood flow + leakage
of plasma

**B- + T-lymphocytes of immune
system** (antigen/antibody response –
see Figure 15.20)

neutrophils
(short-lived) engulf
bacteria identified
by opsonins

engulfed bacterium in 'food vacuole' –
lysosomes with hydrolytic enzymes
fuse, causing destruction of bacterium

Figure 15.17
Inflammation at a damage
site, the processes.

The blood circulation plays a complex part in the resistance to infection. White cells in the blood (Figure 11.2, page 226) fall into two functional groupings that have different roles in the defence against disease. General phagocytic white cells engulf 'foreign' material. These are the neutrophils and the macrophages. **Neutrophils** make up 60% of all white cells in the blood, but they are short-lived. **Macrophages** are the principal 'rubbish-collecting cells' found throughout the body tissues. Other white cells produce the antibody reaction to infection or invasion of foreign matter (see Figure 15.19).

The blood also delivers special proteins (**complement proteins**), which work with white cells in overcoming infections.

Blood clotting

The clotting of blood is the mechanism by which escape of blood is prevented, either at small breaks or at cuts and other wounds. In these circumstances, clotting is normally rapid, and also prevents invasion by bacteria.

Clot formation is not normally activated in the intact circulation because coagulation is triggered only by conditions at the break. The most significant event is that collagen fibres in the walls of damaged arteries or veins are exposed. The subsequent steps to clotting are complex, and can be seen as a fail-safe mechanism. The steps in the blood-clotting mechanism are summarised in Figure 15.18.

Figure 15.18
The blood-clotting mechanism.

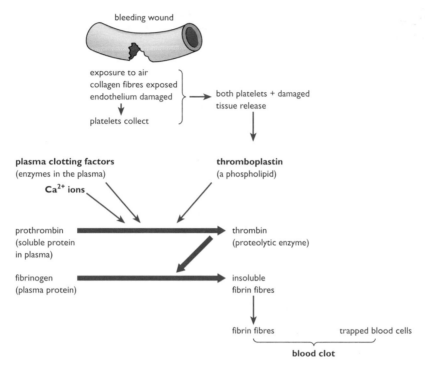

Immunity

The blood circulation plays a complex part in the resistance to infection. Some of the white cells that originate in the bone marrow make up the body's immune system. Immune system white cells are involved in specific resistance to disease.

The immune system is based on the body's ability to distinguish between 'self' (body cells and specific proteins, for example) and 'non-self' substances (produced by an invading organism, for example). Any 'non-self' substance is called an **antigen**. The ability to recognise antigens and to take steps to overcome them is the property of a type of white cell called a **lymphocyte**.

There are two types of these lymphocytes present in the lymph glands, which are known as B- and T-lymphocytes. These lymphocytes have different day-to-day roles (defined below). During their formation, they take different routes between bone marrow and lymph glands, which influence their subsequent activities.

B-lymphocytes

B-lymphocytes (for bone-derived lymphocytes) migrate directly from bone marrow to lymph nodes. In the presence of an antigen they divide rapidly, producing many plasma cells. These plasma cells secrete many **antibodies** (large protein molecules), which attach to the antigen molecules. An antibody is a special kind of protein constructed from two long, identical polypeptide chains (**heavy chain**) and two shorter chains (**light chain**). They are held together in the shape of a Y, whose top contains the antigen-binding site. The amino acid sequences differ at this site in different antibodies, which gives them their specificity (Figure 15.19).

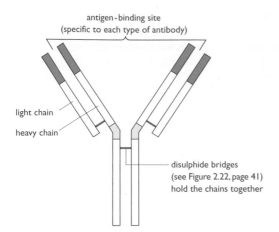

Figure 15.19
Structure of an antibody.

antigen-binding site
(specific to each type of antibody)

light chain

heavy chain

disulphide bridges
(see Figure 2.22, page 41)
hold the chains together

The plasma cells have a life span of only a few days. However, 'memory cells' are also formed and retained in the lymph nodes. Memory cells enable a quick response in the event of the antigen reinvading the body.

Antibodies destroy antigens in different ways:

- toxins (for example, from a bacterium) may be neutralised (inactivated) by reaction with the antibody
- bacterial cells may be clumped together so they 'precipitate' and can be engulfed by phagocytic cells
- antibodies may react with bacterial cells, so ensuring attachment to phagocytic cells
- antibodies may cause destruction of bacterial cell walls, causing lysis (destruction).

T-lymphocytes

4 What are the differences between antigens and antibodies, and where are they found?

T-lymphocytes (for thymus-derived lymphocytes) migrate first to the thymus gland to mature, and this occurs in the fetus. In the thymus the body apparently selects out lymphocytes that would otherwise react to the body's own cells. From the thymus, the mature T-lymphocytes migrate to the lymph nodes. When they are activated by an antigen, three types of T-lymphocyte are formed.

- **Helper cells** activate plasma cells. They also secrete chemicals (called **opsonins**) that attach to the antigens (on bacterial cells, for example), so labelling them for phagocytosis by other white cells.
- **Killer cells** kill body cells that have been invaded by viruses, causing the cells to burst, and so terminating the replication of the virus.
- **Suppressor cells** switch off the immune response once the invasion has been overcome.

These roles are summarised in Figure 15.20.

● **Extension**   Passive immunity

Antibodies are able to cross the placenta membrane (Figure 19.24, page 429) from the mother's blood into that of the fetus. As a consequence, the baby at birth is protected against the same diseases as the mother. This immunity, known as **passive immunity**, fades away after birth because the baby's immune system has not made the antibodies.

Vaccination

Providing immunity artificially is called **immunisation**, and may be brought about by vaccination. In **vaccination**, harmless antigens from a disease-causing organism are introduced into the body, either by injection or by mouth. This stimulates the body's immune system to make antibodies against the antigen. Artificial immunity is established in this way. Successful vaccination results in the presence of antibody-producing cells in the body, which are quickly activated if antigen from the same type of disease-causing organism enters the body. Vaccination works because it induces the production of memory lymphocytes, which persist in the body (Figure 15.20). Protection from many diseases can be obtained in this way, including poliomyelitis.

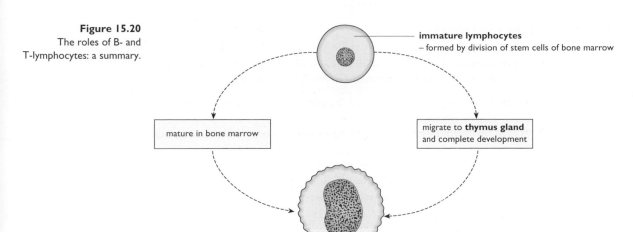

Figure 15.20
The roles of B- and
T-lymphocytes: a summary.

immature lymphocytes
– formed by division of stem cells of bone marrow

mature in bone marrow

migrate to **thymus gland**
and complete development

B-lymphocytes   **T-lymphocytes**

Mature B- and T-lymphocytes circulate in
bloodstream and are stored in the lymph nodes.

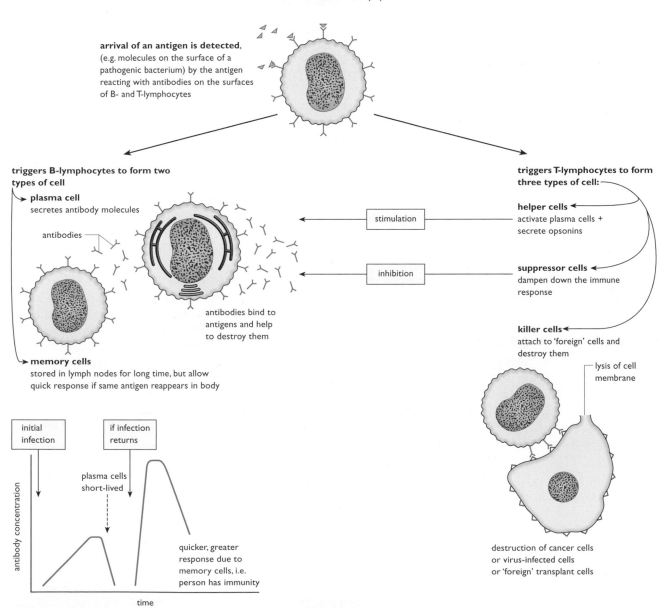

arrival of an antigen is detected,
(e.g. molecules on the surface of a
pathogenic bacterium) by the antigen
reacting with antibodies on the surfaces
of B- and T-lymphocytes

**triggers B-lymphocytes to form two
types of cell**

↳ **plasma cell**
    secretes antibody molecules

antibodies

antibodies bind to
antigens and help
to destroy them

stimulation

inhibition

**triggers T-lymphocytes to form
three types of cell:**

helper cells
activate plasma cells +
secrete opsonins

suppressor cells
dampen down the immune
response

killer cells
attach to 'foreign' cells and
destroy them

lysis of cell
membrane

↳ **memory cells**
    stored in lymph nodes for long time, but allow
    quick response if same antigen reappears in body

initial
infection

if infection
returns

plasma cells
short-lived

antibody concentration

quicker, greater
response due to
memory cells, i.e.
person has immunity

time

destruction of cancer cells
or virus-infected cells
or 'foreign' transplant cells

Types of vaccines

An effective vaccine causes our immune system to respond by producing specific antibodies, and to retain memory lymphocyte cells, **but it does not cause the disease**. This is not always easy to do, and various types of vaccine have had to be devised.

1 A **killed virulent organism** may be used, e.g. dead cells of the bacterium *Bordetella pertussis*, which causes whooping cough when alive.
2 A **live, non-virulent strain** may be used, e.g. strains of the virus that causes Rubella that have been 'crippled' (attenuated) so as not to cause the disease.
3 A **modified toxin**, such as that used against diptheria bacillus.
4 **Isolated antigens** from a pathogen, such as the influenza virus.
5 **Genetically engineered antigens**, such as those grown from genetically modified yeast cells with the gene to produce the protein coat of hepatitis B added. The vaccine is separated from the yeast's growth medium and purified. It is proving highly effective against this deadly viral infection.

Blood groups and blood transfusions

Human blood cells carry antigens on their plasma membrane, of which the ABO system and the Rhesus system are most important as far as blood transfusions are concerned. You may already know your own blood grouping, for each of us has a particular combination, and this has to be determined before we receive a transfusion of blood, should this be needed.

Blood groups are a special example of the antigen–antibody reaction. Looking at the detail of the **ABO system** in Table 15.5, you will notice that people tend to have an antibody in the plasma against whichever antigen they *lack*. This antibody is always present, even though the blood has not been in contact with the relevant antigen. So, for example, if a person of blood group A accidentally receives a transfusion of group B blood, then the anti-B antibodies in the recipient's plasma make the 'foreign' B cells clump together (the term is 'agglutinate'). The clumped blood cells then block blood vessels, which may be fatal. Consequently, you can see why blood of group O is so useful for transfusion purposes: it has neither A nor B antigens on the red cells.

If a small quantity of blood is given in a transfusion, the type of antibodies in the plasma received does not matter because it is diluted so much by the plasma of the recipient's blood. But for a large transfusion, the match of antigens and antibodies needs to be perfect.

The **Rhesus system** is different again. Rhesus negative people (people *without* the Rhesus antigen on their red cells) do *not* carry antibodies in their plasma. That is, unless they have been previously sensitised.

In practice, sensitisation of a Rhesus negative woman may occur if she carries a Rhesus positive fetus in the uterus (that is, the Rhesus factor is inherited). Late on in a pregnancy there is a likelihood of some mixing of maternal and fetal bloods. As a result, the mother is sensitised by Rhesus positive antigens, and she makes Rhesus antibodies. These would remain in the plasma, and should a second pregnancy occur, again with a Rhesus positive fetus, then antibodies would pass across the placenta from her plasma and destroy the red cells of a Rhesus positive fetus. In fact, treatment with anti-Rhesus antibodies, immediately the first pregnancy ends, prevents the problem.

5 Distinguish between the following pairs:

• antibiotics and vaccines
• bacteria and viruses
• infectious and non-infectious disease
• thrombus and embolus
• circulatory and respiratory diseases
• batch culture and continuous culture
• open fermenter and closed fermenter
• vector and host
• inflammation and immunity
• B-lymphocyte and T-lymphocyte.

Table 15.5
Blood grouping and transfusion possibilities.

1 *ABO system:*	Blood group A	Blood group B	Blood group AB	Blood group O
Red cell surface	A antigens	B antigens	A + B antigens	neither
Plasma	anti-B antibodies	anti-A antibodies	neither	both anti-A and anti-B antibodies
Blood groups that may be used for transfusion	A, O	B, O	A, B, AB, O	O

2 *Rhesus system:*	Rhesus$^+$	Rhesus$^-$
Rhesus antigens on red cells	present	absent
Antibodies to Rhesus antigens in blood plasma	none	none (*unless* previously sensitised)

Note: Blood group O is the universal donor blood group. Blood group AB is the universal recipient.

● Extension Monoclonal antibodies

Monoclonal antibodies are a recent invention, now widely used in medicine and research. A **monoclonal antibody** is a large quantity of a single antibody that is stable and can be used over a period of time. Each type of antibody is made by one particular type of B-lymphocyte. Unfortunately, B-lymphocytes are short-lived; they survive for only a few days. Monoclonal antibodies are made by fusing the specific lymphocyte with a cancer cell, which, unlike other body cells, goes on dividing indefinitely. The resulting cell divides to form a clone of cells that persists, and conveniently goes on secreting the antibody.

Monoclonal antibodies are used in:

- **cancer treatment**, for attaching toxins to antigens occurring on the plasma membrane of cancer cells alone
- **medical diagnosis**, for detecting cancer cells and pathogens such as viruses, and in pregnancy testing
- **transplant surgery**, for preventing transplant rejection by targeting T-cells that are causing rejection, rather than using immunosuppressive drugs, which leave the patient vulnerable to diseases.

● Skills task

Taking as your example one of the major threats to health in the human world population, such as tuberculosis, malaria or cardiovascular diseases due to cigarette smoking, prepare an explanatory presentation to your class.

You will need to be able to explain (and to be able to answer questions on) the way health is threatened, how those who have contracted the disease are best treated, and how the disease could be prevented.

Prepare the content of overhead transparencies (or posters) you would use, and the notes needed to talk informally for about 10 minutes.

SUMMARY

● Health is a state of physical, mental and social well-being, not merely the absence of disease. Diseases caused by disease-causing agents are **communicable diseases** since they may be transferred. **Non-communicable diseases and disorders** are not 'caught' from other organisms.

● Cardiovascular disease, malnutrition and respiratory disease due to pollution are examples of non-communicable diseases.

● **Viruses** consist of DNA or RNA, wrapped in a protein coat. Viruses take over host cells and convert the cellular machinery to produce more viruses, which escape and may repeat the process. **Viral diseases** include influenza, poliomyelitis and AIDS.

● **Bacterial diseases** are caused by pathogenic bacteria. Unlike viral diseases, they are vulnerable to antibiotics. Examples of bacterial diseases include tuberculosis, tetanus, cholera and salmonella food poisoning. However, most bacteria do not cause disease at all.

● Diseases caused by **eukaryotic organisms** include: malaria, which is due to the protoctistan *Plasmodium*, and transferred by the mosquito; the intestinal tapeworm, *Taenia*, a flatworm, which has a secondary host, the pig.

● **Parasites** show structural, physiological and reproductive mechanisms characteristic of their way of life.

● Defence against disease is provided by the intact body surfaces. When the skin is damaged the body reacts by **inflammation**. If bleeding occurs the site is sealed by **blood clotting**.

● The **immune system** includes **B- and T-lymphocytes**, which, when sensitised by foreign material (**antigens**), respond in complex ways to overcome the invasion.

● Examination questions

1 Penicillin is an antibiotic which is derived from the fungus *Penicillium chrysogenum*. The antibiotic can be produced on a commercial scale as shown in the diagram below.

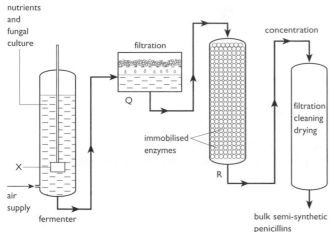

a i What is the purpose of structure X? (1)
ii Why is air supplied to the fermenter? (1)
b Explain the purpose of the filtration carried out at Q. (2)
c i Suggest **one** reason for using enzymes at R. (1)
ii Suggest why they are used as **immobilised** enzymes. (2)

London, AS/A level, Module B/HB4A, Jan 1997

2 a Describe how active immunity to a viral infection can be acquired naturally. (3)
b State **two** ways in which passive immunity may be acquired naturally by a young child. (2)

London, AS/A level, Module B/HB4A, June 1997

3 Chemicals, cells, tissues, organs and systems are all involved in body defence.
a Explain the role of the following chemicals in body defence.
   i Antibodies (2)
   ii Fibrinogen (2)
   iii Histamine (2)
b State the role of the following cells in body defence.
   i T lymphocytes (T cells) (1)
   ii B lymphocytes (B cells) (1)
   iii Neutrophils (1)

OCR (Oxford), A level, 6915, Mar 1999

4 Explain the cause and effect of each of the following:
a Coronary heart disease. (3)
b The smoking of cigarettes can lead to reduced levels of oxygen being carried in the blood. (3)
c AIDS can result in an increased risk of contracting pneumonia, tuberculosis and some cancers. (3)
d Alcohol in excess can result in obesity and liver damage. (3)

OCR (Oxford), A level, 6915, June 1999

5 Several diseases of the gaseous exchange system are caused by smoking.
a State a category of disease that includes such smoking-related diseases. Give a reason for your choice. (1)

The figure shows diagrams of two alveoli from the lungs of a smoker, **A**, and from a non-smoker, **B**, after exhalation is complete.

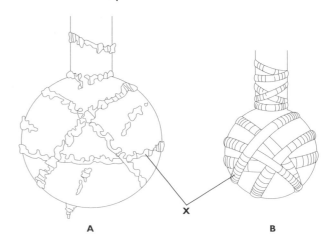

b i Identify the fibres labelled **X** that surround the alveoli. (1)
ii Explain what happened in the smoker's lungs to damage the structure of the fibres, **X**. (3)
iii Describe the expected consequences for breathing and gaseous exchange of the damage to the alveoli shown in the smoker's lungs. (3)
iv Describe the likely appearance of a cross-section of the lungs of **A** when viewed under the light microscope. (4)

OCR (Cambridge), A level, 4808, Nov 1999

IV
ORGANISM
AND
ENVIRONMENT

16 Biodiversity

STARTING POINTS
● **Biodiversity** is a contraction of '**biological diversity**', and refers to the **variety of living things**.
● **Human knowledge of biodiversity** past and present is important because:
  – we share the Earth and its resources with other organisms
  – human activities may threaten the future of habitats and of the organisms that inhabit them
  – nature is the ultimate source of our food, raw materials and medicines
  – the state of living things is one of the ways we monitor the environment.
● In **systematic biology**, scientists discover, describe, name and classify living and fossil organisms.

The scale of biodiversity

There are vast numbers of living things in the world. The word 'biodiversity' is a contraction of 'biological diversity', and is the term we use for this abundance of different types or species of organism. Up to now, about *1.7 million species have been described and named*.
However, there is no international 'library of living things' where new discoveries are automatically checked out. Consequently, some known organisms may have been 'discovered' more than once.

Meanwhile, previously unknown species are being discovered all the time. In the UK alone, several hundred new species have been described in the past decade. We might have expected all the wildlife in these islands to be known, since Britain was one of the countries to pioneer the systematic study of plants and animals. Apparently, this is not the case; previously unknown organisms are frequently found. World-wide, *the number of unknown species is estimated at between 3 and 5 million at the very least*, and possibly as high as 100 million. So scientists are not certain just how many different types of organisms exist. Figure 16.1 is a representation of the proportions of known and unknown species estimated to exist in many of the major divisions of living things, and the relative numbers in these different divisions, shown as a pie chart.

Figure 16.1
Introducing biodiversity.

Proportions of known species:

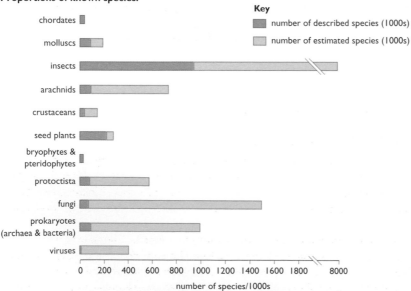

Key
■ number of described species (1000s)
■ number of estimated species (1000s)

number of species/1000s

Data from: '*The web of life; a strategy for systematic biology in the UK*' The UK Systematic Forum, The Natural History Museum, Cromwell Road, London SW7 5BD.

Relative numbers of animal and plant groups:

The 1.7 million described species are more than 50% insects, and the higher plants, mostly flowering plants, are the next largest group. By contrast, only 4000 species of mammals are known, about 0.25% of all known species.

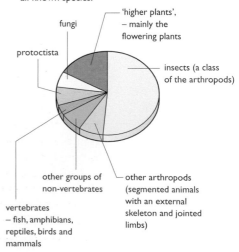

'higher plants', – mainly the flowering plants

fungi

protoctista

insects (a class of the arthropods)

other groups of non-vertebrates

other arthropods (segmented animals with an external skeleton and jointed limbs)

vertebrates – fish, amphibians, reptiles, birds and mammals

Biodiversity and extinctions

From time to time, species become **extinct**. We know about extinctions that happened long ago from the fossilised remains of organisms that are discovered. Today, extinction of species continues at an alarming rate. Most extinctions occur because living space on the surface of the Earth is being profoundly changed. This is largely due to the activities of humans, which impact on so many different habitats. Wild habitats are continually being disturbed and destroyed by the changes people make to the environment. It is now estimated that up to *10% of all species could disappear in the next 25 years*. And as each species dies out it puts other species at a disadvantage, as the fate of organisms is interconnected – by food chains, for example.

Meanwhile, if species have not been discovered then how can they be conserved? From a human viewpoint, nature is the ultimate source of human food, of our raw materials, and of many medicines. We need to protect the Earth's biodiversity in order to protect ourselves, quite apart from the obvious needs of the living things who share the environment with us. You can study human influences on the environment and conservation in Chapter 18. Meanwhile, you can see that the study of the diversity of life and the classification of living things is a very important branch of biology – for all our futures.

What do we mean by 'species'?

We refer scientifically to a particular type of living thing by the term '**species**'. A species is defined simply as 'a group of individuals of common ancestry that closely resemble each other, and are normally capable of interbreeding to produce fertile offspring'.

There are two issues relating to this definition, however. One is that some (very successful) species reproduce asexually, without any interbreeding at all. Organisms that reproduce asexually are very similar in structure, showing little variation between individuals.

The other point is that we now believe that species change with time, and that new species evolve from other species (see Chapter 21, page 458). The fact that species may change makes it impossible to think of a species as constant and unchanging. However, evolutionary change takes place over a long period of time. On a day-by-day basis, the term 'species' is satisfactory and useful.

Taxonomy – the classification of diversity

Classification is essential to biology because there are so many different living things. It would be impossible to sort out and compare them unless they were organised into manageable categories. By using an effective classification system, we can more easily organise our ideas about organisms and make generalisations. The scheme of classification has to be flexible, however, in order to allow newly discovered living organisms to be added into the scheme wherever they fit best. It should also include fossils, since we believe living and extinct species are related.

The process of classification involves:

• giving every organism an agreed name
• imposing a scheme upon the diversity of living things.

The binomial system of naming

Many organisms have local names, but these often differ from locality to locality around the world, so they do not allow people in different places to be confident they are talking about the same thing. Scientists therefore use an agreed international system called the **binomial system** (meaning 'a two-part name'). By this system everyone, anywhere knows exactly which organism is being referred to.

Each organism is given a scientific name consisting of two Latin words. The first (a noun) designates the **genus**, the second (an adjective) the **species**. The generic name comes first, and begins with a capital letter; it is followed by the specific name. Conventionally, this name is written in italics (or is underlined). As shown in Figure 16.2, closely related organisms have the same generic name; only their species names differ. For convenience, when an organism is

Figure 16.2
Naming organisms by the binomial system.

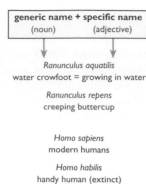

generic name + specific name
(noun)   (adjective)

Ranunculus aquatilis
water crowfoot = growing in water

Ranunculus repens
creeping buttercup

Homo sapiens
modern humans

Homo habilis
handy human (extinct)

referred to frequently its full name is given initially, but in subsequent mentions its generic name is shortened to the first (capital) letter followed by a full stop. For example in an article or scientific paper with a number of references to humans, *Homo sapiens* at the first mention would subsequently be referred to as *H. sapiens*.

The scheme of classification

The science of classification is called '**taxonomy**'. The word comes from '**taxa**' (singular = taxon), which is the general name for groups or categories within a classification system. The taxa used in taxonomy are given in Figure 16.3.

In classification, the aim is to use as many of the organism's characteristics as possible to place similar organisms together and separate the dissimilar ones. Just as similar species are grouped together into the same genus (plural = genera), so too, similar genera are grouped together into families. Families are grouped into orders, then classes, phyla and kingdoms. This is the **hierarchical scheme of classification**: each successive group contains more and more different kinds of organism.

Figure 16.3
The taxa used in taxonomy, and, as an example, applied to the genus *Homo*.

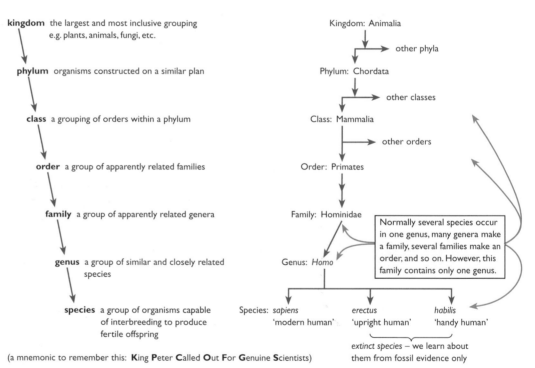

kingdom the largest and most inclusive grouping e.g. plants, animals, fungi, etc.

phylum organisms constructed on a similar plan

class a grouping of orders within a phylum

order a group of apparently related families

family a group of apparently related genera

genus a group of similar and closely related species

species a group of organisms capable of interbreeding to produce fertile offspring

(a mnemonic to remember this: **K**ing **P**eter **C**alled **O**ut **F**or **G**enuine **S**cientists)

Kingdom: Animalia → other phyla

Phylum: Chordata → other classes

Class: Mammalia → other orders

Order: Primates

Family: Hominidae

Genus: *Homo*

Normally several species occur in one genus, many genera make a family, several families make an order, and so on. However, this family contains only one genus.

Species: *sapiens* 'modern human'   *erectus* 'upright human'   *habilis* 'handy human'

extinct species – we learn about them from fossil evidence only

What features are used in classification?

The quickest way to classify living things is according to their immediate and obvious similarities and differences. For example, we might classify together animals that fly, simply because the essential organ – wings – are so easily seen. This would include almost all birds and many insects (as well as the bats and certain fossil dinosaurs). However, resemblances between the wings of the bird and the insect are superficial. Whilst both act as aerofoils (structures that generate 'lift' when moved though the air), they are built from different tissues and have different origins in terms of the development of the body. We say that the wings of birds and insects are **analogous structures** (Figure 16.4). Analogous structures resemble each other in function but differ in their fundamental structure. A classification based on analogous structures is said to be an *artificial* classification.

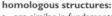

analogous structures:
* resemble each other in function
* differ in their fundamental structure
* illustrate only superficial resemblances

An example of analogous structures are the **wings of birds and insects**, which are similar only in their function as aerofoils.

An example of homologous structures are the **limbs of vertebrates**, all of which appear to be modifications of an ancestral five-fingered (pentadactyl) limb.

homologous structures:
* are similar in fundamental structure
* are similar in position and development, but not necessarily in function
* are similar because of common ancestry

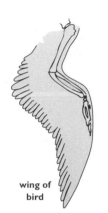

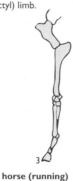

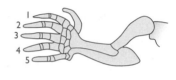

wing of
bird

wing of
insect

horse (running)

basic plan of
pentadactyl limb

mole
(digging)

Figure 16.4
Analogous and homologous
structures.

Conversely, a *natural* classification is based on similarities and differences due to close relationships between organisms resulting from the fact that they share common ancestors. The bone structure of the limbs of all vertebrates suggests they are modifications of a common plan, known as the pentadactyl limb. So, there are many comparable bones in the human arm, the leg of a horse, the limb of a mole and the wing of a bird. Structures built to a common plan, but adapted for different purposes, are called **homologous structures**.

A classification based on evolutionary relationships

A natural classification based on homologous structures is believed to reflect evolutionary relationships. A classification based upon evolutionary relationships is called **phylogenetic**, and this is what taxonomists try to reflect.

Today, similarities and differences in the biochemistry of organisms, as well as structural features, have become important in taxonomy. For example, the composition of nucleic acids and cell proteins often shows us the degree of relatedness between organisms more precisely than structural features. Organisms that are closely related show fewer differences in the composition of specific nucleic acids and cell proteins they all possess. But, despite this additional source of evidence, evolutionary relationships are still only partly understood. So current taxonomy is only partly a phylogenetic classification.

The five kingdoms

At one time the living world seemed to divide naturally into two kingdoms:

the **plants**
– photosynthetic (autotrophic nutrition)
– mostly rooted (that is, stationary) organisms

the **animals**
– ingestion of complex food (heterotrophic nutrition)
– typically mobile organisms

These two kingdoms grew from the original disciplines of biology, namely **botany**, the study of plants, and **zoology**, the study of animals. Fungi and microorganisms were conveniently 'added' to botany!

Initially this presented only one problem: fungi possessed the typically 'animal' heterotrophic nutrition but were 'plant-like' in structure. Later, with the use of the electron microscope, came the discovery of the two types of cell structure, namely prokaryotic and eukaryotic (page 4). As a result, the bacteria with their prokaryotic cells could no longer be 'plants' since plants have eukaryotic cells. The divisions of living things into kingdoms needed overhauling. Today, the agreed division of living things is into five kingdoms:

- **Prokaryote Kingdom**, the bacteria and cyanobacteria (photosynthetic bacteria), predominantly unicellular organisms
- **Protoctistan Kingdom** (eukaryotes), predominantly unicellular, and seen as resembling the ancestors of the fungi, plants and animals
- **Fungal Kingdom** (eukaryotes), predominantly multicellular organisms, non-motile, with heterotrophic nutrition
- **Plant Kingdom** (eukaryotes), multicellular organisms, non-motile, with autotrophic nutrition
- **Animal Kingdom** (eukaryotes), multicellular organisms, motile, with heterotrophic nutrition.

Their possible evolutionary relationship is shown in Figure 16.5.

Figure 16.5
Possible evolutionary relationship of the five kingdoms.

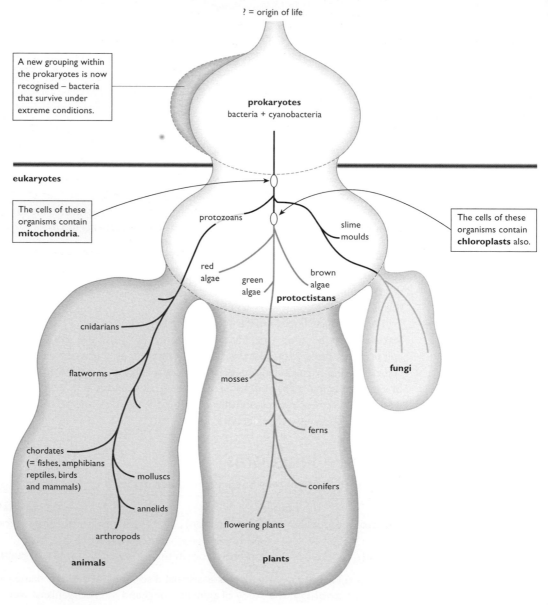

? = origin of life

A new grouping within the prokaryotes is now recognised – bacteria that survive under extreme conditions.

prokaryotes
bacteria + cyanobacteria

eukaryotes

The cells of these organisms contain **mitochondria**.

protozoans

slime moulds

The cells of these organisms contain **chloroplasts** also.

red algae

green algae

brown algae

protoctistans

cnidarians

flatworms

fungi

mosses

ferns

chordates
(= fishes, amphibians reptiles, birds and mammals)

molluscs

conifers

annelids

flowering plants

arthropods

animals

plants

Looking at the range of life

The prokaryotes

The structure of the prokaryotic cell is introduced in Figure 1.23, page 21. Organisms with cells of this structurally simple kind include the **bacteria** and **cyanobacteria** (Figure 16.6). Bacteria have existed on Earth longer than any other organisms; they date back 3.5 billion years (Figure 21.2, page 460). At this early time, Earth's atmosphere contained no oxygen. Despite, or possibly because of, their long evolutionary history, prokaryotes are extremely successful organisms. Many different prokaryote species exist, showing every type of nutrition. The photosynthetic forms, the cyanobacteria, are more recent arrivals: they date back only 2 million years. Only since the cyanobacteria appeared and started to photosynthesise has oxygen gas accumulated in the atmosphere. Indirectly, oxygen in the atmosphere allowed organisms to move on to the land, and permitted the eventual evolution of complex, compact body structures of the larger animals and plants.

Figure 16.6
Introducing the prokaryotes.

The prokaryotes include the bacteria and cyanobacteria:

* unicellular or filamentous organisms consisting of very small cells, 0.5–5.0 μm
* genetic material is circular DNA, naked (no protein attached) in the cytoplasm, attached to plasma membrane
* no membranous organelles, but ribosomes present (smaller than those of eukaryotes)
* rigid cell wall of polysaccharide with amino acid.

TEM of *Escherichia coli* (×40 000) – a bacterium

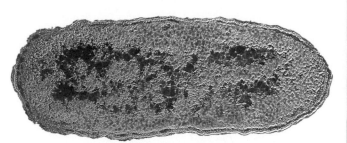

E. coli **is a rod-shaped bacterium**, part of the normal gut 'flora' of humans and other vertebrates. It feeds on the food molecules among which it lives (saprotrophic nutrition).

drawing of *E. coli* cell

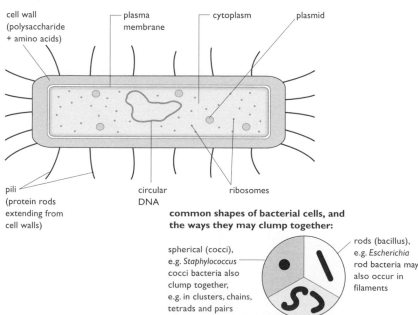

cell wall (polysaccharide + amino acids)

plasma membrane

cytoplasm

plasmid

pili (protein rods extending from cell walls)

circular DNA

ribosomes

common shapes of bacterial cells, and the ways they may clump together:

spherical (cocci), e.g. *Staphylococcus* cocci bacteria also clump together, e.g. in clusters, chains, tetrads and pairs

rods (bacillus), e.g. *Escherichia* rod bacteria may also occur in filaments

spiral, e.g. *Spirillum*   **or**   comma (vibrio), e.g. *Vibrio*

SEM of *Anabaena* filament (×2000) – a cyanobacterium

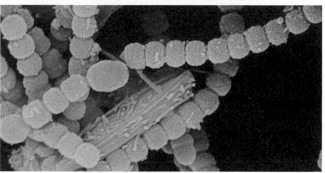

Anabaena **is a filamentous cyanobacterium**, a photosynthetic organism (autotrophic nutrition) that also fixes atmospheric nitrogen (N_2) to the ammonium ion, which the cells then use to make amino acids and proteins.

drawing of cells of *Anabaena* filament

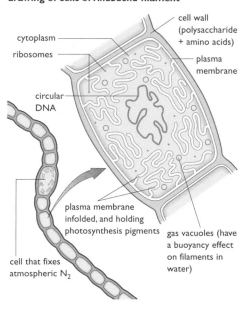

cytoplasm

ribosomes

cell wall (polysaccharide + amino acids)

plasma membrane

circular DNA

plasma membrane infolded, and holding photosynthesis pigments

gas vacuoles (have a buoyancy effect on filaments in water)

cell that fixes atmospheric N_2

The Protoctista

The Protoctista are a kingdom of eukaryotes that are unicellular, colonial or of relatively simple multicellular construction. They are organisms that do not easily fall into the Plant, Animal or Fungal Kingdoms. They are all found in aquatic habitats. The Protoctista comprise **algae**, including the multicellular seaweeds, **protozoans**, and certain simple fungi, the **slime moulds**, which are motile by means of their flagella (Figure 16.7). From this rather strange collection of organisms you may have guessed (correctly) that the Protoctista are classified together as a group on the basis of their relatively simple level of organisation, rather than being a truly natural grouping of closely related organisms.

Figure 16.7
Introducing the protoctista.

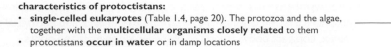

characteristics of protoctistans:
- **single-celled eukaryotes** (Table 1.4, page 20). The protozoa and the algae, together with the **multicellular organisms closely related** to them
- protoctistans **occur in water** or in damp locations

- the **protozoa** are single-celled animal-like organisms with holozoic or parasitic nutrition (Figure 7.2, page 141)

- the **algae** are photosynthetic organisms with a cell structure like that of green plants
- show **diversity of structure**, from unicellular and simple filament forms to huge, multicellular seaweeds

Amoeba proteus (×200)

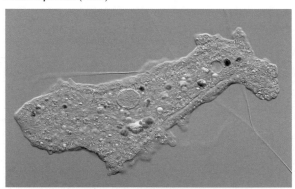

Chlamydomonas, a motile unicellular alga of pond water (×1600)

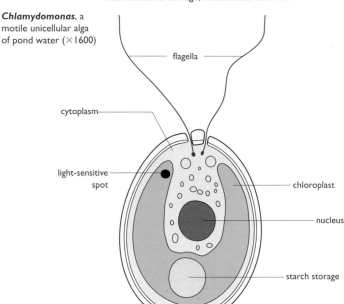

flagella

cytoplasm

light-sensitive spot

chloroplast

nucleus

starch storage

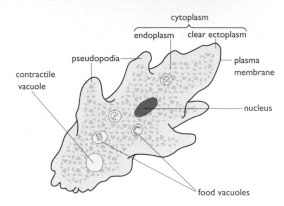

cytoplasm
endoplasm   clear ectoplasm
pseudopodia
contractile vacuole
plasma membrane
nucleus
food vacuoles

Trypanosoma, a blood parasite of humans and cattle, transmitted between hosts by the tsetse fly. In humans it causes 'sleeping sickness' (x400)

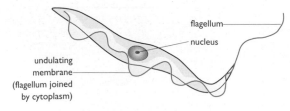

flagellum
nucleus
undulating membrane (flagellum joined by cytoplasm)

Another protozoan is *Paramecium*, which has a body covered by cilia (Figure 7.3, page 142)

Fucus, a brown seaweed (×0.5)

plant body of:
- holdfast (attaches plant to rock/breakwater)
- stalk
- blade or thallus

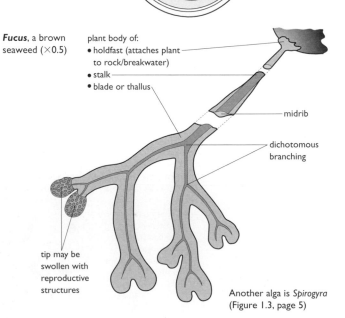

midrib
dichotomous branching
tip may be swollen with reproductive structures

Another alga is *Spirogyra* (Figure 1.3, page 5)

The fungi

The fungi include the moulds, yeasts, mildews, mushrooms, puffballs and rusts (Figure 16.8). The study of fungi is called **mycology**, and this group of organisms is of great economic importance. The fungus 'body' is known as a **mycelium**, and consists of fine, tubular **hyphae**. These, though plant-like, have walls, not of cellulose, but **chitin** (page 31). The nutrition of fungi also distances them from plants, for fungi are heterotrophic. Many feed on dead organic matter (saprotrophic nutrition) but others are parasites, particularly of plants. Fungi reproduce by the production of **spores**, which are typically dispersed by air currents.

Figure 16.8
Introducing the fungi.

the structure of the fungal mycelium, showing eukaryotic organisation:

tip of hypha enlarged

mycelium of hyphae

— vacuole — ribosome — nucleus — mitochondrion

— hyphal wall — Golgi apparatus — vesicle

characteristics of fungi:
- eukaryotic organisms with a protective wall made of **chitin**
- 'body' of fungus a **mycelium** of branching, tube-like **hyphae** – often divided by cross-walls (septa) into short, multinucleate sections
- no chlorophyll present – fungi are **heterotrophic**, feeding on dead organic matter, which is externally digested (saprotrophs) or, parasitically, particularly on higher plants
- reproduction is by means of **spores**, produced by asexual and sexual processes
- common fungi are the **moulds**, **mildews**, **yeasts** and **mushrooms**

mould fungi, e.g. *Rhizopus*

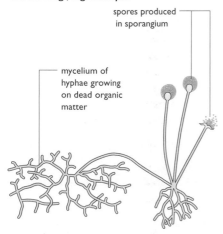

spores produced in sporangium

mycelium of hyphae growing on dead organic matter

yeast, e.g. *Saccharomyces*, yeast cells growing in sugar solution (x 5000)

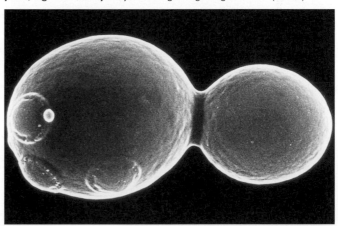

mushroom, e.g. *Amanita muscaria*, mushroom in section

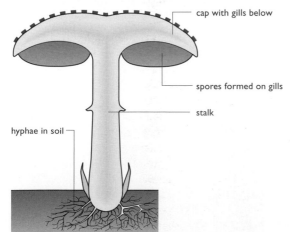

cap with gills below

spores formed on gills

stalk

hyphae in soil

Amanita muscaria (x 0.5)

Plants

The green plants are terrestrial organisms, adapted to life on land, although some do occur in aquatic habitats. They are eukaryotic organisms, with cell walls containing **cellulose**. In their nutrition, green plants are autotrophic organisms, manufacturing sugar by **photosynthesis** in their chloroplasts. The sugar is then stored or used immediately to sustain the whole of their metabolism.

A distinctive feature of green plants is their rather complex life cycle, for there are two stages or generations, and these generations alternate.

- The **gametophyte generation** has cells with haploid nuclei (*n*) which contain the basic set of chromosomes. The gametophyte generation produces gametes. Gametes fuse to form a zygote, and this develops into a sporophyte.
- The **sporophyte generation** has cells with diploid nuclei (2*n*), which contain two sets of the basic set of chromosomes. The sporophyte generation forms haploid spores by meiosis, and these germinate to form gametophytes.

The phyla that make up the green plants

Figure 16.9
Green plant diversity.

The chief characteristics of the phyla that make up the green plants are summarised in Figure 16.9. In the different phyla of green plants, the two generations have differing degrees of prominence.

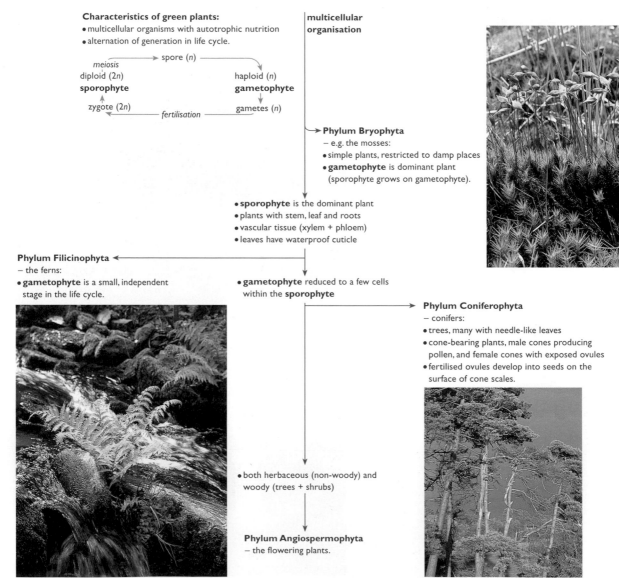

Characteristics of green plants:
- multicellular organisms with autotrophic nutrition
- alternation of generation in life cycle.

multicellular organisation

meiosis → spore (*n*)
diploid (2*n*) **sporophyte** → haploid (*n*) **gametophyte**
zygote (2*n*) ← *fertilisation* ← gametes (*n*)

Phylum Bryophyta
– e.g. the mosses:
- simple plants, restricted to damp places
- **gametophyte** is dominant plant (sporophyte grows on gametophyte).

- **sporophyte** is the dominant plant
- plants with stem, leaf and roots
- vascular tissue (xylem + phloem)
- leaves have waterproof cuticle

Phylum Filicinophyta
– the ferns:
- **gametophyte** is a small, independent stage in the life cycle.

- **gametophyte** reduced to a few cells within the **sporophyte**

Phylum Coniferophyta
– conifers:
- trees, many with needle-like leaves
- cone-bearing plants, male cones producing pollen, and female cones with exposed ovules
- fertilised ovules develop into seeds on the surface of cone scales.

- both herbaceous (non-woody) and woody (trees + shrubs)

Phylum Angiospermophyta
– the flowering plants.

352

The **mosses** and liverworts (**bryophytes**) are all land plants, but are poorly adapted to terrestrial conditions. Internally they are without lignified cells such as fibres, and they contain no vascular tissue. Lack of internal support and transport tissues may explain why they are all relatively small plants. They are also without true roots, being anchored by tiny **rhizoids**. The leaves are simple structures mostly one cell thick, and without a waxy cuticle.

In the bryophytes, the gametophyte is the conspicuous and dominant generation. The sporophyte generation grows on the gametophyte, almost like a parasite, and is dependent upon it. The moss *Funaria* is an example, illustrated in Figure 16.10.

Figure 16.10
Introducing bryophytes.

characteristics of mosses and liverworts (Phylum Bryophyta):

- Multicellular eukaryotic organisms with cells having cellulose cell walls. Mosses are small, leafy structures with spirally arranged leaves. There is no cuticle.
- The plant lacks water-conducting vessels (xylem) and elaborate food-conducting tissues (phloem). The plant has no roots, but is anchored by hair-like rhizoids.
- Nutrition is autotrophic, with sugar produced in organelles called chloroplasts, by photosynthesis.
- The life history shows two generations that alternate. In bryophytes the gametophyte is the conspicuous and dominant generation. The sporophyte grows on the gametophyte, and is dependent on it.
- Most bryophytes grow on land, but they are largely restricted to damp environments.

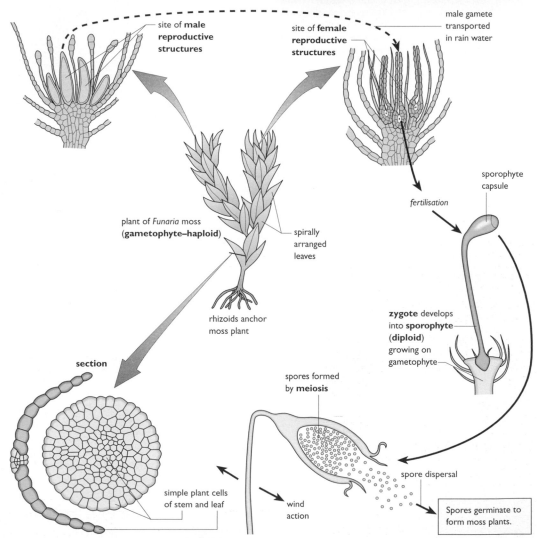

site of **male reproductive structures**

site of **female reproductive structures**

male gamete transported in rain water

plant of *Funaria* moss (**gametophyte–haploid**)

spirally arranged leaves

rhizoids anchor moss plant

fertilisation

sporophyte capsule

zygote develops into **sporophyte** (**diploid**) growing on gametophyte

section

spores formed by **meiosis**

spore dispersal

simple plant cells of stem and leaf

wind action

Spores germinate to form moss plants.

The present-day **ferns** are relatively small survivors of an ancient group of plants. In the Carboniferous period, about 355 million years ago (Figure 21.2, page 460), huge forests grew across swampy land, and contained tree-like ferns and related plants. When these organisms died and decayed they became peat deposits that were gradually converted to coal. This is why, when we burn fossil fuel today, we are adding carbon dioxide to our atmosphere that has been locked away as coal or oil for millions of years.

In comparison with mosses, today's ferns are well adapted to terrestrial life. They have finely divided leaves, often called **fronds**. The leaves have a waxy cuticle, and stomata through which gas exchange occurs. Leaves, stems and roots are connected by vascular tissue and are supported by fibres strengthened with lignin (page 316). Ferns are found growing on the ground, between rocks and on trees (plants growing on other plants are called **epiphytes**). In the ferns, the sporophyte is the dominant plant, and the gametophyte is a small, inconspicuous but sturdy independent plant. The fern *Dryopteris* is illustrated as an example in Figure 16.11. Unlike the bryophytes, ferns do not require very damp conditions for reproduction.

Figure 16.11 Introducing ferns.

characteristics of ferns (Phylum Filicinocophyta):
* Ferns are green plants with stem, leaves and roots, and are well adapted to terrestrial conditions. Vascular tissue (xylem and phloem) is present. Their leaves are elaborate structures with a waxy, waterproof covering (cuticle) with pores (stomata) in the leaves.
* The life history shows two generations that alternate. The fern plant is the diploid sporophyte generation. Spores are produced in spore containers (sporangia) on the lower surface of leaves, in clusters called sori.
* The spores germinate to form the gametophytes, small independent plants. The gametophyte produces gametes. Gametes fuse to form the zygote, which grows into the sporophyte.

Dryopteris **fern plant (diploid sporophyte)**

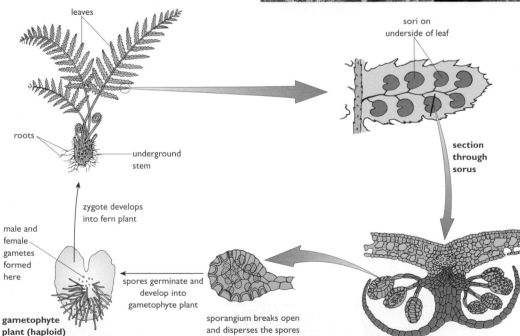

The range of green plants also includes the **conifers**, or cone-bearing trees. In a cone, simple seeds may be formed. The biology of conifers is largely outside the scope of this book, although you may come across these plants in ecological studies. They are certainly of economic importance today. (Consequently, the main features of conifers are shown in the context of the diversity of green plants, in Figure 16.9.)

The flowering plants or **angiosperms** are now the dominant land plants, in almost every habitat across the world. Some angiosperms take the form of trees and shrubs, but many are non-woody (herbaceous) plants. Whether woody or herbaceous, a flowering plant is the sporophyte generation in the life cycle. The gametophyte generation is so drastically reduced as to be nothing more than tiny cells or nuclei within the sporophyte reproductive structures.

The chief characteristic of flowering plants is their reproductive structure: the **flower**. Flowers are unique to these plants; from the flower comes seeds. With the evolution of the flower and seed has come complex mechanisms of pollen transfer and seed dispersal which sometimes exploit the activities of other organisms. For example, species of insects including bees and butterflies are attracted to flowers and carry out pollination (the transfer of pollen between flowers). A wider range of animals may be involved in fruit and seed dispersal. Some plants rely on the wind either for pollination or seed dispersal, or both.

The seed contains an embryo plant and food store. The embryonic leaves are called **cotyledons**. As a phylum, the angiosperms are divided into two classes of plants on the basis of the number of seed leaves the embryo plant forms (Figure 16.12). The flowering plant *Ranunculus* is illustrated here as an example, and the steps to seed formation are shown in Chapter 19, page 413.

Figure 16.12
Introducing flowering plants.

characteristics of flowering plants (Phylum Angiospermophyta):
- The angiosperms are the dominant group of land plants. Many are herbaceous (non-woody) plants, others are trees and shrubs.
- The flowering plant has stem, leaf and root tissue, Vascular tissue (xylem and phloem) is present. Leaves are elaborate structures with a waxy, waterproof covering (cuticle) with pores (stomata) in the surface.
- In the flowering plant life cycle the sporophyte is the dominant generation, with the gametophyte severely reduced and retained inside sporophyte structures as a few cells or nuclei.
- The flower is unique to the angiosperms, and from it are formed seeds. The seeds are enclosed in an ovary. After fertilisation, the ovary develops into a fruit.

flowering plants are divided into:

dicotyledons
e.g. buttercup, sunflower, oak:
- in the seed the embryo plant has two seed leaves
- parts of the flowers occur in 2s, 4s or 5s

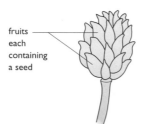
fruits each containing a seed

monocotyledons
e.g. grasses (wild + cultivated), iris:
- in the seed the embryo plant has one seed leaf
- parts of the flowers occur in 3s

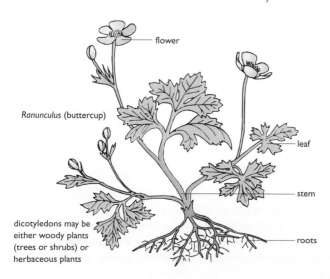
Ranunculus (buttercup)
flower
leaf
stem
roots
dicotyledons may be either woody plants (trees or shrubs) or herbaceous plants

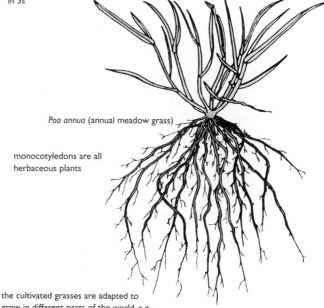
Poa annua (annual meadow grass)
monocotyledons are all herbaceous plants

the cultivated grasses are adapted to grow in different parts of the world, e.g.
- wheat – in temperate regions, relatively dry
- maize – in tropical/subtropical regions (page 183)
- rice – in shallow swamps (page 384)
- sorghum – in semi-arid regions (page 382)

Animals

Characteristics of animals

Animals are multicellular, eukaryotic organisms with heterotrophic nutrition (Figure 7.2, page 141). The cells of animals are without chloroplasts and without a wall surrounding the plasma membrane, in contrast to those of plants. Typically, the cells of an animal's body are highly specialised by their structure and physiology to perform particular functions, such as muscle cells for movement. Specialised tissues are often combined together to form organs that perform a particular function in the body as a whole. Most animals have some form of nervous system to coordinate their body actions and responses.

Another contrast with plants is the simplicity of the life cycle of many animals, although some parasitic animals are an exception to this. The life cycle of animals is diploid (Figure 19.2, page 411), with the adult producing haploid gametes (sperms and ova) by meiosis. After fertilisation, the zygote divides to produce an embryo that, early in development, becomes a characteristic hollow ball of cells, called a **blastula**.

Animal lifestyle and body plan

In contrast with green plants and fungi, many animals are in more or less constant movement, often in search of food, for example. The symmetry of the body of motile organisms is typically **bilateral**, meaning that there is only one plane that cuts the body into two equal halves (Figure 16.13). Also with motility comes a compact body, elongated in the direction of movement. Shaped like this animals offer the minimum of resistance to the surrounding medium, whether air or water. Since the front (anterior) end of the animal experiences the changing environment first, sense organs become located there. The result is the evolution of a head distinct from the rest of the body – a developmental process called **cephalisation**.

The body of animals with non-motile (sessile) lifestyles typically shows **radial symmetry**. Here the body is approximately cylindrically organised, with the body parts arranged around a central axis. There are many planes through which the body can be cut into equal halves.

The phylum of animals that illustrate radial symmetry, the Cnidaria (Figure 16.15), have a body wall composed of just two layers of cells, a condition described as **diploblastic**. The outer layer of tissue is called the **ectoderm**, and the inner layer the **endoderm**. These two layers are separated by a jelly layer, the **mesoglea**. This simple body wall surrounds the gut cavity or **enteron**.

Figure 16.13
Animal lifestyle and body symmetry.

radial body symmetry of *Hydra*, typical of a sedentary (sessile) lifestyle

Body is more or less a cylinder, with many planes of symmetry around a central axis.

Front (anterior) of motile animal experiences the environment first, and most sense organs are arranged here = **cephalisation**.

bilateral symmetry of a fish, typical of a motile lifestyle

in bilateral symmetry the two sides of the animal are the same, but upper (dorsal) and lower (ventral) are different, as are the front (anterior) and rear (posterior)

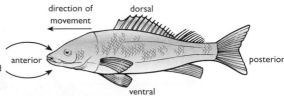

direction of movement
dorsal
anterior
posterior
ventral

All other animal phyla have a body of three layers of cells, a condition called **triploblastic**. The middle layer of cells, called the **mesoderm**, is the origin of the majority of the body organ systems. In many triploblastic phyla a cavity develops within the mesoderm, called the **coelom**. The flatworms (Phylum Platyhelminthes) are triploblastic animals without a coelom (Figure 16.14). However, a coelom is seen in many phyla, including the segmented worms (Phylum Annelida) and the vertebrates.

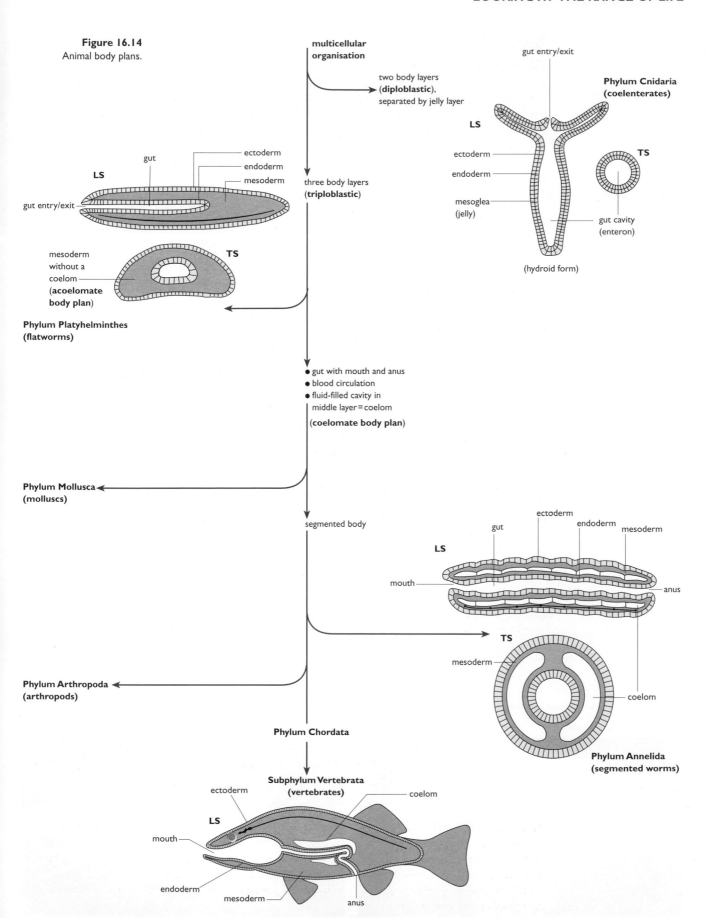

Figure 16.14
Animal body plans.

Some important animal phyla

The **cnidarians** include the jellyfish, sea anemones and corals (Figure 16.15). Cnidarians may exist in one of two forms, either as a stationary polyp, like *Hydra*, or as a floating medusoid form, like the jellyfish. Some, like *Obelia*, exist as both. Both forms have two layers to their body walls, the ectoderm and endoderm (diploblastic organisation), separated by a layer of jelly. In the jelly layer there is a simple 'nerve net' that connects the cells of both layers and coordinates behaviour and responses. The body structure of cnidarians is radially symmetrical and they have tentacles. Food is trapped using characteristic stinging cells, the **cnidoblasts**, and is pushed into the body cavity by the tentacles.

Figure 16.15
Introducing the cnidarians.

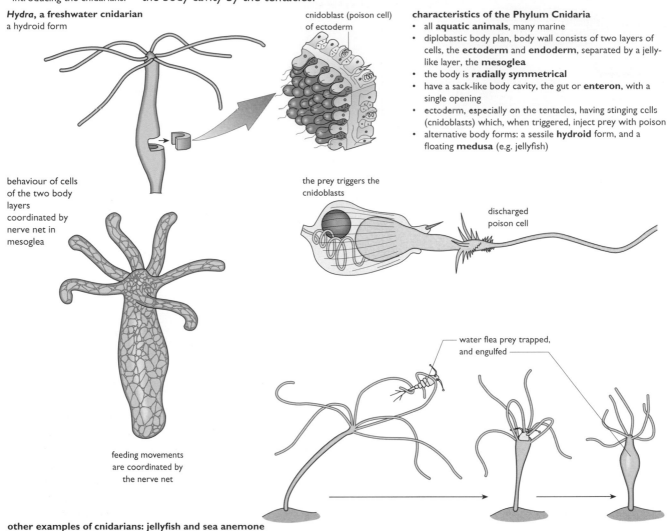

Hydra, a freshwater cnidarian
a hydroid form

cnidoblast (poison cell) of ectoderm

behaviour of cells of the two body layers coordinated by nerve net in mesoglea

feeding movements are coordinated by the nerve net

the prey triggers the cnidoblasts

discharged poison cell

water flea prey trapped, and engulfed

characteristics of the Phylum Cnidaria
- all **aquatic animals**, many marine
- diplobastic body plan, body wall consists of two layers of cells, the **ectoderm** and **endoderm**, separated by a jelly-like layer, the **mesoglea**
- the body is **radially symmetrical**
- have a sack-like body cavity, the gut or **enteron**, with a single opening
- ectoderm, especially on the tentacles, having stinging cells (cnidoblasts) which, when triggered, inject prey with poison
- alternative body forms: a sessile **hydroid** form, and a floating **medusa** (e.g. jellyfish)

other examples of cnidarians: jellyfish and sea anemone

a jellyfish floats near the surface

a sea anemone attached to rock

The **platyhelminthes** are unsegmented animals with a body built from three cell layers (triploblastic organisation). They have no cavity or coelom in the middle layer. They have a gut that has a mouth but no anus. There is no circulatory system in the platyhelminth body but, since the body is generally small, thin and often flat, oxygen can diffuse easily to most of the cells. Platyhelminthes often have both male and female reproductive organs in one individual (hermaphrodite organisation). Some are free-living flatworms, but others are parasitic flukes or tapeworms (Figure 16.16).

Figure 16.16
Introducing the platyhelminthes.

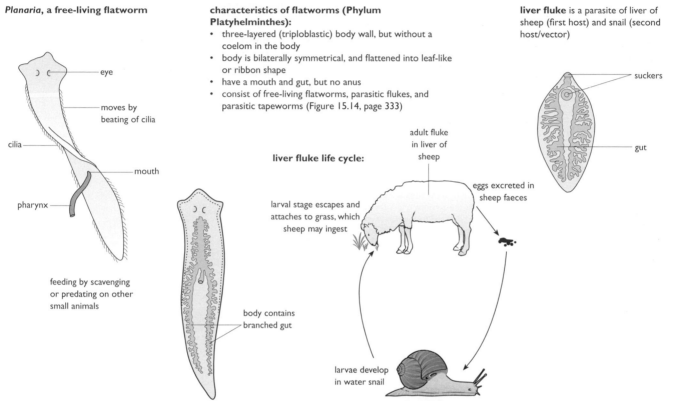

Planaria, a free-living flatworm

- eye
- moves by beating of cilia
- cilia
- mouth
- pharynx
- feeding by scavenging or predating on other small animals
- body contains branched gut

characteristics of flatworms (Phylum Platyhelminthes):
- three-layered (triploblastic) body wall, but without a coelom in the body
- body is bilaterally symmetrical, and flattened into leaf-like or ribbon shape
- have a mouth and gut, but no anus
- consist of free-living flatworms, parasitic flukes, and parasitic tapeworms (Figure 15.14, page 333)

liver fluke is a parasite of liver of sheep (first host) and snail (second host/vector)

- suckers
- gut

liver fluke life cycle:
- adult fluke in liver of sheep
- eggs excreted in sheep faeces
- larval stage escapes and attaches to grass, which sheep may ingest
- larvae develop in water snail

The **molluscs** include the slugs, snails, limpets, mussels and octopuses (Figure 16.17). They are triploblastic, coelomate animals with generally soft, flexible bodies that show little or no evidence of segmentation. The molluscs are a huge and diverse group of organisms – the second largest group in terms of numbers of species. The body is divided into a head, a flattened, muscular foot and a hump or visceral mass that is often covered by a shell. This is secreted by a layer of tissue called the **mantle**. We cannot do justice to the range of structure and diversity of molluscs at this level. Most are aquatic, and found in freshwater or marine habitats, but a few are terrestrial. The compact body shape of molluscs means that diffusion is not an effective method for the transport of nutrients. So molluscs have gills or occasionally lungs for gaseous exchange, as well as a well-developed blood circulation.

Figure 16.17
Introducing the molluscs.

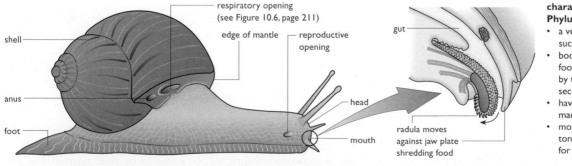

- respiratory opening (see Figure 10.6, page 211)
- edge of mantle
- reproductive opening
- gut
- shell
- anus
- foot
- head
- mouth
- radula moves against jaw plate shredding food

characteristics of the Phylum Mollusca:
- a very diverse and successful group
- body divided into head, foot, and hump covered by the mantle, which secretes the shell
- have gills or lungs in the mantle cavity
- most have a rasping, tongue-like radula used for feeding

other examples of the molluscs are the marine **mussel** (bivalve), the **octopus**, and **squid**

The **annelids** are the segmented worms (Figure 16.18). Their body consists of a series of repeating units or 'segments'. This form of body organisation is known as **metameric segmentation**. The functioning of the body segments is coordinated by a ventral nerve cord with nerves running to the organs of each segment, and there is a concentration of nerve cells at the front of the body (a degree of cephalisation). Annelids have a well-developed circulatory system in which blood is transported to all parts of the body in arteries and is drained away in veins. The blood contains an oxygen-transporting pigment. Annelids have a soft body without a rigid skeleton. There is no waterproof covering over their body surface so they live in moist places, and gaseous exchange occurs over the body surface. The muscles of the body wall bring about movement by working against the pressure of the fluid of the coelom. They have a flexible, hydrostatic skeleton.

Figure 16.18
Introducing the annelids.

characteristics of the segmented worms (Phylum Annelida):
- worm-like animals with a body built of a fixed number of similar segments
- each segment contains the same pattern of nerves, muscles, blood vessels, and excretory organs
- this is **metameric segmentation**, and is visible externally as rings
- internally, the segments are separated by septa that divide the coelom into compartments
- the collection of sense organs and the feeding structures at the anterior end – the cephalisation process, modifies the segmentation pattern somewhat
- a solid (not tubular) ventral nerve cord runs the length of the body

the earthworms, e.g. *Lumbricus*

The roles of the hydrostatic skeleton (coelum fluid), the muscles of the body wall, and the bristles (chaetae) in each segment in movement are shown in Figure 14.12, page 315.

Gaseous exchange occurs through the whole body surface, which is kept moist (Figure 10.6, page 211).

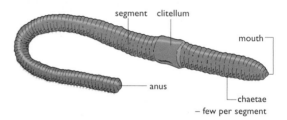

segment   clitellum

mouth

anus

chaetae
– few per segment

the leeches, e.g. *Hirudo*, the medical leech

marine worms with numerous bristles to each segment, e.g. *Nereis*, the ragworm

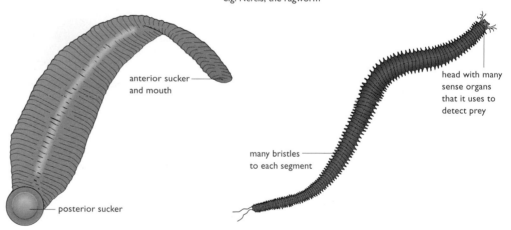

anterior sucker
and mouth

posterior sucker

head with many
sense organs
that it uses to
detect prey

many bristles
to each segment

The **arthropods** are also segmented animals, but they have a hard external skeleton, together with jointed limbs (from which their name comes)(Figure 16.19). They are triploblastic, coelomate animals. However, the coelom body cavity, clearly obvious in annelids, is reduced. Much of their body cavity is a blood-filled **haemocoel**, with blood bathing the body organs. The nervous system is similar to that of annelids. Arthropods are more numerous than any other group of animals, both in numbers of species and in numbers of individuals. The insects are by far the most numerous of these.

The arthropods have a relatively strong exoskeleton or **cuticle** made of chitin, secreted by the outer layer of body cells, and made waterproof. Many arthropods live successfully in dry, terrestrial habitats. The cuticle cannot grow with the animal, so it has to be shed periodically, and replaced by a larger one into which the enlarging animal grows.

Figure 16.19
Introducing the arthropods.

characteristics of the Phylum Arthropoda (the arthropods):
- these are the most numerically successful of all animals (Figure 16.1, page 344); divided into five distinct groups: the **crustaceans**, the **arachnids**, the **centipedes**, the **millipedes** and the **insects**
- the body is segmented, and is covered by a hard external skeleton made of chitin
- the exoskeleton is shed and replaced by a larger one periodically (moulted), in order to allow growth of the body
- there are jointed limbs present, typically one pair per segment, although this pattern has been lost from some arthropods
- the blood circulation is 'open', with blood in a haemocoel cavity surrounding all the organs of the body; a tubular heart pumps blood into the haemocoel

Subphylum Crustacea (the crustaceans):
- a wide range of animals, mostly aquatic, that show great variation in form
- dorsal part of the body covered by a shield called the carapace
- exoskeleton usually hardened by calcium salts
- two pairs of antennae, e.g. *Armadillium* (woodlouse) and *Daphnia* (water flea)

Class Arachnida (the arachnids):
- body divided into cephalothorax (head + thorax = six segments) and abdomen (= 13 segments)
- four pairs of legs attached to the cephalothorax
- no antennae present, e.g. *Araneus*, the garden spider

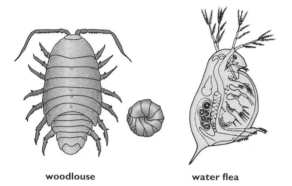

woodlouse   **water flea**

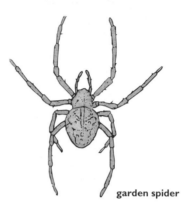

garden spider

Class Chilopoda (the centipedes):
- dorsi-ventrally flattened body of numerous, leg-bearing segments, the legs typically long
- well-developed head and jaws (e.g. poison claws) present
- one pair of antennae present, e.g. *Lithobius* (centipede)

Class Diplopoda (the millipedes):
- cylindrical body of numerous segments, many segments with two pairs of legs
- head with simple eyes but no poison claws
- one pair of antennae present, e.g. *Iulus* (millipede)

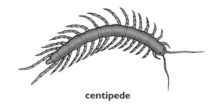

centipede

millipede

Class Insecta (the insects):
- body divided into head (six fused segments), thorax (three segments) and abdomen (11 segments)
- adult insects have only three pairs of legs, one to each segment of the thorax; most have two pairs of wings, also attached to the thorax
- a pair of compound eyes and one pair of antennae are present on the head
- head has mouthparts that are modified paired limbs
- air is piped to the tissues by a system of tubes called tracheae (Figure 10.10, page 215), e.g. *Locusta* (the locust), and *Pieris* (the cabbage white butterfly)

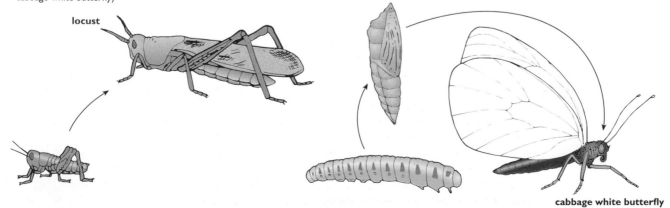

locust

cabbage white butterfly

Figure 16.20
Introducing the
vertebrates.

Characteristics of the Subphylum Vertebrata:
At some stage in their development vertebrates have:
• a tubular, hollow dorsal nerve cord
• a vertebral column (backbone)
• a postanal tail

• gill slits in the throat, known as visceral clefts
• a blood circulation in which blood flows back down the body dorsally, and forwards ventrally

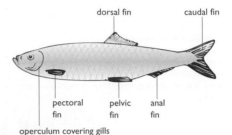

Class Osteichthyes (the bony fish):
• fish with a skeleton of bone
• mouth at a terminal position on the head
• the gills are covered by a body flap, the operculum
• the fins are supported by bony rays, e.g. *Clupea* (herring)

Class Amphibia (the amphibians):
• amphibians have moist skin and use the skin for respiratory gas exchange
• largely terrestrial animals that breed in water, where fertilisation is external. The larval stage (the tadpole) is aquatic
• the tadpole undergoes metamorphosis into a terrestrial adult, e.g. *Rana* (frog)

Class Reptilla (the reptiles):
• terrestrial vertebrates, with dry, impervious skin protected by overlapping scales
• gaseous exchange occurs in lungs
• fertilisation is internal, but the fertilised eggs are laid with a shell
• typically, reptiles have four pentadactyl limbs, but in the snakes the limbs are reduced or absent, e.g. *Lacerta* (lizard)

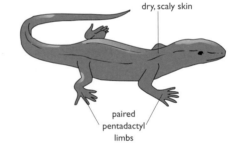

Class Aves (the birds):
• birds have a strong, light skeleton; limb bones are hollow with internal strutting for strength
• the skin of the body is covered by scales
• the forelimbs are modified as wings; massive flight muscles are anchored to the pectoral girdle
• birds are endothermic, with a high and constant body temperature
• fertilisation is internal; eggs are laid with a food store (yolk) and a hard calcareous shell, e.g. *Columba* (pigeon)

Class Mammalia (the mammals)
Subclass Eutheria (the placental mammals):
• the skin of mammals has hair
• mammals have four pentadactyl limbs
• the body cavity is divided by a muscular diaphragm between thorax and abdomen
• mammals are endothermic, with a relatively high and constant body temperature
• fertilisation is internal; the young complete their early development in the uterus; when born they are fed on milk produced in mammary glands, e.g. *Homo sapiens* (human)

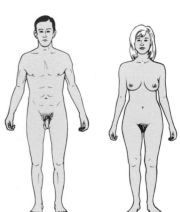

The **chordates** are a phylum that includes the vertebrates, but also some non-vertebrate groups, for instance the tunicates (sea squirts). They are triploblastic, coelomate animals that have a dorsal strengthening structure (called a **notochord**) in their bodies for at least some part of their development. Lying above the notochord is a dorsal, tubular **nerve cord**. In the pharynx region of the body is a series of pharyngeal slits, opening between the pharynx (between mouth and oesophagus) and the outside of the animal. There is also a postanal tail. All these features are present in all chordates, but not necessarily for all stages of their life. In some vertebrates, for example, some of these features are only briefly present, being lost early in embryological development. Here, we are concerned with the vertebrates only.

The **vertebrates** are those members of the Phylum Chordata that have a **vertebral column** in place of the supporting rod, the notochord. The vertebrates include the fish, amphibia, reptiles, birds and mammals. The features of these classes of vertebrates are introduced in Figure 16.20. Much of animal biology in this book concerns the vertebrates, particularly the human animal.

SUMMARY

- ● '**Biodiversity**' refers to the vast numbers of living things that exist. About 1.7 million different species are known, but a much larger number of organisms may exist, undiscovered.
- ● By **species** we refer to a group of individuals of common ancestry that closely resemble each other and are normally capable of interbreeding to form fertile offspring.
- ● The process of **classification** involves naming organisms by the binomial system so that each has a generic and a specific name. Genera are further grouped into a hierarchical classification of families, orders, classes, phyla and kingdoms. A kingdom is the largest and most inclusive category.
- ● The **Prokaryote Kingdom** includes the bacteria and cyanobacteria, all characterised by very small cells without a true nucleus (page 4).
- ● The **Protoctistan Kingdom** contains the single-celled eukaryotic organisms (protozoa and unicellular algae) and the multicellular organisms closely related to them, including the seaweeds.
- ● The **Fungus Kingdom** contains the multicellular eukaryotes with heterotrophic nutrition and a protective wall of chitin to the hyphae that make up the fungus 'body' of mycelium.
- ● The green **Plant Kingdom** contains multicellular eukaryotes that have autotrophic nutrition. Their cells are surrounded by a cellulose cell wall, and they are sedentary, mostly rooted organisms.
- ● The **Animal Kingdom** contains the multicellular eukaryotes that are mostly motile, and show heterotrophic nutrition.

● Examination questions

1 The diagram shows the way in which four species of monkey are classified.

  a This system of classification is described as hierarchical. Explain what is meant by a *hierarchical* classification. (1)

  b i To which genus does the green monkey belong? (1)
    ii To which family does the red colobus belong? (1)

  c What does the information in the diagram suggest about the similarities and differences in the genes of these four species of monkey? (2)

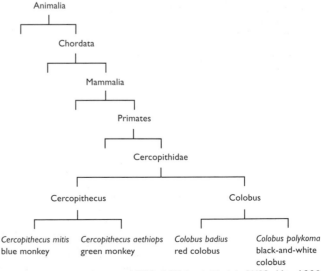

NEAB, AS/A level, Module BY02, Mar 1998

2 Read through the following passage, which refers to different types of skeleton in various animal groups, then write on the dotted lines the most appropriate word or words to complete the account.

A .... skeleton is typical of earthworms. Insects have an .... skeleton, which contains a material called .... The skeletons of mammals, however, are found .... their bodies, and are made of bone, which is strengthened with mineral ions such as ...., and ....(6)

London, A level, Module B3, Jan 1997

3 The diagram below shows an organism of the genus *Rhizopus*.

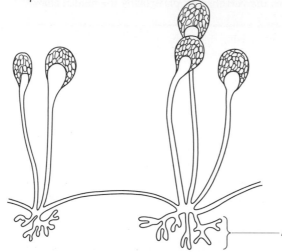

a Name the major taxonomic group to which this organism belongs and give *one* external feature characteristic of this group. (2)
b Describe the role of part **A** in the nutrition of the organism. (2)
c Explain how parasitic nutrition differs from the nutrition of *Rhizopus*. (2)

London, AS/A level, Module B2, June 1998

4 Complete the table below by stating *one* external feature characteristic of the group.

Group	Characteristic external feature
cnidarians	
mosses	
arthropods	
ferns	

(4)

London, AS/A level, Module B2, June 1996

5 The diagram below is a simple dichotomous key which could be used to separate three groups of terrestrial plants: mosses, ferns and angiosperms.

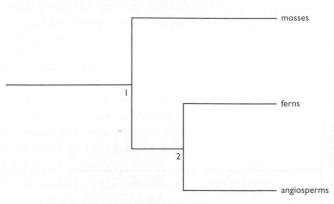

a I State *two* external features shown by both ferns and angiosperms but not by mosses, which could be used to make the separation at I on the diagram. (2)
   ii State *two* external features of angiosperms which could be used to separate them from ferns. (2)
b State *one* feature which distinguishes fungi from mosses, ferns and angiosperms. (1)

London, AS/A level, Module B2, Jan 1997

6 The table below refers to characteristics of different taxonomic groups of animals.

If a feature is present, place a tick (✓) in the appropriate row and if the feature is absent, place a cross (✗) in the appropriate row.

Feature	Chordates	Arthropods	Annelids
postanal tail			
exoskeleton			
compound eyes			
chaetae			
visible external segmentation			

(5)

London, AS/A level, Module B2, Jan 1996

17 Ecology: the interdependence of organisms

STARTING POINTS
- Ecology is the **study of living things in their environment**.
- **Where organisms live** and the **sizes of their populations** are affected by interactions with other organisms and with the non-living parts of their environment.
- **Energy** enters green plants as light, is transferred from organism to organism as chemical energy during feeding, and eventually returns to the environment as heat.
- **Nutrients** that are required by living things are used again and again by being recycled between organisms and their environment.
- From studies of the ecology of organisms it is sometimes possible to assess the **impact of human actions on the environment**. This application of ecology is developed in Chapter 18.

● Introducing ecology

Ecology is the study of living things within their environment. It is an essential part of modern biology. Understanding the relationships between organisms and their environment is just as important as knowing about the structure and physiology of animals and plants, for example.

One of the ideas that ecologists have introduced into biology is that of the '**ecosystem**'. This is defined as a community of organisms and their surroundings, the environment in which they live. An ecosystem is a basic functional unit of ecology since the organisms that make up a community cannot realistically be considered separately from their physical environment. Examples of ecosystems, such as woodland or a lake, illustrate two important features of an ecosystem, namely that it is:

- a largely **self-contained unit**, since most organisms of the ecosystem spend their entire lives there, and their essential nutrients will be endlessly recycled around and through them
- an **interactive system**, in that the kind of organisms that live there is largely decided by the physical environment, and the physical environment is in turn constantly altered by the organisms.

It is a good idea to begin by identifying the ideas that ecologists have introduced and regularly use, to establish exactly what each means. Table 17.1 gives definitions of these ecological terms; you can refer to it as the need arises.

Table 17.1
An introduction to ecological terms.

Biosphere:	only a part of planet Earth, its land, oceans and atmosphere is inhabited. The majority of organisms live in a narrow belt, from the upper soil to the lower atmosphere. Or, if marine, many live near the ocean surface. This restricted zone which living things inhabit is called the biosphere
Ecosystem:	an ecosystem is a stable, settled unit of nature consisting of a community of organisms, interacting with each other and with their surrounding physical and chemical environment. Examples of ecosystems are ponds or lakes, woods or forests, sea shores or salt marshes, grassland, savanna or tundra. Ecosystems are necessarily very variable in size
Population:	a population consists of all the living things of the same species in a habitat at any one time. The members of a population have the chance of interbreeding (assuming the species concerned reproduces sexually). The boundaries of populations are often hard to define, but those of aquatic organisms occurring in a small pond are clearly limited by the boundary of the pond
Community:	a community consists of all the living things in a habitat – the total of all the populations, in fact. So, for example, the community of a well-stocked pond would include the populations of rooted, floating and submerged plants, the populations of bottom-living animals, the populations of fish and non-vertebrates of the open water, and the populations of surface-living organisms – typically a very large number of organisms, in fact

continued

Habitat:	the habitat is the locality in which an organism occurs. It is where the organism is normally found. If the area is extremely small we call it a **microhabitat**. The insects that inhabit the crevices in the bark of a tree are in their own microhabitat. Conditions in a microhabitat are likely to be very different from conditions in the surrounding habitat
Niche:	the niche of an organism is how it feeds and where it lives. For example, the sea birds known as the cormorant and shag feed in the same water and nest on the same cliffs and rocks, so they share the same habitat. However, the cormorant feeds on sea-bed-living fish, such as flatfish, whereas the shag feeds on surface-swimming fish such as herring. Since these birds feed differently they have different niches
Competition:	resources of every sort are mostly in limited supply, and so organisms must compete for them. For example, plants may compete for space, light and mineral ions. Animals may compete for food, shelter and a mate. Whatever resource is in short supply and preventing unlimited growth is known as a **limiting factor**. Competition between individuals of the same species, **intraspecific competition**, occurs when individuals compete for a mate, for example. Competition between individuals of different species, **interspecific competition**, occurs when the red and grey squirrel compete for hazel nuts in autumn, for example
Environment:	environment is a term we use for 'surroundings'. We talk about the environment of cells in an organism, or the environment of organisms in a habitat. It is our term for the external conditions affecting the existence of organisms, too, so 'environment' is a rather general unspecific term, but useful none the less

Energy flow through ecosystems

Producers, consumers and decomposers

Think of an ecosystem such as a broad-leaved woodland in summer time, with its community of plants, animals, fungi and microorganisms, all engaged in their characteristic activities. The essence of survival is activity. To carry out these activities organisms need energy. The immediate source of energy in cells is the molecule adenosine triphosphate (ATP) (page 48). A great deal of the ATP required is produced by **respiration**. The energy that ATP contains has been transferred from sugar and other organic molecules, called the respiratory substrates. These organic molecules are obtained from **nutrition**.

The nutrition of the green plants in the habitat is autotrophic. Plants make their own organic nutrients from an external supply of inorganic nutrients, using energy from sunlight in photosynthesis. In contrast, animals can use only existing organic nutrients, and they must digest the food that they eat so that the organic molecules within it can be released and used. Animal nutrition is therefore dependent upon plant nutrition, either directly or indirectly. Animal nutrition is heterotrophic.

In ecology, organisms are often conveniently classified by their feeding relationships. Green plants are **producers**, animals are **consumers**, and, in the process of feeding, energy is transferred. Some of the consumers, known as **herbivores**, feed directly and exclusively on plants. Herbivores are **primary consumers**.

Animals that feed exclusively on other animals are called **carnivores**. Carnivores feeding on primary consumers are known as **secondary consumers**. Carnivores that feed on secondary consumers are called **tertiary consumers**, and so on.

Eventually all producers and consumers die and decay. Organisms that feed on dead plants and animals, and on the waste matter of animals, are a category of feeders known as **detritivores** or **decomposers**. Feeding by detritivores releases inorganic nutrients from the dead organic matter. These inorganic nutrients are absorbed by green plants, sooner or later, and reused.

Food chains and food webs

The feeding relationship describing which carnivore eats a herbivore that has eaten plants is called a **food chain**. Since the plant material at the start of the food chain may be either living or dead, the food chains are of two types. Herbivores feeding on living plants are said to be browsing or grazing, and the food chain of these herbivores is called a **grazing chain**. Herbivores feeding on dead plant material, degrading and decomposing the organic matter in the process, are part of a **decomposer chain**.

I What is the main difference between the terms 'niche' and 'habitat' in ecology?

In fact, most food chains, both grazing and decomposer chains, interconnect with other chains. This is because most prey have more than one predator. The interconnected food chains form a **food web**. Food chains and a food web for a deciduous woodland are shown in Figure 17.1. Note that food chains tell us about the feeding relationships of organisms in an ecosystem, but they are *qualitative* relationships (we know which organisms are present) rather than *quantitative* (we do not know the numbers of organisms at each level).

Figure 17.1
Woodland food chains and food web.

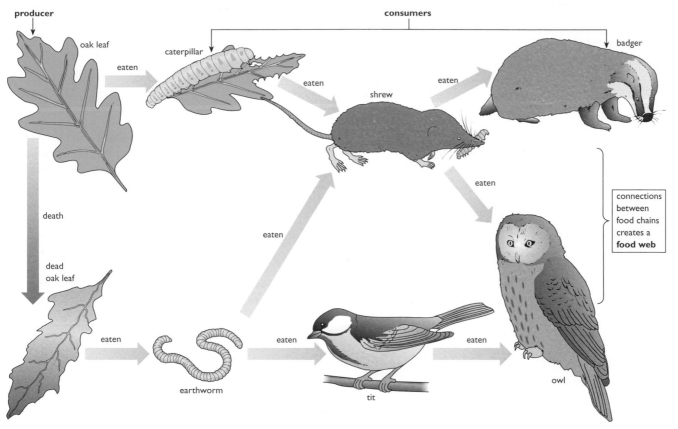

Trophic levels

The level at which an organism feeds in a food chain is called its feeding or **trophic level**. In this way of classifying feeding relationships, the producers are designated as trophic level 1, simply because their energy has been transferred once, from Sun to plant. All the herbivores comprise level 2, because here the energy has been transferred twice, and so on. The trophic levels for the grazing chain of Figure 17.1 are shown in Table 17.2.

Table 17.2
Trophic levels.

Trophic level		
1	oak leaf	primary producer
2	caterpillar	primary consumer
3	shrew	secondary consumer
4	badger	tertiary consumer

So, by definition, between each trophic level there is an energy transfer. As energy is transferred from one organism to another in a food chain, some is lost to the surrounding environment. Only about 10% of what is eaten, in fact, becomes built into the organism's body. Part of the reason for this reduction is that some of the food consumed remains undigested, passing through the consumer unchanged, and is lost in the faeces. There is also some loss of energy in the processes and reactions of feeding, digestion and excretion. In consequence, some of the chemical energy taken in as food is ultimately given off as heat energy from the organism. This point is summarised in Figure 17.2.

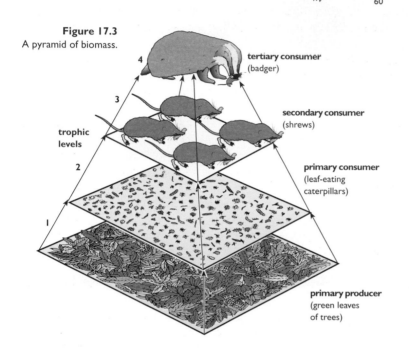

Figure 17.2
Loss of energy between trophic levels.

Imagine 100 units of energy being eaten. Only 10 units get to be tissues; the rest is lost in respiration and as waste products.

respiration
30

tissue
10

eaten
100

gas, faeces
and waste
60

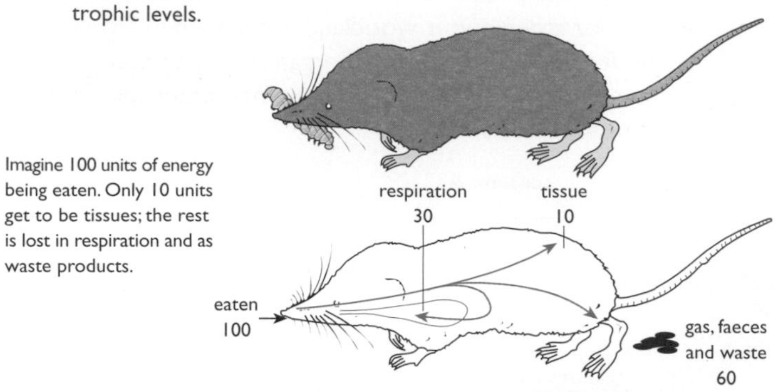

The energy loss at transfer between trophic levels is the reason why most food chains are fairly short. Since typically only about 10% of the energy taken on board by organisms at any one level of a food chain is available to the browser or predator that feeds on it, after a few levels the supply of energy has become too low to be useful. It is very uncommon for food chains to have more than four or five links between the primary producer and top carnivore.

Figure 17.3
A pyramid of biomass.

4   tertiary consumer
                     (badger)

3

                     secondary consumer
                     (shrews)

trophic
levels

2   primary consumer
                     (leaf-eating
                     caterpillars)

1

                     primary producer
                     (green leaves
                     of trees)

Analysis of feeding relationships and the energy changes involved shows us that ecosystems are structured a bit like **pyramids**. At the start of the grazing chain shown in Figure 17.1 is a large biomass of green plant leaves. This supports a smaller biomass of primary consumers, which in turn supports an even smaller biomass of secondary consumers. An ecosystem pyramid diagram showing the structure of an ecosystem in terms of the biomass of organisms at a given time at each trophic level is illustrated in Figure 17.3.

Pyramids of numbers, pyramids of biomass and pyramids of energy

Ecological pyramids are a way of analysing ecosystems. They can be used to express seasonal changes in one ecosystem, or to compare different ecosystems at comparable times, for example. It can be difficult, though, to decide at which trophic level every organism feeds. For example, omnivores feed as both primary consumers (level 2) and secondary (or higher) consumers (level 3).

When first used as a way of analysing ecosystems, ecological pyramids were considered as **pyramids of number**. To produce such an ecological pyramid diagram, all the organisms at each trophic level within a given area were recognised and counted. This information could be relatively easily obtained, without destroying the organisms. At the time it was argued that this 'numbers' approach was correct since:

- ecosystems typically contain a very large number of small animals and a progressively smaller number of larger animals
- predators are larger than their prey because they have to be able to overpower them easily
- prey is never so small that it takes the predator a long time to catch sufficient numbers of them
- small animals reproduce faster than large animals, so maintaining their numbers despite predation.

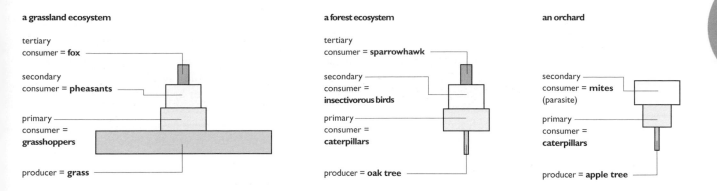

Figure 17.4
Examples of ecological pyramids of numbers.

The results were presented as rectangular blocks, stacked on top of each other, representing the numbers of organisms at each trophic level in a bar diagram (for example, the 'grassland ecosystem' in Figure 17.4).

The problems with this approach was that no allowance was made for the differences in size of individual organisms. A giant oak tree and a single microscopic green alga both counted as one! Consequently, 'pyramids' of numbers sometimes create strange-shaped pyramids of limited meaning.

This problem was overcome by producing **pyramids of biomass**. At the start of the grazing chain shown in Figure 17.1 is a large **biomass** of green plant leaves. This supports a smaller biomass of primary consumers, which in turn supports an even smaller biomass of secondary consumers. An ecosystem pyramid diagram showing the structure of an ecosystem in terms of the biomass of organisms at a given time at each trophic level is illustrated in Figure 17.3. The fieldwork to do this involves estimating the numbers of organisms of each type at each trophic level, and then finding the biomass (dry weight) of a representative sample of each type of organism. The dry mass is found by heating a weighed sample to a temperature that is hot enough to drive off all the water (about 80°C) but not hot enough to burn away any organic matter. Cooled samples were weighed and heated, cooled and reweighed. This process was repeated until two consecutive readings gave the same mass, showing that all the water had been driven off.

A problem with the accuracy of biomass measurements is that different tissues contain different amounts of energy. Consequently, a **pyramid of energy** is sometimes considered to be the most useful form of ecological pyramid. However, to obtain the information needed for this, representative samples of the organisms present in the food chain have to be burnt in a calorimeter (Figure 9.1, page 192) in oxygen. The energy released raises the temperature of the water surrounding the combustion chamber. The mass of water in the calorimeter is known, so the amount of heat energy released from the rise in water temperature can be calculated. Carried out on all organisms at every trophic level, this is a time-consuming and destructive activity. In practice, pyramids of biomass can be converted to pyramids of energy using published values of energy content, made in previous experiments in habitats that are comparable.

2 In a food chain, a large amount of plant material supports a smaller mass of herbivores and an even smaller mass of carnivores. Why is this so?

● **Extension** Productivity

Productivity is the amount of energy built into the organism of a trophic level in the food chain. It is expressed in units of kilojoules per square metre per year ($kJ\ m^{-2}\ yr^{-1}$). For example, the **primary productivity** is the rate at which the green plants convert light energy into chemical energy. However, they also convert some of the organic molecules produced back to carbon dioxide and water and lose the energy as heat to the environment, in the process of growth and development. The remaining energy, known as the **net primary productivity**, is built into the cells and tissues of plants, and is available to herbivores.

net primary productivity = primary productivity − energy used in plant respiration

continued

To estimate the net primary productivity of an ecosystem, representative samples of the plants growing in an ecosystem must be harvested, and the dry mass found (after all water present has been driven off by prolonged, gentle heating). Figures for the primary productivity of various habitats are shown in Figure 17.5, including some agricultural systems.

In natural ecosystems (those experiencing minimal disturbances by humans), productivity is highest in the tropics and in the oceans. The tropics (regions of low latitude/regions close to the equator) get higher temperatures and more light, both of which are favourable environmental factors for plant growth. Temperatures are much lower in the oceans, but here the upwelling currents raise valuable plant nutrients from the depths, which favours plant growth. Productivity is lowest in ecosystems of high latitude (that is, regions close to the poles) and deserts (of ice or sand) where either low temperatures or low rainfall, and a poor supply of nutrients like nitrates and phosphates, slow plant growth.

Figure 17.5
Primary productivity of some natural and agricultural ecosystems.

In agriculture, humans tend to 'import' nutrients (by adding inorganic fertilisers for plant crops, and giving manufactured animal feeds to the stock) and thereby distort the figures for productivity, compared with more natural environments.

dry desert

temperate forests

tropical rain forests

continental shelf waters

ice desert

grassland agriculture

intensive horticulture

deep oceans

productivity: ($\times 10^3$ kJ m^{-2} yr^{-1})

less than 2.0	12.5–42.0	42.0–105.0	42.0–2.0

Nutrient cycling

Living things require energy to drive the activities of life, but they also require nutrients. Nutrients provide the chemical elements that make up the biochemical molecules of cells and organisms. Organisms are made of carbon, hydrogen and oxygen, together with the mineral elements nitrogen, calcium, phosphorus, sulphur and potassium, and several others, in increasingly small amounts. The full list of mineral elements required by organisms is in Table 3.2, page 58.

Plants obtain their essential nutrients as carbon dioxide and water, from which they manufacture sugar. With the addition of mineral elements absorbed as ions from the soil solution, they build up the complex organic molecules they require. Animals obtain nutrients as complex organic molecules of food, which they digest, absorb and assimilate into their own cells and tissues.

3 What is the source and final fate of most energy of ecosystems?

The **movement of nutrients and energy through an ecosystem is quite different**. Energy flows through food chains from sunlight energy to the chemical energy of organic molecules, and finally to heat energy, all of which is ultimately lost to space. Nutrients, on the other hand, are **recycled and reused** continuously. Recycling is essential for the survival of living things, because the available resources of many elements are strictly limited. When organisms die their bodies become broken down and decomposed, mainly by bacteria and fungi, and the nutrients are released. Elements may become part of the soil solution, and some may react with chemicals of soil or rock particles before becoming part of living things again by being reabsorbed by plants. The cycling processes by which essential elements are released and reused are called **biogeochemical cycles**. These cycles are summarised in Figure 17.6.

All the essential elements take part in biogeochemical cycles. Here we give two examples. One is the **carbon cycle**. Both photosynthesis and respiration play important parts in the cycling of carbon, as shown in Figure 18.11, page 396. Carbon becomes part of the atmosphere as carbon dioxide, and it is in this form that it re-enters the food chain.

The other example is the **nitrogen cycle**.

Figure 17.6
Cycling of nutrients and the flow of energy within an ecosystem – a summary.

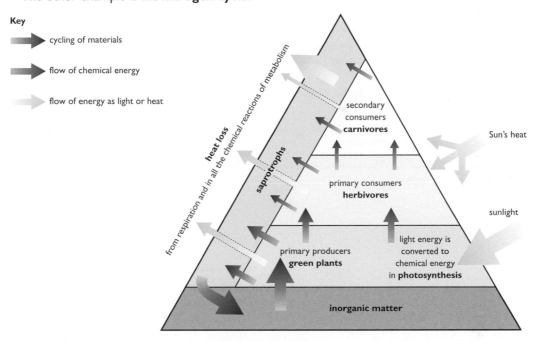

The nitrogen cycle

Nitrogen is a component of proteins and nucleic acids, and hence an essential element for all living things. There is an abundance of nitrogen in the biosphere since it makes up almost 80% of the atmosphere. However, nitrogen molecules in the air are not directly available to plants and animals. This is because the bonds in molecules of nitrogen (N_2, or dinitrogen) are strong and a great deal of energy is needed to break them. Plants and animals cannot do this. Instead plants take up nitrogen from the soil in a 'combined' form, as nitrate and ammonium ions. From these combined forms of nitrogen, plants are able to manufacture the amino acids they require. Animals take in proteins in their diet, digest them to amino acids and absorb them for use in the body.

Biological nitrogen fixation

Whilst eukaryotic organisms cannot make use of nitrogen gas, many prokaryotes (the bacteria and cyanobacteria, page 349) are able to break the bonds in dinitrogen using energy from respiration, by a process called **nitrogen fixation** (Figure 17.7). The nitrogen atoms are then reduced to ammonia by addition of hydrogen from reduced NAD (from respiration – see Figure 9.11, page 200). The ammonia in the form of ammonium ions is combined with organic acid to form amino acids, from which the larger nitrogen-containing compounds of cells are built up.

Figure 17.7
Nitrogen fixation
by prokaryotes.

$$\underbrace{N_2 \xrightarrow[\text{(nitrogenase)}]{\text{enzyme}} NH_3}_{\substack{\text{nitrogen} \\ \text{fixation}}} \xrightarrow{\text{+ organic acids}} \underbrace{\text{amino acids}}_{\substack{\text{amino acid} \\ \text{synthesis}}} \longrightarrow \underbrace{\text{proteins}}_{\substack{\text{protein} \\ \text{synthesis}}} \begin{cases} \longrightarrow \text{enzymes} \\ \longrightarrow \text{cytoplasm +} \\ \quad \text{membrane proteins} \end{cases}$$

energy from ATP   **reducing power** (NADH + H⁺) from respiration

1 Some nitrogen-fixing prokaryotes are free-living, like the cyanobacteria that occur in pond water and damp mud. An example is the filamentous cyanobacterium *Anabaena* (Figure 17.8). Cyanobacteria like *Anabaena* are effectively 'green manure' on the Earth's surface, occurring anywhere it is light and moist enough for them to survive. The cyanobacteria of paddy fields of tropical and subtropical regions (for example, in Asia and India) have been calculated to 'fix' annually a great deal of nitrogen. The combined nitrogen in cyanobacteria is released when they die and decay, and so becomes available to other green plants (such as the rice plants of the paddy fields — see Figure 17.21, page 384) and, through them, to the animal life present as well. Human agriculture has benefited from nitrogen fixation by the cyanobacteria for many hundreds of years, long before plant nutrition was understood.

Figure 17.8
Nitrogen-fixation in
Anabaena species.

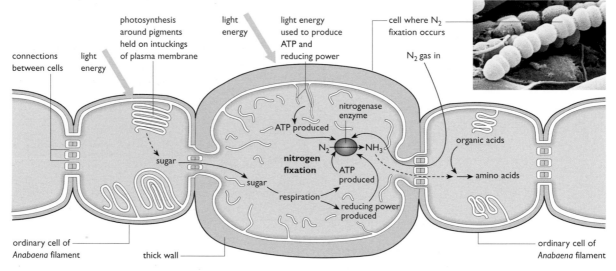

2 The bacterium *Rhizobium* occurs in soil where it feeds saprotrophically, but is also able to enter the cells of the cortex of roots of leguminous plants, such as peas, beans, clover, soya and many others. The bacterium causes the plant root tissue to form a nodule around the 'infected' cells. In the nodule, conditions are favourable for the bacterium, and it responds by synthesising the enzyme nitrogenase and then converting nitrogen gas to ammonia:

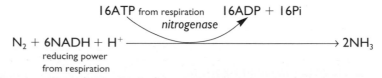

$$N_2 + 6NADH + H^+ \xrightarrow[\substack{\text{reducing power} \\ \text{from respiration}}]{\overset{\substack{16ATP \text{ from respiration} \qquad 16ADP + 16Pi}}{\textit{nitrogenase}}} 2NH_3$$

The energy for this reduction reaction is supplied by respiration in the bacterium, using sugar supplied by the host plant. Ammonia is converted to amino acids, many of which are used by the plant host. Thus the relationship between plant and bacterium is described as **mutualistic**, since the bacterium receives sugar from its host and in return supplies excess amino acids. A plant with these root nodules is able to grow well in conditions where nitrates are absent or in poor supply. The structure of the root nodule is illustrated in Figure 17.9.

Figure 17.9
Rhizobium in the root nodules of leguminous plants.

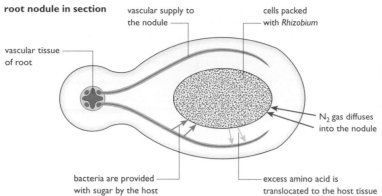

root nodule in section

vascular tissue of root

vascular supply to the nodule

cells packed with *Rhizobium*

N₂ gas diffuses into the nodule

bacteria are provided with sugar by the host

excess amino acid is translocated to the host tissue

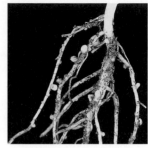

photograph of roots of a leguminous plant with root nodules in which N₂ fixation occurs

Other forms of nitrogen fixation

Atmospheric nitrogen is also fixed during thunderstorms, when the electrical energy of the lightning bolt passes through the air, forming oxides of nitrogen. These chemicals are washed into the soil and may be absorbed by plants.

As a result of human activities quite a lot of nitrogen is fixed, some of it intentionally. For example, in an industrial process known as the **Haber–Bosch process**, dinitrogen is reduced to ammonia under conditions of high temperature and pressure and in the presence of an industrial catalyst. The ammonia is used to produce fertilisers, as well as other industrial reagents. Industrially produced plant fertilisers are extremely effective in enhancing crop productivity, but they are expensive products. Some of the poorest farmers of the world cannot afford to use them at all.

In the internal combustion engines of cars and lorries, nitrogen present in air drawn into the cylinders of the engine is fixed to oxides of nitrogen by the ignition sparks, for example. It is later released back into the atmosphere as a component of exhaust fumes. (See also Figure 17.10, page 374).

Combined nitrogen in the soil

Ammonification

After death, the bodies of living things are broken up by the activities of carrion feeders and detritivores, as part of decomposer food chains. Eventually, the combined nitrogen in proteins, amino acids and nucleic acids is converted to ammonia, as a result of bacterial decomposition. The ammonia reacts with soil chemicals to form ammonium salts. These are soluble and so dissolve in the soil solution around soil particles. The urea present in animal urine is also converted to ammonia in the soil.

Nitrifying bacteria of the soil

In the soil are chemosynthetic bacteria (page 374). These autotrophic organisms use chemical energy from particular reactions they catalyse, in order to synthesise sugar, in much the same way as green plants use the energy from sunlight. The chemical reactions they use involve the combined nitrogen of the soil. These bacteria are called **nitrifying bacteria**. One group of the nitrifying bacteria, known as *Nitrosomonas*, convert ammonium salts to nitrites. Others, known as *Nitrobacter*, convert nitrites to nitrates. It is mostly as nitrate ions that nitrogen is absorbed from the soil solution into plant roots.

Denitrifying bacteria

In the absence of oxygen in soil (anaerobic conditions, such as occur in waterlogged soil where all the air has been driven out) another group of chemosynthetic bacteria may flourish. These bacteria, known as **denitrifying bacteria**, reduce nitrates and ammonium salts to nitrogen gas. They reverse the effects of nitrifying bacteria, and for agriculture and plant growth they are disastrous. Farmers drain land to prevent it from becoming waterlogged. These bacteria also occur in compost heaps, and may be responsible for loss of a considerable amount of combined nitrogen from the food chain. In sewage works denitrifying bacteria can be extremely useful, however (Figure 18.17, page 403).

The nitrogen cycle is summarised in Figure 17.10.

4 What is the difference between the flow of nutrients and of energy in the biosphere?

Figure 17.10
The nitrogen cycle.

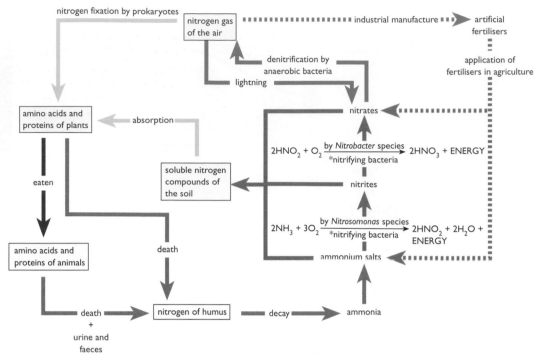

*Nitrifying bacteria are chemosynthetic autotrophs, using energy from exothermic chemical reactions.

Population ecology: how populations grow

One of the ways we can understand what goes on in an ecosystem is to find out how the separate populations that make up the ecosystem grow and maintain themselves. Remember, a population is defined as a group of individuals of the same species that have the potential to breed with each other. In an ecosystem such as a wood or lake, the numbers of some species remain remarkably stable, but other species have periods of rapid growth, and sometimes populations 'crash'. What are the factors in an ecosystem that control population size?

Population growth

Think of the situation when a small number of rabbits are allowed to enter a large, well-stocked meadow area from which other rabbits continue to be excluded. The rabbits initially familiarise themselves with the new territory, and establish burrows. Then, benefiting from the more or less unrestricted access to food supplies, breeding commences. The population of rabbits would increase very rapidly, but eventually, because of the very large numbers of rabbits produced, the vegetation would be used up faster than it grew. Further increases in population would stop. In this situation, the supply of food has become a **limiting factor** in the growth of the rabbit population. If we had maintained a careful count of rabbit numbers throughout this experiment, a graph of number of individuals plotted against time would give us an **S-shaped (sigmoid) curve**.

This growth curve of a population in the wild can be duplicated in the laboratory. A quantity of microbiological growth medium, called a broth, can be inoculated by a few bacteria, under controlled laboratory conditions, and the growth of the bacterial population measured. Bacteria reproduce by a process called **binary fission** (see Figure 19.1, page 411), in which fully grown bacteria each divide into two and these cells then grow to full size. The bacteria feed on the nutrients in the medium (such as glucose, amino acids and growth factors), slowly using them up. Waste products start to accumulate. The typical change in its population with time is shown in Figure 17.11. We see that the population numbers pass through distinct phases, and each phase is identified by a descriptive name. Organisms first adapt to the medium (**lag phase**), then growth proceeds at an exponential rate (**log phase**), then at a more steady rate (**linear growth**), and finally growth slows down and stops (**stationary phase**).

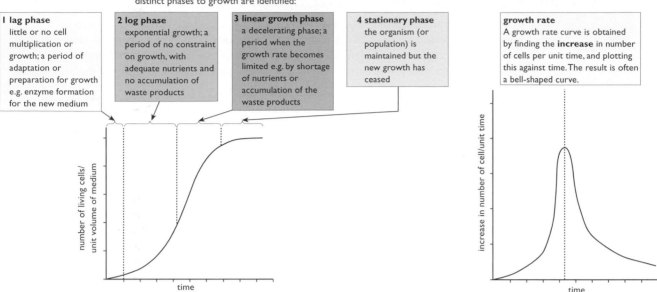

The pattern of growth of a population of microorganisms after being inoculated into a fresh medium sample is shown. The distinct phases to growth are identified:

1 lag phase
little or no cell multiplication or growth; a period of adaptation or preparation for growth e.g. enzyme formation for the new medium

2 log phase
exponential growth; a period of no constraint on growth, with adequate nutrients and no accumulation of waste products

3 linear growth phase
a decelerating phase; a period when the growth rate becomes limited e.g. by shortage of nutrients or accumulation of the waste products

4 stationary phase
the organism (or population) is maintained but the new growth has ceased

growth rate
A growth rate curve is obtained by finding the **increase** in number of cells per unit time, and plotting this against time. The result is often a bell-shaped curve.

Figure 17.11
The sigmoid curve of growth.

Exponential growth cannot be maintained

When a small population has access to ideal conditions there is an exponential period of growth, whether it is a population of mammals or of microorganisms. In **exponential growth** a population doubles in each generation: one individual becomes 2, then 4, 8, 16, 32, 64, 128, 256 and so on. This type of increase in a population is quick, but is not maintained, simply because there are insufficient resources for it. As a population increases it begins to experience **environmental resistance**, since space and resources are reduced and competition for them increases. So, the population tends to stabilise at a level which ecologists call the **carrying capacity** of its habitat. If the population numbers start to increase above the carrying capacity, then shortage of resources reduces the numbers of offspring produced, and the population regulates itself at the level of the carrying capacity. If the population is reduced, say by heavy predation, then the additional resources available lead to an increase in reproductive rate, and the carrying capacity is again reached. In other words, populations tend to be naturally self-regulating.

Why populations fluctuate in the wild

In ecosystems the numbers of each population may naturally fluctuate over time. In fact, population sizes vary for the following reasons.

- The **birth rate** varies.
- The **death rate** varies.
- Mobile members of the population may move away to new habitats; this is referred to as **emigration**.
- New members of the species may arrive from other habitats; this is referred to as **immigration**.
- There may be a sudden, rapid change in one or more of the physical or chemical components of the environment, known as **abiotic factors**. They may either reduce the size of the population or reduce the birth and death rates. Examples include severe drought, or intense cold. The effects of such factors are unrelated to the density of the population. They are therefore known as **density-independent factors**.
- The presence of other members of the population and of members of other populations, may affect the population numbers adversely. For instance, there may be competition for resources, predation and grazing, or parasitism. The effects of these factors, known as **biotic factors**, increase with increasing population numbers. They are therefore known as **density-dependent factors**.

● Extension   Estimating populations in an ecosystem

In the study of an ecosystem it is often important to collect information on the size of populations. A total count of *all* the members of a population is called a **census**. However, this is often impractical because of the size of the ecosystem, the movements of animals, and the numbers of individual plants usually involved. Instead, we can take a **sample** of the population.

Estimating a plant population

Quadrats are commonly used to estimate plant populations. A quadrat is a square frame that is placed over a known area for the purpose of sampling it. The choice of size of quadrat depends upon the size of the individuals of the population. A 10 cm² quadrat, for example, is useful for assessing epiphytic *Pleurococcus* on trees, but 1 m² quadrats are more useful for estimating large herbaceous plants.

Quadrats need to be placed randomly in order to obtain a representative sample. The area is first divided into a grid of numbered sampling squares. Then the quadrats are chosen according to a random number generator. The different species present in the quadrat are identified. Then an estimate is made of the density, frequency, abundance or cover of plant species in a habitat. The steps are outlined in Figure 17.12.

Figure 17.12
Estimating plant
populations using
a quadrat.

Use of the quadrat:
*   positioned at random within habitat being investigated
*   different species present are then identified
*   without destroying the plants present and the microhabitats beneath them, plant species' density, frequency, abundance, **or** cover can be estimated:

density = mean number of individuals of each species per unit area (time-consuming and may be hard to assess separate individuals)

frequency = number of quadrats in which a species occurs, expressed as % (rapid and useful for comparing two habitats)

cover = the % of ground covered by a species (useful where it is not possible to identify separate individuals)

abundance = subjective assessment of species present, using the DAFOR scale:
D = dominant, A = abundant,
F = frequent, O = occasional, R = rare
(same observer must make 'abundance' judgements, which may be useful as *comparisons* of two or more habitats, rather than objective scores)

The optimum size of quadrat: this varies with the habitat, and the size of plants found. Look at the example here. In the 1 m quadrat there are six species present. How many different species are counted in the quadrat of sides 10, 20, 30, 40, 50, 60, 70, 80 and 90 cm? The optimum quadrat size is reached when a further increase in size adds no or very few species as present.

How many quadrats?
When there is no further increase in the number of species found, sufficient quadrats have been analysed in that habitat.

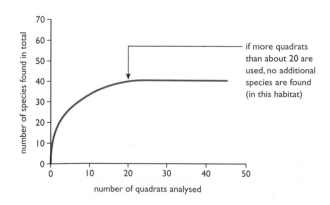

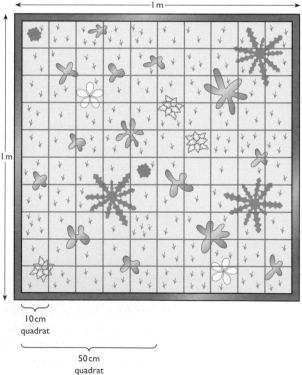

if more quadrats than about 20 are used, no additional species are found (in this habitat)

continued

Capture, mark, release and recapture (MRR, or the Lincoln Index) technique

This is a method for estimating population sizes of mobile animals, such as small mammals or birds, woodlice or insects, that can be captured and marked with a ring, tag or dab of white coloured pigment. It is necessary to be able to trap relatively large samples for significant results. The method assumes the marked individuals are not harmed, and that they distribute themselves randomly in the population upon release. MRR may be demonstrated on populations of woodlice discovered sheltering under stones, flower pots, etc. in an area of a garden or woodland. 'Captured' samples are marked with typing correction fluid or coloured nail varnish. Animals must not be more vulnerable to predation after they are marked. The steps are outlined in Figure 17.13.

Figure 17.13
Estimating animal populations using 'mark, release and recapture'.

an illustration of the principle 'mark, release and recapture' as a technique for estimating population size

Note that relatively large samples must be caught for significant results. For example, what would have been the estimated size of this population if the second sample had caught two woodlice, not one?

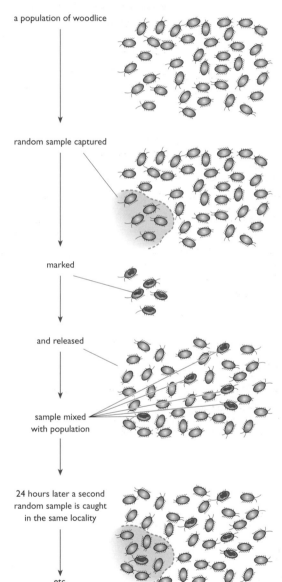

a population of woodlice

random sample captured

marked

and released

sample mixed with population

24 hours later a second random sample is caught in the same locality

etc.

The population is estimated using the formula:

$N = n_1 \times n_2/n_3$

where N = the population being estimated

n_1 = number of captured, marked and released

n_2 = total number captured on the second occasion

n_3 = number of marked individuals recaptured

$N = 5 \times 8/1 = 40$

Ecosystems: abiotic and biotic factors

An ecosystem is a stable unit of nature consisting of a community of organisms interacting both between themselves and with the physical and chemical environment. The living things are known as the **biota**, and their physical environment as the **abiotic environment**. Both aspects of ecosystems are so closely related as to be almost inseparable. To learn about the working of the ecosystem, however, we need to look at both aspects in more detail.

Introducing the abiotic factors

The abiotic factors, the physical and chemical components of an ecosystem, more or less determine the physical conditions in which populations live. The abiotic factors of a terrestrial habitat are of three types, relating to:

- **climate**, including factors such as solar radiation, temperature, rainfall and wind
- **soil**, including factors such as the parent rock, soil water and soil chemistry, and the mineral nutrients available
- **topography**, including factors such as the slope and aspect of the land, and the altitude.

We can illustrate the far-reaching impact of abiotic factors by looking at the effects of solar radiation. Light is the ultimate source of energy for the ecosystem; green plants grow only where there is sufficient light for their autotrophic nutrition. This need of green plants for light has an effect on the structure of plant communities. For example, a woodland is stratified into **layers**: the canopy above, the shrub layer below, field layer (herbaceous plants) and the ground layer (mosses). Each layer has particular plant life adapted to the amount of light (and its variation) and its own fauna. In aquatic habitats, plant life is largely confined to a region close to the surface.

The duration and type of illumination is the environmental trigger for inducing flowering in many plants. It also influences the timing of reproduction, migration and hibernation of animals, as light enables animals to see and be seen, and it also affects the level of brain hormones concerned with reproduction.

Sunlight is the major source of heat. Very few organisms grow if the temperature of their environment falls outside the range 0–40 °C. The effect of temperature on organisms is direct, for temperature influences the rate of all biochemical reactions. At low temperatures ice crystals may form in cells, disrupting the cytoplasm. At the other extreme, high temperatures denature enzymes. However, certain bacteria found in hot springs have evolved tolerance of temperatures above 100 °C.

The length of daily illumination and the intensity of the light is determined by latitude, season, aspect (slope), time of day and the extent of cloud cover. Through its effects on temperature, light intensity also influences humidity.

Interactions of abiotic factors

In fact the interactions of abiotic factors (and biotic factors) of ecosystems are complex, as shown in Figure 17.14. For example, landscape and soil are steadily changed by the actions of climate as well as by living things. This is illustrated in Figure 17.15.

Figure 17.14
Abiotic and biotic factors and their interactions – a summary.

Key
→ effects of factors on the organism
┈▸ effects of factors on one another

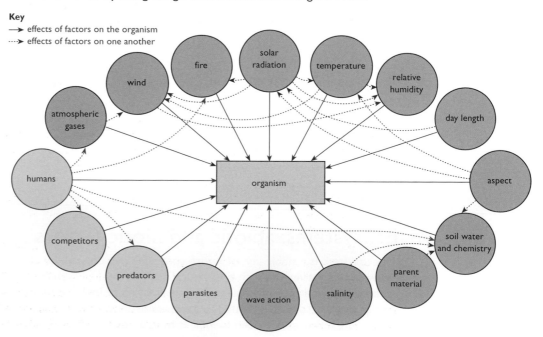

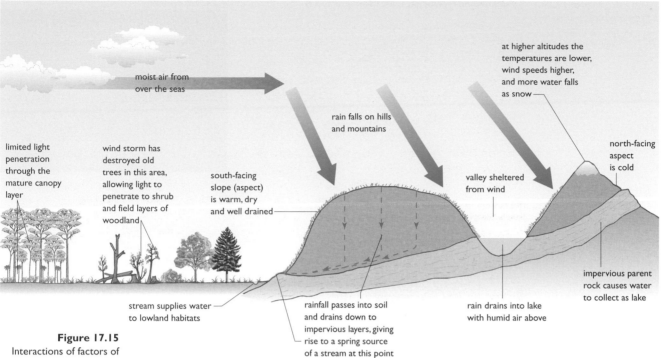

moist air from over the seas

rain falls on hills and mountains

at higher altitudes the temperatures are lower, wind speeds higher, and more water falls as snow

north-facing aspect is cold

limited light penetration through the mature canopy layer

wind storm has destroyed old trees in this area, allowing light to penetrate to shrub and field layers of woodland

south-facing slope (aspect) is warm, dry and well drained

valley sheltered from wind

impervious parent rock causes water to collect as lake

stream supplies water to lowland habitats

rainfall passes into soil and drains down to impervious layers, giving rise to a spring source of a stream at this point

rain drains into lake with humid air above

Figure 17.15
Interactions of factors of climate, soil and topography in terrestrial ecosystems.

Introducing the biotic factors

All the organisms of an ecosystem affect each other. Interactions between organisms, known as the biotic factors, include those between members of the same species (**intraspecific competition**) and between members of different species (**interspecific competition**).

Competition

Resources of every sort are limited and so organisms have to compete for them. Plants compete for space, light and mineral nutrients. Animals compete for food, shelter and a mate. To lose out in competition for resources means the individual grows and reproduces more slowly, and in extreme cases, dies. When the fastest-growing competitor eliminates the slower-growing competitor, it takes over the area completely. This is known as the principle of **competitive exclusion**. Competition between individuals of different species takes the form of predation, grazing or parasitism.

Predation and grazing relations

A **predator** is an organism that feeds on a living species. Predators are normally larger than their prey, and they tend to kill before they eat. The predator's prey is another animal. The eating of plants by herbivorous animals is a very similar process, but is referred to as **grazing** or **browsing**. All food webs show numerous examples of both predation and grazing.

Prey–predator relationships may be studied in a laboratory. Experiments show that both populations naturally oscillate (Figure 17.16). Predators feed on their prey and the population of the prey starts to decline. Meanwhile, the predators breed so their numbers start to increase. Eventually their food source starts to become scarce. The result is some starvation among the predators, so their numbers in turn decline. A decline in the number of predators allows the number of prey to increase again, and so on.

This relationship is not easy to demonstrate in nature, since a particular predator and a single prey population are rarely 'locked in' together in such a tight relationship. However, there is a record of prey and predator pelts, received by the Hudson Bay Trading Company of Canada, from trappers over a 100-year period, which seems to be a clear example. A less clear-cut example may be the decline in small mammals associated with changes in farming and harvesting patterns in recent years, but it is difficult to rule out the effect of other factors.

Figure 17.16
Prey–predator oscillation
in the laboratory (**1**)
and in nature (**2**).

1 *Paramecium* feeding on yeast (*Saccharomyces*)

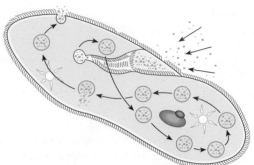

yeast cells (x 300)

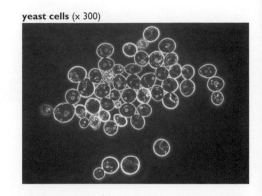

**the results of a laboratory study of *Paramecium* and
Saccharomyces populations over several days**

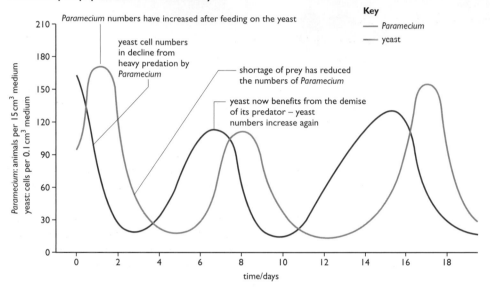

Paramecium numbers have increased after feeding on the yeast

yeast cell numbers
in decline from
heavy predation by
Paramecium

shortage of prey has reduced
the numbers of *Paramecium*

yeast now benefits from the demise
of its predator – yeast
numbers increase again

Key
— *Paramecium*
— yeast

Paramecium: animals per 15 cm³ medium
yeast: cells per 0.1 cm³ medium

time/days

2 Evidence for prey–predator oscillations in nature: the fluctuations in numbers of pelts
that hunters were able to trap, 1845–1945, of snowshoe hare (prey) and lynx (predator)

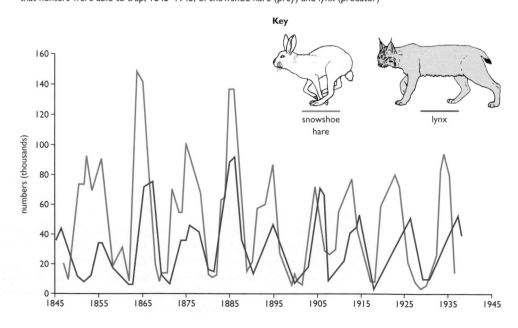

Key

snowshoe
hare

lynx

numbers (thousands)

380

Parasitism

Symbiosis is the name we give to a relationship between two or more organisms living in intimate association. It simply means 'living together'. Parasitism is one form of symbiosis, in which the parasite lives on or in another organism, the **host**, for all or much of its life cycle. The parasite depends on the host for food and the host receives no benefit at all. **Endoparasites** live in the body of their host, like the tapeworm (page 333), and the malarial parasite (page 332). **Ectoparasites** live on the body of their host, like the aphids that tap the phloem sieve tubes of plants (page 248).

A parasite may affect the growth and reproduction of its host. In these cases the parasite is a limiting factor for the host species. In fact, the effects of parasitic associations show a gradation. They range from those that normally kill the host (like the myxoma virus on the rabbit, causing the fatal myxomatosis disease) to associations so bland that the parasite virtually leaves its host unharmed.

● **Extension** ## Mutualism

Mutualism is a form of symbiosis in which the two organisms of different species, living in intimate association, do so to mutual advantage. Mutualism is an example of a favourable interaction between organisms.

An example is the **lichens**. These are structurally simple organisms that are able to colonise the most barren and exposed surfaces of rocks, wood (for example, fence posts) and the like. Lichens are an association between fungi and algae. It seems they succeed by mutual support where either of the two organisms alone would not. The alga produces sugar by photosynthesis, and the fungus is able to retain water and mineral ions whenever these are available. Together, fungus and alga can lie 'dormant' in the most adverse conditions of drought, for example.

Another example of mutualism is the **mycorrhizal association** between the roots of plants, particularly trees, and the hyphae of particular species of soil fungi (Figure 17.17). The fungus benefits from sugar supplied by the plant. In turn, it feeds back to the tree's roots the excess mineral ions, like phosphate, potassium and nitrate, that it has absorbed from the soil immediately these have been released (often at times of the year when the tree's growth is minimal). Since trees are very important as a resource for human activities, the mycorrhizal relationship is of great ecological and economic significance.

Figure 17.17
Mycorrhizal relationship as an example of mutualism.

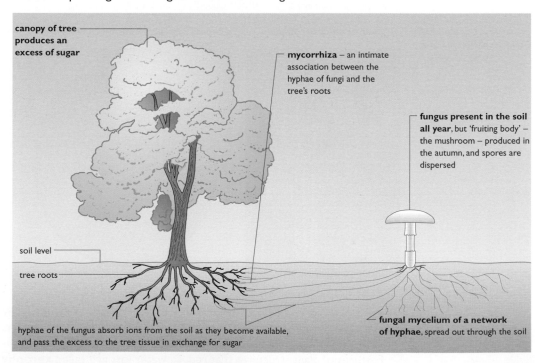

canopy of tree produces an excess of sugar

mycorrhiza – an intimate association between the hyphae of fungi and the tree's roots

fungus present in the soil all year, but 'fruiting body' – the mushroom – produced in the autumn, and spores are dispersed

soil level

tree roots

hyphae of the fungus absorb ions from the soil as they become available, and pass the excess to the tree tissue in exchange for sugar

fungal mycelium of a network of hyphae, spread out through the soil

Succession

When new land is exposed it is invaded and colonised by organisms. In fact, a sequence of communities develops with time by a process known as **ecological succession**. When the succession sequence starts on entirely new land, then the process is known as a **primary succession**.

Primary succession; pioneer plants and soil formation

New land is formed on the Earth's surface at river deltas, at sand dunes and from cooled volcanic larva, for example. At these sites, all that is initially present is the material forming the mineral particles of soil.

The **mineral** component of **soil** is formed partly by erosion of the parent rock mass. Erosion breaks off solid rock into smaller particles. Mechanisms of erosions include the expanding and contracting effects of extremes of temperatures, the action of wind and water, and chemical reactions that occur, such as when slightly acid rain falls. Mineral particles are also blown or washed in from elsewhere. The resulting mineral skeleton comprises particles of a wide range of sizes from small stones and coarse sand to the finest clay particles.

Soil, when it has fully formed, includes organic matter known as **humus** wrapped around these particles of the mineral skeleton. Humus is a substance derived from dead plant and animal remains, together with animal faeces, that have been decomposed by the actions of microorganisms. Humus is a dark-coloured, sticky substance. Its decay process continues for some time, releasing mineral nutrients for plants. It also helps the soil to hold water. Between these mineral particles and humus linings are innumerable pockets of **air**. Also present in soil is a huge flora and fauna (including microorganisms and small animals), adapted to life in this habitat.

Humus is first added to soil by plant invaders in the primary succession, known as **pioneer plants**. The pioneer plants are typically lichens and cushions of moss. They are followed by tiny herbaceous plants, many with features that help them survive where water is scarce. Until the soil is fully formed it retains little water, even when this is freely available. Some specialised plants are able to survive drought. They are called **xerophytes**, and they have special features to reduce water loss. Table 17.3 lists the common **xeromorphic features**, primarily of leaves. Sorghum is a cultivated grass plant showing many **xerophytic features** (Figure 17.18). Another example is marram grass, which colonises sand dunes (see Figure 10.7, page 212).

Figure 17.18 Sorghum and *Ammophila* sp. as xerophytes.

sorghum growing in habitat   photomicrograph – TS leaf of *Ammophila* sp. (marram grass)

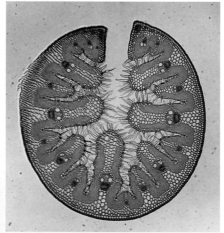

Water loss occurs as vapour, mostly through the stomata of the leaves by transpiration. The structure of the leaf in relation to transpiration and structure of the stomata is shown in Figures 11.21 and 11.22 on page 242.

Features of plant structures that reduce water loss are called **xerophytic features**.

Table 17.3
Xeromorphic features of plants – a summary.

Xeromorphic feature	Effect
thick cuticle to leaf and stem	prevents water loss through the ordinary epidermal cells
layer of hairs on the epidermis	traps moist air over the leaf and reduces the diffusion gradient
leaves in a rosette at ground level	leaves held close together in moist air
reduction in the number of stomata	reduces the outlets through which moist air can diffuse
stomata in pits or grooves	moist air trapped outside the stomata, reducing diffusion
leaves reduced to little more than scales on a photosynthetic stem	reduces area from which transpiration can occur
leaf rolled or folded when short of water and leaf cells flaccid	(see Figure 10.7, page 212)
ability to obtain water when scarce by having: i superficial roots	taps overnight condensation
or ii deep and extensive roots	taps deep water table in soil

5 Distinguish between the following pairs:

- biotic and abiotic factors
- food chain and food web
- primary producers and primary consumers
- density-dependent factors and density-independent factors
- primary succession and secondary succession
- predation and grazing
- consumer and detritivore
- nitrifying bacteria and denitrifying bacteria
- autotrophic nutrition and heterotrophic nutrition
- carnivore and omnivore.

The growth and death of the pioneer plants add humus, and so some soil water is retained. Nutrients are added to the soil when organisms die, and the nutrients available to plants increase steadily. A wider range of plants now grow, and start to shade out the pioneers. The conditions in the soil are increasingly favourable to microorganisms and soil animals, which invade the habitat from the surroundings. Herbaceous plants are followed by shrubs and small trees, all growing from seeds that are carried in by wind, water or the activities of animals. Perhaps in thirty or more years a small wood will have been formed.

So succession can be seen as a **directional change in a community with time**. Initially abiotic factors have the greater influence on the survival and growth of organisms. Later, as the numbers of living organisms build up, biotic factors affect survival too.

The eventual outcome of the succession is perhaps a stable woodland community where once there was bare rock or dry sand. Whatever the nature of the specific community that results, an important feature of a succession is the progressive increase in the number of species present. As more and more species occur in a habitat the food webs are likely to be more diverse and complex. If so, in the event that one population crashes (such as when a disease sweeps through the members of a species) the alternative food chains may be sufficient to supply the higher trophic levels.

The stages in a succession are called **seral stages**, and the whole process is termed a **sere**. When the primary succession starts from dry conditions, then the sere is called a **xerosere**. The stable community that is the outcome of the sere is called a **climax community** (Figure 17.19).

Figure 17.19
A primary succession on dry land – a xerosere.

This succession sequence is not a rigid ecological process, but an example of what may happen. It is influenced by factors like:
a how quickly humus builds up and soil forms
b rainfall or drought, and the natural drainage that occurs
c invasions of the habitat by animals and seeds of plants.

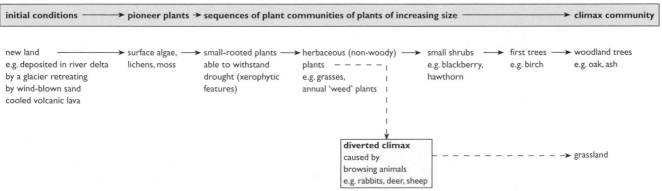

A **xerosere** = succession under dry, exposed conditions where water supply is an abiotic factor limiting growth of plants, at least initially.

Primary successions also develop in aquatic habitats, such as in a pond formed and fed by a spring. Here the sequence of pioneer plants differs from those in a dry land primary succession. However, the result may well still be a woodland climax community. The succession in this case is called a **hydrosere** (Figure 17.20). Certain plants are adapted to aquatic or permanent swamp conditions. They are known as **hydrophytes**. Rice is a cultivated grass plant showing hydrophytic features (Figure 17.21).

Figure 17.20
A primary succession from open water – a hydrosere.

spring-maintained **lake** of water low in nutrients ⟶ **woodland** community, with some wetland (bog or fen)

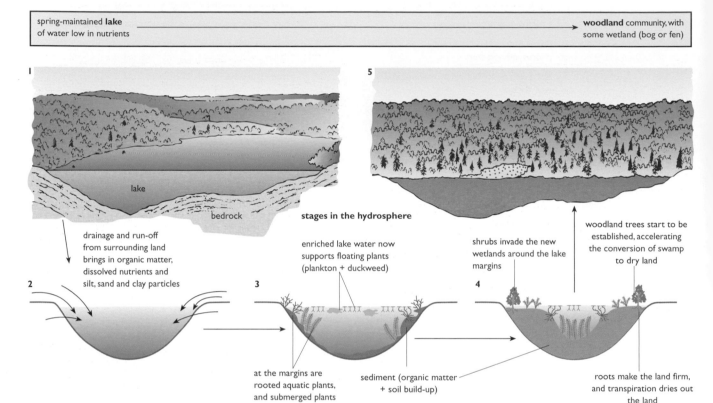

1

lake

bedrock

2

drainage and run-off from surrounding land brings in organic matter, dissolved nutrients and silt, sand and clay particles

stages in the hydrosphere

3

enriched lake water now supports floating plants (plankton + duckweed)

at the margins are rooted aquatic plants, and submerged plants

sediment (organic matter + soil build-up)

4

shrubs invade the new wetlands around the lake margins

roots make the land firm, and transpiration dries out the land

5

woodland trees start to be established, accelerating the conversion of swamp to dry land

Figure 17.21
The rice plant as a hydrophyte.

rice growing in habitat, with growing part submerged

inflorescence, showing rice grains forming

photomicrograph – TS of root tissue (×100)

air spaces are continuous throughout the plant – O_2 diffuses to submerged roots

Secondary succession

Sometimes an established community is suddenly disrupted and destroyed. This occurs, for example, when fire destroys a large area of vegetation. Or it may occur as a result of human activities. In these habitats, soil has already been formed, but the existing biota are largely or totally destroyed. The successions that result start from existing soil. They are known as **secondary successions** (Figure 17.22). Secondary successions normally happen quite quickly, since the necessary soil for plant life is already present. Plants are established as their seeds are blown in. Or they may spread in at the edges from neighbouring unharmed climax communities.

Figure 17.22
An example of secondary succession – a recolonisation of woodland after a fire.

woodland devastated by fire

regrowing woodland, a few years later

● **Extension** Species diversity and succession

Early on in the development of a succession, for example at the pioneer plants stage on new land (Figure 17.19), the number and diversity of species is low. At this stage the populations of organisms present are usually dominated by abiotic factors. For example, if extreme, unfavourable abiotic conditions occur, the numbers of organisms may be severely reduced.

On the other hand, in a stable climax community many different species are usually present, many in quite large numbers. In these conditions, adverse abiotic conditions are less likely to have such a dramatic effect on the numbers of organisms present. In fact, in a well-established community the dominant plants set the way of life for many other inhabitants. They provide the nutrients, determine the habitats that exist, and may influence the environmental conditions. The plants are likely to modify and reduce the effects of extreme abiotic conditions. Thus, the **diversity of species** present in a habitat is a possible indicator of the stability of the community. Species diversity of a plant community may be measured by applying the formula:

$$\text{diversity} = \frac{N(N-1)}{\sum n(n-1)}$$

where N = the total number of plants,
and n = the number of plants per species.

To work out the index of diversity, data is obtained by analysing samples of the plant community, counting all the plants present and the number of different species.

● **Skills tasks**   The growth of a population of the common rough woodlouse *Porcellio scaber* was investigated by MRR (page 377) over a 28-day period with the following results:

Day	0	7	14	21	28
Captured	12	14	16	18	15
Including recaptured woodlice	–	7	6	6	5

1 Calculate the size of the population at day 7, 14, 21 and 28.
2 Plot graphs of: **a** population size against time, and **b** change in population size with time.

SUMMARY
- ● Ecology is the **study of organisms in relation to their environment**. The majority of living things occur in a relatively narrow belt known as the **biosphere**, which extends from the upper soil to the lower atmosphere. In the sea, most organisms occur near the ocean surface.
- ● An **ecosystem**, such as a lake, woodland or salt marsh, is a stable, settled unit of nature consisting of a **community of organisms interacting** with each other and with their surrounding physical and chemical environment.
- ● Living things require **energy** to drive the activities of life, but energy transfer through organisms is one way. In **food chains**, energy is passed from **producers** (photosynthetic green plants) to **primary consumers** (herbivores), to **secondary and tertiary consumers** (carnivores). Each level of the food chain is called a **trophic level**.
- ● **Nutrient cycles**, such as the **carbon cycle** and the **nitrogen cycle**, show how matter circulates around an ecosystem. These cycles have a **biological** component (when the element concerned is part of an organism) and a **geochemical** component (when the element is in the soil, water or atmosphere).
- ● A **population** consists of all the living things of the same species in a habitat that have the chance to interbreed. A population may initially grow exponentially, but is prevented from doing so indefinitely by **environmental resistance**, which takes many different forms. When a population's numbers have become stable it is said to be at the **carrying capacity** of the environment.
- ● The **abiotic environment** with which organisms interact, and which may limit growth, includes climatic factors (solar radiation, temperature, rainfall and wind), soil factors (parent rock, soil water and chemistry, and mineral nutrients) and topography (slope and aspect of land, and altitude).
- ● Interactions between organisms of the ecosystem, known as **biotic factors**, take the form of **competition** for resources, and may involve **predation** (by carnivores) or **grazing** (by herbivores), **parasitism**, or **mutualism**.
- ● The change in species found in a community over time is known as **succession**. **Primary successions** are the colonisation of previously unoccupied spaces such as land where the biota are destroyed by fire, the recolonisation process is called a **secondary succession**.

● Examination questions

1 a The diagram shows part of a food web in a marine ecosystem.

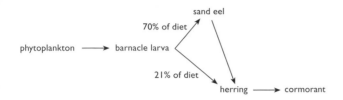

Draw and label a pyramid of numbers for the food chain:

(1)

b Explain, in terms of energy, why food chains with the fewest steps are most efficient. (2)

c If the barnacle population were to decrease as a result of pollution, explain how the herring population may be affected. (2)

AQA(NEAB), A/AS level, Module BY05, Mar 1999

2 The diagram shows a simplified food web.

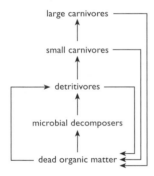

a What is the difference between the ways in which microbial decomposers and detritivores obtain their nutrients? (2)

b Explain **two** ways in which the presence of detritivores may increase the activity of microbial decomposers. (4)

AQA(NEAB), A/AS level, Module BY01, June 1999

3 a Define the following terms:
  i habitat (1)
  ii niche (1)
  iii community (1)
  iv population. (1)

In the United Kingdom, deciduous trees lose their leaves in October – November and new leaf growth takes place in April – May of the following year.

Figure 1 shows a pyramid of biomass for a deciduous woodland in July in the United Kingdom.

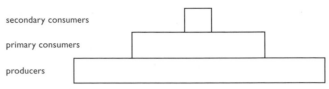

Figure 1

b Explain
  i how the biomass of the second trophic level would be determined; (4)
  ii why the biomass decreases at each trophic level. (2)

Figure 2 represents a pyramid of biomass for the same woodland in January. This pyramid is drawn to the same scale as Figure 1.

Figure 2

c With reference to both figures, explain the changes in biomass of each of the trophic levels, between the woodland in July and in January. (4)

UCLES, AS/A level, 4802, June 1998

4 The diagram below shows part of the nitrogen cycle.

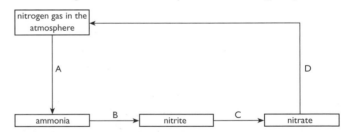

a Name a genus of bacteria which is responsible for each of the reactions A, B, C and D. (4)

b Describe the conditions in which the bacteria responsible for reaction D will thrive. (2)

London, AS/A level, Module B2, Jan 1998

5 The table shows net primary productivities in some types of aquatic community.

Community type	Mean net primary productivity
swamp and marsh	2000
continental shelf	360
lake and stream	250
open ocean	125

continued

a i Explain what is meant by net primary productivity. (1)

ii In what units could net primary productivity be measured? (1)

b Suggest why the mean net primary productivity is much higher for the continental shelf community than in the open ocean. (4)

c The diagram shows a pyramid of biomass for a lake during June.

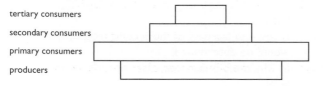

tertiary consumers
secondary consumers
primary consumers
producers

i Explain how it is possible for the biomass of the producers to be smaller than the biomass of primary consumers. (1)

ii Sketch a pyramid of energy for the trophic levels shown in the diagram. (1)

NEAB, AS/A level, Module BY05, Mar 1998

6 The figure shows the changes in the size of a yeast population with time when grown in a flask containing a sterile solution of sucrose.

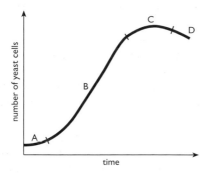

number of yeast cells

time

a Name the phase of growth and explain the shape of the curve at each of periods **A** to **D**. (8)

b Explain what is meant by the term *carrying capacity*. (1)

c With reference to a **named** example, explain how limiting factors determine the final size of a population in nature. (3)

UCLES, A level, 4803, Nov 1996

7 The number of earthworms in a field may be estimated by using frame quadrats. The quadrats are placed at random on the surface of the area being sampled. The ground is then watered with a very dilute solution of formalin. The earthworms which come to the surface are collected and washed.

a i Explain why the quadrats should be placed at random. (1)

ii Throwing a quadrat does not ensure a random distribution. Describe a method by which you could ensure that the quadrats would be placed at random. (2)

b Give **one** advantage of describing the size of the population in terms of biomass rather than as the number of earthworms collected. (1)

c Similar sized populations of earthworms were kept in soils at different temperatures. The earthworms were fed on discs cut from leaves. The table shows the number of leaf discs eaten at each temperature.

Temperature/°C	Number of leaf discs eaten
0	0
5	178
10	204
15	174
20	124

Using information in the table, explain how mean soil temperature and feeding activity might affect the size of the earthworm population. (3)

AQA(NEAB), A/AS level, Module BY05, June 1999

18 Humans and the environment

STARTING POINTS
● The world **human population** is very large. Humans have brought about change in every part of the biosphere.
● Human lifestyles and the industries that support them cause **pollution** of Earth's atmosphere, land, lakes and oceans.
● **Biodiversity** is reduced by the changes our presence and activities bring about in ecosystems.
● **Conservation** measures often clash with the immediate needs of farmers, fishermen, foresters and tourists.

Humans influence the biosphere

In the long history of life on Earth, humans are very recent arrivals. Life originated about 3500 million years ago, but our own species arose only a little over 100 000 years ago. Initially, human activities had little impact on the environment. For one thing, during early human 'prehistory' the population numbers were low. *Homo sapiens* were a rather 'struggling' species, living among many very successful ones. Our earliest ancestors were probably scavengers, only later becoming hunters and gatherers of food. At this stage, survival must have been a very chancy affair.

The first significant increase in the human population occurred with the development of settled agriculture. This change began in the 'fertile crescent' in the Middle East about 10 000 years ago. It is known as the Neolithic ('New Stone Age') Revolution. After then, the human population started to increase in numbers, but only at a very slow rate (Figure 18.1).

The current **human population explosion** began at about the beginning of the Industrial Revolution, some 200 years ago. It is still continuing, and no one is certain when this rate of growth will slow down, as it surely must. When we plot world human population against time we see a steeply rising **J-shaped curve**. This curve can be compared to the first half of the sigmoid curve of growth of microorganisms, shown in Figure 17.11, page 375.

The human population therefore appears to be in a 'log phase' of growth. This is due to high birth rates and lowering of death rates, leading to a rising life expectancy (that is, people are living very much longer) (Figure 18.2). This increased life expectancy is most notable among people of the developed nations but is a trend in many human populations.

Figure 18.1
The changing pattern of the estimated world human population.

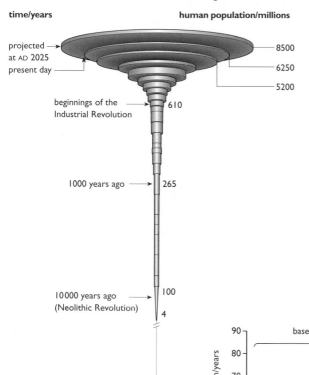

time/years

human population/millions

projected at AD 2025
present day

- 8500
- 6250
- 5200

beginnings of the Industrial Revolution → 610

1000 years ago → 265

10 000 years ago (Neolithic Revolution) → 100

4

Homo sapiens origins (over 100 000 years ago)

Figure 18.2
Expectation of life at birth in England over approximately the past 500 years.

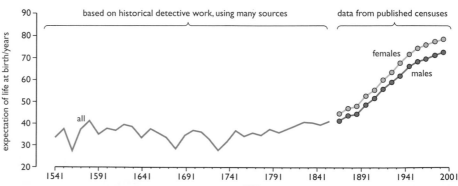

based on historical detective work, using many sources

data from published censuses

females

males

all

expectation of life at birth/years

year

389

Today the impact of humans on the environment is very great indeed. There is virtually no part of the biosphere that has not come under human influence and been changed to some extent. It continues to be changed by us – both the physical and chemical (abiotic) environment and the living organisms in it (the biota). In this chapter we can see some of the ways in which the world's land, sea and atmosphere are being changed by human activities. Then, the issue of conservation of the remaining resources is considered.

Degradation of terrestrial habitats

Deforestation

When our planet is examined by satellite photography from space we see that large, stable vegetation zones occur over most of the Earth's land surface. Biologists call these zones **biomes**. Examples of biomes include the tropical rain forests, temperate grasslands and deciduous and coniferous forests.

The dominant plants in a biome set the way of life of other living things in it. This is because the plants provide the principal source of nutrients and many different habitats. The dominant plants also influence the physical and chemical conditions, playing a key part in setting the environmental conditions of all the other organisms of the biome.

Figure 18.3 is a world map showing the biomes. A point to notice is that 'forests' are a major climax community in many terrestrial ecosystems, in fact more or less everywhere except where the climate is too dry or too cold. Trees of some sort cover about one-third of the land's surface, or at least they once did before the intervention of humans.

Figure 18.3
The biomes of the world.

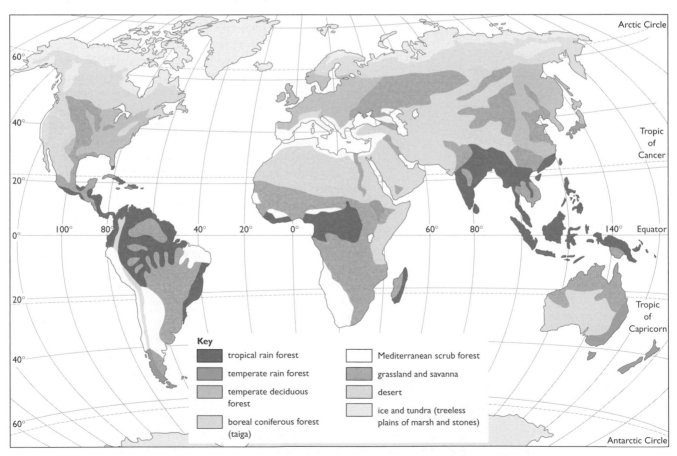

Key

tropical rain forest

temperate rain forest

temperate deciduous forest

boreal coniferous forest (taiga)

Mediterranean scrub forest

grassland and savanna

desert

ice and tundra (treeless plains of marsh and stones)

Trees in the forests are harvested for materials for construction work, firewood and paper manufacture, and are also felled because the land is needed for growing crops. Around the world the felling process mostly occurs faster than replanting, or faster than the forest can regenerate itself naturally.

Destruction of trees is environmentally unfavourable for several reasons:

- Removal of forests destroys the habitats of numerous species of animals, plants, fungi and bacteria, which consequently decline in numbers. In many cases, organisms are in danger of extinction. Extinction reduces genetic diversity (page 406).
- Trees influence the climate favourably. This is because, through evaporation and transpiration from the leaves, water is recycled as vapour, forming clouds and later raining on the land below.
- Tree canopies lessen the impact of intense rain. They slow and scatter it, allowing water to pass more gently to the leaf litter, so that it percolates slowly through to the soil rather than running off it quickly. The tree roots also stabilise the soil so that erosion from heavy rain is prevented. These effects are especially important on the slopes of mountains.
- Until a tree is cut down and burnt or allowed to decay, the wood is a reservoir of carbon that might otherwise be present in the atmosphere as carbon dioxide gas, contributing to an enhanced greenhouse effect (page 395).

1 In what ways do large areas of forest influence climate in a region?

Figure 18.4
Three different views of the destruction of rain forest.

Globally, **deforestation** is a major environmental concern, but it is not a new threat. For example, Britain and much of the rest of Europe was once largely covered by forests of various types. These were long since cut down and the land used for agriculture, housing, transport and industry. In many parts, few forests remain, and many of our remaining trees, found in hedgerows, are also threatened by changes in agricultural practices. Meanwhile, the northern coniferous forests of Canada and Russia, and the tropical rain forests of South America, Africa and Asia are being cut down at an alarming rate. The destruction of the rain forests has become a political issue, with developed and less-developed countries often on opposite sides of the fence (Figure 18.4).

1 Rain forest is sometimes removed in **'slash and burn' agriculture**, in which local people clear the vegetation and burn it to release the nutrients for the growing of a cash crop. But the soil is poor at retaining nutrients, the land is not productive for long, and farming is soon abandoned. However, the rain forest may not fully regrow; species are lost.

2 **Selective logging**, in which about 10% of the (mature) trees are taken, may destroy 50% of the rain forest because of the heavy machinery used. Also woody vines covering trees may bring down young trees as they are pulled out with the felled trees.

3 **Some criticism of logging by developing nations** comes from rather thoughtless voices in countries where the same process has been carried out earlier, and where little or nothing is now done to reduce the output of CO_2 from fossil fuels, which it is hoped the rain forests will counter for them.

Desertification

Deserts are also natural biomes (Figure 18.3). The ice caps around the poles are described as 'ice deserts', but here we are focusing on dry deserts. The annual rainfall of dry desert regions is low enough for the land to be almost permanently dry, and plant life is virtually absent. When wind blows across the land there is nothing to bind the soil together. Fine, light particles of humus, clays and silts are removed in a dust cloud, leaving coarse sand. This process is called **desertification**.

Around the margins of deserts is land of low rainfall that very easily becomes desert in particular environmental conditions. Some desert regions are expanding in this way. Desertification is speeded up by the following:

- **Overgrazing** of land that supports only sparse vegetation leads to the few plants that are there being destroyed.
- **Deforestation** causes rainfall to be allowed to pass quickly over the land, washing away the soil, and extends the time when the land is dry (Figure 18.5).
- **Salination** (is the build-up of salts in soil to a level where the soil solution is too concentrated for normal plants to survive). Salts build up in soils of arid regions if these are frequently irrigated with groundwater, or by water from local rivers. A quantity of salts are dissolved in the water; these remain in the soil when the water evaporates. Salts therefore accumulate each time irrigation is repeated.
- **Climate change** may result in less rainfall in marginal areas around existing deserts (page 397).

Some evidence suggests that dry desert regions are on the increase, but other evidence disputes this. In prolonged periods of drought, marginal lands may appear to lose all their plants, but there may be a bank of viable seeds in the soil that survives unharmed for very long periods. Land of this sort normally fills with dense vegetation following the return of the rains. To be certain that deserts are spreading we have to separate cases of severe and prolonged drought from those of permanent desertification.

Figure 18.5
Deforestation may lead to desertification.

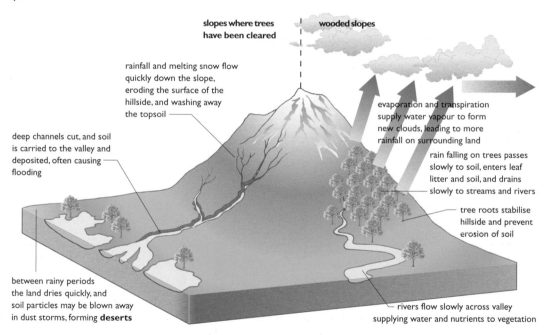

slopes where trees have been cleared

wooded slopes

rainfall and melting snow flow quickly down the slope, eroding the surface of the hillside, and washing away the topsoil

evaporation and transpiration supply water vapour to form new clouds, leading to more rainfall on surrounding land

deep channels cut, and soil is carried to the valley and deposited, often causing flooding

rain falling on trees passes slowly to soil, enters leaf litter and soil, and drains slowly to streams and rivers

tree roots stabilise hillside and prevent erosion of soil

between rainy periods the land dries quickly, and soil particles may be blown away in dust storms, forming **deserts**

rivers flow slowly across valley supplying water and nutrients to vegetation

Pesticides

Wild plants and animals have evolved alongside their predators and parasites, and most live in balance with them. Our cultivated crops and herds have been selected to be especially productive and high yielding. However, they may have limited resistance to certain local parasites and predators, especially when they are intensively cultivated. Whole fields of a single variety of crop plants are called '**monocultures**'. In all forms of intensive cultivation, when disease attacks one plant or animal, many others are likely to be affected.

Pesticides are substances used to control harmful organisms that are a danger to crops or herds. These substances are designed to kill specific types of pest, including plant weeds (by **herbicides**), insects (by **insecticides**), and fungi (by **fungicides**). Pesticides have enormously improved productivity in agriculture, but their use has generated problems in the environment. Herbicides are the most widely used group of pesticides, but insecticides are also widely used and they may cause greater problems for humans.

Herbicides

Competition for space, light and nutrient ions between weed and crop plants (interspecific competition, page 379) decreases yields in agriculture. Therefore, herbicides are used to kill weeds.

Herbicides were developed after the discovery that indoleacetic acid (IAA or auxin, see below), whilst effective as a growth regulator at low concentrations, is highly toxic to plants at higher concentrations. Many substances chemically related to IAA (Figure 18.6) have been found to be effective in killing specific groups of plants (that is, selective weedkillers), such as broad-leaved weeds among corn crops, or grasses among broad-leafed crops. These herbicides are called systemic pesticides since they are absorbed into the leaves and carried to the stem and roots through the plant's vascular system (see Figure 11.19, page 240). Here they may fatally interfere in the biochemistry of metabolism and growth.

The ecological harm done by herbicides is largely due to their efficiency. They are sprayed under pressure on to crops from wide-armed tractor attachments or from low-flying aircraft (Figure 18.6). If the air were always still when applied then little of this herbicide would drift on to hedgerows and neighbouring wild land. In fact, though, the uncultivated land of the countryside around farms has a reduced flora, owing to application in inappropriate weather conditions. Roadside verges were also once important reservoirs of plants. Application of herbicides there has removed many wild flowers and the animal life dependent on them.

Figure 18.6
The application of herbicide by spraying, and analogues of IAA used as herbicides.

Application of herbicide in quite still air, but the spray can be seen to drift and some may be carried outside the crop areas at the sides of the field.

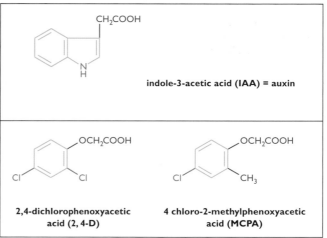

indole-3-acetic acid (IAA) = auxin

2,4-dichlorophenoxyacetic acid (2, 4-D)

4 chloro-2-methylphenoxyacetic acid (MCPA)

These are highly toxic to broad-leaved plants (dicotyledons) growing in lawns and cereal crops, but harmless to the grass family (monocotyledons).

Insecticides

Insects are the most numerous of all animal groups (Figure 16.1, page 344) and flowering plants and insects have evolved together. It is no surprise, therefore, that some plants produce natural insecticides in their tissues as a defence mechanism. The substance pyrethrum, a chemical with strong insecticidal properties, occurs in relatives of the *Chrysanthemum* plant. There are other substances in various species that also protect against insect attack. Humans were not the first organisms to apply biological warfare principles to the insects!

The revolution in the chemical control of insect pests came when a particular substance known as dichlorodiphenyltrichloroethane (**DDT**), was found to be a very effective insecticide. The DDT molecule has chlorine atoms attached to hydrocarbon rings, and was the first of a family of **organochlorine** insecticides. DDT is a nerve poison to insects, causing rapid death even when applied in low concentrations. It was economical to use because the molecule was stable when dispersed in the biosphere, remained lethal for a very long time and was effective against a very wide range of insect pests (that is, a broad spectrum insecticide). In the concentrations needed to kill insects it did not do any direct harm to vertebrates, and so it was liberally used. During the Second World War and subsequently it was especially effective against the mosquito, the vector for malaria (Figure 15.13, page 332). Of course, very many insect predators of pest species were also killed by DDT.

DDT is fat soluble, however, and so it is selectively retained in fatty tissues of animals, rather than circulating in their blood to be excreted by the kidneys. As a result, DDT accumulates at each stage of the food chain, a process known as **bioaccumulation**. In the concentrations that accumulate in non-vertebrates, fish and birds, DDT is extremely toxic, and it becomes further concentrated in the top carnivores (Figure 18.7). Once the harmful effects of DDT were discovered the quality of 'stability' was renamed '**persistence**'. Although DDT is not a nerve poison in birds and mammals, in breeding birds it does inhibit the deposition of calcium in the eggshell. Affected birds lay thin-shelled eggs that easily crack (Figure 18.8). This effect caused a rapid decline in numbers of our birds of prey after DDT had become widely used in agriculture.

Figure 18.7
Bioaccumulation of DDT.

a food chain in which DDT was concentrated

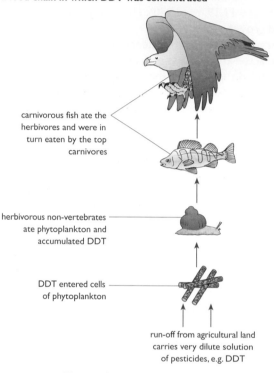

carnivorous fish ate the herbivores and were in turn eaten by the top carnivores

herbivorous non-vertebrates ate phytoplankton and accumulated DDT

DDT entered cells of phytoplankton

run-off from agricultural land carries very dilute solution of pesticides, e.g. DDT

pyramids of biomass of the food chain, showing typical concentrations of DDT in ppm/organism

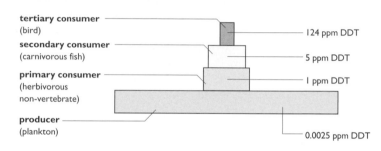

tertiary consumer (bird) — 124 ppm DDT
secondary consumer (carnivorous fish) — 5 ppm DDT
primary consumer (herbivorous non-vertebrate) — 1 ppm DDT
producer (plankton) — 0.0025 ppm DDT

Figure 18.8
Eggshell thickness studies in sparrowhawks.

eggshell thickness study of British sparrowhawks 1870–1970 more than 2000 clutches of eggs were measured; each dot represents the mean shell thickness of a clutch (typically five eggs)

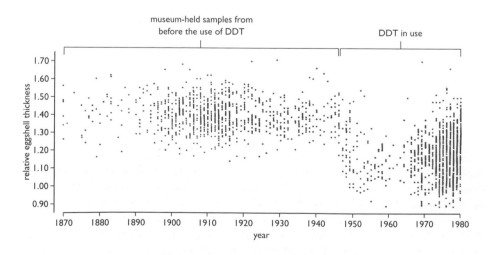

museum-held samples from before the use of DDT

DDT in use

food web of sparrowhawk (DDT widely used in agriculture at this time)

Sparrowhawk flies fast and low, relying on surprise to catch its prey.

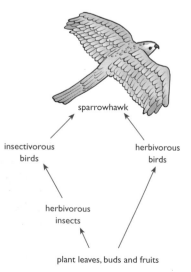

sparrowhawk

insectivorous birds

herbivorous birds

herbivorous insects

plant leaves, buds and fruits

Once the effects of organochlorine pesticides were recognised a ban was imposed, at least in the developed countries. In its place, insecticides that are **biodegradable** (not persistent) in the biosphere and more specific in their actions were sought. Initially, organophosphate insecticides were favoured because they break down in the soil. They work by blocking the synapses of the nervous system; but they are now suspected of being harmful to humans. If tiny quantities of pesticide persist in the food chain, these residues may accumulate in humans.

Subsequently, substances called carbamates and the pyrethroids, which are synthetic derivatives of pyrethrum, have been developed. These are much less toxic to mammals and also biodegradable. However, they are lethal to fish and must not be used near streams, rivers or lakes.

2 How may the application of pesticide at concentrations harmless to most wildlife cause death of organisms higher up in a food chain?

Air pollution
Greenhouse effect

The radiant energy reaching the Earth from the Sun, which includes visible light and infrared radiation (heat), warms up the sea and land. As it is warmed, the Earth radiates infrared radiation back out from its surface towards space. However, much of this heat does not escape from our atmosphere. Some is reflected back to the Earth's surface by clouds and much is absorbed by gases in the atmosphere which are warmed. In this respect, the effect of the atmosphere is like the glass in a greenhouse. This is why this phenomenon of Earth warming has come to be known as the '**greenhouse effect**' (Figure 18.9), and the gases that absorb infrared radiation are referred to as '**greenhouse gases**'. Carbon dioxide and water vapour are naturally occurring greenhouse gases, and so too is methane. The greenhouse effect is very important to life on the Earth, for without it the Earth's surface temperatures would be too cold for life to survive.

Figure 18.9
The greenhouse effect.

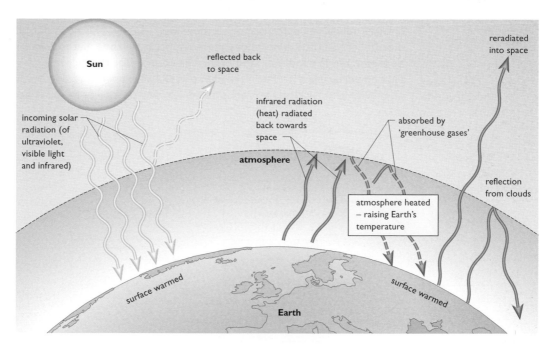

Does an enhanced greenhouse effect lead to global warming?

The composition of the atmosphere has changed over the course of time. The levels of carbon dioxide in the atmosphere in earlier times has been measured in bubbles of gas obtained from cores of ice drilled out of the deep, permanent ice layers in Antarctica. These data tell us how variable carbon dioxide levels have been over the past 160 000 years, but not *why* they have changed so much. We can only assume that when the carbon dioxide levels were raised in earlier periods of Earth's history, this was due to processes like volcanic eruptions and the weathering of chalk and limestone rocks adding additional carbon dioxide to the atmosphere.

Atmospheric carbon dioxide concentration and temperature change over the past 100 years.

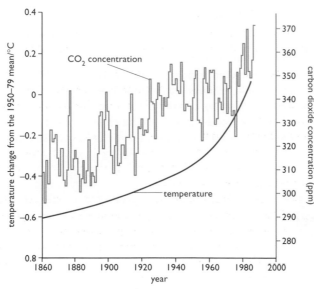

Figure 18.10
Carbon dioxide level and temperature.

In Figure 18.10 we can see how much the level of carbon dioxide has been rising recently. Since the Industrial Revolution, in the developed countries of the world (the past 200 years or so) the levels have been rising steeply. This latter rise is due to the burning of the **fossil fuels** coal and oil. Fossil fuels were mostly laid down in the Carboniferous Period (Figure 21.2, page 460). So we are now adding carbon dioxide to our atmosphere that had been 'locked away' in solid or liquid form for about 350 million years.

However, the situation is more complex than this. Not all the carbon dioxide released into the air stays in the atmosphere, as the carbon cycle shows (Figure 18.11). This is because carbon dioxide is soluble in water. Here, hydrogencarbonate ions are fixed in photosynthesis by phytoplankton. This is clearly illustrated by the appearance of algal blooms (see Figure 18.14) that occur in spring as waters warm up and after nutrients have been brought up from the depths by winter storms. Later, almost all the organic matter sinks to the bottom and is deposited there.

An increase in carbon dioxide concentration in the air around green plants also increases the rate of photosynthesis of land plants (Figure 8.10, page 176). Carbon dioxide is removed from the air during daylight hours by the leaves of the tree canopies of the world's forests.

Estimates and measurements of changing temperature levels show that mean temperature changes appear to match carbon dioxide levels closely. This does not prove that rising carbon dioxide levels in the atmosphere cause temperature rises, but it does suggest that the two may be associated in some way. We cannot be certain that the increasing level of atmospheric carbon dioxide will cause a further marked rise in global temperature. However, '**global warming**' is a possibility, and currently it is considered a strong possibility by many people.

Figure 18.11
The carbon cycle.

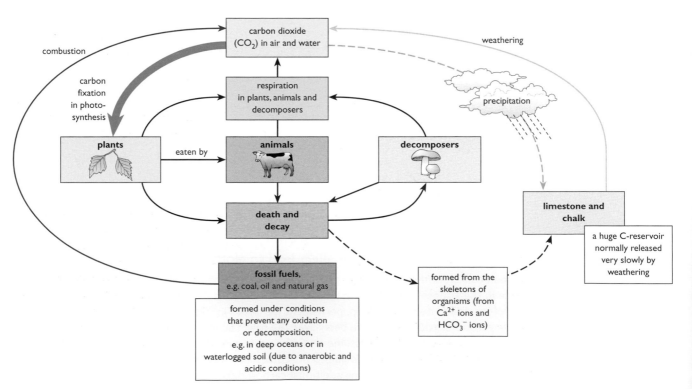

What effect might global warming have?

Nobody knows what the effects will be for certain. Numerous predictions have been made, some to support the international calls for action. The most likely effects include the following:

- **The polar ice caps will melt** as the mean temperature rises. This would cause the sea level to rise all over the world, and lowland areas on all continents would be subject to increased flooding. In these areas, as diverse as Bangladesh in Asia and the Netherlands in Europe, large numbers of the human population currently live.
- There will be **greater evaporation of water** at the higher mean temperatures, increasing the quantity of water vapour in the atmosphere. Water vapour is a greenhouse gas, so the greenhouse effect might be further enhanced. This might increase the precipitation of snow at the poles, thereby increasing the polar ice caps again.
- There will be **enhanced plant growth** anywhere that plants grow with access to adequate water and mineral nutrients. This would include the algae members of the phytoplankton, growing where currents of water are welling up, bringing up mineral nutrients from the ocean beds. Also many terrestrial plants including trees, might show enhanced growth rates.
- There will be **changes in local weather patterns**, warming some regions of the globe, but cooling others. Similarly, rainfall may increase in some regions but decrease in others. If these sorts of change occur, they would certainly change the distribution of species over the Earth, and might cause extinctions in some regions.

Ozone layer

Ozone is a form of oxygen that contains three atoms of oxygen combined together. It occurs naturally in the Earth's atmosphere, forming an ozone layer in the region of the atmosphere called the stratosphere. This layer is at a height of 15–40 km above the Earth's surface, so it is described as **high-level ozone**. Ozone (O_3) is formed in the upper atmosphere by the action of ultraviolet (UV) radiation on molecular oxygen (O_2), which is split into two highly reactive atoms of oxygen. Each oxygen atom then reacts with a molecule of oxygen to form ozone:

$$O_2 \xrightarrow{+\ UV\ light} O + O$$
$$O + O_2 \xrightarrow{\hspace{2cm}} O_3$$
$$+\ UV\ light$$

At the top of the stratosphere there is much incoming UV radiation but little oxygen; closer to the Earth's surface there is much oxygen but little UV radiation. Consequently, the highest concentration of ozone is at a midpoint of the stratosphere.

Ozone of the stratosphere is maintained by the action of UV light on ozone, and this ceaseless cycle of changes leaves the composition of the atmosphere unchanged, and most of the incoming UV light absorbed. The energy of UV light creates ozone from the molecules of oxygen, and much of the incoming UV radiation is used in the process, fortunately. The stratosphere is slightly warmed by the reactions, but the heat is lost to space:

$$O_3 \underset{}{\overset{+\ UV\ light}{\rightleftharpoons}} O + O_2$$

Any UV radiation that reaches the Earth's surface is very harmful to living things because it is absorbed by the organic bases (adenine, guanine, thymine, cytosine and uracil) of nucleic acids (DNA and RNA) and causes them to be modified (by mutation, see page 466). Consequently, the maintenance of the high-level ozone layer is important to the survival of life. The most serious outcome of UV exposure in humans is skin cancer. This may arise after many years of high UV exposure. If the melanin-producing cells of the skin mutate, causing changes to pre-existing moles or forming new, dark, irregular, spreading patches, malignant melanoma is the result. Affected melanocytes may spread widely in the body. If so, the melanoma may be incurable and fatal.

Other likely dangers of UV exposure are damage to the skin's immune system, and damage to the eye, causing cataracts in the lenses.

Atmospheric pollution destroys high level ozone

Certain gaseous pollutants are threatening the ozone layer. These pollutants include substances such as **chlorofluorocarbons** (CFCs). CFCs are unreactive molecules that have been manufactured by the chemical industry for use as propellants in aerosol cans and as the coolant in refrigerators. When these gases escape into the atmosphere they are slowly carried up to the stratosphere. This process may take as long as five years.

Once in the stratosphere, CFCs are broken down by UV light. Highly reactive single chlorine radicals (Cl·) are released, and these break down ozone molecules in the following cyclic reaction:

$$O_3 + Cl· \longrightarrow ClO + O_2$$
$$ClO + O \longrightarrow Cl· + O_2$$

The outcome is that, in the presence of CFCs, ozone molecules are broken down faster than they can be reformed by the natural reaction between molecular oxygen and UV light.

Large quantities of CFCs were released into the atmosphere before this danger was realised. Because of the time taken for CFCs to reach the upper atmosphere, ozone depletion will continue for many years yet, despite the current steps to replace CFCs by safer chemicals.

The thinning of the ozone layer is greater over some countries than others. However, for all organisms exposed to sunlight on land, the thinning ozone layer (called an '**ozone hole**') is a potential problem. Protective clothing and UV-blocking creams are necessary to avoid the danger of skin cancer, the risk of which is increasing for people in Chile, South Africa, New Zealand and Australia, for example.

Other gaseous pollutants

'Acid rain'

When fossil fuels are burnt the elements contained in the fuel are oxidised. This occurs in coal-, oil- and gas-fired power stations, in domestic and industrial boilers, and in the internal combustion engines of trains, buses, cars and lorries. Large quantities of carbon dioxide are formed (see 'global warming', page 395), as well as smaller quantities of sulphur dioxide (SO_2) and oxides of nitrogen (NO_2 and NO). These acidic pollutants may be deposited immediately out of the air as 'dry deposition'. Or they may dissolve in moisture in the atmosphere, and then fall as '**acid rain**' (Figure 18.12). Sulphur dioxide dissolves in water to form sulphurous acid. It is also oxidised to sulphur trioxide. Many common atmospheric pollutants of air are catalysts of this oxidation. Sulphur trioxide dissolves in water to form sulphuric acid.

Clean rain water has a pH of 5.6 (this is due to carbon dioxide dissolved as carbonic acid). However, rain polluted with these oxides of sulphur and nitrogen may have a pH as low as 4.0–4.5. There are other sources of sulphur dioxide gas in the atmosphere, apart from fossil fuels. These include rotting vegetation, and emissions from volcanoes. Certain types of marine plankton, including those of the spring 'bloom' in the seas of the northern hemisphere (see Figure 18.14), discharge an organic form of sulphur called dimethyl sulphide into the air.

4 How does the exhaust gas of cars contribute to the formation of low level ozone?

The harm that 'acid rain' causes is mainly to soil, lake and river waters, and to animals and plants within these habitats. In acidified soil the more valuable ions (potassium, calcium, magnesium and trace elements) are leached away, and insoluble aluminium ions are brought into solution at poisonous concentrations. Aluminium ions accumulate in lake and river water and reach concentrations that kill fish. The growth of the crowns of tree canopies may also be harmed by acid rain.

Much is now done to remove sulphur dioxide from the flue gases of power stations. Low sulphur content fuels are favoured, and the gas is 'scrubbed' from the flue gases. The exhaust gases of many cars are passed through a catalytic converter to turn oxides of nitrogen into nitrogen gas. Diesel fuel that is low in sulphur content is now produced.

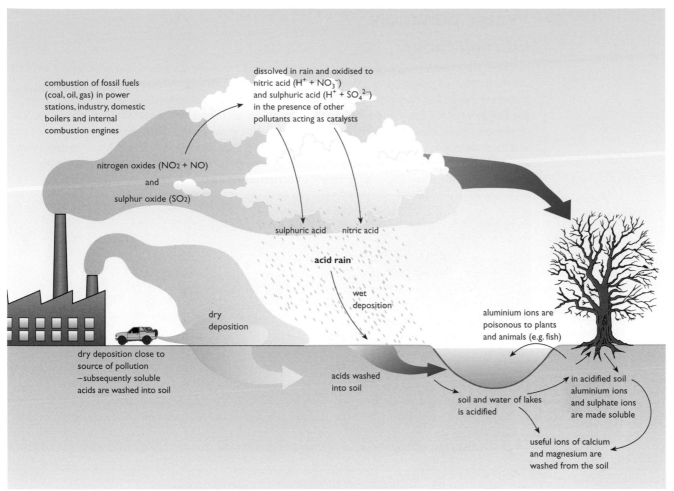

combustion of fossil fuels (coal, oil, gas) in power stations, industry, domestic boilers and internal combustion engines

dissolved in rain and oxidised to nitric acid ($H^+ + NO_3^-$) and sulphuric acid ($H^+ + SO_4^{2-}$) in the presence of other pollutants acting as catalysts

nitrogen oxides ($NO_2 + NO$) and sulphur oxide (SO_2)

sulphuric acid   nitric acid

acid rain

wet deposition

dry deposition

dry deposition close to source of pollution – subsequently soluble acids are washed into soil

acids washed into soil

aluminium ions are poisonous to plants and animals (e.g. fish)

soil and water of lakes is acidified

in acidified soil aluminium ions and sulphate ions are made soluble

useful ions of calcium and magnesium are washed from the soil

Figure 18.12
Acid rain.

Low-level ozone

Ozone, a valuable component of the upper atmosphere, is also formed in the lower atmosphere by reactions between components of car exhaust fumes. These are mainly oxides of nitrogen and hydrocarbon vapours, which are emitted as unburnt fuel. The reactions take place in sunlight, so ozone concentrations are higher in the day and lower at night. **Low-level ozone** is harmful to plants, sometimes causing death of the leaves, and also to the respiratory system of animals.

In conditions of very bright sunlight, the cocktail of chemicals released from traffic, industry and houses forms a deadly mixture known as **photochemical smog** (Figure 18.13). In some cities the surrounding hills may help trap the smog. Along with the ozone, oxides of nitrogen and sulphur and hydrocarbon fuel vapours are trapped by dust particles, so the smog appears as a foul-smelling yellow cloud. Also present in the smog are the extremely fine dust particles that are emitted by incorrectly adjusted diesel engines. The finest of these particles, known as PM10s, are too tiny to be trapped in the mucus lining the tubes of the lungs, and they damage the cells of the alveoli.

Figure 18.13
Photochemical smog over a Californian city, formed in bright sunshine.

solar radiation is the energy source that drives the chemical reactions that form photochemical smog and ozone, e.g. from hydrocarbon vapour (unburnt fuel) and oxides of nitrogen

cold air trapped below warm air

exhaust gases from cars trapped with dust particles

Water pollution

Eutrophication

In water enriched with inorganic ions, plant growth is normally luxuriant. Ion enrichment may be due to accidental pollution by raw sewage, or stockyard effluent. Alternatively, an excessive or incorrect use of fertilisers on farm crops results in excess soluble fertiliser being leached from the soil by rain. Of the many ions beneficial to plants, an increased concentration of ammonium, nitrate and phosphate ions particularly increases plant growth. In spring, water temperatures rise and then the algae of seas, lakes and rivers undergo a population explosion. This is known as an **algal bloom** (Figure 18.14). The enrichment of waters with inorganic nutrients, causing an excess of aquatic plant life, is an example of **eutrophication**.

Figure 18.14
Extensive seasonal algal blooms of the oceans observed in satellite images.

This 'false colour' photograph of the Earth's surface, taken from a satellite, shows where **algal blooms** (orange) are most common, and where algal growth is least (purple areas).

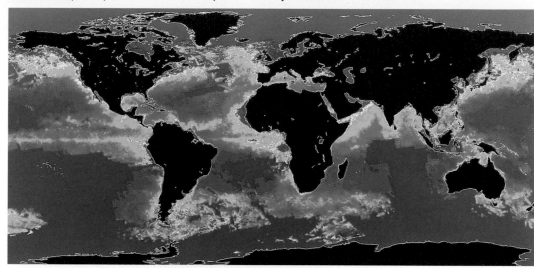

Figure 18.15 (below)
The effect of pollution of a river with untreated sewage.

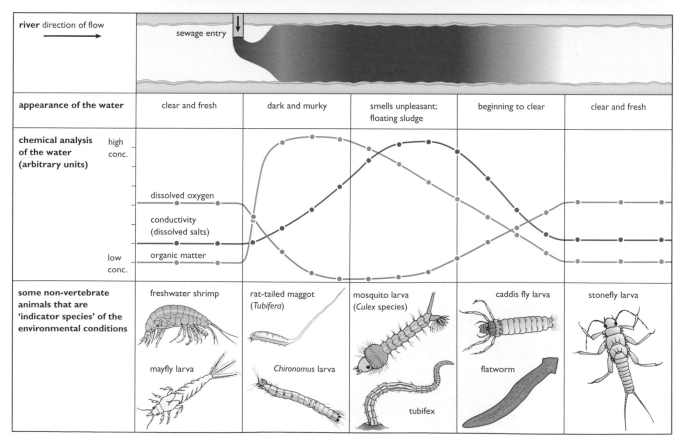

river direction of flow →	sewage entry ↓				
appearance of the water	clear and fresh	dark and murky	smells unpleasant; floating sludge	beginning to clear	clear and fresh
chemical analysis of the water (arbitrary units) high conc. — low conc. — dissolved oxygen — conductivity (dissolved salts) — organic matter					
some non-vertebrate animals that are 'indicator species' of the environmental conditions	freshwater shrimp · mayfly larva	rat-tailed maggot (*Tubifera*) · *Chironomus* larva	mosquito larva (*Culex* species) · tubifex	caddis fly larva · flatworm	stonefly larva

Later, after the algal bloom of rivers and lakes has died back, the organic remains of the plants are decayed by saprotrophic aerobic bacteria. As a result the water becomes deoxygenated, causing anaerobic decay and formation of hydrogen sulphide. The few organisms that can survive in these conditions prosper. However, many aquatic organisms die, including fish, because they need oxygen and cannot tolerate hydrogen sulphide. The sequence of events when a river is polluted with raw sewage is very similar, and is summarised in Figure 18.15.

Note that, in the absence of pollution, eutrophication still occurs as a natural process, but only very slowly. In rivers and lowland ponds and lakes the amount of dissolved nutrients steadily increases (Figure 18.16). In contrast, the water of mountain lakes or tarns, and the streams that feed them, are typically low in dissolved nutrients. Here the surrounding land is often stony, with poor soil. The result is that few dissolved ions are present and aquatic plants show little growth. This condition is known as **oligotrophic**.

Figure 18.16
An oligotrophic and eutrophic environment compared.

mountain lake (oligotrophic environment):

surrounding land is stony and with very little plant life

water that runs into lake is low in ions

no floating or rooted aquatic plant life visible

water is clear, and the stony lake bed can be seen

ions accumulate very slowly in this water and, so far, are insufficient to support plant life

lowland pond (eutrophic environment):

surrounding land has rich vegetation and soil contains soluble ions and humus

organic matter (e.g. dead leaves) falls into water and decays

water contains a rich flora of floating and rooted aquatic plants

human activities may contribute to build-up of nutrients (e.g. as slurry from farmyard animals, sewage overspill, and frequent use of fertilisers on surrounding land) – but nutrients build up naturally too – just more slowly

ions have accumulated in the pond water and support a luxuriant flora

Biological oxygen demand

The rate at which oxygen is used up by a sample of water is called its **biological oxygen demand** (**BOD**). This is a useful indicator of pollution. The higher the BOD the greater is the amount of organic matter present. The number of aerobic saprotrophic bacteria in the water, feeding on the organic matter, also increases. BOD is measured by finding the rate at which oxygen is taken up by a sample of water held in the dark at 20 °C over a period of 5 days.

Testing for microbiological pollution

Water that is contaminated by sewage may contain human pathogens. Several serious diseases are caused by intestinal bacteria (for example, cholera and typhoid) or viruses (for example, poliomyelitis). However, the tests for contamination of drinking water by human sewage look not for pathogens in water (these are likely to be very uncommon if present, and therefore hard to detect), but rather for the presence of extremely common, harmless bacteria of the human gut, such as *Escherichia coli*, a commensal organism (page 162). This is because faeces contain large numbers of these harmless organisms. It is easier to establish water contamination by the presence of this bacterium.

Industrial pollutants

Some industrial processes deliberately produce substances not found in nature that are potentially harmful. The organochlorine and organophosphate insecticides are examples. Other industrial pollutants are naturally occurring substances released in damaging concentrations. Among these are substances such as heavy metal ions, which persist indefinitely. Other pollutants, whilst extremely harmful, are quite rapidly biodegraded. Crude oil is an example.

Heavy metal ions

Several heavy metal ions, such as copper and zinc, are necessary for cell function when present at very low concentrations but highly toxic at high concentrations. Others, including lead, cadmium and mercury ions, are toxic at almost any concentration as they inactivate enzymes. Mercury and lead are widely used in industry, and therefore frequently occur in the environment. Mercury is converted by bacteria in water into an organic form, methyl mercury, which is far more toxic than the metal ion. Methyl mercury is taken up by fish, and moves through the food chain. It causes acute nervous disorders in humans.

The mental performance of children has been shown to be impaired by lead present in their bloodstream. Lead is a substance that was once added to some petrols in significant amounts, and was consequently emitted in the exhaust in the form of minute particles. Lead was also previously very extensively used in plumbing and in paints. Lead in petrol is now being phased out, domestic plumbing is now copper based, and lead is excluded from paints.

● **Extension**   ## Water pollution and the steps to the supply of clean water

The bulk of rain falling on the land has evaporated from the oceans. Rain mostly drains through the ground to rivers and returns to the sea immediately, or it is taken up by plants and evaporates into the air to form clouds, and finally again falls as rain. This rapid cycle (the water cycle, which typically takes only 14 days for a complete cycle) is driven by solar energy.

Water for human uses either comes from surface sources (rivers, lakes and reservoirs) or is obtained from deep ground sources (water that has passed down through soil and permeable rock to collect above an impermeable layer). Water obtained from rivers includes water from sewage treatment plants upstream, as well as water that has drained from agricultural land.

Clean water is a precious resource. Before it is drunk, all water requires treatment to remove suspended solids and bacteria. Treatment is by filtration, and by the addition of chlorine to kill microorganisms. Chemically pure water is unknown in nature; water naturally contains small quantities of dissolved atmospheric gases, including carbon dioxide (water is a dilute solution of carbonic acid). It also contains some inorganic ions dissolved in it when passing through soil. Nitrate ions are thought to be harmful to humans if large quantities are present in drinking water; regulations stipulate no more than 50 ppm of nitrate ions should be present.

continued

Figure 18.17
Sewage treatment, and the reduction of nitrate in drinking water.

So the task for an efficient sewage works is to remove the organic matter, destroy pathogenic bacteria, and reduce nitrate levels if they are higher than regulations permit. The steps to water purification are summarised in Figure 18.17.

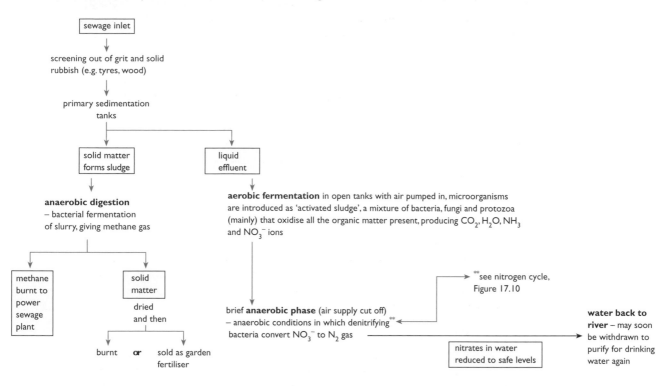

a sewage treatment works viewed from the air

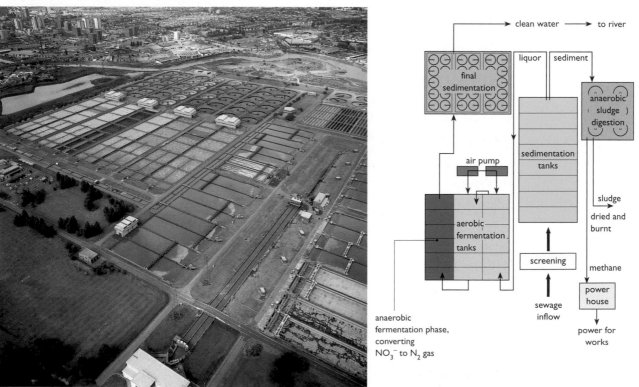

Crude oil

Crude oil escapes from damaged tankers and pipelines, seeps from marine and coastal installations, and is flushed from tankers when ballast water is pumped out (Figure 18.18). The oil floats on water as a slick, and does harm to wildlife, including marine birds, by matting their plumage. Flight and feeding dives become impossible. Crude oil also destroys seaweeds, molluscs and crustaceans, when an oil slick is driven on to rocky shores. After initial losses, however, oil spills are rapidly dispersed by bacterial decomposition, because crude oil is quite quickly biodegradable. The use of chemical dispersants, although removing the crude oil scum from sight, has been found to do further harm to the whole marine food chain. Many dispersants are toxic and non-biodegradable.

Figure 18.18
The 'Sea Empress',
15 January 1996.

The 'Sea Empress', loaded with 130 000 tonnes of crude oil, ran aground at Milford Haven, Pembrokeshire on 15 January 1996. By the time she reached harbour, 6 days later, more than 50% of the cargo had been spilt. About 120 miles of rocky coast was polluted, including two coastal nature reserves and one marine reserve; 70 000 sea birds were 'oiled'.

Conservation

The impact of human activities has caused much environmental destruction. As a result, there is an urgent need to conserve the natural environment. Studies of the ecology of ecosystems may allow us to assess the impact of human activities. **Conservation** involves using this knowledge to manage the environment to maintain biodiversity (page 344). Conservation is an active process, not simply a case of preservation. Currently there are four strategies for conservation, as follows.

1 Maintaining representative sites

Completely natural ecosystems unchanged by humans no longer exist. Conservation measures are designed to preserve the full range of semi-natural habitats. The setting aside of land for restricted access and controlled use allows the maintenance of biodiversity. This now takes the form of:

- Setting up of **statutory conservation areas**: the National Parks of Britain, introduced by Act of Parliament, are under the control of separate national organisations for England, Wales and Scotland. Also identified are Areas of Outstanding Natural Beauty (AONB), which are singled out for special treatment by the community. National Parks and AONBs occupy about 20% of the land surface of the UK. The national Nature Conservancy body has established National Nature Reserves and identified Sites of Special Scientific Interest (SSSIs), which amount to over 6000 protected locations.

Currently, government funds are also available for Environmentally Sensitive Areas (ESAs), where support is given to farmers to maintain traditional agriculture. In future, European environmental initiatives, through the European Habitat Directive, will help to maintain biodiversity by identifying Special Areas of Conservation, which will become protected under European law.

- Initiatives of national and local **non-government organisations** (**NGOs**): in the UK, membership of organisations such as the National Trust (NT), the Royal Society for the Protection of Birds (RSPB), and the various county wildlife trusts is widespread and growing. These organisations own and manage sites of every description across the UK. Much of the conservation work they achieve is carried out by volunteers.

2 Balanced use of resources

Conflict between economic and conservation interests is extremely common. Increasing demand for food, and the need for economic returns to farmers and land owners, fishermen, forest dwellers and tree loggers, for example, have to be balanced with our obvious need to sustain the resources themselves. The development and implementation of global and national policies for the sustainable use of natural resources is probably one of the most important current conservation issues. Consumers and voters in a democracy have a part to play, 'thinking globally and acting locally'.

The scale of **commercial fishing** in the seas around Britain and the rest of Europe has been so intensive as to have depleted the fish stocks (Figure 18.19). Currently the European Commission is attempting to limit the 'take' of fishing fleets by imposing quotas, restrictions on net size, close seasons and exclusion zones. The success of initiatives like this is vital. However, they are dependent on local people, as consumers, politicians and fishermen, seeing that there is no real conflict between the fishing industries' long term needs and successful conservation.

Figure 18.19
Overfishing in European waters. This graph shows the decline of North Sea cod stocks as a result of overfishing.

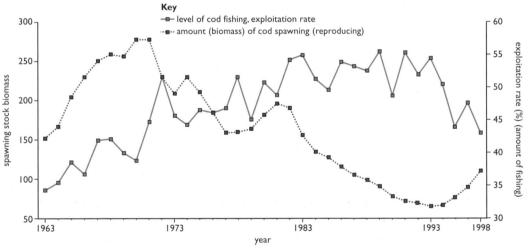

As the amount of fishing has been reduced (since about 1990), the decline in spawning fish had been reversed. With time, this trend may allow stocks to recover completely.

Another example of this conflict that must be resolved is in the **sustainable use of the world's forests**. In the countries directly concerned, forestry provides employment for millions of local people. Local problems of poverty, population growth and landlessness cannot be ignored. At the same time, huge world markets also seek raw materials.

To overcome the destruction of forests, including the tropical rain forests, alternative, sustainable forestry projects are needed to supply markets and provide employment. Sustainable forestry recognises that a number of mature trees can be removed in a given area without interrupting maintenance of the forest or decreasing biodiversity there, and sees they are cut and removed in a way that does not damage the trees that will be left to replace them. This is a tall order, however, given the extensive demand for resources from the developed world, the scale of poverty and debt in many countries with the trees, and the massive logging machinery used to harvest the timber.

3 Conservation of endangered species

Species must be preserved if our actions threaten them; we have no right to eliminate other organisms, and should not be prepared to allow it to happen through indifference. Our own self-interest requires their preservation, too, for several reasons. Wild organisms contribute to a pool of genetic diversity that is useful to genetic engineers (page 120). Many wild plants are sources of compounds of medicinal value as new drugs. In particular ecosystems some wild organisms are more efficient energy converters than existing crops and herds. It is also essential to maintain a diverse flora and fauna to ensure the continuation of the processes of evolution of new species in response to the changing environments of the Earth.

When a particular species becomes extinct, its genes are permanently lost, and the total pool of genes on which life operates is diminished. The loss of major habitats around the world effectively decreases the genetic heritage. **Genetic conservation** seeks to prevent such losses. Currently, the rate of extinctions is exceptionally high. Survival of endangered species is sought by maintaining habitat diversity (see 1 on page 404), and by maintaining local, national and international actions to ensure protection of the vulnerable organisms. The International Union for the Conservation of Nature and Nature Reserves coordinates the updating of the **Red Data Books**. These books list endangered species, identifying those for which special conservation efforts are needed. The information these books contain has been the basis on which many countries agree not to import or export endangered species under the CITES (Convention on International Trade in Endangered Species) initiative.

Preservation of species on the brink of extinction may involve the use of botanical gardens, the maintenance of viable seed banks, and captive breeding programmes at zoological gardens.

Note:
You can keep in touch with international issues on conservation of endangered species at these Web sites:
The World Wide Fund for Nature UK:
www.wwf-uk.org
CITES:
www.cites.org

4 Pollution control

Control of pollution in the atmosphere

International action to avoid long-term damage to the environment as a consequence of 'acid rain', 'global warming' and the longer-term threat to the ozone layer has begun and controls are being set up. These have followed upon the United Nations Conference on the Environment and Development (the 'Earth Summit'), held in Rio de Janeiro in June 1992. In this summit, world leaders signed a global environment and development action plan called '**Agenda 21**', which was based on the concept of sustainable development (that is, 'development which meets the needs of the present without compromising the ability of future generations to meet their own needs').

Control of pesticides

Concern over the long-term consequences of using pesticides arises from the fact that:

- the natural predators of pests and other useful organisms are often eradicated more speedily than pests
- pest populations rapidly develop resistance to pesticides
- residues of the pesticides pass into the food chain and accumulate in other wildlife, and in humans as well.

Consequently, it is now recognised that, where no effective biological control measures exist, pest control is best achieved (and environmental pollution best avoided) by combining a variation in cultivation methods and a rotation of the crops with minimal use of well-targeted pesticides. This approach is referred to as '**integrated control of pests**'.

Biological control exploits natural enemies to regulate the population of pest species. Recently chemical messengers known as pheromones, which are produced by many animal species, have been exploited. Pheromones are volatile chemicals. Sometimes they are used by males or females of a species to attract partners for mating. Synthetic pheromones of these types can be deployed to lure pests into traps laced with pesticide. Traps are sited away from the crops, where pests can be killed without harm to their natural enemies.

4 Distinguish between the following pairs:

- biome and ecosystem
- deforestation and desertification
- 'greenhouse' gases and 'acid rain'
- infra-red and ultraviolet radiation
- Neolithic and Industrial Revolutions
- dry deposition and wet deposition
- molecular oxygen and trioxygen (ozone)
- conservation and preservation in the countryside
- chlorofluorocarbons and oxides of nitrogen
- control by pesticide and biological control.

Figure 18.20
An ethanol powered car in Brazil, a development of the 'Gashol' project.

Crops of sugar cane yield sugar that is fermented to ethanol solution and distilled to form liquid fuel (95% ethanol).

A domestic 'biogas' fermenter in an Indian village.

Anaerobic decay in below-ground fermenters of dung and other organic waste yields methane gas a a fuel.

5 Renewable sources of energy

So-called renewable energy comes from the exploitation of wave power, wind power, tidal power, solar energy, hydroelectric power and from biological sources. Many of the sources have a low environmental impact and are often described as 'environmental friendly'. For example, biological sources of power exploit the ability of green plants to photosynthesise. One example is the use of green crops to produce ethanol as a liquid fuel for vehicles. Another is the conversion of organic waste matter to methane, a gaseous fuel to use in cooking, heating and power generation. Both of these are alternatives to the use of fossil fuels.

● **Skills task**   Articles frequently occur in the press, concerning some aspect of human interaction with the global environment, such as deforestation, global warming or the effects of pesticides. These articles sometimes adopt a sensational approach or make exaggerated claims of benefits or dangers. Select one article and read it carefully. Then:

1 Produce a concise version of the points made (often called a 'précis') in a way that you can present to others.
2 Produce a similarly brief list of points that you feel restore balance to the presentation. Be ready to present both sides of the argument to your peers.

SUMMARY
● The exponential expansion of human numbers is a relatively recent phenomenon, but the current **size of the human population** makes huge demands on the world's living space and resources, so that many environments are being degraded and biodiversity reduced.
● Forest biomes predominate on much of the habitable land surface, but human activities have removed many trees, and **deforestation** of tropical rain forests and northern pine forests continues. In some areas, the destruction of trees has speeded up soil loss, leading to **desertification** at the fringes of arid areas.
● In modern agriculture, the high level of productivity of crops requires the widespread use of **pesticides** to control insects and weeds, but residues of the poisonous chemicals used have tended to accumulate in the food chain, harming wildlife and humans.
● Atmospheric carbon dioxide and other gases help to keep the Earth warm, rather like the glass in a greenhouse. Increasing levels of atmospheric carbon dioxide, released in the burning of fossil fuels, may be enhancing the natural '**greenhouse effect**', possibly leading to **global warming**.
● Chlorofluorocarbons (CFCs), used as propellants in aerosol cans, have reached the upper atmosphere and released active atoms responsible for damaging the high-level **ozone layer**. This has increased the amount of UV radiation reaching the Earth's surface.
● Sulphur dioxide and oxides of nitrogen, which are released when fossil fuels (coal, oil and gas) are burnt, dissolves in rain to form '**acid rain**'. These pollutants acidify soil and freshwater habitats, speeding removal of useful ions and releasing soluble aluminium ions, which are poisonous to fish and plants.
● A cocktail of substances, including unburnt hydrocarbons, are released into the lower atmosphere when fuels are burnt. These react together and form ozone, particularly in bright sunlight. **Low-level ozone** harms plant leaves and the respiratory system of animals.

continued

- The build-up of valuable nutrients in lakes, rivers and oceans, known as **eutrophication**, enhances plant growth there. An example of this is springtime 'algal blooms'. When the plants die the organic matter is decayed by aerobic bacteria, and other aerobic organisms (for example, fish) may be killed by lack of oxygen. Human activities, including excessive use of fertilisers on the land, may speed up eutrophication.
- **Industrial effluents** discharged into the environment include the occasional escape of untreated sewage, the release of crude oil and the discharge of heavy metal ions such as mercury and cadmium. All of these are pollutants that may cause environmental harm in the food chains affected.
- **Conservation** is the management of resources and habitats so as to maintain the existing range of habitats, and to prevent future reductions in biodiversity.

Examination questions

1 The figure shows changes in the atmospheric carbon dioxide concentrations at Mauna Loa, a site on an island in the middle of the Pacific Ocean, between 1958 and 1988.

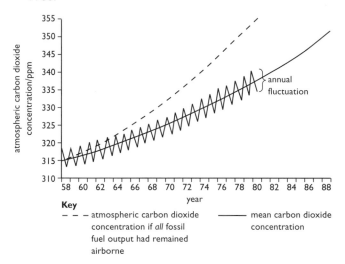

Key
– – – atmospheric carbon dioxide concentration if *all* fossil fuel output had remained airborne

——— mean carbon dioxide concentration

a Suggest why Mauna Loa is regarded as a particularly suitable place to measure concentrations of carbon dioxide. (2)

b With reference to the figure,
i explain why there is an annual fluctuation in the concentration of carbon dioxide; (2)
ii showing your working, calculate the percentage increase in carbon dioxide concentration over the 30 years between 1958 and 1988; (2)
iii state the year in which the 1988 mean carbon dioxide concentration would have been reached if all the carbon dioxide from the burning of fossil fuels had remained in the atmosphere. (1)

c Explain why all the carbon dioxide from the burning of fossil fuels does **not** remain in the atmosphere. (2)

Although chlorofluorocarbons (CFCs) are more powerful greenhouse gases than carbon dioxide, it is the increasing concentrations of carbon dioxide which are blamed for enhancing the greenhouse effect.

d i Explain what is meant by the *greenhouse effect*. (4)
ii Explain why carbon dioxide is of more concern than CFCs. (1)
iii Suggest **one** other factor in the atmosphere which contributes to the increased concentrations of carbon dioxide. (1)

UCLES, A level, 4803, Nov 1997

2 Read the following passage

Wetlands – Water, water everywhere?
Wetlands are areas where land and water meet. They are found in almost every country in the world and vary enormously in size from a small pond to the vast 10 million hectare bays in the Canadian Arctic. The movement of water is slow in wetlands, allowing sediments to settle to the bottom. Wetland plants, and the bacteria associated with them, absorb and break down substances, such as organic wastes, that would otherwise pollute rivers, ponds and lakes downstream.

However, there is a limit to how many pollutants wetlands can absorb. In some areas, excessive amounts of sewage, slurry and fertilisers are being pumped into the water. Air pollution falls on wetlands as acid rain. Sediments from road-building and construction block out the light, and heavy metal ions accumulate.

Many flat, low-lying wetlands have been drained for development or the animal communities living there severely depleted through overhunting or overfishing. One of the greatest threats to UK wetlands has been excessive extraction of peat. Nearly 100 wetlands of international importance have been identified in the UK and many conservation organisations are involved in protecting these sites.

(Reproduced from an article by permission of John Grace, first published in *The Guardian*.)

a Describe how the following pollutants could affect wetland ecosystems.
i fertilisers (6)
ii heavy metal ions (3)
b Explain the benefits of conserving wetlands. (3)

NEAB, AS/A level, Module BY05, Mar 1998

V
LIFE
GOES ON

Reproduction

STARTING POINTS ● Reproduction, the **production of new individuals** by sexual or asexual means, is a characteristic of living things.
● **Asexual reproduction** can occur in a number of different ways; the offspring are **genetically identical to the parent**.
● In **sexual reproduction**, two **haploid gametes** fuse to form a **diploid zygote**, which grows into a new individual that is **genetically different from the parents**.

● Reproduction: new generations of individuals

Reproduction is the production of new individuals by an existing member or members of the same species. It is a fundamental characteristic of life; the ability to self-replicate in this way sets the living world apart from the non-living. In reproduction, a **parent generation** effectively passes on a copy of itself, in the form of genetic material, to another generation: the **offspring**. The genetic material of an organism consists of its chromosome(s), which are made of nucleic acid (see Chapter 5).

The period of time from the beginning of an organism's life until it reproduces is called the **life cycle**. Young organisms must first grow and develop before they can reproduce. In nature, not all individuals survive to adulthood and sexual maturity. Since many organisms die young, reproduction by those who survive to be adults is the way a population is maintained, and the continuity of the species is ensured. When conditions are very favourable, more offspring may be produced than die, and then there is an increase in numbers. By reproduction, populations can therefore also grow and spread.

Organisms reproduce either asexually or sexually; many reproduce by both these methods. How do these processes differ?

Asexual reproduction

In **asexual reproduction** a single organism produces new individuals. Organisms that can reproduce in this way often do so as soon as they become established in a new habitat or reach a certain size, provided they are well supplied with nutrients.

Asexual means 'non-sexual': no gametes are formed in asexual reproduction. The cells of the new offspring are normally produced by **mitosis** (the replicative nuclear division, see page 100), so the progeny are identical both to the parent and to each other. Identical offspring are called **clones**. The technique of artificially producing clones is called **cloning**.

The advantage of asexual reproduction is that a large number of new individuals are produced rapidly, by a single parent, so that a suitable habitat can be colonised and exploited quickly. New individuals all have the qualities of the successful parent, since they are genetically identical.

In the five kingdoms of living things, asexual reproduction is common among the prokaryotes, protoctists, fungi and plants, but uncommon among animals. Different forms of asexual reproduction are shown in Figure 19.1.

● Extension   Application of cloning

Cloning does not occur naturally in vertebrate animals. However, it can be carried out artificially, for example by taking an embryo before the cells have specialised, and teasing out the cells into small groups. By repeating this process, many copies of a useful animal can be produced. Cloning of humans is banned on ethical grounds (in the UK) but cloning of animals has applications in genetic engineering and animal breeding.

In plants it is widely practised in the artificial propagation of useful plants in the taking of cuttings, and in tissue culture techniques (Figure 6.11, page 132).

Figure 19.1
Forms of asexual reproduction.

in prokaryotes:
binary fission in a bacterium, the bacterium divides into two separate cells after the circular chromosome has duplicated

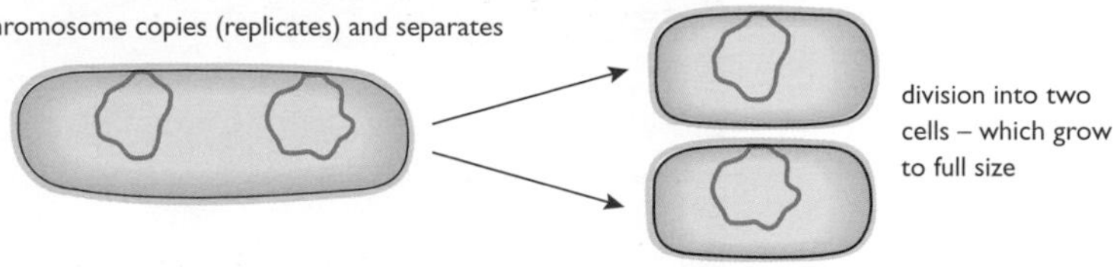

chromosome copies (replicates) and separates

division into two cells – which grow to full size

in protoctistans:
multiple fission in *Plasmodium* (malaria-causing organism), nucleus divides by mitotic divisions to form 6–24 nuclei, and then the cytoplasm divides around them to form cells that are released into the bloodstream and infect fresh blood cells

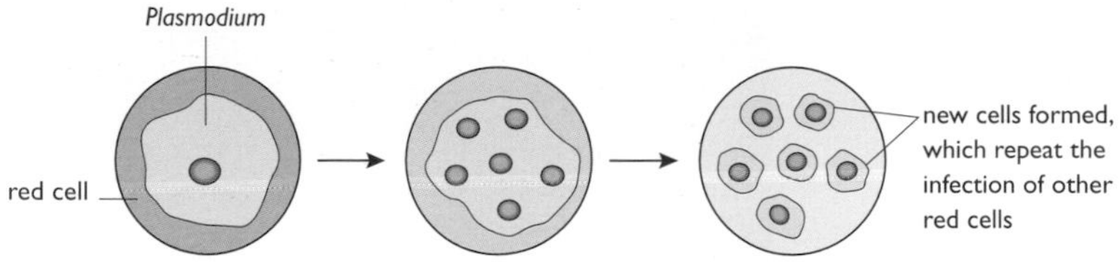

Plasmodium

red cell

new cells formed, which repeat the infection of other red cells

in fungi:
spore formation in *Rhizopus*, a sporangium (spore-container) forms at the tip of an upright hypha and the contents divide into spores, which are released; spores transported to new food surfaces may grow and eventually release spores themselves

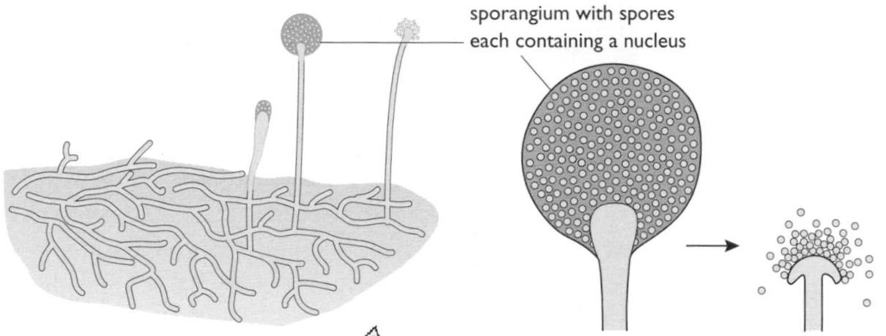

sporangium with spores each containing a nucleus

in plants:
stolon formation in blackberry plants, a shoot grows out and when the growing tip reaches the ground it roots and forms a new plant; later this plant becomes cut off from the parent plant and forms new stolons itself

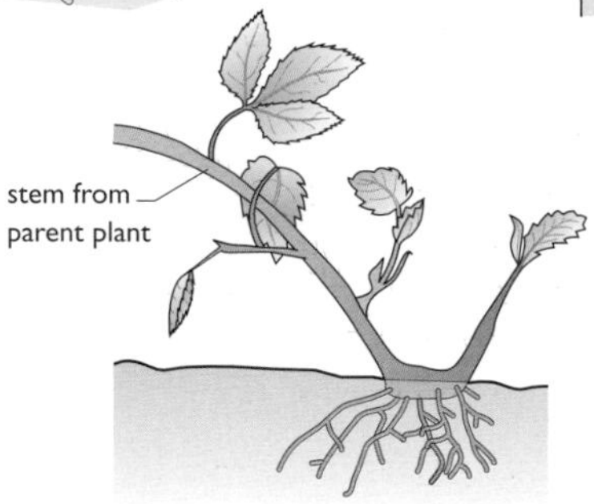

stem from parent plant

in animals:
budding of a new individual from *Hydra*, a bulge forms in the two-layered body wall of *Hydra* and develops into a new individual with a mouth and tentacles before it becomes detached from the parent

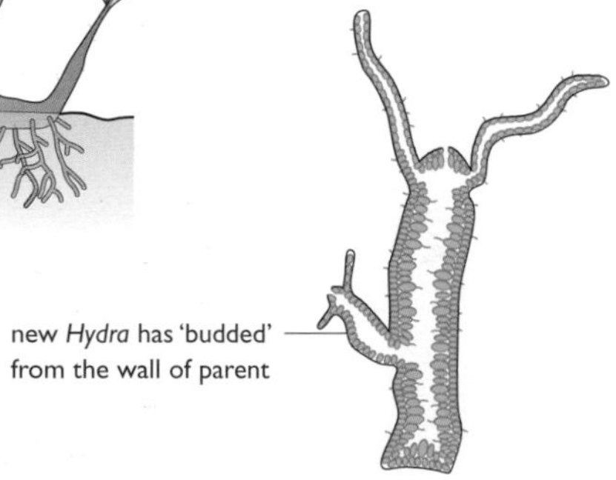

new *Hydra* has 'budded' from the wall of parent

Figure 19.2
Meiosis and the diploid life cycle.

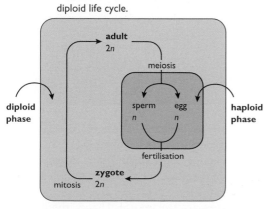

diploid phase

adult
2*n*

meiosis

sperm
n

egg
n

haploid phase

fertilisation

zygote
2*n*

mitosis

Self-fertilisation = sperm + egg from same individual.
Cross-fertilisation = sperm + egg from different individuals.

Sexual reproduction

In **sexual reproduction** two **gametes** fuse to form a **zygote**, which then grows into a new individual. Fusion of gametes is called **fertilisation**. The process of gamete formation involves a **meiotic division**, halving the normal chromosome number (Figure 19.2). That is, gametes are **haploid**, and fertilisation restores the **diploid** number of chromosomes. Without the reductive nuclear division in the process of sexual reproduction, the chromosome number would double in each generation.

The offspring produced by sexual reproduction are unique, in complete contrast to offspring formed by asexual reproduction. There are genetic differences between the nuclei formed by meiosis. These differences, together with the random nature of fertilisation, mean that the new individuals differ both from their parents and from each other. These differences, although small, are important in the eventual production of new species by natural selection (see Chapter 21).

Figure 19.3
SEM of oogamous sexual reproduction in the gametes of a human.

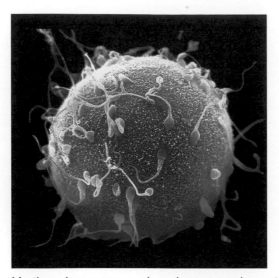

Typically, male and female gametes differ in size and behaviour. Male gametes are small and motile. Female gametes are large and stationary, and usually have stored food reserves. This is because of the different roles. The role of the male gamete is to move efficiently to reach the female gamete, ahead of its rivals, and achieve fertilisation. The union of unlike gametes like these is called **oogamy** (Figure 19.3). By contrast, some algae (these organisms are protoctistans, page 350), have gametes of the same size. Fusion of gametes of the same size is called **isogamy**.

Motile male gametes, such as the sperms shown in Figure 19.3, require a watery medium in which to move. In aquatic animals such as fish and amphibians, the male and female gametes are shed into the water, and **fertilisation occurs externally** (Figure 19.4). In organisms that have colonised the land and mastered life there, such as mammals, birds and the flowering plants, **internal fertilisation** in an environment suitable for transport of the male gamete is necessary. Internal fertilisation in most terrestrial organisms involves the male gametes being introduced into the female's reproductive organs.

Figure 19.4
External and internal fertilisation.

external fertilisation in frogs

internal fertilisation in birds

Some organisms produce both male and female gametes in one individual. These are described as **bisexual** or **hermaphrodite**. The earthworm and the garden snail are examples of hermaphrodite organisms. Many flowers are also hermaphrodite. In hermaphroditic organisms **self-fertilisation** may be possible, but frequently there are mechanisms to ensure that **cross-fertilisation** occurs. The same is true of many flowers.

Many animals, including all mammals and most vertebrates, are **unisexual**. That is, the male and female gametes are produced in different individuals. In unisexual organisms, fertilisation occurs between different individuals, ensuring cross-fertilisation.

Sexual reproduction in flowering plants

Flower structure

Flowering plants, known as the Angiospermophyta (page 355), contain reproductive organs in their **flowers**. The flower develops from the tip of a shoot. A group of flowers occurring together on a stem is known as an **inflorescence**. Many flowers are hermaphroditic structures, containing both male and female parts. The different parts of flowers occur in rings or whorls, attached to the swollen tip of the flower stalk, which is called the **receptacle**. Botanists regard the parts of the flower as being modified leaves.

The outer whorl of the flower is the **sepals**. These are green, small, leaf-like structures that protect the flower in the bud stage. The sepals are known collectively as the **calyx**.

The next whorl is the **petals**. These are known collectively as the **corolla**. In flowers that attract insects, petals are typically brightly coloured and conspicuous. Another feature of most insect-pollinated flowers are **nectaries**, in which a sugary solution called nectar is produced and secreted. Part of the receptacle, calyx or corolla may be modified for this role.

The male parts of the flower are the **stamens**. Each stamen consists of an **anther** at the end of a stalk-like **filament**. The stamens are known collectively as the **androecium**. The anthers contain the **pollen grains** in **pollen sacs**.

The female parts are the **carpels**. A flower may contain a single carpel or many carpels, and the carpels may be free or fused together. For example, in the buttercup flower there are numerous carpels, but they are not fused. Each carpel consist of an **ovary**, which contains one or more **ovules**, a **stigma** (which is the receptive surface for pollen grains) and the **style**, which connects stigma and ovary. The carpels are known collectively as the **gynaecium**. The ovule contains an **embryo sac**, in which are contained the **egg cell** and the **endosperm nucleus**.

The structure of the buttercup flower is shown in Figure 19.5.

Figure 19.5
The structure of the buttercup flower.

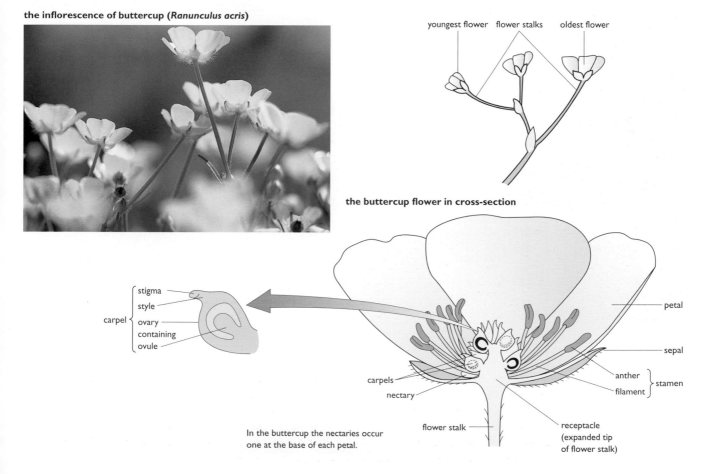

the inflorescence of buttercup (*Ranunculus acris*)

youngest flower   flower stalks   oldest flower

the buttercup flower in cross-section

carpel {
stigma
style
ovary
containing
ovule
}

petal

sepal

anther
filament
} stamen

carpels

nectary

flower stalk

receptacle
(expanded tip
of flower stalk)

In the buttercup the nectaries occur
one at the base of each petal.

Pollen grain formation

The immature anther has four pollen sacs, each containing a central mass of cells that will develop into pollen grains. These cells are called **pollen mother cells**, and they are surrounded by a layer of cells that provide nutrients (the tapetum).

The pollen mother cell divides by meiosis, producing four haploid nuclei. The cytoplasm divides around them, and new cell walls are laid down. This forms a 'tetrad' of pollen grains. The walls of pollen grains have an outer layer with a sculptured surface (the 'exine'), which is thick and extremely resistant. The pattern of this sculpting is characteristic of the species, and this is very useful to scientists. The species of pollen deposits can be identified by examination with a microscope. As the wall of the pollen grain is highly resistant to decay, pollen grains have survived for millions of years as fossil deposits, given the right conditions. Ancient pollen deposits, when rediscovered, provide evidence about the flora in earlier times.

The pollen grains then separate and the haploid nucleus inside each divides by mitosis, forming two nuclei. One of these is known as the **generative nucleus** and the other as the **pollen tube nucleus** (Figure 19.6). Before fertilisation occurs, the generative nucleus divides further into two male nuclei. Both of these are involved in fertilisation, in a most unusual act of double fertilisation that occurs in flowering plants (see Figure 19.9).

When the pollen grains are fully formed the anther walls split open ('dehisce'), releasing the pollen grains for transport, hopefully to an appropriate stigma.

Figure 19.6
Formation of pollen grains.

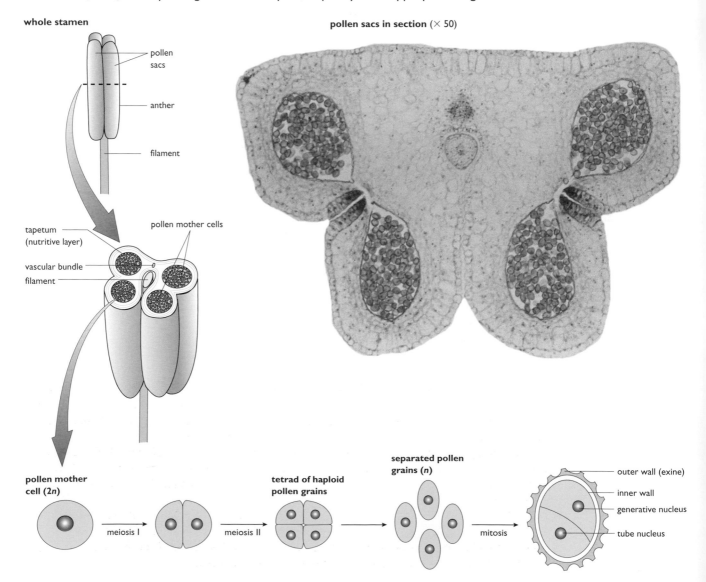

whole stamen

- pollen sacs
- anther
- filament

pollen sacs in section (× 50)

- tapetum (nutritive layer)
- vascular bundle
- filament
- pollen mother cells

pollen mother cell (2n) → meiosis I → meiosis II → **tetrad of haploid pollen grains** → **separated pollen grains (n)** → mitosis →

- outer wall (exine)
- inner wall
- generative nucleus
- tube nucleus

Pollination and fertilisation

Pollination is the transfer of pollen from a mature anther to a receptive stigma. The pollen may come from the anthers of the same flower or flowers of the same plant, in which case the process is referred to as **self-pollination**. Alternatively, pollen may come from flowers on a different plant of the same species; this is referred to as **cross-pollination**.

Transfer of the pollen usually takes place by the wind or by insects, although in the flowers of certain habitats, running water, birds or bats carry out pollination. **Wind-pollinated** flowers produce and release vast amounts of pollen. This increases the chances of some reaching the stigma of an appropriate plant. **Insect-pollinated flowers** produce a sugar solution, nectar, which attracts insects to visit the flower. There are a range of differences between wind- and insect-pollinated flowers, which are listed in Figure 19.7.

Figure 19.7
The differences between insect- and wind-pollinated flowers.

insect-pollinated flowers, e.g. buttercup (page 413):
- flowers in conspicuous positions
- insects are attracted by colour of conspicuous petals or by scent, or both, and carry pollen from flower to flower
- nectaries secrete nectar
- stamens enclosed in the flower
- pollen variable in size, with sculptured exine
- stigma small and in a position to make contact with visiting insects

wind-pollinated flowers, e.g. grass flower:
- flowers may be produced before the leaves
- air currents carry pollen, some of which may reach a flower of same species
- nectaries not present
- stamens hang outside the flower
- large quantities of light, smooth pollen
- stigma large and feathery, and hanging outside the flower

part of a grass flower

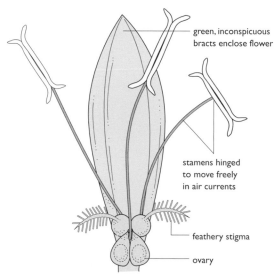

green, inconspicuous bracts enclose flower

stamens hinged to move freely in air currents

feathery stigma

ovary

Embryo sac formation

The female gamete, an **egg cell**, is formed in an embryo sac within an ovule, inside the ovary of the flower. The ovule has an outer covering, called the **integuments**; at the tip is a tiny pore, called the **micropyle**.

In the immature ovule is an **embryo sac mother cell**, which undergoes meiosis to form four haploid cells. Only one of the cells develops further. This forms the embryo sac containing a single, haploid nucleus. The steps to development of the embryo sac are shown in Figure 19.8, where the series of nuclear divisions that occur next are also shown.

The **embryo sac nucleus** undergoes mitosis three times to form eight nuclei. These arrange themselves within the sac so there are four at each end. One nucleus from each group then migrates to the centre of the sac. These two nuclei fuse, forming a diploid nucleus: the **primary endosperm nucleus**. We'll return to this later.

The three nuclei remaining at each end form into cells. Those at the end of the embryo sac nearest the micropyle form the egg apparatus, consisting of an egg cell supported by two cells, called **synergids**. At the opposite end the three cells are called the **antipodal cells**. Synergids and antipodal cells play no further significant role in reproduction.

Figure 19.8
Formation of the
embryo sac.

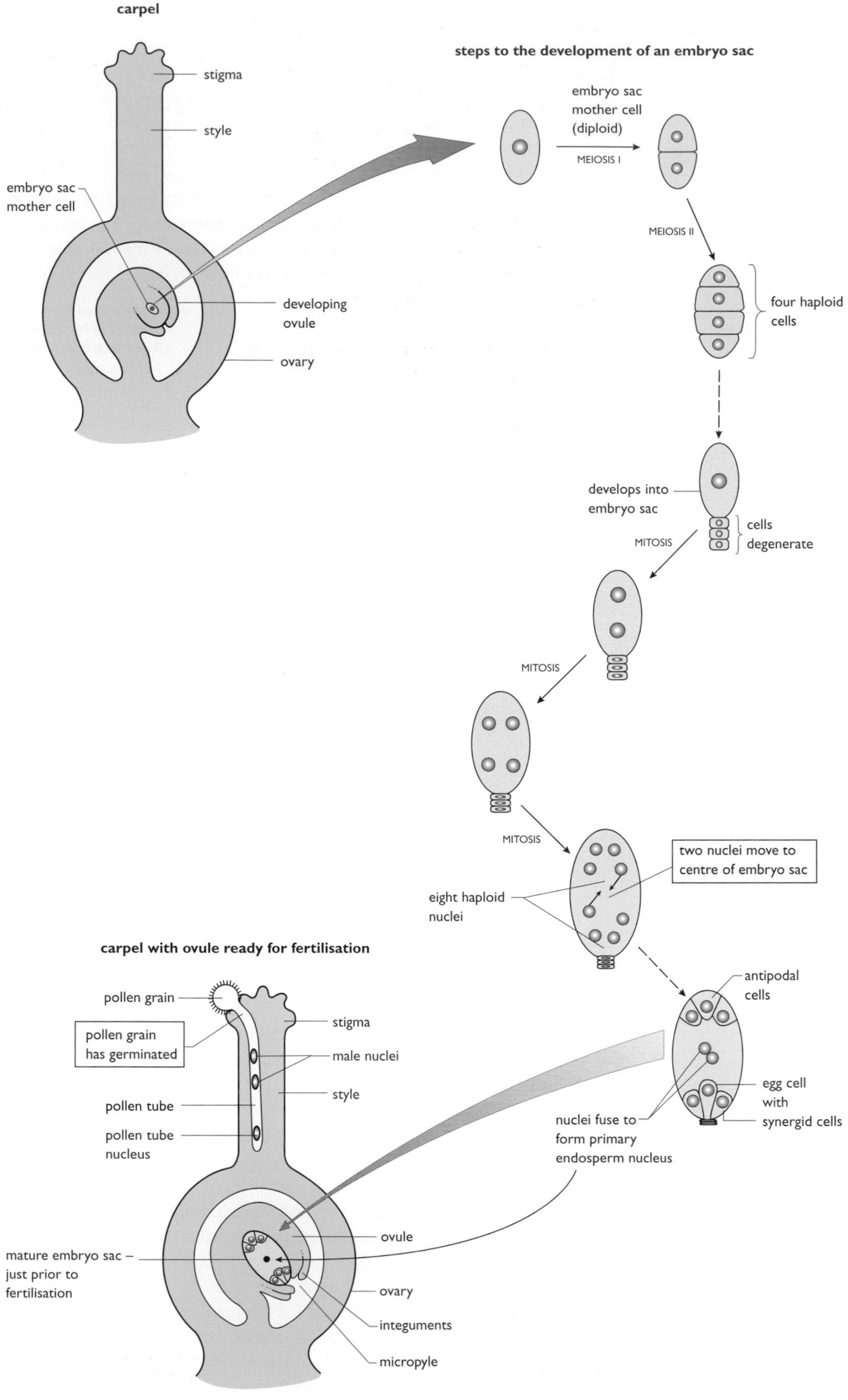

carpel

steps to the development of an embryo sac

stigma

style

embryo sac
mother cell

developing
ovule

ovary

embryo sac
mother cell
(diploid)

MEIOSIS I

MEIOSIS II

four haploid
cells

develops into
embryo sac

cells
degenerate

MITOSIS

MITOSIS

MITOSIS

eight haploid
nuclei

two nuclei move to
centre of embryo sac

antipodal
cells

egg cell
with
synergid cells

nuclei fuse to
form primary
endosperm nucleus

carpel with ovule ready for fertilisation

pollen grain

pollen grain
has germinated

pollen tube

pollen tube
nucleus

stigma

male nuclei

style

mature embryo sac –
just prior to
fertilisation

ovule

ovary

integuments

micropyle

Extension   How cross-pollination is ensured

If self-fertilisation occurs the offspring produced will show less variation from their parents than if the gametes from different individuals were involved. Self-fertilisation is also known as **inbreeding**. Since many flowers are hermaphrodites they have a potential for self-fertilisation not seen in a unisexual organism. So it is interesting to discover that there are several mechanisms that prevent self-fertilisation common in hermaphroditic flowers, including:

- stamens and stigmas that mature at different times, so that when the stigma is receptive the stamens are not releasing pollen grains, and *vice versa*
- physiological differences between stigma tissue and pollen grains, preventing pollen that lands on the stigma from germinating if it belongs to the same plant (or, if it germinates, preventing the pollen tube from growing).

Fertilisation in flowering plants can occur only after an appropriate pollen grain has landed on the stigma, and germinated there. The pollen grain produces a pollen tube, which grows down between the cells of the style, through the micropyle and into the embryo sac (Figure 19.9). Growth of the pollen tube is under the control of the tube nucleus (see Figure 19.6), but is also influenced by conditions in the style.

The pollen tube delivers the two male nuclei into the embryo sac. One of the two male nuclei then fuses with the egg nucleus in the embryo sac, forming a diploid zygote. The other fuses with the endosperm nucleus, forming a triploid endosperm nucleus. This unique process is called **double fertilisation**.

Figure 19.9
Fertilisation.

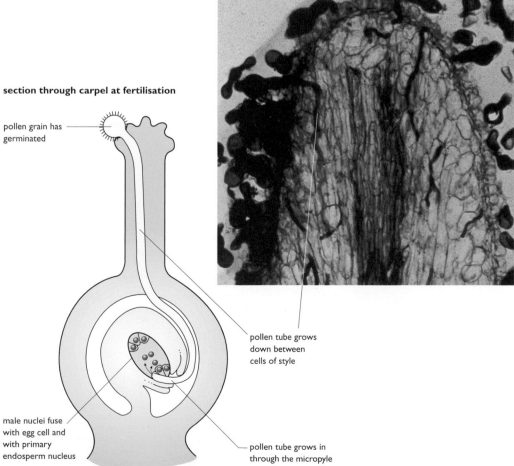

photomicrograph of LS through stigma, showing germinating pollen grains (× 200)

section through carpel at fertilisation

pollen grain has germinated

pollen tube grows down between cells of style

male nuclei fuse with egg cell and with primary endosperm nucleus

pollen tube grows in through the micropyle

1 Explain the differences between pollination and fertilisation.

Seed and fruit development

The **seed** develops from the fertilised ovule. It contains an embryo plant and a food store (Figure 19.10). The following changes occur immediately double fertilisation has taken place:

- The zygote grows by repeated mitotic division to produce cells that form an embryonic plant. This consists of a **radicle** (the developing root), a **plumule** (the developing stem) and a single seed leaf or two seed leaves, the cotyledons. The phylum of flowering plants divides into two classes, according to the number of embryonic seed leaves the plant possesses. The **monocotyledons** have a single seed leaf; the **dicotyledons** have two (Figure 16.12, page 355).
- The **triploid endosperm nucleus**, formed by the fusion of the second male nucleus with the diploid endosperm nucleus, divides repeatedly by mitosis. This forms endosperm tissue, which is the food store of the seed. Note that formation of the endosperm tissue commences only if fertilisation occurs. In the absence of fertilisation, no food reserves are moved into the unfertilised ovule.

In some mature seeds the endosperm (stored food) is held in the cotyledons. This is the case in peas and beans, for example. Here the endosperm material is taken up into the cotyledons, which enlarge, and they make up most of the seed.

In other seeds, the food store is held separately, and becomes an endosperm tissue laid down around the embryo, densely packed with stored food. This is the case in sunflower seeds and wheat.

As the seed matures, the outer layers of the ovule (the integuments) become the seed coat or **testa**. The ovule has developed into a seed, and the remains of the ovary become the fruit, which encloses and surrounds the seed(s).

Dormancy

The water content of the seed decreases as the seed moves into a **dormancy period**. This content can fall as low as 10–15%. In this condition the seed is able to survive unfavourable conditions. Some plants complete the development of the embryo during the dormancy period; the other parts of the flower also dry out and shrivel. The ovule has then developed with a seed, and the remains of the ovary becomes a fruit, which encloses and surrounds the seed(s).

Figure 19.10
Seed formation.

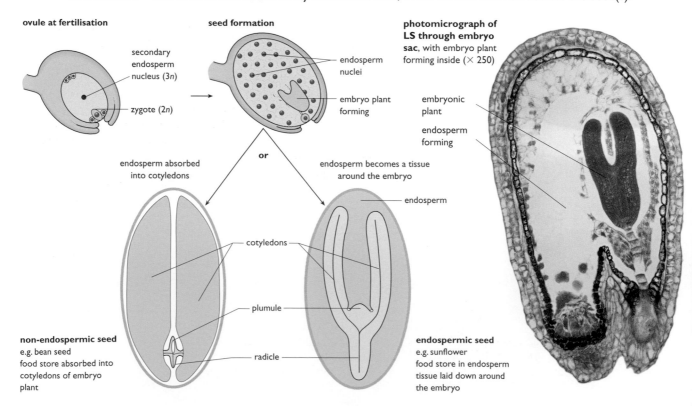

ovule at fertilisation

secondary endosperm nucleus (3*n*)

zygote (2*n*)

seed formation

endosperm nuclei

embryo plant forming

photomicrograph of LS through embryo sac, with embryo plant forming inside (× 250)

embryonic plant

endosperm forming

endosperm absorbed into cotyledons

or

endosperm becomes a tissue around the embryo

endosperm

cotyledons

plumule

radicle

non-endospermic seed
e.g. bean seed
food store absorbed into cotyledons of embryo plant

endospermic seed
e.g. sunflower
food store in endosperm tissue laid down around the embryo

Germination of seeds

The dormant seed is a way for the plant to survive the unfavourable season. It is also one way that plants may be dispersed, prior to **germination** and the growth of new plants. There are two forms of seed germination, as the cotyledons may remain below ground (**hypogeal germination**) or be raised above the ground (**epigeal germination**), as shown in Figure 19.11.

Figure 19.11
Seed germination.

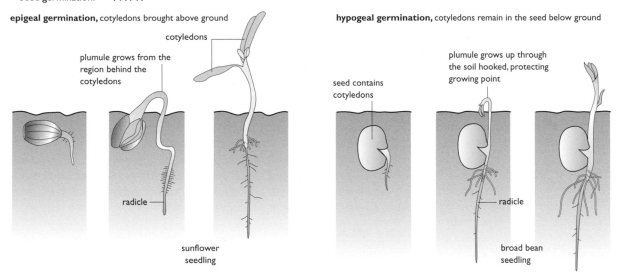

epigeal germination, cotyledons brought above ground

cotyledons

plumule grows from the region behind the cotyledons

radicle

sunflower seedling

hypogeal germination, cotyledons remain in the seed below ground

seed contains cotyledons

plumule grows up through the soil hooked, protecting growing point

radicle

broad bean seedling

● Extension   Life cycles of plants

The life cycle of a simple green plant like a moss (Figure 16.9, page 352) is apparently quite different from that of flowering plants. In the moss, there is a spore-producing stage, the diploid sporophyte, and a gamete-producing stage, the haploid gametophyte. In the moss life cycle the sporophyte and gametophyte stages alternate. However, in moss the gametophyte is dominant.

Botanists believe that the flowering plants share a common ancestry with these plants, and that their life cycle provides evidence of this. The flowering plant life cycle (Figure 19.12) is not a straightforward diploid life cycle with haploid gametes (as is typical of mammals – for example, as shown in Figure 19.2, page 411). Botanists believe there is evidence of 'alternation of generations' in flowering plant life cycles. On this interpretation of the flowering plant life cycle, the sporophyte is the dominant stage, and the gametophyte is reduced to a few redundant nuclei or cells. If this is correct, then the flowering plant is a sporophyte that forms two types of spores: the microspores (pollen grains) and the megaspores (embryo sac).

Figure 19.12
The life cycles of flowering plants.

The angiosperms are a highly successful group of plants that reproduce by means of seeds. Many flowering plants are also capable of reproducing vegetatively (asexually), that is, when parts of the parent plant become separated and grow independently.

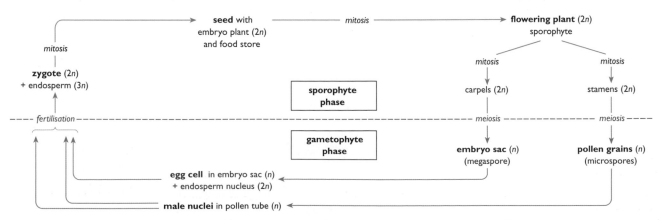

Extension What controls dormancy and flowering?

Seeds germinate under conditions favourable for growth, rather than under conditions in which the seedling will perish. Also, plants flower at different times of the year; species have a precise season when flowers are produced. How is dormancy switched off and flowering switched on by environmental conditions? The answer is that day length provides important signals.

Plant development and phytochrome

A blue–green pigment called **phytochrome** is present in green plants in very low concentrations. The amount of phytochrome is not sufficient to mask chlorophyll, and it has been difficult to isolate and purify this substance from plant tissue, although this has been done. Phytochrome is a very large conjugated protein (protein molecule + pigment molecule combined), and it is highly reactive. It is not a plant growth substance, but a **photoreceptor pigment**. It is able to absorb light of a particular wavelength, and change its structure as a consequence. It is then likely to react with different molecules around it, according to its structure.

We know that phytochrome exists in two interconvertible forms. One form, referred to as P_R, is a blue pigment that absorbs mainly red light of wavelength 660 nm ('$_R$' stands for 'red'). The other form is P_{FR}, a blue-green pigment that absorbs mainly far-red light of wavelength 730 nm. When P_R is exposed to light (or to red light on its own) it is converted to P_{FR}. In the dark (or if exposed to far-red light alone) P_{FR} is converted back to P_R.

$$P_R \underset{\substack{\text{\textit{darkness (or far-red light alone)}} \\ \text{(slow)} \qquad\qquad \text{(fast)}}}{\overset{\substack{\text{\textit{light (or red light alone)}} \\ \text{(slow)} \qquad\qquad \text{(fast)}}}{\rightleftharpoons}} P_{FR}$$

The influence of light on plant growth and development is known as **photomorphogenesis**. Phytochrome is the pigment system involved in photomorphogenesis. We know this because the red/far-red absorption spectrum of phytochrome corresponds to the action spectrum of some specific effects of light on development. (The terms 'absorption spectrum' and 'action spectrum' are introduced in Figure 8.8, page 175, in the context of chlorophyll and photosynthesis.)

It appears that it is P_{FR} that is the active form of phytochrome in photomorphogenesis. It stimulates some effects in plant development and inhibits others. In particular, it influences the phenomena of seed dormancy and controls the onset of flowering. We will look into these further.

Seed dormancy

Seeds that fail to germinate despite suitable external conditions (for example, sufficient moisture, a suitable temperature, etc.) are said to be **dormant**. Most seeds pass through a period of dormancy, which may be imposed internally. For example, the embryo of the seed may be incompletely developed, or dormancy may be due to the presence of abscisic acid, which is a growth inhibitor (page 300).

Dormancy in seeds often coincides with the time that external conditions (for example, winter) are unfavourable for a seedling. In some species, dormancy may be overcome by a period of low temperature treatment (2–3 weeks at 0–5 °C, for example), after which germination occurs as soon as suitable conditions for plant growth arise.

Light-requiring seeds

Many seeds of wild plants also require light before germination can occur (for example, foxglove, *Digitalis purpurea*, and an old variety of lettuce called 'grand rapids' in which the phenomenon was discovered). In these cases white light or red light alone will trigger germination. Conversely, far-red light inhibits germination, even if administered as a brief flash only, after treatment with red light. (Note, however, that sensitivity to light works only in seeds that have taken up sufficient water for germination. It seems that only under these conditions is the seed's phytochrome in a condition to respond.)

continued

The biochemical mechanism by which P_R breaks dormancy and triggers germination is unknown. In wild plants there is an obvious advantage to coordinating germination with the availability of sufficient water and light, particularly in species with small seeds that have very limited stores of food for early growth. Also, many wild seeds will fall into positions where there is insufficient light, and only occasionally will chance events bring them into a position favourable for growth.

Flowering

Photoperiodism is the response of an organism to the changing length of the day. In many animals the breeding season is determined by day length. Many plants flower only at a particular time of the year. Plants where flowering is controlled by day length fall into two categories (Figure 19.13):

- **Short-day plants**: these are plants that flower only if the period of darkness is longer than a certain critical length. If darkness is interrupted by a brief flash of red light the plant will not flower, but this is reversed by a flash of far-red light.

    Interpretation: Phytochrome in P_{FR} form *inhibits* flowering in short-day plants. The very long nights required by short-day plants allow the concentration of P_{FR} to fall to a low level, removing the inhibition. A flash of light in the darkness reverses this, but a flash of far-red light reverses this once again, and flowering still takes place.

- **Long-day plants**: these are plants that flower only if the period of uninterrupted darkness is less than a certain critical length each day.

    Interpretation: Phytochrome in P_{FR} form *promotes* flowering in long-day plants. The long period of daylight causes the accumulation of P_{FR}, because P_R is converted to P_{FR}.

Figure 19.13
Flowering related to day length.

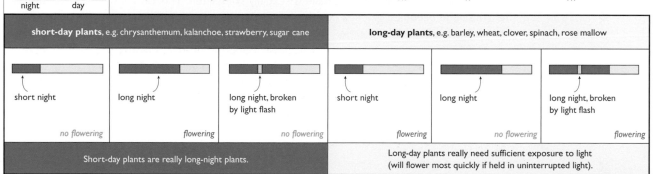

Key 24 hours
night day

short-day plants, e.g. chrysanthemum, kalanchoe, strawberry, sugar cane			long-day plants, e.g. barley, wheat, clover, spinach, rose mallow		
short night	long night	long night, broken by light flash	short night	long night	long night, broken by light flash
no flowering	*flowering*	*no flowering*	*flowering*	*no flowering*	*flowering*
Short-day plants are really long-night plants.			Long-day plants really need sufficient exposure to light (will flower most quickly if held in uninterrupted light).		

Figure 19.14
Phytochrome and flowering: a suggested hypothesis.

The conversion of vegetative buds to flower buds

It is the leaves of plants that are sensitive to day length, yet the structural switch to flowering occurs in the stem apex. It has been assumed that a growth regulator substance is formed in leaves under the correct regime of light and dark, and is then transported to the stem apex where it causes the switch in development. For example, a leaf that has been exposed to the correct photoperiod, if immediately grafted on to another plant of the same type, will cause it to flower.

A hormone is believed to exist, and has been named 'florigen', but it has not been isolated. Since it is P_{FR} that is enzymically active, this substance might cause the formation of an enzyme that promotes the formation of florigen in long-day plants but inhibits its formation in short-day plants. Much remains to be discovered about the control of flowering. A suggested mechanism is shown in Figure 19.14.

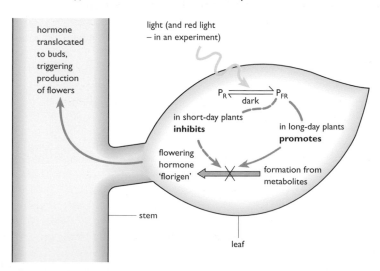

Sexual reproduction in mammals

In mammals, like most vertebrates, the sexes are separate (unisexual individuals). In the body, the reproductive and urinary (excretory) systems are closely bound together, especially in the male, so biologists refer to these as the 'urinogenital system'. Here we consider only the reproductive systems. The gametes are produced in paired glands called **gonads**. The male gametes, **spermatozoa** (singular spermatozoon) or sperms, are produced in testes. The female gametes, **ova** or **oocytes** (singular ovum/oocyte), are produced in ovaries.

The reproductive system

The **male reproductive system** (Figure 19.15) consists of the following:

- The two **testes** (singular testis) produce sperms. These glands are situated in the scrotal sac, which hangs outside the main body cavity. This arrangement allows the testes to be kept at a temperature 2–3 °C lower than the normal body temperature – the optimum temperature for sperm production. Testes also produce the male sex hormone, **testosterone**, so the testes are also endocrine glands (page 292).
- The **ducts** store the sperms, and carry them in a fluid called **seminal fluid** to the outside of the body during a process called ejaculation.
- The exocrine glands that secrete the nutritive seminal fluid in which the sperms are transported include the **seminal vesicles** and **prostate gland**.
- The **penis** is a duct through which the urethra runs. This carries to the outside both semen during an ejaculation and urine during urination. The penis also contains spongy erectile tissue that can fill with blood when the male is sexually stimulated. This causes the penis to enlarge, lengthen and become rigid, in a condition known as an erection. The erect penis penetrates the vagina in sexual intercourse.

Figure 19.15
The male urinogenital system.

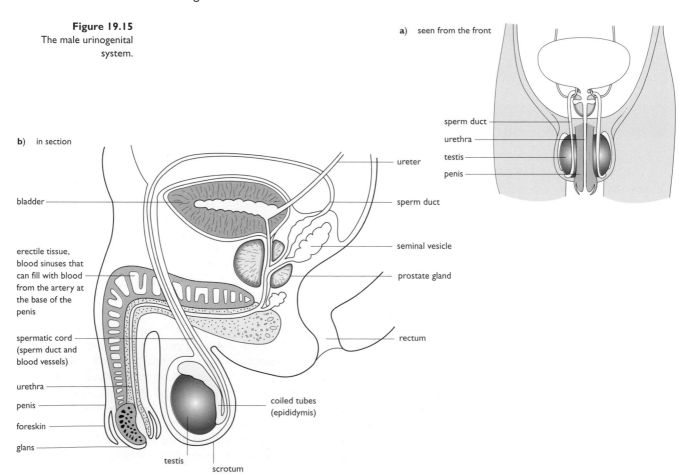

a) seen from the front

sperm duct
urethra
testis
penis

b) in section

ureter

bladder

sperm duct

erectile tissue, blood sinuses that can fill with blood from the artery at the base of the penis

seminal vesicle

prostate gland

spermatic cord (sperm duct and blood vessels)

rectum

urethra

penis

coiled tubes (epididymis)

foreskin

glans

testis

scrotum

The **female reproductive system** (Figure 19.16) consists of the following:

- The **ovaries** produce the ova. The ovaries are held near the base of the abdominal cavity. They are also endocrine glands, and secrete the female sex hormones **oestrogen** and **progesterone**.
- A pair of **oviducts** extend from the uterus and open as funnels close to the ovaries. The oviducts transport oocytes, and are the site of fertilisation.
- The **uterus**, or womb, is about the size and shape of an inverted pear. It has a thick muscular wall, together with an inner lining of mucous membrane richly supplied with arterioles. This lining, called the **endometrium**, undergoes regular change in a 28-day cycle. Each month the lining is built up in preparation for implantation and early nutrition of a developing embryo, should fertilisation of an oocyte occur. If this does not occur, the endometrium disintegrates and menstruation starts.
- The **vagina** is a muscular tube that can enlarge to allow entry of the penis, and exit of a baby at birth. The vagina is connected to the uterus at the cervix, and it opens to the exterior at the vulva.

Figure 19.16
The female urinogenital system.

a)   seen from the front

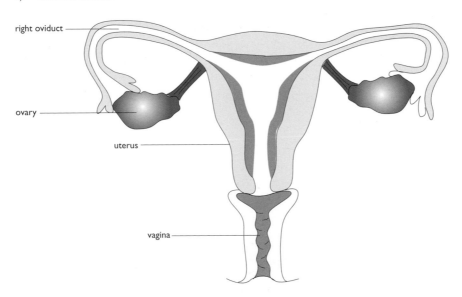

b)   in section

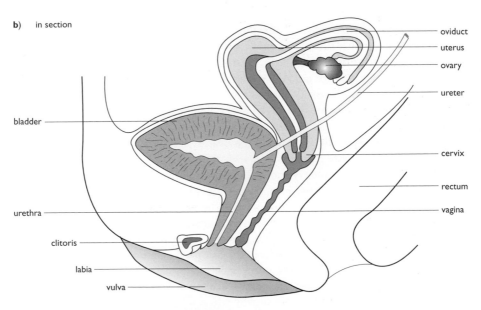

Gamete formation

Many gametes are produced, very few of which are used in reproduction. **Gametogenesis**, or the formation of gametes, occurs in both the testes and the ovaries. In the process of gamete formation there is a common sequence of phases. First there is **multiplication**, in which the gamete mother cells divide by mitotic cell division. This division is repeated to produce many cells that become gametes. Then each cell undergoes **growth**. Finally **maturation** occurs, which involves meiosis and results in the formation of the haploid gametes. These phases are summarised in Figure 19.17, where the differences in sperm and ovum production are also shown.

Figure 19.17
The phases and changes during gametogenesis.

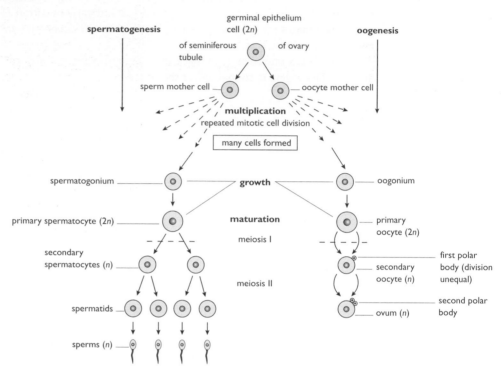

Spermatogenesis (Figure 19.18) begins in the testes at puberty and continues throughout life. The testis consists of **seminiferous tubules** lined by germinal epithelial cells that divide repeatedly. The cells formed, called **spermatogonia**, grow to form primary **spermatocytes**. Then by meiosis I, secondary spermatocytes are formed, which become **spermatids** by meiosis II. These are released into the lumen of the tubules. Also present in the tubules are nutritive cells, which sustain the spermatids as they mature into sperms.

Oogenesis (Figure 19.19) begins in the ovaries of the fetus before birth, but the final development of oocytes is completed in adult life. The germinal epithelium, which lines the outer surface of the ovary, divides by mitotic cell division to form **oogonia**. These cells migrate into the connective tissue of the ovary, where they grow and enlarge to form the primary **oocytes**. Each oocyte becomes surrounded by layers of follicle cells, and the whole structure is called a **primary follicle**. At birth, the ovaries contain about 200 000 primary follicles. These remain dormant until puberty.

Between puberty and the cessation of ovulation at menopause, typically at 45–55 years of age, primary follicles begin to develop. Several start to grow each month, but usually only one matures. The others degenerate. The primary oocyte in its follicle then undergoes meiosis I. The cytoplasmic division that follows is unequal, forming a tiny polar body and a secondary oocyte. The second meiotic division, meiosis II, begins but does not go to completion. In this condition, ovulation occurs. The secondary oocyte is released from its secondary follicle and from the ovary by rupture of the ovary wall. The remains of the primary follicle immediately develop into a 'yellow body', called the **corpus luteum**. This is an additional but temporary endocrine gland, of which more will be said shortly.

Figure 19.18
The testis, and stages in spermatogenesis.

testis, in section, part dissected

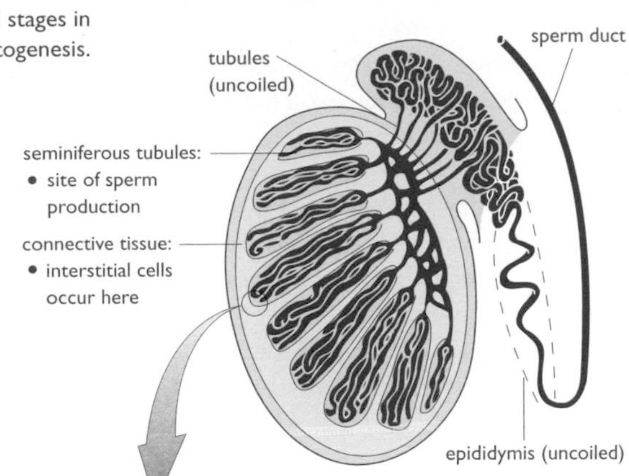

tubules (uncoiled)

sperm duct

seminiferous tubules:
• site of sperm production

connective tissue:
• interstitial cells occur here

epididymis (uncoiled)

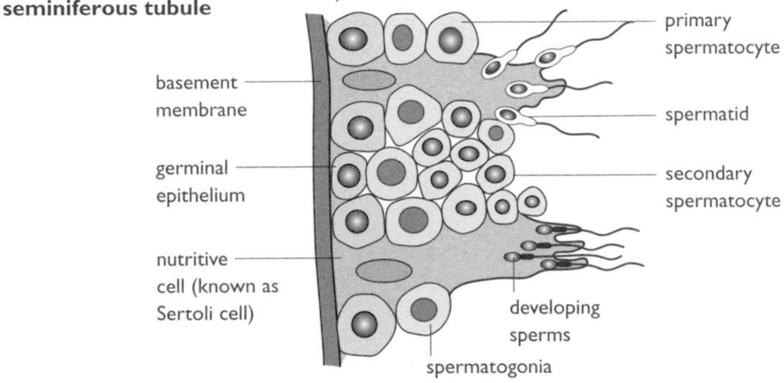

photomicrograph of TS of seminiferous tubule, HP

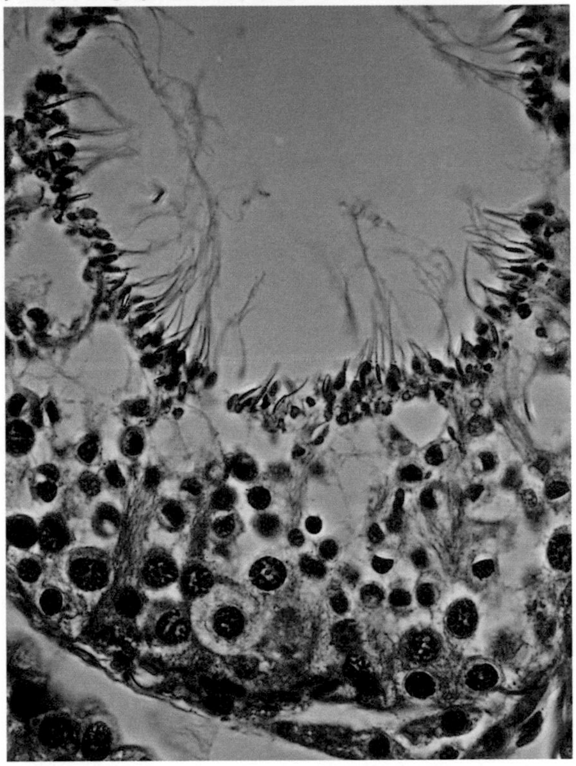

TS part of the seminiferous tubule

basement membrane

germinal epithelium

nutritive cell (known as Sertoli cell)

primary spermatocyte

spermatid

secondary spermatocyte

developing sperms

spermatogonia

ovary in section, showing stages in development of secondary oocyte

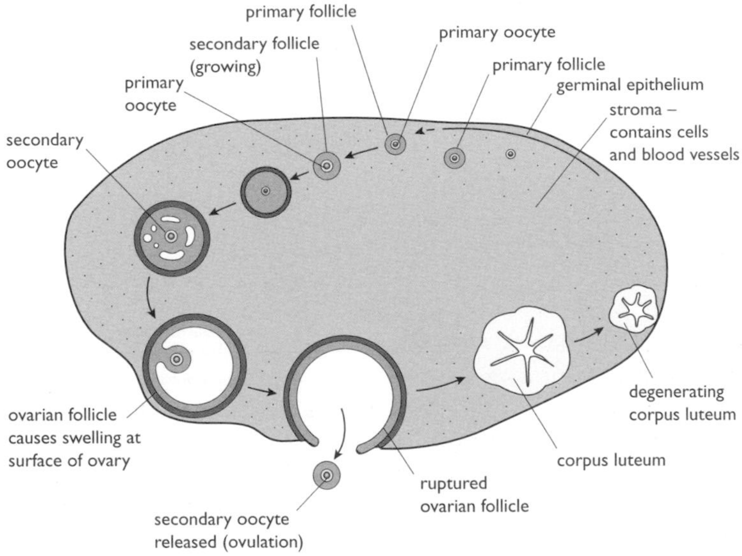

primary follicle

secondary follicle (growing)

primary oocyte

secondary oocyte

primary oocyte

primary follicle

germinal epithelium

stroma – contains cells and blood vessels

ovarian follicle causes swelling at surface of ovary

degenerating corpus luteum

corpus luteum

ruptured ovarian follicle

secondary oocyte released (ovulation)

photomicrograph of mammalian ovary, LP

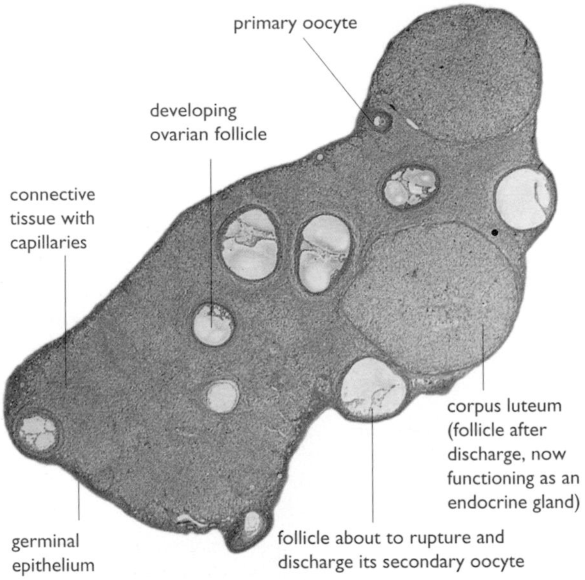

primary oocyte

developing ovarian follicle

connective tissue with capillaries

corpus luteum (follicle after discharge, now functioning as an endocrine gland)

germinal epithelium

follicle about to rupture and discharge its secondary oocyte

Figure 19.19
The ovary, and stages in oogenesis.

Fertilisation

In mammals, fertilisation is internal and occurs in the upper part of the oviduct. The sperms are introduced into the female during sexual intercourse. The erect penis is placed in the vagina, and semen may be ejaculated (3–5 cm^3 in humans) close to the cervix. Typically, more than one hundred million sperms are deposited. The pH of the vagina is quite acid, but the alkaline secretion of the prostate gland, a component of the semen, helps to neutralise the acidity and provides an environment in which sperms can survive. Waves of contractions in the muscular walls of the uterus and the oviducts assist in drawing semen from the cervix to the site of fertilisation. In this way, a few thousand of the sperms reach the upper uterus and swim up the oviducts. One or more of the few sperms reach a secondary oocyte, passing between the follicle cells surrounding it. Next, the coat that surrounds the oocyte, made of glycoprotein and called the **zona pellucida**, has to be crossed. This is made possible by hydrolytic enzymes which are packaged in the tip of the head of the sperm (called the 'acrosome'). When this is in contact with the zona pellucida, these enzymes are released and digest a pathway for the sperm to reach the oocyte membrane. This process is part of the activation process, called '**capacitation**', in which sperms are prepared for fertilisation.

The head of the sperm, containing the male nucleus, is at last able to fuse with the oocyte membrane (Figure 19.20). The nucleus enters the oocyte. As this happens, granules in the outer cytoplasm of the oocyte release their contents outside the oocyte by exocytosis (Figure 3.27, page 71). These prevent the oocyte plasma membrane being crossed by another sperm.

As the sperm nucleus enters the oocyte, completion of meiosis II is triggered, and the second polar body is released. Only at this point do the male and female haploid nuclei come together to form the diploid nucleus of the zygote. Fertilisation is completed. Figure 19.21 summarises the stages of fertilisation.

Figure 19.20
Fertilisation of a human secondary oocyte.

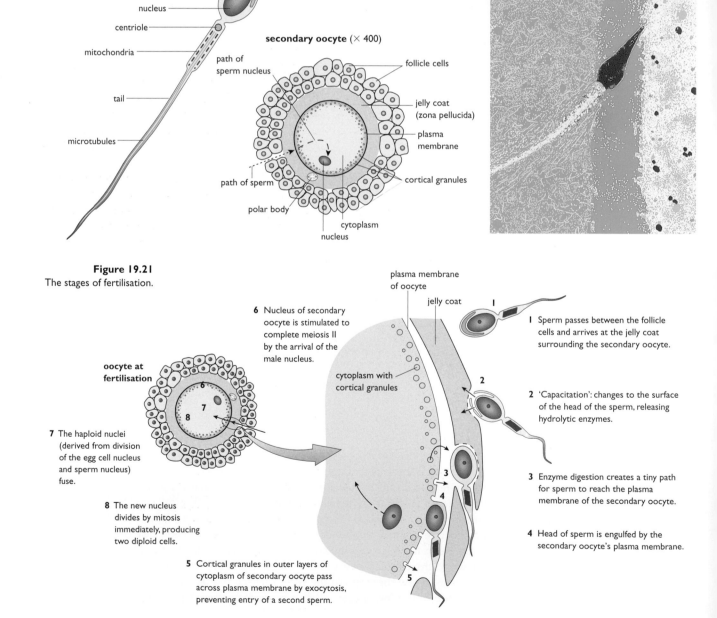

human sperm and secondary oocyte at fertilisation

sperm (× 800)
- acrosome (hydrolytic enzyme)
- nucleus
- centriole
- mitochondria
- tail
- microtubules

secondary oocyte (× 400)
- path of sperm nucleus
- follicle cells
- jelly coat (zona pellucida)
- plasma membrane
- cortical granules
- path of sperm
- polar body
- cytoplasm
- nucleus

TEM of fertilisation, showing the head of the sperm penetrating the glycoprotein coat, HP

Figure 19.21
The stages of fertilisation.

oocyte at fertilisation

6 Nucleus of secondary oocyte is stimulated to complete meiosis II by the arrival of the male nucleus.

plasma membrane of oocyte

jelly coat

cytoplasm with cortical granules

1 Sperm passes between the follicle cells and arrives at the jelly coat surrounding the secondary oocyte.

2 'Capacitation': changes to the surface of the head of the sperm, releasing hydrolytic enzymes.

7 The haploid nuclei (derived from division of the egg cell nucleus and sperm nucleus) fuse.

3 Enzyme digestion creates a tiny path for sperm to reach the plasma membrane of the secondary oocyte.

8 The new nucleus divides by mitosis immediately, producing two diploid cells.

4 Head of sperm is engulfed by the secondary oocyte's plasma membrane.

5 Cortical granules in outer layers of cytoplasm of secondary oocyte pass across plasma membrane by exocytosis, preventing entry of a second sperm.

Extension   Oestrus in animals

In animals, including farm animals, sexual activity (mating) is usually coordinated with the most favourable time of the year for rearing the young. For example, the breeding season for sheep occurs in late summer or autumn, after a time when food has been readily available and the female's body is likely to be prepared for the demands that reproduction will place on her. During the breeding season the female has times of sexual activity or **oestrus** ('heat'), alternating with times of sexual inactivity. Ewes come on heat for about 24 hours or so every 16–17 days at this time. The signs of oestrus are the restlessness of the animal, which may mount or be mounted by others in the herd. A ewe in oestrus has enlarged external genitalia; the vulva becomes red and swollen and there may be a discharge. The ewe produces various secretions that act as pheromones (volatile hormones), inducing sexual activity in the male. The ewe will then allow mating to occur, but all sexual activity ends when pregnancy starts. The ewe is then 'in lamb' for about 5 months. Each ewe produces between one and three lambs.

The environment provides the stimulus for the onset of oestrus in animals. The length of daily illumination falling on the eyes controls the release of releasing hormone by the hypothalamus (see Figure 19.25). In males, sperm production by the testes is increased. Changes in the male and female are coordinated to ensure that mating occurs when both are most fertile.

Early development and implantation

Fertilisation occurs in the upper oviduct. As the zygote is transported down the oviduct, aided by cilia, mitosis and cell division commences (Figure 19.22). The process of the division of the zygote into a mass of daughter cells is known as **cleavage**. This is the first stage in the growth and development of a new individual. Note that the embryo does not increase in mass at this stage, but by the time the embryo has reached the uterus it is a solid ball of tiny cells called **blastomeres**. Division continues and the blastomeres next organise themselves into a fluid-filled ball, called a **blastocyst**.

In humans, by day seven the blastocyst consists of about one hundred cells. At this point it starts to embed itself in the endometrium – a process known as **implantation**. Implantation takes from day 7 to day 14 approximately. At this stage, some of the blastomeres appear to be grouped together; they are known as the **inner cell mass**, and it is these cells that will eventually become the fetus proper. Once implanted, the embryo starts to receive nutrients directly from the endometrium of the uterus wall.

Figure 19.22
The site of the earliest stages of development of the embryo.

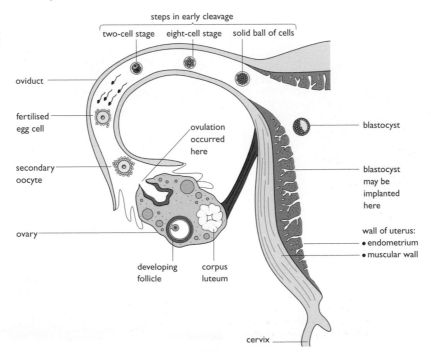

Human gestation: zygote to embryo to fetus

The period of development in the mother's body, lasting from conception to birth, is known as **gestation** (it lasts for 40 weeks in humans). The rate of growth and development during gestation is much greater than in any other stage of life. During the first 2 months of gestation the developing offspring is described as an **embryo** (Figure 19.23). By the end of 2 months' development the beginning of the principal adult organs can be detected, the **embryonic membranes** have appeared and the **placenta** is operational. During the rest of gestation, the developing offspring is called a **fetus**.

The structure and role of the placenta

The outer layers of the embryo grow and give rise to the placenta and the membranes (Figures 19.23 and 19.24). The placenta and membranes support and protect the embryo proper. The innermost membrane (the amnion) surrounds a fluid-filled cavity (the amniotic cavity), in which the fetus becomes suspended, cushioned against mechanical damage. By the end of the 12th week the embryo has formed most of its organ systems. The fetus exchanges nutrients and waste products with the maternal blood system through the fully formed placenta, to which it is connected by the **umbilical cord**. The placenta is a disc-shaped structure composed of both maternal (endometrial) and fetal membrane tissues. Here the maternal and fetal blood circulations are brought very close together over a huge surface area, but they do *not* mix. The placenta and fetus are connected by two fetal arteries and a fetal vein, in the umbilical cord.

Exchange in the placenta is by diffusion and active transport. The exchanges and other functions of the placenta are as follows:

- **Respiratory gases are exchanged**. Oxygen diffuses across the placenta from the maternal haemoglobin to the fetal haemoglobin (see page 239). Carbon dioxide diffuses in the opposite direction.
- **Water** crosses the placenta by osmosis, **glucose** by facilitated diffusion, and **ions** and **amino acids** are transported actively.
- **Excretory products** leave the fetus, including urea.
- **Antibodies present** in the mother's blood cross the placenta. The fetus is protected from the same diseases to which the mother has antibodies. This form of immunity (passive immunity, see page 338) gradually disappears after birth as the fetus's own immune system has not manufactured the antibodies.
- It acts as an **endocrine gland**, initially producing HCG (page 432), and later progesterone and oestrogen, taking over from the corpus luteum.
- It acts as a **barrier to bacteria** (although some viruses can cross).

2 Why is it so important that the blood of mother and offspring do not mix together in the placenta?

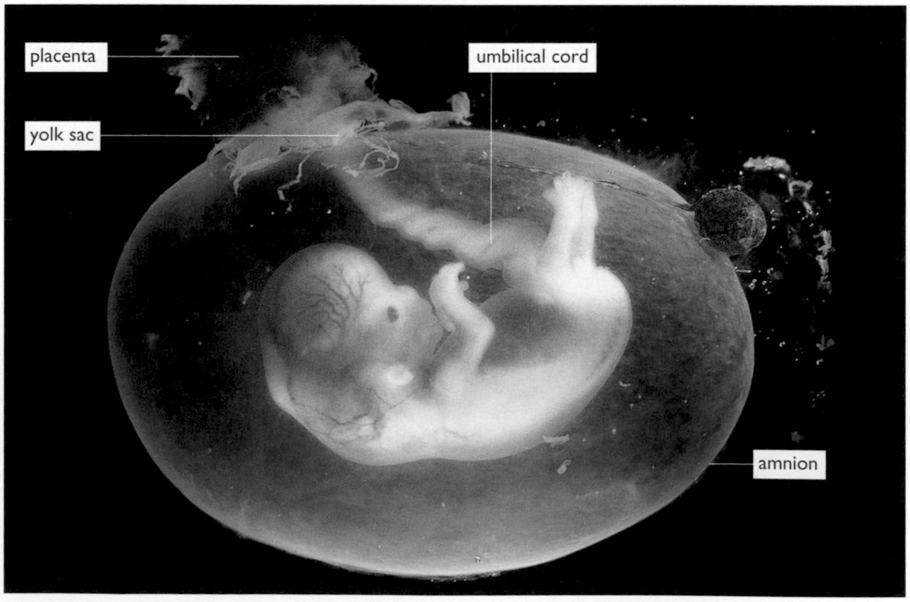

Figure 19.23
Human embryo at 6 week stage.

placenta

umbilical cord

yolk sac

amnion

Figure 19.24
The placenta.

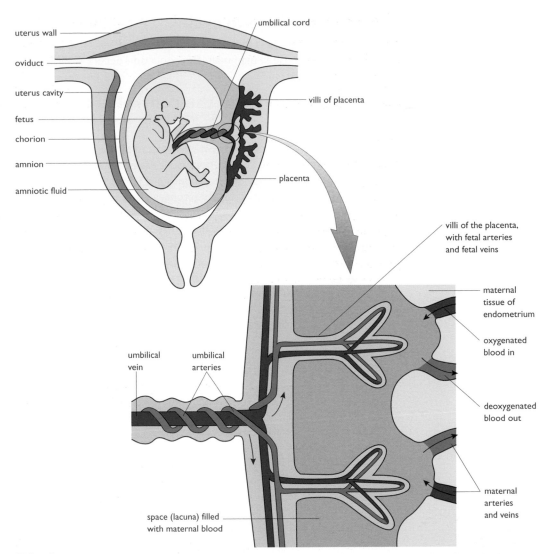

Birth

Shortly before birth a hormone, **oxytocin**, relaxes the elastic fibres that join the bones of the pelvic girdle, especially at the front. It thus aids widening (dilation) of the cervix for the head (the widest part of the offspring) to pass through. Powerful, intermittent waves of contraction of the muscles of the uterus wall occur, starting at the top and moving towards the cervix. During this process, known as 'labour', the rate and strength of the contractions increase to expel the offspring. Finally, less powerful uterine contractions separate the placenta from the endometrium, and cause the discharge of the placenta and remains of the umbilicus, known as 'afterbirth'.

Lactation

During pregnancy, the **mammary glands** are prepared for **milk production** by the action of the hormones. Just before birth, **lactation** commences. Lactation is the production, secretion and ejection of milk, and is controlled by a hormone, **prolactin**, from the anterior pituitary gland.

In the first 2–3 days the milk, called **colostrum**, provides sugar and protein, but no fat. Also present are antibodies that aid survival during first exposures to potentially dangerous microorganisms. Later-formed milk is an almost complete diet, providing 1.5–2.0% protein, 3.5% fat, 6.5% milk sugar (lactose), and 0.3% vitamins and minerals (for example, Ca^{2+}, vitamins A and B, although milk is relatively deficient in vitamins C and D) with water. Milk is deficient in iron, however, and offspring have to rely on the iron stored in their liver until their diet changes and develops.

The mammalian life cycle

The mammalian life cycle is diploid, with haploid gametes. The diagram in Figure 19.2 (page 411) represents the life cycle in mammals. Reproduction occurs sexually, and no form of asexual reproduction occurs.

Roles of hormones in the control of reproduction

In females

There are two **female sex hormones**, secreted by the ovaries, known as **oestrogen** and **progesterone**. These are steroid hormones (as is the male hormone testosterone, see page 432). Secretion of the female sex hormones are under the direct control of two other hormones, which are secreted by the pituitary gland (anterior lobe) (Figure 19.25). These hormones, made of protein, are called **luteinising hormone (LH)** and **follicle stimulating hormone (FSH)**. LH and FSH are also present in the male. They are known as 'gonadotrophic hormones' or 'gonadotrophins' because their roles are to stimulate the gonads. Secretion of gonadotrophic hormones is initiated at puberty (and thereafter maintained) by the action of a fourth hormone, called **gonadotrophin releasing hormone (GnRH)**. This releasing hormone originates in the hypothalamus, a part of the brain to which the pituitary gland is connected.

Oestrogen and progesterone bring about the increase in size of the reproductive organs, and secondary sexual characteristics of the female, such as the growth of the breasts. Another effect

Figure 19.25
Hormone regulation of the menstrual cycle.

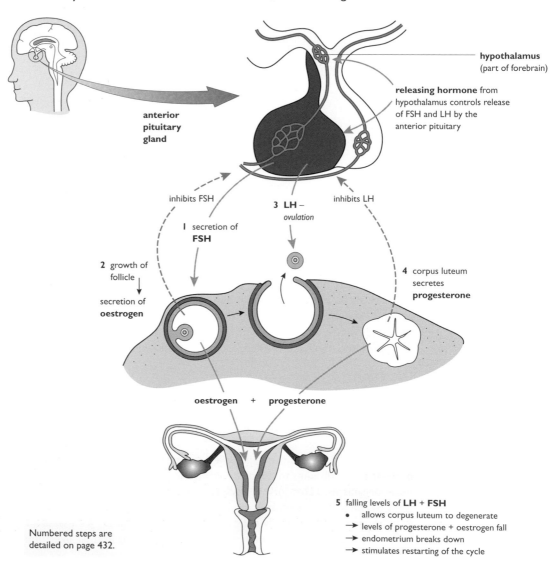

hypothalamus
(part of forebrain)

releasing hormone from hypothalamus controls release of FSH and LH by the anterior pituitary

anterior pituitary gland

inhibits FSH

3 LH –
ovulation

inhibits LH

I secretion of **FSH**

2 growth of follicle

secretion of **oestrogen**

4 corpus luteum secretes **progesterone**

oestrogen + progesterone

Numbered steps are detailed on page 432.

5 falling levels of **LH + FSH**
- allows corpus luteum to degenerate
→ levels of progesterone + oestrogen fall
→ endometrium breaks down
→ stimulates restarting of the cycle

they have is to stimulate muscle protein formation and bone growth. Because of this, they are known as 'anabolic steroids' ('anabolic' means 'build up'), but the effects of the female sex hormones are less marked, in this respect, than those of testosterone in the male. Nevertheless, when female sex hormone levels fall after menopause, some women experience loss of bone density, a disease known as osteoporosis.

In the female the secretion of sex hormones is cyclical, rather than occurring at a steady rate. In fact, there are two cycles of change at work, one in the ovaries and one in the uterus lining. Together these sets of change make up the **menstrual cycle** (Figure 19.26). 'Menstrual' means monthly, and the cycle takes 28 days.

Figure 19.26
The changing levels of hormones in the menstrual cycle.

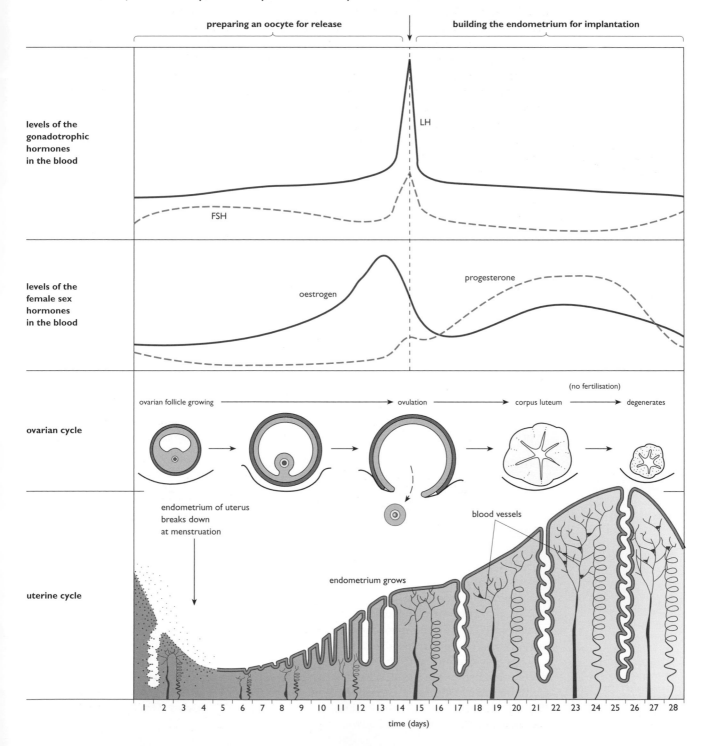

By convention, the first day of this cycle is taken as the first day of menstruation (bleeding), which is the shedding of the endometrium lining of the uterus. The steps, which are also depicted in Figure 19.25, are as follows:

1 FSH is secreted by the **pituitary gland**, and stimulates development of several primary follicles in the ovary. Only one will complete development into an ovarian follicle (see Figure 19.19).

2 The **developing follicle** then secretes oestrogen. Oestrogen has two targets. In the uterus it stimulates the build-up of the endometrium, which prepares the lining for a possible implantation of an embryo, should fertilisation take place. In the pituitary gland, it inhibits the further secretion of FSH. This prevents the possibility of other follicles being stimulated to develop. It is an example of negative feedback control (see page 253).

3 Meanwhile, the concentration of oestrogen continues to build-up, increasing to a peak value just before the midpoint of the cycle. This high and rising level of oestrogen suddenly stimulates the secretion of LH and, to a slightly lesser extent, FSH, by the **pituitary gland**. LH stimulates **ovulation**.

As soon as the ovarian follicle has discharged its secondary oocyte, LH also stimulates the conversion of the vacant follicle into a corpus luteum.

4 The **corpus luteum** now secretes progesterone and to a lesser extent, oestrogen. Progesterone has two targets. In the uterus it continues the build-up of the endometrium, further preparing for a possible implantation of an embryo, should fertilisation take place. In the pituitary gland the effect of the progesterone is to inhibit further secretion of LH, and also of FSH. (This is a second example of negative feedback control.)

5 The levels of FSH and LH in the bloodstream are now rapidly decreasing. Low FSH and LH levels allow the corpus luteum to degenerate. As a consequence, the levels of progesterone and of oestrogen also fall. Soon the levels of these hormones are low. Under these conditions, the extra lining of the uterus is no longer maintained. The endometrium breaks down and is lost through the vagina in the first 5 days or so of the new cycle.

Falling levels of progesterone mean the release of FSH by the pituitary is no longer inhibited, so that FSH is again secreted. A new cycle is under way.

6 **If the secondary oocyte discharged at ovulation is fertilised**, then the woman becomes pregnant. The developing embryo itself immediately becomes an endocrine gland, secreting a hormone called **human chorionic gonadotrophin** (**HCG**). This circulates in the blood and maintains the corpus luteum as an endocrine gland, for at least the first 16 weeks of the pregnancy. When eventually the corpus luteum does break down, the placenta takes over as an endocrine gland, secreting oestrogen and progesterone. These hormones continue to prevent ovulation, maintain the endometrium and prepare the mammary glands for lactation.

In males

In the male, the secretion of sex hormone is a continuous process, rather than cyclic. At puberty, releasing hormones from the hypothalamus trigger the secretion of FSH and LH by the anterior lobe of the pituitary (as in the female). In the male, however, LH stimulates the endocrine cells of the testes (interstitial cells – they occur in the connective tissue between the seminiferous tubules) to secrete **testosterone**, the male sex hormone.

Secretion of testosterone at this stage in development causes the enlargement of the penis, growth of body hair, enlargement of the larynx and growth of muscles and bone (remember, testosterone is an anabolic steroid hormone). These features are referred to as the **secondary sexual characteristics**. Testosterone also stimulates growth of the germinal epithelium of the seminiferous tubules, and sperm production commences. Testosterone and FSH trigger development of the nutritive (**Sertoli**) cells. Testosterone secretion continues throughout life.

Overactivity of the testes is regulated by negative feedback control. For example, a very high level of testosterone in the blood inhibits secretion of LH, and the concentration of LH in the blood then falls. Testosterone production decreases. Similarly overactivity of the nutritive (Sertoli) cells causes a hormone inhibitor to be produced and released. This inhibits FSH and spermatogenesis is then slowed down.

3 Distinguish between the following pairs:

• sexual and asexual reproduction
• calyx and corolla
• androecium and gynaecium
• pollination and fertilisation
• ovule and ovary
• endosperm nucleus and egg cell
• endospermic and non-endospermic seeds
• unisexual and hermaphrodite
• external and internal fertilisation
• prostate gland and seminal vesicles
• nutritive cells and interstitial cells
• ovaries and oviducts
• ovarian follicle and corpus luteum
• umbilical cord and placenta
• pregnancy and lactation.

● **Extension** Hormones and human fertility

Use of hormones in contraception

Hormone methods of contraception (the 'pill') work by interfering with natural hormone levels and gamete production. For example, the female contraceptive pill is a mixture of synthetic forms of oestrogen and progesterone. If the pill is taken as prescribed, the raised level of these hormones in the blood acts through negative feedback. The secretion of releasing hormones by the hypothalamus is suppressed. The effect of this is to lower the concentrations of LH and FSH in the blood. Remember, it is the very high concentration of LH and FSH that naturally triggers ovulation. So the lowering of LH and FSH levels has the effect of:

* preventing ovulation
* preventing maintenance of the endometrium at a level that allows implantation
* maintaining a cervical mucus that is too viscous to permit entry of sperms.

Hormones in infertility treatment

Infertility may affect as many as 15% of the adult population in developed countries. It has many causes, but most commonly it can be attributed to failure to ovulate by the female partner, or the absence of sperms or a very low count of sperms in semen. One way that conception can be aided is the process of *in vitro* **fertilisation** (**IVF**). This technique involves:

* use of 'fertility drugs' (LH and FSH) to stimulate the ovaries to release many oocytes ('superovulation')
* collection of oocytes directly from the ovaries by microsurgery techniques
* collection of a sperm sample from the partner or a donor
* '*in vitro*' (literally 'in glass') fertilisation by mixing sperms and eggs in a dish under controlled laboratory conditions
* laboratory incubation of fertilised ova to check normal, healthy cell divisions and growth
* return of a selection of healthy embryos (typically at the blastocyst stage) to the uterus for implantation. Normally three embryos are reintroduced, in the anticipation that one may implant.

The first child born as a result of IVF (1978) is now a young adult. Many cases of infertility have been overcome by this technique.

● **Extension** Menopause and HRT

Menopause is the ending of the monthly menstruations. It is due to a gradual failure of the ovaries, which occurs after the age of 50 years. The physical and psychological symptoms of menopause are mostly due to reduced oestrogen levels. One of the long-term changes involved, loss of bone density, leads to the disease osteoporosis. The symptoms are prevented by taking oestrogen in pill form, by skin implant or by skin patch. This treatment is known as **hormone replacement therapy** (**HRT**).

● **Skills task** Humans may intervene in their reproduction in the following ways:
* contraception (prevention of fertilisation), birth control (prevention of birth) and abortion (induced, as opposed to spontaneous abortion)
* treatment of male infertility (low sperm count, abnormal sperms or impotence) and female infertility (failure to ovulate or damage to oviducts or uterus)
* *in vitro* fertilisation techniques, including artificial insemination or egg donation, and surrogacy.

Taking one major aspect of these developments, investigate:
1 the part played by advances in reproduction physiology, genetics and medical technology
2 the main ethical issues that arise.

Prepare to report concisely on your findings to your peers, including a personal evaluation of the ethical issues.

Examination questions

1 The diagram represents a flower.

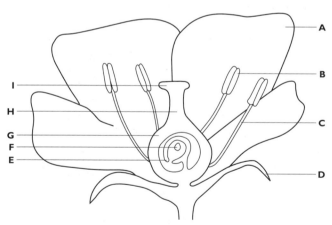

a Give the letter of the structure which:
  i becomes the fruit wall;
  ii becomes the testa (seed coat);
  iii produces pollen grains. (3)
b Explain **two** ways, shown in the diagram, in which this flower is adapted for insect pollination. (2)

AQA(AEB), A level, 0607/1, June 1999

2 a Distinguish between *pollination* and *fertilisation* in flowering plants. (1)
b Describe the development of a flowering plant embryo sac from an embryo sac mother cell. (4)

The figure shows an embryo sac of *Epipactis helleborine*, with an unfertilised ovule. The chromosome number of this plant is $2n = 40$.

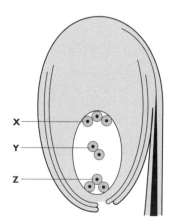

© MEYER & ANDERSON, *Plant Physiology* (Van Nostrand, 1952), Thomson Learning

c State the number of chromosomes in structures **X** and **Y**. (1)
d Outline what happens to structures **Y** and **Z** at fertilisation. (4)

UCLES, A level, 4805, Mar 1997

3 The diagram shows the relationship between some of the glands and hormones controlling the oestrous cycle.

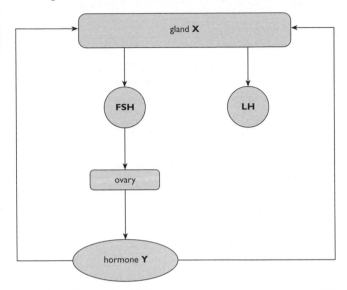

a i Name gland **X**. (1)
  ii Name hormone **Y**. (1)

The graphs show the change in concentrations of follicle stimulating hormone (FSH), luteinising hormone (LH) and hormone **Y** in the blood, during part of an oestrous cycle.

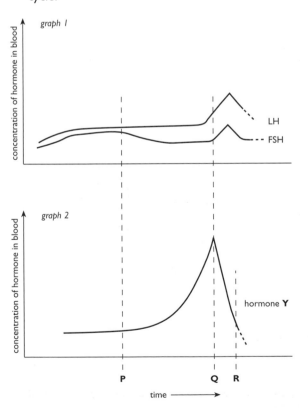

b i Use the letter '**O**' to show on graph 1 when ovulation is most likely to occur. (1)

ii What is the term given to the effect hormone **Y** has on FSH between times **P** and **Q**? (1)
iii What causes the change of concentration of hormone **Y** between times **Q** and **R**? (1)

AQA(NEAB), AS/A level, BY01, June 1999

4 The table below refers to four hormones associated with the human menstrual cycle.

If the statement is correct, place a tick (✓) in the appropriate row and if the statement is incorrect place a cross (✗) in the appropriate row.

Hormone	Secreted by ovaries	Reaches highest level in blood before ovulation
follicle stimulating hormone (FSH)		
luteinising hormone (LH)		
oestrogen		
progesterone		

(4)

London, A level, Module B3, June 1997

5 The diagram below shows the structure of part of a mammalian placenta and the umbilical cord, which is attached to a developing fetus.

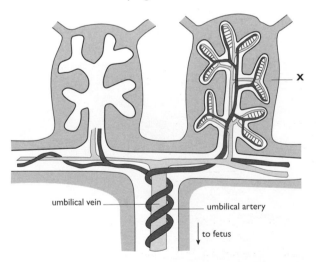

a State *two* substances which would be present in a higher concentration in the umbilical vein than in the umbilical artery. (2)
b The cavity labelled **X** contains maternal blood. Suggest why it is an advantage for this blood to be in a cavity rather than in a vessel. (2)

London, A level, Module B3, Jan 1997

20 Inheritance

STARTING POINTS
● Genetics is the study of **inheritance** of characteristics by offspring from their parents.
● In sexual reproduction **haploid gametes** fuse to form a **diploid zygote** which grows and develops into an **offspring**.
● Gametes are formed by meiotic cell division, and differ from each other because:
— **independent assortment** of maternal and paternal chromosomes into the four gametes occurs in meiosis, forming new combinations of chromosomes
— **crossing over** of segments of individual maternal and paternal homologous chromosomes occurs in meiosis, forming new combinations of genes
— **fertilisation is random**, so any sperm may fuse with any egg cell.
● Consequently, **offspring differ genetically** both from each other and from their parents.

● Variation

Individuals of a species are strikingly similar, which is exactly how we identify them, for example, as humans, buttercups or houseflies. But individuals also show numerous differences, although we may initially have to look carefully for them in members of species other than our own. Certainly, within families there are remarkable similarities between parents and their offspring. However, no two members of a family are genetically identical, apart from identical twins.

Genetics is the science of **heredity**. It is the study of how **variation** arises and how the **characteristics** of individuals are passed from generation to generation.

Variation in living things may be due to genetics or to an effect of the environment on the individual, or both. Genetic differences are controlled by **genes**. Some variations among the individuals of the crowd in Figure 20.1 are due to genetic difference alone – such as their sex. Other variations between individuals are due to the environment they experience – such as an illness due to a vitamin or mineral deficiency. Other variations are possibly due to the interaction of both genetics and environment – such as their weights.

Figure 20.1
All the same species, but they show many variations!

Discontinuous and continuous variations

Variations are of two types (Figure 20.2). Discrete or **discontinuous variations** are ones in which the characteristic concerned is one of two or more types, but with no intermediate forms. Examples include the garden pea plant, which may be tall or dwarf, the fruits of the maize cob, which may be yellow or purple, and cattle, which may be horned or hornless (polled). In humans, the ear lobe is either formed free from the side of the head or is attached. Similarly, in ABO blood grouping, humans are found to be one of the A, B, AB or O groups. There are no intermediate forms in any of these examples. Discontinuous variations are genetically determined. That means they are controlled by genes, as we shall see later.

In **continuous variation** the variable is not discrete. Here there is a merging or blending of the different alternative forms giving a continuous distribution of physical types. Height in humans is a good example. The heights obtained from the measurement of a very large sample of adult humans may take any value between the lower and upper extremes, though they will show a **normal** distribution (for each sex), with most people being somewhere in the middle. Continuous variations may be genetically determined, or they may be due to environmental and genetic factors working together.

Figure 20.2
Discontinuous and continuous variables.

examples of discontinuous variation

I horned and hornless (polled) cattle

 2 free-lobed and attached lobe (external ear)

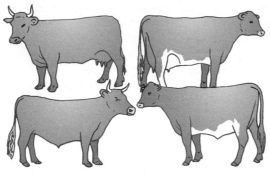

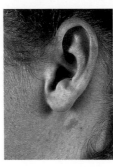
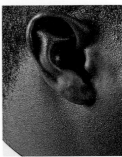

3 dwarf and tall pea plant – variation in height above ground

The heights of these plants fall into two discrete groups, in both of which there is a normal distribution of variation, but with no overlap between the groups.

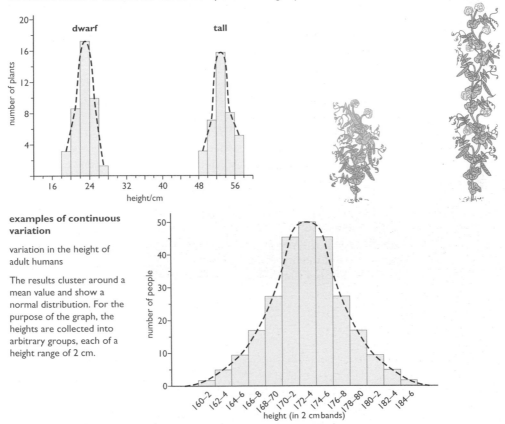

examples of continuous variation

variation in the height of adult humans

The results cluster around a mean value and show a normal distribution. For the purpose of the graph, the heights are collected into arbitrary groups, each of a height range of 2 cm.

Inheriting genes in sexual reproduction

In sexual reproduction, haploid gametes are formed, by meiosis, from the nuclei of diploid cells in the gonads (page 422). So, each gamete contains only one copy of each gene. The units of heredity are genes: sections of the DNA molecule running the length of a chromosome (page 438). The genes control the different characteristics of organisms.

At fertilisation, male and female gametes fuse to form a zygote. Consequently, the zygote is a diploid cell with two sets of chromosomes, known as **homologous pairs**, one from each parent. Thus there are *two copies* of each gene. These lie in the same positions, or **loci**, on the two homologous chromosomes (Figure 20.3). The alternative forms of a gene are called **alleles**. There are at least two alleles of every gene.

Figure 20.3
An homologous pair of chromosomes.

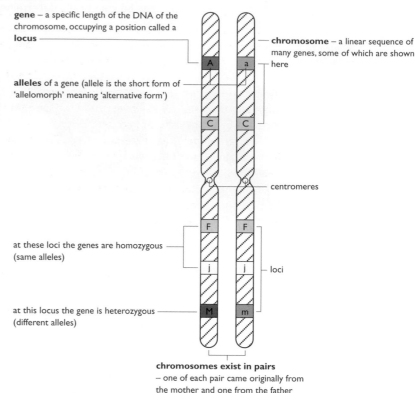

The **loci** are the positions along the chromosomes where genes occur, so alleles of the same gene occupy the same locus.

gene – a specific length of the DNA of the chromosome, occupying a position called a **locus**

alleles of a gene (allele is the short form of 'allelomorph' meaning 'alternative form')

chromosome – a linear sequence of many genes, some of which are shown here

centromeres

at these loci the genes are homozygous (same alleles)

loci

at this locus the gene is heterozygous (different alleles)

chromosomes exist in pairs – one of each pair came originally from the mother and one from the father

Genotype and phenotype

The alleles that an organism carries (which are present in every cell) make up the genotype of that organism. A genotype in which the two alleles of a gene are the same is said to be **homozygous** for that gene. If the alleles are different then the organism is **heterozygous** for that gene.

The **genotype** is the genetic constitution of an organism. Alleles interact in various ways, and the genotype also interacts with environmental factors. The outcome is the phenotype. The **phenotype** is the way in which the genotype of the organism is expressed – for example, in the appearance of the organism.

Table 20.1 is a summary of these and other basic genetic terms.

Table 20.1
Essential genetic terms.

genotype:	the genetic constitution of an organism
phenotype:	the characteristics displayed by the organism – the way in which the genotype is expressed (appearance of an organism)
gene:	the basic unit of inheritance by which inherited characteristics are transferred from parents to offspring, consisting of a length of DNA on a chromosome
allele:	alternative forms of a gene, occupying a specific position (locus) on a chromosome
dominant allele:	an allele that affects the phenotype of the organism whether present in the heterozygous or homozygous condition; represented by a capital letter in a genetic cross
recessive allele:	an allele that affects the phenotype of the organism only when the dominant allele is absent (that is, in homozygous recessive individuals); represented by a lower-case letter in a genetic cross
homozygous:	a diploid organism that has inherited the same allele (for any particular gene) from both parents
heterozygous:	a diploid organism that has inherited different alleles from each parent

Patterns of inheritance

Inheritance of a single pair of contrasting characteristics

A breeding experiment in which the inheritance of the alleles of a single gene is investigated is called a **monohybrid cross**. The example chosen here is one that was used when the mechanism of inheritance was first successfully investigated. Experiments were conducted into the inheritance of contrasting characteristics of the garden pea plant, *Pisum sativum*. In this case the investigation centred on the height of stem in the garden pea plant, which may be either 'tall' (say about 48 cm), or 'dwarf' (about 12 cm). This characteristic is controlled by a single gene with two alleles.

The plants used as the **parental generation (P)** in this cross were one tall and one dwarf plant, and they were **pure breeding** plants. 'Pure breeding' plants are ones that, when crossed among themselves, always gives rise to offspring that are like the parents. The geneticist's term for pure breeding is homozygous.

The garden pea plant naturally self-pollinates (and therefore fertilises itself), even though the flowers open and insects such as the honey bee visit for pollen and nectar, and transport pollen between flowers. So, in order to carry out a genetic 'cross' between different garden pea plants, self-pollination had to be prevented. This was achieved by removing the male parts of the flowers, the stamens, whilst the flower was still immature (that is before the pollen had been formed). Pollen was then introduced from a flower on a plant with the contrasting characteristic (that is, pollen from a flower of a tall plant was introduced on to the stigma of a dwarf plant, and vice versa). This technique is shown in Figure 20.4

Figure 20.4
Cross-pollination of the garden pea plant.

Flowers of the pea family have five petals: a rear **standard**, two lateral **wings**, and two **keels** arranged like a boat, surrounding the male (stamens) and female (stigma, style and ovary) parts of the flower.

Insects, such as bees, part the keels on landing, expose the stamens and stigma, and may pollinate the flower.

three steps to cross-pollination of the pea plant:

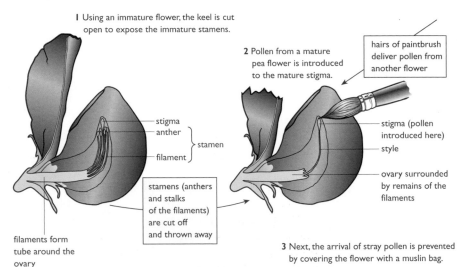

1 Using an immature flower, the keel is cut open to expose the immature stamens.

2 Pollen from a mature pea flower is introduced to the mature stigma.

hairs of paintbrush deliver pollen from another flower

stigma
anther
filament } stamen

stamens (anthers and stalks of the filaments) are cut off and thrown away

filaments form tube around the ovary

stigma (pollen introduced here)
style
ovary surrounded by remains of the filaments

3 Next, the arrival of stray pollen is prevented by covering the flower with a muslin bag.

Note: the garden pea plant is naturally self-pollinated even though it is visited by insects.

Figure 20.5
The monohybrid cross in summary.

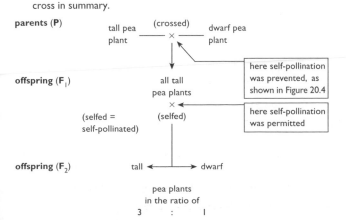

parents (P)   tall pea plant (crossed) × dwarf pea plant

offspring (F₁)   all tall pea plants

here self-pollination was prevented, as shown in Figure 20.4

(selfed = self-pollinated)   (selfed) ×

here self-pollination was permitted

offspring (F₂)   tall ← → dwarf

pea plants in the ratio of
3 : 1

The offspring from this cross were a large number of peas that, when planted, all grew into tall plants. The offspring are known as the **first filial generation** (shortened to **F₁**). Plants of the F₁ generation were then allowed to self-pollinate (and so self-fertilise) to form the **second filial generation** (or **F₂**). The offspring were a large number of pea seeds that, when planted, grew into a mixture of tall and dwarf plants in the ratio of three tall to one dwarf. (This cross is summarised in Figure 20.5.) How is this 3 : 1 ratio brought about? What is its significance?

INHERITANCE

Interpreting the monohybrid cross

We can understand the outcome of the monohybrid cross in terms of the behaviour of genes and alleles in meiosis, fertilisation and development (Figure 20.6). We use the symbol **T** to represent the allele for tall and the symbol **t** to represent the allele for dwarf.

The parents were homozygous for height alleles, meaning that the parent of phenotype 'tall' had a genotype **TT** and the parent phenotype 'dwarf' had a genotype **tt**. The parents each produce only one type of gamete; the tall parent produced gametes containing an allele for 'tall' (**T**), and the dwarf parent produced gametes containing an allele for 'dwarf' (**t**).

Fertilisation produced offspring with a genotype that is heterozygous for 'height' alleles (**Tt**). The phenotype of the F₁ generation was 'tall', so we say that in the heterozygous nucleus, the 'tall' allele is **dominant** and the 'dwarf' allele is **recessive**. Geneticists say that the dominant allele is **expressed** in the phenotype. (Note that the recessive allele is not lost or destroyed, but rather is temporarily inactive. We say it is 'not expressed'.)

The F₁ generation are all heterozygous tall (**Tt**). When they form gametes, half will carry the **T** allele and half the **t** allele. So, each heterozygous parent produces two types of gamete. Fertilisation involves the random fusion of male and female gametes. So a **T** male gamete may be equally likely to fuse with a **T** or a **t** egg cell, and a **t** male gamete may be equally likely to fuse with a **T** or a **t** egg cell. The outcome is easily shown in a matrix called a **Punnett square** (in Figure 20.7), which is named after the biologist who first used it.

As a consequence, provided a large number of offspring are formed from the cross, about $\frac{1}{4}$ of the offspring are homozygous tall (**TT**), $\frac{1}{2}$ are heterozygous tall (**Tt**) and $\frac{1}{4}$ are homozygous dwarf (**tt**). Meanwhile, the ratio of the phenotypes is 3 tall to 1 dwarf. This ratio is typical of a monohybrid cross where one allele is dominant and one allele is recessive. A genetic cross is represented as a **genetic diagram** (Figure 20.7), which shows the genotypes of parents, gametes and offspring, and explains the ratios to be anticipated in the offspring.

Another outcome of this breeding experiment is that we can confirm that the characteristics of an organism are controlled by pairs of alleles that separate in equal numbers into different gametes as a result of meiosis (Figure 20.6). This is known as the principle or **Law of Segregation**.

1 Using the example of the gene for height in a garden pea plant, explain the difference between alleles and genes.

Figure 20.6
The behaviour of alleles in the monohybrid cross.

In the pea plant, 'height' is controlled by a single gene.

In this cross a pea plant homozygous for tall was crossed with a pea plant homozygous for dwarf. The offspring were allowed to self-pollinate (and so self-fertilise) to produce the second generation.

The garden pea plant has seven pairs of chromosomes per nucleus (and therefore seven chromosomes in its gametes), but only one pair is represented here, for clarity.

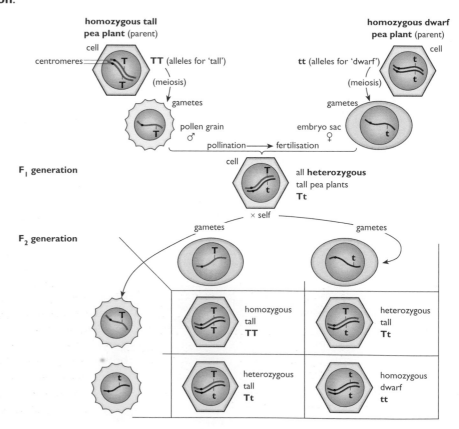

The offspring of self-fertilising ('selfing') heterozygous tall pea plants were in the ratio 3 tall : 1 dwarf.

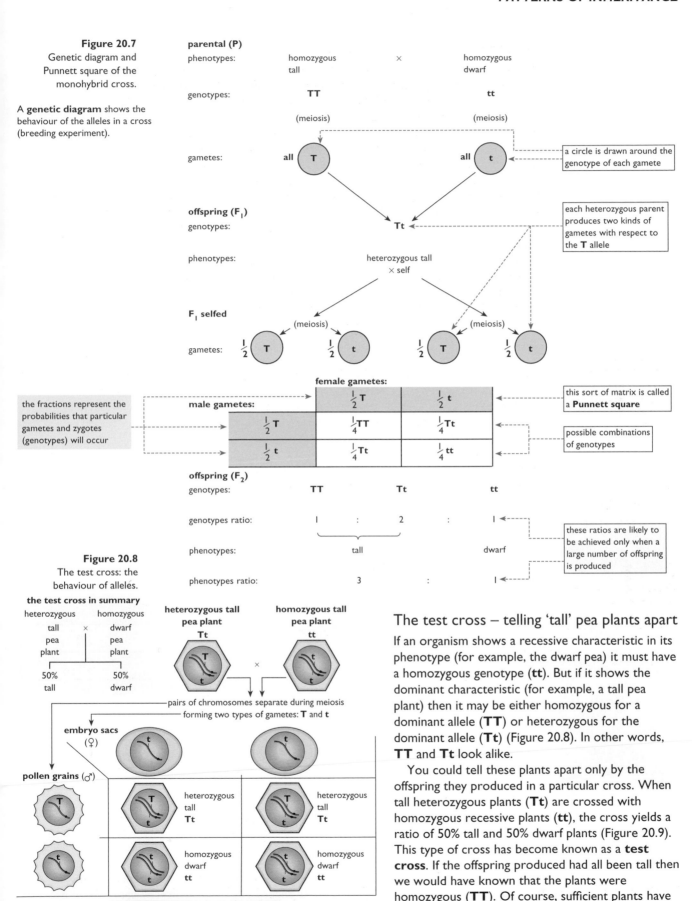

Figure 20.7
Genetic diagram and Punnett square of the monohybrid cross.

A **genetic diagram** shows the behaviour of the alleles in a cross (breeding experiment).

a circle is drawn around the genotype of each gamete

each heterozygous parent produces two kinds of gametes with respect to the **T** allele

the fractions represent the probabilities that particular gametes and zygotes (genotypes) will occur

this sort of matrix is called a **Punnett square**

possible combinations of genotypes

these ratios are likely to be achieved only when a large number of offspring is produced

Figure 20.8
The test cross: the behaviour of alleles.

the test cross in summary

pairs of chromosomes separate during meiosis forming two types of gametes: T and t

embryo sacs (♀)

pollen grains (♂)

Offspring were in the ratio of 1 tall : 1 dwarf

The test cross – telling 'tall' pea plants apart

If an organism shows a recessive characteristic in its phenotype (for example, the dwarf pea) it must have a homozygous genotype (**tt**). But if it shows the dominant characteristic (for example, a tall pea plant) then it may be either homozygous for a dominant allele (**TT**) or heterozygous for the dominant allele (**Tt**) (Figure 20.8). In other words, **TT** and **Tt** look alike.

You could tell these plants apart only by the offspring they produced in a particular cross. When tall heterozygous plants (**Tt**) are crossed with homozygous recessive plants (**tt**), the cross yields a ratio of 50% tall and 50% dwarf plants (Figure 20.9). This type of cross has become known as a **test cross**. If the offspring produced had all been tall then we would have known that the plants were homozygous (**TT**). Of course, sufficient plants have to be used to obtain these distinctive ratios.

Figure 20.9
Genetic diagram
of the test cross.

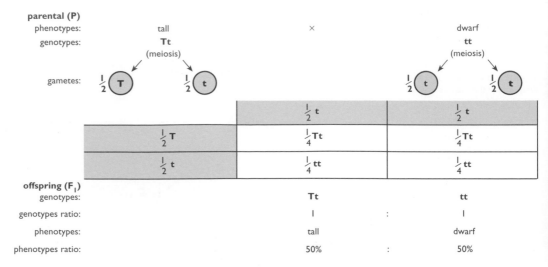

parental (P)			
phenotypes:	tall	×	dwarf
genotypes:	**Tt**		**tt**
	(meiosis)		(meiosis)

gametes: $\frac{1}{2}$ (T) $\frac{1}{2}$ (t) $\frac{1}{2}$ (t) $\frac{1}{2}$ (t)

		$\frac{1}{2}$ t	$\frac{1}{2}$ t
	$\frac{1}{2}$ T	$\frac{1}{4}$ Tt	$\frac{1}{4}$ Tt
	$\frac{1}{2}$ t	$\frac{1}{4}$ tt	$\frac{1}{4}$ tt

offspring (F₁)			
genotypes:	**Tt**		**tt**
genotypes ratio:	1	:	1
phenotypes:	tall		dwarf
phenotypes ratio:	50%	:	50%

Another example of monohybrid inheritance

Figure 20.10
Monohybrid inheritance in
the leopard and panther
(*Panthera pardus*).

The leopard and panther were traditionally thought of as separate but closely related species, but we now know their differences are due to just one pair of alleles (Figure 20.10). The panther is a black variety of the leopard, just as the dwarf garden pea is related to the tall pea! This genetic connection was discovered by breeding in captivity.

For a long time the leopard and panther were thought to be different species. In fact they are the same species, one in which coat/fur type is controlled by a single gene.

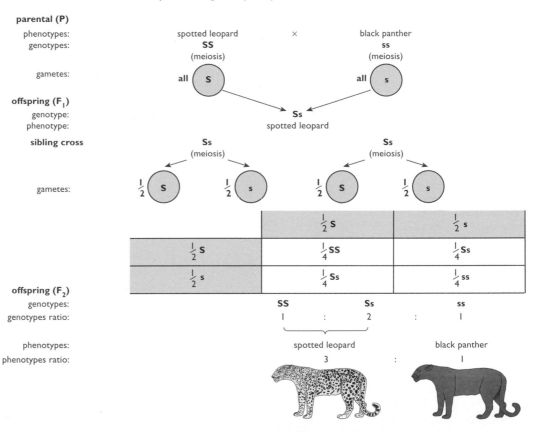

parental (P)			
phenotypes:	spotted leopard	×	black panther
genotypes:	**SS**		**ss**
	(meiosis)		(meiosis)
gametes:	all (S)		all (s)

offspring (F₁)	
genotype:	**Ss**
phenotype:	spotted leopard

sibling cross Ss (meiosis) Ss (meiosis)

gametes: $\frac{1}{2}$ (S) $\frac{1}{2}$ (s) $\frac{1}{2}$ (S) $\frac{1}{2}$ (s)

		$\frac{1}{2}$ S	$\frac{1}{2}$ s
	$\frac{1}{2}$ S	$\frac{1}{4}$ SS	$\frac{1}{4}$ Ss
	$\frac{1}{2}$ s	$\frac{1}{4}$ Ss	$\frac{1}{4}$ ss

offspring (F₂)				
genotypes:	**SS**		**Ss**	**ss**
genotypes ratio:	1	:	2	: 1
phenotypes:		spotted leopard		black panther
phenotypes ratio:		3	:	1

Human inheritance investigated by pedigree chart

Of course, study of human inheritance by experimental crosses (with selected parents, sibling crosses and the production of large numbers of progeny) is out of the question. Instead, we may investigate the pattern of inheritance of a particular characteristic by researching **family pedigrees**, where appropriate records of the ancestors exist. A human pedigree chart uses a set of rules, as outlined in Figure 20.11.

Figure 20.11
An example of a human pedigree chart.

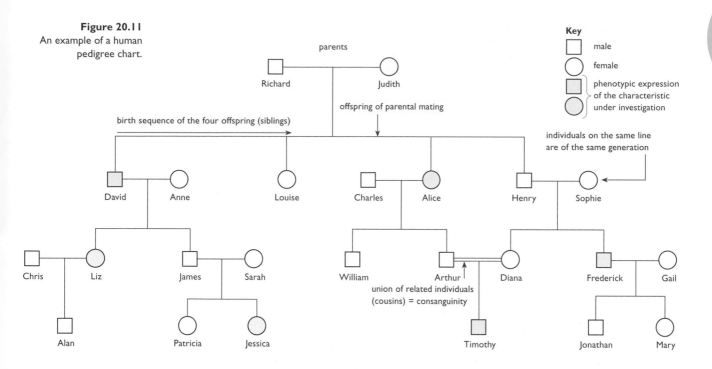

Figure 20.12
Pedigree chart of a family with albino members.

We can use a pedigree chart to detect conditions due to dominant or recessive alleles. In the case of a characteristic due to a dominant allele, the characteristic tends to occur in one or more members of the family in *every* generation. On the other hand, a recessive characteristic is seen infrequently, skipping many generations. For example, **albinism** is a rare inherited condition of humans (and other mammals) in which the individual has a block in the biochemical pathway by which the pigment melanin is formed. Albinos have white hair, very light-coloured skin and pink eyes. Albinism shows a pattern of **recessive monohybrid inheritance** in humans (Figure 20.12).

Albino people must be homozygous for the recessive albino allele (**pp**). People with normal skin pigmentation may be homozygous normal (**PP**) or carriers (**Pp**).

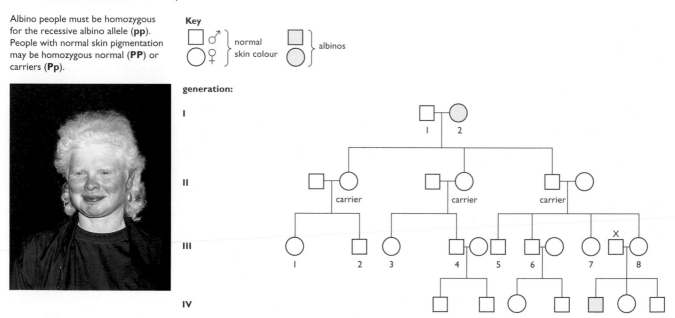

This is a typical family tree for inheritance of a characteristic controlled by a recessive allele. In **generation 1**, individual 1 may be **PP** or **Pp**, but individual 2 must be **pp** (albino). In **generation 2**, all offspring must be carriers (**Pp**) because they all inherited a recessive allele (**p**) from their albino parent. In **generation 3**, the offspring may or may not be carriers, but individual 8 *must* be a carrier (**Pp**) *and* her partner X must also be a carrier (**Pp**) since their offspring include an albino (**pp**).

Sex determination in humans

Gender is determined in humans by specific chromosomes, known as the **sex chromosomes** (Figure 20.13). Humans have one pair of sex chromosomes (either XX or XY) along with the 22 other pairs (known as **autosomal chromosomes**). The embryonic gonads of the very young human embryo will develop into ovaries *unless* 'instructed' otherwise. This is what happens where the sex chromosomes are XX. But, in an embryo with XY, the presence of a gene on the Y chromosome triggers development of the gonad tissue into testes. This switch is due to the presence of a **testis-determining gene** on the Y chromosome (see Figure 20.16, page 446). This switch in development occurs about 7–8 weeks into the growth of an embryo. Subsequently, many other genes, some present on the sex chromosomes but others present on autosomal chromosomes, control the differentiation of male or female characteristics of the fetus.

Figure 20.13
X and Y chromosomes and the determination of sex.

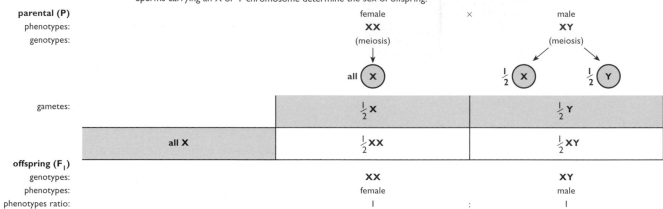

Humans have one pair of sex chromosomes (XX or XY) and 22 other pairs.
Sperms carrying an X or Y chromosome determine the sex of offspring.

Gender is determined differently in some organisms, but an X/Y system is the rule in mammals. It is also common to many other vertebrates, and in many insects, including the fruit fly *Drosophila*. In grasshoppers and butterflies, in contrast, the males are XX and the females XO (where O = 'absent').

Sex linkage

Genes present on the sex chromosomes are inherited with the sex of the individual. They are said to be **sex-linked characteristics**. The inheritance of these sex-linked genes is different from the inheritance of genes on the autosomal chromosomes. This is because the X chromosome is much longer than the Y chromosome, and for most of their length the X and Y chromosomes are non-homologous (see Figure 20.16, page 446). The characteristics that are controlled by genes on the non-homologous part of the X chromosome will appear in the male even if the allele concerned is recessive. Meanwhile, in a female, a single recessive allele is often masked by a dominant allele on the other X chromosome and the recessive allele is not expressed.

Examples of conditions controlled by recessive alleles on the X chromosome are red–green colour blindness, Duchenne muscular dystrophy and haemophilia. In the case of a male, if a single recessive allele is present it will be expressed, in the same way as the unpaired alleles of the Y chromosome are all expressed in the male. (However, these are concerned with male structures and male functions.) In the case of females, the condition will be expressed *only* if she is homozygous. If she has a single copy of the gene, she will carry it on to the next generation.

Red–green colour blindness

A red–green colour blind person sees the colours green, yellow, orange and red as all the same colour. This condition afflicts about 8% of males, but only 0.4% of females in the human population. This is because a female with normal colour vision may be homozygous for the normal colour vision allele ($X^{RG}X^{RG}$) or she may be heterozygous for normal colour vision ($X^{RG}X^{rg}$). For a female to be red–green colour blind, she must be homozygous recessive for this allele ($X^{rg}X^{rg}$), and this occurs extremely rarely. On the other hand, a male with a single recessive allele for red–green colour vision ($X^{rg}Y$) will be afflicted.

The inheritance of red–green colour blindness is illustrated in Figure 20.14. It is helpful for those who are red–green colour blind to recognise their inherited condition. Red–green colour blindness is detected by the use of multicoloured test cards.

Figure 20.14
Detection and inheritance of red–green colour blindness.

Colour blindness is detected by multicoloured test cards. A mosaic of dots is arranged on the cards so that those with normal vision see a pattern that is not visible to those with colour blindness.

inheritance of red–green colour blindness

parental (P)

phenotypes: carrier female   ×   normal male

genotypes: $X^{RG}X^{rg}$ $X^{RG}Y$

(meiosis)   (meiosis)

gametes: $\frac{1}{2}$ X^{RG} $\frac{1}{2}$ X^{rg} $\frac{1}{2}$ X^{RG} $\frac{1}{2}$ Y

	$\frac{1}{2}$ X^{RG}	$\frac{1}{2}$ Y
$\frac{1}{2}$ X^{RG}	$\frac{1}{4}$ $X^{RG}X^{RG}$	$\frac{1}{4}$ $X^{RG}Y$
$\frac{1}{2}$ X^{rg}	$\frac{1}{4}$ $X^{RG}X^{rg}$	$\frac{1}{4}$ $X^{rg}Y$

offspring (F$_1$)

genotypes: $X^{RG}X^{RG}$ $X^{RG}X^{rg}$ $X^{RG}Y$ $X^{rg}Y$

phenotypes: normal   carrier   normal   colour blind

females   males

2 Haemophilia results from a sex-linked gene. The disease is most common in males, but the haemophilia allele is on the X chromosome. Can you explain this anomaly?

Haemophilia

In the circulatory system of a mammal, if a break occurs in a vessel there is a risk of uncontrolled bleeding. This is normally overcome by the **blood-clotting mechanism**, which plugs any gaps that appear from injury (Figure 15.18, page 337). Haemophilia is a rare, genetically determined condition in which the blood will not clot normally. The result is frequent, excessive bleeding.

There are two forms of haemophilia, known as haemophilia A and haemophilia B. They are both due to a failure to produce adequate amounts of particular blood proteins that are essential to the complex blood-clotting mechanism. Today, haemophilia is effectively treated by the administration of the clotting factor that the patient lacks.

Haemophilia is a sex-linked condition; the genes controlling production of the blood proteins concerned are located on the X chromosome. It is caused by a recessive allele. Because of this, it is largely a disease of the male since in males a single X chromosome carrying the defective allele (X^hY) will result in disease. For a female to have the disease, she must be homozygous for the recessive gene (X^hX^h). However, this condition is usually fatal *in utero*, typically resulting in a natural abortion.

A female with only one X chromosome with the recessive allele (X^HX^h) is described as a '**carrier**'. She has normal blood clotting, but when she is partnered by a normal male there is a 50% chance of the daughters being carriers and a 50% chance of the sons being haemophiliac (Figure 20.15).

Figure 20.15
The inheritance of haemophilia.

parental (P)

phenotypes: carrier female   ×   normal male

genotypes: X^HX^h X^HY

(meiosis)   (meiosis)

gametes: $\frac{1}{2}$ X^H $\frac{1}{2}$ X^h $\frac{1}{2}$ X^H $\frac{1}{2}$ Y

	$\frac{1}{2}$ X^H	$\frac{1}{2}$ Y
$\frac{1}{2}$ X^H	$\frac{1}{4}$ X^HX^H	$\frac{1}{4}$ X^HY
$\frac{1}{2}$ X^h	$\frac{1}{4}$ X^HX^h	$\frac{1}{4}$ X^hY

offspring (F$_1$)

genotypes: X^HX^H X^HX^h X^HY X^hY

phenotypes: normal   carrier   normal   haemophiliac

females   males

● **Extension**   Pairing of X and Y chromosomes in meiosis

We know that homologous chromosomes pair up early in meiosis (Figure 5.5, page 104). Pairing is an essential step in the mechanism of meiosis. However, only a very small part of the X and Y chromosomes of humans can and do pair up during meiosis (that is, **complementary alleles**) (Figure 20.16). In fact, the bulk of both sex chromosomes contain genes that have *no* corresponding alleles on the other type of sex chromosome. Thus, the short Y chromosome carries genes that are specific for male sex determination and sperm production, including the 'male' gene coding for the **testis-determining factor** (**TDF**). This factor switches development of embryonic gonad tissue to testes early in embryonic development. Meanwhile the X chromosome carries an assortment of genes, very few of which are concerned with sex determination.

Figure 20.16
The pairing of X and Y chromosomes in meiosis.

During meiosis homologous chromosomes pair. When chromosomes pair, two X chromosomes will do so along their whole length, but X and Y chromosomes have few corresponding alleles and they pair for only a short part of their length. Consequently, no crossing over between X and Y chromosomes can occur along most of their lengths.

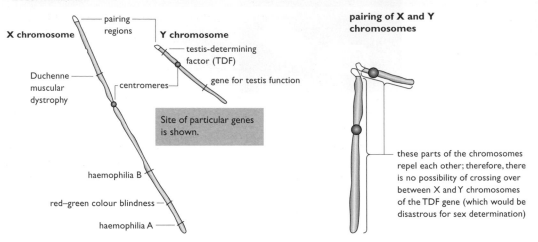

Modification of the 3 : 1 monohybrid ratio

In certain types of monohybrid cross the 3 : 1 ratio is not obtained. Two of these situations are illustrated next.

Multiple alleles

The genes introduced so far exist in only two forms (two alleles) – for instance, the 'height' gene of the garden pea, which has tall or dwarf alleles. Not all genes are like this. In fact, very many genes exist in more than two alternatives, and these are known as cases of **multiple alleles**. An example of multiple alleles is those controlling the ABO blood group system of humans (Table 15.5, page 340). Our blood belongs to one of the A, B, AB or O groups (Figure 20.17). The alleles are represented by the symbols I^A, I^B and I^o. The ABO blood group system is determined by some combination of the alleles. In each individual only two of these alleles exist, but they are inherited as if they were alternative alleles of a pair. However, alleles I^A and I^B are dominant to I^o, which is recessive; I^A and I^B are codominant alleles (Figure 20.18).

Multiple alleles are common. For simplicity, we began this chapter on inheritance with a gene (height of the garden pea) for which there are just two alleles. However, *most* genes have more than two alleles.

Figure 20.17
The ABO blood group system.

possible genotypes: where allele I^A and allele I^B are codominant and I^o is recessive to alleles I^A and I^B

	$I^A I^A$ $I^A I^o$	$I^B I^B$ $I^B I^o$	$I^A I^B$	$I^o I^o$
phenotypes:	blood group A	blood group B	blood group AB	blood group O
red cell surface:	A antigens	B antigens	A + B antigens	neither
plasma:	anti-B antibodies	anti-A antibodies	neither	both anti-A and anti-B antibodies

an example of the inheritance of blood groupings A, B, AB and O

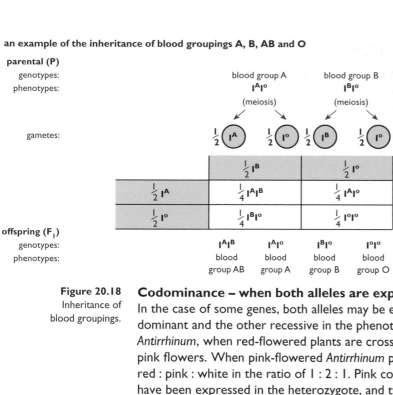

parental (P)

genotypes:
phenotypes:

blood group A
I^A I^O

blood group B
I^B I^O

(meiosis)   (meiosis)

gametes:

½ I^A   ½ I^O   ½ I^B   ½ I^O

	½ I^B	½ I^O
½ I^A	¼ I^A I^B	¼ I^A I^O
½ I^O	¼ I^B I^O	¼ I^O I^O

offspring (F₁)

genotypes:
phenotypes:

I^A I^B   I^A I^O   I^B I^O   I^O I^O

blood   blood   blood   blood
group AB group A   group B   group O

> **3** One busy night in an understaffed maternity unit, four children were born at about the same time. Then the babies were muddled up by mistake; it was not certain which child belonged to which family. Fortunately the children had different blood groups:
>
> A, B, AB and O
>
> The parents' blood groups were also known:
>
> Mr and Mrs Jones   A × B
> Mr and Mrs Smith   B × O
> Mr and Mrs Matthews   O × O
> Mr and Mrs Reynolds   AB × O
>
> The nurses were able to decide which child belonged to which family. Can you work out how?

Figure 20.18
Inheritance of blood groupings.

Codominance – when both alleles are expressed

In the case of some genes, both alleles may be expressed simultaneously, rather than one being dominant and the other recessive in the phenotype. For example, in the common garden flower *Antirrhinum*, when red-flowered plants are crossed with white-flowered plants, the F₁ plants have pink flowers. When pink-flowered *Antirrhinum* plants are crossed the F₂ offspring are found to be red : pink : white in the ratio of 1 : 2 : 1. Pink coloration of the petals occurs because both alleles have been expressed in the heterozygote, and two pigment systems are present, rather than that of a dominant allele only. 'Red' and 'white' are said to be **codominant alleles**. In genetic diagrams, each of the codominant alleles has a superscript capital letter, in recognition of their equal influence (Figure 20.19).

Figure 20.19
Codominance in the garden flower, *Antirrhinum*.

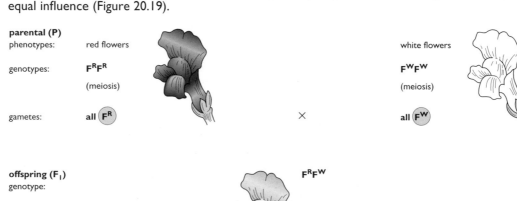

parental (P)

phenotypes: red flowers

genotypes: F^R F^R

(meiosis)

gametes: all F^R

×

white flowers

F^W F^W

(meiosis)

all F^W

offspring (F₁)

genotype:

phenotype:

F^R F^W

pink flowers

> **4** Try for yourself (with pencil and paper) the monohybrid cross between cattle of a variety with a gene for coat colour with codominant alleles: 'red' and 'white' coat. Homozygous parents produce 'roan' offspring (that is, red and white hairs together). What offspring will you expect, in what proportions, when a sibling cross (equivalent to 'selfing' in plants) occurs between roan offspring?

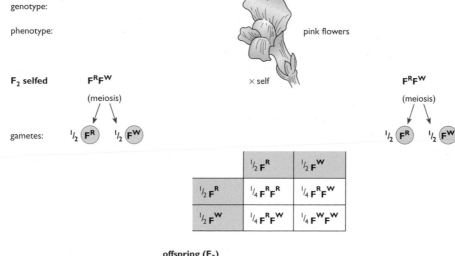

F₂ selfed   F^R F^W

(meiosis)

gametes: ½ F^R   ½ F^W

× self

F^R F^W

(meiosis)

½ F^R   ½ F^W

	½ F^R	½ F^W
½ F^R	¼ F^R F^R	¼ F^R F^W
½ F^W	¼ F^R F^W	¼ F^W F^W

offspring (F₂)

genotypes: F^R F^R   F^R F^W   F^W F^W

genotypes ratio: 1   :   2   :   1

phenotypes: red   pink   white

Inheritance of two pairs of contrasting characteristics

Now we move on to examine the fate of two genes in a genetic cross. The simultaneous inheritance of two pairs of contrasting characters is referred to as a **dihybrid cross**. We can illustrate this by an experiment with the fruit fly *Drosophila*.

Drosophila is a small insect that occurs around rotting vegetable materials (Figure 20.20). This fly exists as a **common form** (originally called the '**wild type**'), and has various naturally occurring **mutants**. *Drosophila* is useful to experimental geneticists for a number of reasons, but basically because it is easy to work with and to interpret results from. For example, *Drosophila* has only four pairs of chromosomes, and a generation time of about 10 days, when reared at 25 °C. More importantly, one female produces hundreds of offspring, which means that statistically significant results are produced by a single cross. These flies are cultured on sterilised artificial medium in glass bottles in a laboratory, and they can be temporarily anaesthetised without permanent harm, for setting up cultures and sorting offspring.

Figure 20.20
Drosophila and some common mutants.

photomicrograph of *Drosophila* (× 15)

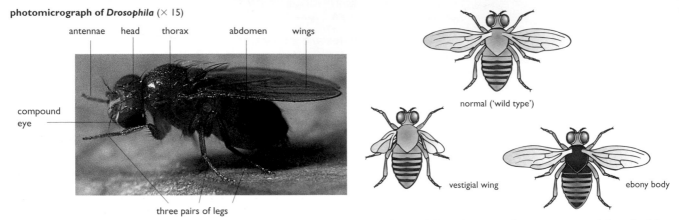

A suitable investigation of a dihybrid cross in *Drosophila* is the cross between normal flies ('wild type') and flies homozygous for the mutant conditions of vestigial wing and ebony body (because these mutant forms are easily recognised). From the outcome of crosses with these genes (Figure 20.21) we know that the allele for normal wing is dominant over the allele for vestigial wing, and that the allele for normal body is dominant over the allele for ebony body. Consequently, the allele for normal wing is represented by **W**, for vestigial wing by **w**, for normal body by **G** and for ebony body by **g**.

Figure 20.21
The dihybrid cross in summary.

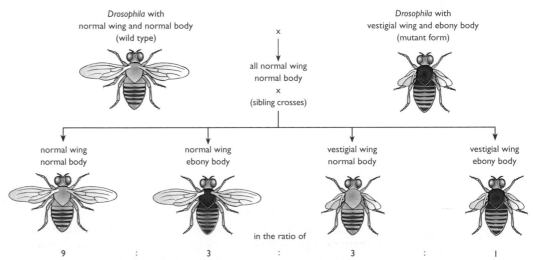

Thus the genotypes of the parents are **WWGG** and **wwgg** respectively (this is always written in that order, never as **WGWG**, for example). The offspring of the first generation (F₁) are all heterozygous normal wing and normal body (**WwGg**). Incidentally, this confirms that the 'normal' alleles are dominant and the mutant alleles are recessive.

The heterozygous normal wing and normal body (**WwGg**) individuals produce four types of gametes. Why? The answer lies in meiosis (Figure 5.5, page 104), and the fact that independent assortment of bivalents occurs in metaphase I (Figure 5.6, page 105). It is helpful to look at these diagrams again, now.

You can see that, since the alleles **W** and **G** and **w** and **g** are on different chromosomes, they may line up in one of two combinations in metaphase I of meiosis, and will give four different combinations of gametes (Figure 20.22). Consequently, when random mating occurs between a very large number of male and female gametes, the following offspring are formed:

Figure 20.22
Genetic diagram showing the behaviour of alleles in the dihybrid cross.

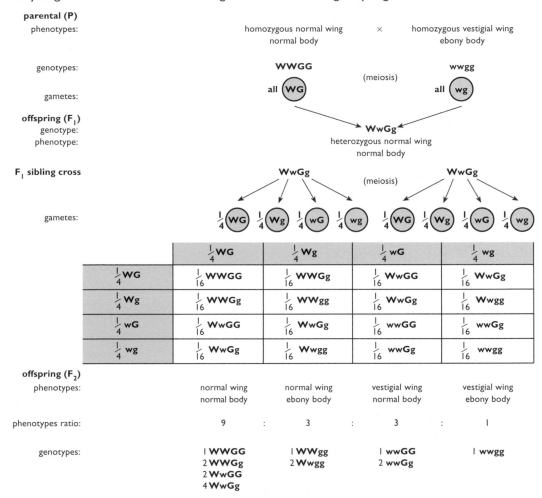

This 9 : 3 : 3 : 1 ratio is typical of the dihybrid cross, where random assortment happens of the chromosomes on which the alleles occur. The conclusion of the dihybrid cross is that 'two or more pairs of alleles segregate independently of each other as a result of meiosis, provided the genes concerned are not linked by being on the same chromosome'. This is known as the principle or **Law of Independent Assortment**.

The dihybrid test cross

Look back to page 441 to remind yourself of the issue the monohybrid test cross sorts out. Why is a test cross sometimes necessary?

In the case of dihybrid inheritance, too, homozygous recessive genotypes *can* be recognised in the phenotype (for example, flies with vestigial wings and ebony bodies). However, homozygous normal wing/normal body flies and flies heterozygous for normal wing/normal body *look the same*. They can be distinguished only by the progeny they produce. When, in a test cross, heterozygous normal wing/normal body flies are crossed with homozygous vestigial wing/ebony body flies, the four phenotypes of the dihybrid cross are formed, but in equal numbers (Figure 20.23). The genetic diagram for this cross is shown in Figure 20.24.

5 Peas that are homozygous for round and yellow seeds were crossed with peas that are homozygous for wrinkled and green seeds. The offspring (F₁) were all round, yellow peas. Produce a genetic diagram for this cross that also shows the ratio of the offspring that would be produced by selfing the F₁ peas.

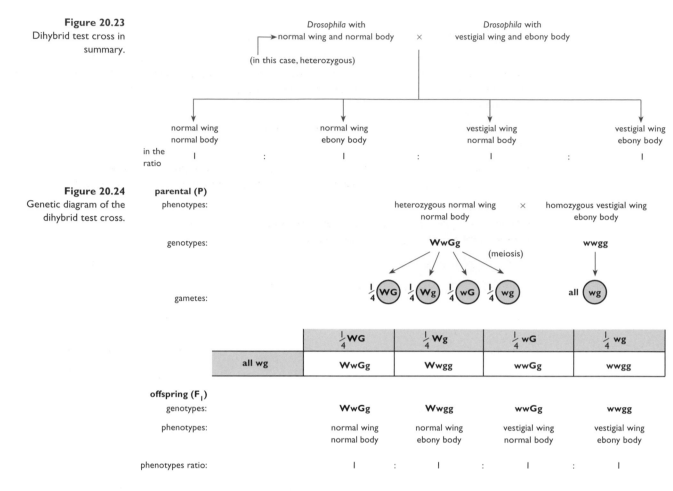

Figure 20.23
Dihybrid test cross in summary.

Figure 20.24
Genetic diagram of the dihybrid test cross.

Extension   Mendelian genetics

The first principles of modern genetics were established by an Austrian monk called Gregor Mendel who lived from 1822 to 1884. He worked at a time before chromosomes had been observed and genes had been described.

Mendel actually worked out the existence of genes and alleles from his investigations of monohybrid and dihybrid crosses of contrasting characteristics of the garden pea plant (the experimental procedures he designed), and by the mathematical interpretation of his results. His experiments involved growing large samples of pea plants, so the outcomes of his experiments were statistically significant.

From the ratios of the progeny he obtained in monohybrid and dihybrid crosses, Mendel argued that:

- within each organism are genes (he called them 'breeding factors') controlling contrasting characteristics of organisms, such as 'tall' and 'dwarf' in the garden pea
- there are two alleles (factors) for each characteristic in each cell, and one allele has come from each plant
- the alleles for each characteristic separate in reproduction (we now call this 'independent assortment'), and either of them can enter an offspring
- the allele for 'tall' is an alternative form of the allele for 'dwarf', and the 'tall' allele is dominant over the 'dwarf' allele.

Mendel's work established that the factors (genes/alleles) that controlled the characteristic of organisms did not 'blend' in any way, even though particular characteristics may not be seen for a generation. (Blending inheritance was the generally accepted explanation of inheritance in his time.) Nevertheless, his work was not appreciated in his lifetime.

Extension   Probability and chance in genetic crosses

We can see that there is an 'expected' ratio of offspring of 9 : 3 : 3 : 1 when a dihybrid cross is carried out. Actually, the offspring produced in a dihybrid cross experiment do not exactly agree with the expected ratio. For example, in one experiment the numbers of progeny were:

normal wing, normal body	normal wing, ebony body	vestigial wing, normal body	vestigial wing, ebony body
315	108	101	32

These results do not exactly fit the 9 : 3 : 3 : 1 ratio. What, if anything, went 'wrong'?

Well, we can expect this precise ratio among the progeny only if three conditions are met:

- fertilisation is random
- there are equal opportunities for survival among the offspring
- large numbers of offspring are produced.

So, in the experiment above, the exact ratio may not be obtained because, for example:

- more male flies of one type may have succeeded in fertilising females than those of the other type
- more females of one type may have died before reaching egg-laying condition than those of the other type
- fewer eggs of one type may have completed their development than those of the other type.

Experimental geneticists are often in the situation of asking 'Do the observed values differ significantly from the expected outcome?' This question is resolved by a simple statistical test, known as the **chi-squared (χ^2) test**, which is used to estimate the probability that any differences between the observed and the expected results are due to chance (Figure 20.25).

Figure 20.25
The chi-squared test of dihybrid cross results.

$$\chi^2 = \frac{\Sigma\,(O - E)^2}{E}$$

where O = observed result
E = expected result assuming a ratio of 9 : 3 : 3 : 1 and a total of 556 flies
and Σ = the sum of

The chi-squared test of the dihybrid cross results given in Figure 20.22

Category	Predicted	O	E	$O - E$	$(O - E)^2$	$(O - E)^2/E$
normal wing, normal body	9	315	312.75	2.25	5.062	0.016
normal wing, ebony body	3	108	104.25	3.75	14.062	0.135
vestigial wing, normal body	3	101	104.25	− 3.25	10.562	0.101
vestigial wing, ebony body	1	32	34.75	− 2.75	7.562	0.218
		total = 556				Σ = 0.47

Thus χ^2 = 0.47.

There were four categories, and therefore only three degrees of freedom (i.e. for any one condition there are three alternatives).

Values for χ^2 for three degrees of freedom (taken from statistical tables):

Probability	0.99	0.95	0.9	0.7	0.5	0.3	0.1	0.05	0.01	0.001
df = 3	0.115	0.35	0.58	0.71	1.39	3.66	6.25	7.82	11.34	16.27

This value (0.47) lies between a probability of 0.95 and 0.90. This means that a deviation of this size is due to chance.

It can be expected 90–95% of the times the experiment is carried out.

There is no significant deviation between the observed (O) and the expected (E) results.

Polygenes

We began the story of genetics with an investigation of the inheritance of height in the garden pea (page 437), where one gene with two alleles gave tall or dwarf plants. This clear-cut difference in an inherited characteristic is an example of discontinuous variation (Figure 20.2), in that there is no intermediate form, and no overlap between the two phenotypes.

In fact, very few characteristics of organisms are controlled by a single gene. Mostly, the characteristics of organisms are controlled by a number of genes, known as **polygenes**. The genes that make up a polygene are often (but not necessarily always) located on different chromosomes. The effects of any one of these genes make a very small or insignificant effect on the phenotype, but the combined effect of all the genes of the polygene is to produce infinite variety among the offspring. Many features of humans are controlled by polygenes, including height. The graph of the variation in the heights of a population of 400 people in Figure 20.2 (page 437) shows continuous variation in height between the shortest at 160 cm and the tallest at 186 cm, and a mean height of 173 cm.

In fact the number of genes controlling a characteristic does not have to be large before the variation in a phenotype becomes more or less continuous within a large group of offspring. Characteristics controlled by polygenes show continuous variation. Nevertheless, the individual genes concerned are inherited in accordance with the principles established above. It is simply the case that there are so many intermediate combinations of alleles that discrete ratios are not observed.

Environmental effects

If plants of a tall variety of a pea are deprived of nutrients (nitrates and phosphates, for example) in the growing phase of development then full size may not be reached. A 'tall' plant may appear dwarf. The same might arise with humans who have been seriously and continuously underfed as growing children. Many characteristics of organisms are affected by both the environment and their genotype. In fact the **phenotype** is the product of:

genotype + influences of the environment

For example, in colonies of the honey bee (*Apis mellifera*) there are three phenotypes (workers, drones and queens) but only two genotypes. These phenotypes are determined by both genotype and environment (their diet). The drones are the community's males, and they develop from unfertilised eggs (their genotype is haploid). The queen and the workers develop from fertilised eggs. These latter two types of contrasting individuals have *identical genotypes*. The queen, who is a much larger organism, differs from her workers only by the diet she is fed in the larval stage. The protein-rich food prepared for her by the nurse worker bees in the colony, not available to the larvae that will be workers, makes the difference.

Extension   Linkage and crossing over

Linkage

The dihybrid cross shown in Figure 20.21 (page 448) concerns the inheritance of two pairs of contrasting characteristics controlled by two genes occurring on *different chromosomes*. Because chromosomes behave independently during meiosis (known as **independent assortment** – Figure 5.6, page 105), any one homologous chromosome can arrive in a gamete with any other. All possible combinations of alleles can occur.

In all organisms there are many thousands of genes per cell, but relatively few chromosomes (Table 20.2). We visualise a chromosome as a linear series of a very large number of genes (Figure 20.3, page 438). So, very many of the genes of an organism occur on the same chromosome. Independent assortment is not normally possible where the genes occur on the same chromosome. These genes are linked together and are almost certainly inherited together (Figure 20.26). **Linked genes** cannot normally assort independently.

continued

Figure 20.26
The inheritance of genes on the same chromosome.

Genes on the same chromosome are likely to be inherited together.
Here, alleles **A** and **B** occur on the same chromosomes, as do alleles **a** and **b**.
Consequently, no genotypes of **AAbb** or **aaBB** are formed.

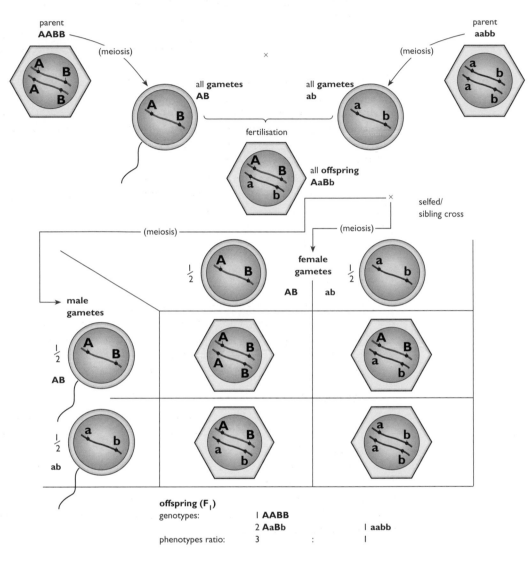

offspring (F₁)
genotypes: I **AABB**
                2 **AaBb**   I **aabb**
phenotypes ratio: 3   :   I

Table 20.2
Chromosomes per diploid cell: some examples.

garden pea (*Pisum sativum*)	14
meadow buttercup (*Ranunculus acris*)	14
dandelion (*Taraxacum officinale*)	24
human (*Homo sapiens*)	46
mouse (*Mus musculus*)	40
crayfish (*Astacus pallipes*)	200

Crossing over

The other source of genetic variation created each time meiosis occurs is **crossing over** between chromatids in the bivalents (Figure 5.7, page 106). Segments are exchanged between adjacent chromatids of homologous pairs early in meiosis, which may give rise to new combinations of characteristics. Almost every pair of homologous chromosomes shows crossing over during meiosis.

continued

The outcome of crossing over is offspring with combinations of characteristics that are not found in either of the parents. These offspring are called **recombinants**. The progeny of crosses where a large number of offspring are produced is a combination of both 'parental types' and 'recombinant types', at least where contrasting characters are controlled by genes on the *same* chromosomes. This is illustrated in *Drosophila* (Figure 20.27), where a homozygous fly with ebony body and curled wing is crossed (test cross) with a heterozygous fly with normal body and straight wing. Note that the characteristic 'curled wing' is a different one from the characteristic 'vestigial wing' shown in the cross in Figure 20.21, which concerns contrasting characteristics controlled by genes on *separate chromosomes*.

Figure 20.27
Linkage and crossing over in *Drosophila*.

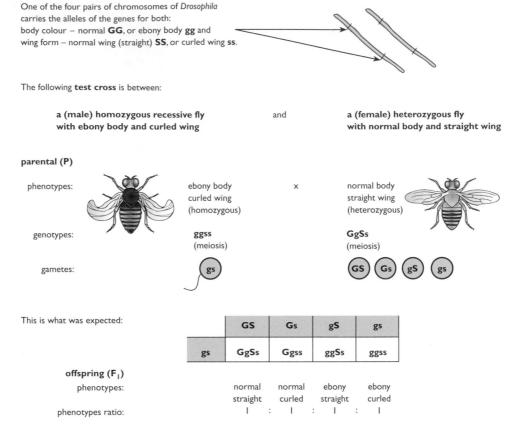

One of the four pairs of chromosomes of *Drosophila* carries the alleles of the genes for both:
body colour – normal **GG**, or ebony body **gg** and
wing form – normal wing (straight) **SS**, or curled wing **ss**.

The following **test cross** is between:

| a (male) homozygous recessive fly with ebony body and curled wing | and | a (female) heterozygous fly with normal body and straight wing |

parental (P)

phenotypes: ebony body curled wing (homozygous)   x   normal body straight wing (heterozygous)

genotypes: **ggss** (meiosis)   **GgSs** (meiosis)

gametes: gs   GS Gs gS gs

This is what was expected:

	GS	Gs	gS	gs
gs	GgSs	Ggss	ggSs	ggss

offspring (F₁)

phenotypes: normal straight   normal curled   ebony straight   ebony curled

phenotypes ratio: 1 : 1 : 1 : 1

But this is what happened:

Offspring		Phenotypes	Genotypes	Numbers obtained
1 parental types:		normal body, straight wing	**GgSs**	536
		ebony body, curled wing	**ggss**	481
2 recombinant types:		normal body, curled wing	**Ggss**	101*
		ebony body, straight wing	**ggSs**	152*

Note the **majority of the offspring were parental types**, so the genes for body colour and wing shape must be on the same chromosomes, i.e. **linked**; however, **crossing over** between these genes has occurred (*).

● Extension Human Genome Project

The Human Genome Project is a coordinated international effort to map the entire human genome that was begun in 1990, coordinated by an organisation called HUGO (the Human Genome Organisation). The work has been shared between more than 200 laboratories around the world to avoid duplication of effort. There are about 2 metres of DNA in each human nucleus, organised into the 23 pairs of matching chromosomes. Our chromosomes contain an average of about 2200 genes. Mapping the genome involves locating all the genes on the chromosomes (their positions relative to each other), and then working out the nucleotides in each gene (Figure 20.28). The task is a huge one, for there are about 3×10^9 base pairs to map. However, much of the work is automated. In fact, the first sequence of a whole human chromosome was published in the scientific journal *Nature* in 1999.

The advantages of this information, apart from satisfying the human quest for knowledge, include the location of genes causing known (and as yet unknown) genetic diseases that are, to date, incurable. This should allow work on prevention as well as on improved treatment of the symptoms. There is the possibility of unprecedented insights into human disease and development.

Figure 20.28
This cytogeneticist is arranging photographs of human chromosomes for diagnostic purposes. Much of the analytical process is now automated, and computers record gene sequences and the sequence of bases (T, G, C and A) or individual genes.

The disadvantages include the cost (similar to that involved in putting a human on the Moon in the 1960s). Should so much money be used in these ways, when many humans are daily deprived of sufficient food and clean water? Who owns this information and how should it be used? There are potential dangers for the individual who is screened genetically, in the uterus or later. Is the information about individuals private? What use might the State, the medical profession or businesses (such as insurance companies) make of it? There are many social, legal and ethical issues for societies to take decisions on.

● Skills task

What steps are involved when an allele is inherited and causes a particular characteristic to appear in the offspring? Take as your example an allele that controls height in the pea plant, or coat colour in the cow, or body colour in *Drosophila*.

- Think about this issue, and look into Chapter 5 again.
- Discuss your ideas with your fellow students and also your teacher.

Then, prepare a short presentation to your group, explaining the steps to gene action in the working cells and tissues.

SUMMARY

- **Genetics** is the study of **inheritance**. Heredity is responsible for many of the similarities and differences (variations) between parents and offspring. **Variations** that are inherited may be discrete or **discontinuous variations** (such as 'tall' or 'dwarf' pea plants) or variation that is a continuous distribution of variables (such as height in humans), known as **continuous variations**.

- Many characteristics of organisms are controlled by **genes**. Genes occur as a linear series along chromosomes. Diploid organisms contain two copies of each gene in each of their cells. Different forms of a gene are called **alleles**. In sexual reproduction, gametes are formed containing one copy of each gene. Offspring receive two copies of each gene (two alleles), one from each parent.

- Alleles may be **dominant** or **recessive** or show incomplete dominance. An organism with two identical alleles of a gene is **homozygous**. An organism with different alleles of a gene is **heterozygous** for that gene. The genetic make-up of an organism is its **genotype**. The resulting appearance of the organism is called its **phenotype**.

- In a **monohybrid cross** the inheritance of a contrasting characteristic controlled by a gene, such as tall and dwarf height in garden pea plants, is investigated. When parents homozygous for the contrasting characteristic are crossed, the first generation (F_1) are heterozygous, for example, the allele for 'tall' in the pea is expressed, showing the allele for 'tall' is dominant to the allele for 'dwarf' which is recessive. When the F_1 generation self-fertilise (or the siblings are crossed in animals), the recessive parent characteristic re-emerges in the ratio of 3 : 1, provided many offspring are formed. This shows that *only one allele of a gene can be carried in a single gamete.*

- The genotype of an organism showing dominant characteristics may be homozygous or heterozygous for the gene concerned. The genotype of this organism can be determined by a **test cross** with an organism that is homozygous recessive for the characteristic.

- Studying inheritance in humans by experimental crosses is out of the question. Instead, the pattern of inheritance of a particular characteristic is followed through many generations, and recorded as a **family pedigree**.

- Gender is determined in humans by the **sex chromosomes**: XX in the female, and XY in the male. The X chromosome is longer than the Y, and carries alleles for genes not present on the Y chromosome. In the male, recessive alleles on the single X chromosome cannot be masked by dominant alleles as often happens in the female. Rare recessive conditions of this type occur more frequently in males, for example, red–green colour blindness, haemophilia and Duchenne muscular dystrophy.

- Exceptions to the monohybrid ratio arise from the existence of alleles that are **codominant**, rather than dominant or recessive, and of more than two alleles for genes, which are known as **multiple alleles**. The human ABO blood group is an example. It is controlled by two of three possible alleles, giving four possible phenotypes, A, B, AB or O blood groupings.

- A **dihybrid cross** concerns the inheritance of two pairs of contrasting characteristics located on different chromosomes. The results confirm that each allele of a gene is equally likely to be inherited with each allele of another gene, a reflection of the independent assortment of chromosomes that occurs in meiosis.

- Many characteristics are controlled by two or more genes, known as **polygenes**, which may be located on different chromosomes. Polygenic inheritance, illustrated by human height, produces a range of values seen as continuous variation, as opposed to the discontinuous variation of characteristics controlled by a single gene with two alleles, one dominant and one recessive.

- **Environmental conditions** of an organism may also influence the expression of alleles, such as when a genetically tall organism is deprived of sufficient nutrients and has a phenotype that is short. Characteristics influenced by the environment also tend to show continuous variation.

- Genes present on the same chromosome are called **linked genes**, and are inherited together. **Crossing over** between chromatids during meiosis produces a small proportion of offspring with new combinations of characteristics (**recombinants**), additional to parental characteristics.

Examination questions

1 Sickle cell anaemia is a recessive inherited condition affecting the red cells (erythrocytes). In Britain approximately 10 births per million show this condition whilst in Africa it has a much greater incidence. In the homozygous condition it may be fatal without treatment.

a What is meant by *the homozygous condition?* (1)

b Describe the genetic and biochemical basis of sickle cell anaemia. (3)

c Suggest how this condition arose. (1)

d Account for the much higher incidence of the disease in Africa than in Britain. (1)

e Explain how this condition may be detected in the fetus. (3)

OCR (Oxford), A level, 6912, Mar 1999

2 The inheritance of ABO blood groups is controlled by three alleles of the same gene, I^A, I^B, and I°. The alleles I^A and I^B are codominant. Both I^A and I^B are dominant to the allele I°.

a Explain what is meant by an allele. (1)

b **i** Complete the table to show the missing genotypes.

Blood group phenotype	Possible genotype
A	$I^A I^A$, ...
B	$I^B I^B$, ...
AB	....
O	....

ii Children of blood groups A and O were born to parents of blood groups A and B. Compose the genetic diagram to show the possible ABO blood group phenotypes of the children which could be produced from these parents. (3)

AQA(NEAB), AS/A level, Module BY02, Mar 1999

3 a Distinguish between the terms *gene* and *allele*. (3)

b The diagram below shows a family tree in which the blood group phenotypes are shown for some individuals.

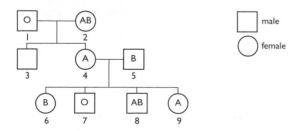

i Using the symbols I^A, I^B and I° to represent alleles, indicate the genotypes of people 1, 2, 4, 5 and 6. (5)

ii State the possible blood groups of person 3. Explain your answer. (3)

London, AS/A level, Module B/HB1, Jan 1997

4 In the fruit fly, *Drosophila melanogaster*, the allele for grey body colour, **G**, is dominant to that for ebony body colour, **g**. The allele for normal wings, **N**, is dominant to that for curled wings, **n**. A student crossed a grey-bodied, normal-winged fly with an ebony-bodied, curled-winged fly. The offspring were as follows:

Phenotype	Numbers
grey body and normal wings	33
grey body and curled wings	23
ebony body and curled wings	28
ebony body and normal wings	16

a Show how this cross should have produced offspring in the ratio 1:1:1:1. (2)

b **i** The chi-squared (χ^2) test can be used to test whether the observed results fit the expectation. Complete the table below in which **E** represents the number of each type of fly expected in the above cross and **O** represents the number actually observed.

Phenotype	Number observed (O)	Number expected (E)	Difference (O−E)	Difference squared (O−E)²
grey body, normal wings	33			
grey body, curled wings	23			
ebony body, curled wings	28			
ebony body, normal wings	16			

(2)

ii Calculate the value of χ^2 using the formula:

$$\chi^2 = \sum \frac{(O-E)^2}{E}$$

(1)

iii Use the following extract from the χ^2 table to decide whether the observed numbers of offspring are significantly different from those expected. Explain how you reached your answer. (3)

Degrees of freedom	Probability (P)						
	0.90	0.50	0.20	0.10	0.05	0.02	0.01
1	0.02	0.46	1.64	2.71	3.84	5.41	6.64
2	0.21	1.39	3.22	4.61	5.99	7.82	9.21
3	0.58	2.37	4.64	6.25	7.82	9.84	11.34
4	1.06	3.36	5.99	7.78	9.49	11.67	13.28

AEB, AS level, 0979/1, June 1997

21 Evolution

STARTING POINTS ● Evolution is the **development of life** in geological time since its beginning about **3500 million years ago**.
● **Fossils** in rock layers that have been accurately dated tell us about the history of life.
● Evolution is believed to occur by **natural selection**.

Life through geological time

By **evolution** we mean the **development of life in geological time**. The word 'evolution' is used very widely, but in biology it specifically means the processes by which life has been changed from its earliest beginnings to the diversity of organisms we know about today, both living and extinct.

We learn about the history of life from the evidence of the **fossils** that have been found (Figure 21.1). Fossilisation is an extremely rare, chance event. This is because predators, scavengers and bacterial action normally break down dead plant and animal structures before they can be fossilised. Of the relatively few fossils formed, most remain buried. If they do become exposed, they are likely to be overlooked or accidentally destroyed before discovery. Nevertheless, numerous fossils have been found. Table 21.1 reviews the ways fossils are formed. Where the fossil or the rock that surrounds it can be accurately dated, we have good evidence of the history of life. The extension box shows how **natural radioactivity** is used to estimate the age of rocks and fossils.

Figure 21.1 Fossilisation.

steps to fossil formation:

1 Dead remains of organisms may fall into lake or sea, and become buried in silt/sand, in anaerobic, low temperature conditions.

2 Hard parts of skeleton/lignified plant tissues may persist and become impregnated by silica/carbonate ions, hardening them.

3 Remains hardened in this way become compressed, in layers of sedimentary rock.

4 After millions of years, upthrust may bring rocks to the surface and erosion of these rocks commences.

5 Land movements may expose some fossils, and few are discovered by chance, but of the relatively few organisms fossilised, very few will ever be found by humans.

sedimentary rock layers with fault line and remains of extinct fossil species

Table 21.1 Forms of fossilisation.

petrification – organic matter of the dead organism is replaced by mineral ions

mould – the organic matter decays, but the space left becomes a mould, filled by mineral matter

trace – an impression of a form, for example a leaf or a footprint, made in layers that then harden

preservation – of the intact whole organism, for example in amber – resin exuded from a conifer which then solidified, or in tar, or in ice – freezing of complete specimens, or in anaerobic, acidic peat

Extension   Radiometric dating

The age of rocks may be dated precisely by radiometric dating techniques. Radioactivity results from spontaneous disintegration of the nuclei of certain (unstable) atoms. Atoms of radioactive isotopes (page 482), such as carbon-14 or potassium-40, decay at a constant rate, forming as a product stable (non-radioactive) atoms. The rate of decay is expressed as the **half-life** of the isotope: the time taken for the amount of radioactive isotope to fall by half. Isotopes that take millions of years to decay may be useful in dating fossils or rocks. By comparing the amounts of these isotopes to that of other isotopes of the element, or to their decay product, it is possible to estimate their age. Two techniques are illustrated here.

Using ^{14}C

Most carbon is ^{12}C, but due to cosmic radiation ^{14}C is also formed at a low, steady rate. Whilst alive, organisms absorb the ratio of ^{12}C : ^{14}C of the environment in which they live. After death, accumulation of radioactive (and other) atoms stops. Meanwhile the ^{14}C steadily breaks down:

$$^{14}\text{C} \xrightarrow[\text{5.6} \times 10^3 \text{ years}]{\text{half-life of}} {}^{14}\text{N}$$

So the ratio of ^{14}C : ^{12}C in a fossil decreases with age: the less ^{14}C, the older is the fossil.

Using the ratio of ^{40}K : ^{40}Ar

When sedimentary rock layers containing fossils are covered by layers of volcanic lava, then accurate dating of fossils and rocks is possible. For example, lava contains potassium-40, which decays to argon-40, as shown:

$$^{40}\text{K} \xrightarrow[\text{1.3} \times 10^9 \text{ years}]{\text{half-life}} {}^{40}\text{Ar (gas)}$$

In *hot* lava argon gas boils away into the atmosphere. Once lava has solidified by cooling, the argon gas that is formed by radioactive decay is trapped in the rock. By measuring the ratio of ^{40}K : ^{40}Ar in laval deposits it is possible to estimate the exact ages of the lava and the approximate age of the sedimentary rocks (and their fossils) below and above these larval layers.

The age of the Earth and the history of life

Today we realise that the history of life on Earth has been very long indeed – many hundreds of millions of years, in fact. This has not always been the case. In Western culture, the biblical account of creation was generally accepted as authorative, at least until the eighteenth century. The chronology given in the Bible suggested that life had appeared on Earth a mere few thousand years ago. For example, in 1654 Archbishop James Ussher calculated that the Creation had occurred in 4004 BC. On his timescale the Earth was only 5000–6000 years old!

In the eighteenth and nineteenth centuries, the ways that weathering of the landscape occurred was noticed. This led to the idea that rocks are endlessly recycled. The sedimentary rocks of existing mountains had once been the bedrock of lakes and seas and, before that, had probably been the rock of even older mountains. Geologists concluded that the Earth was very old indeed. Today, we estimate the age of the Earth as being 4500 million years, and that life originated 3500 million years ago (mya).

The geological timescale is shown in Figure 21.2. The length of time involved is so huge it is hard to imagine. The 24 hour clock diagram in Figure 21.2 may help you to appreciate the relative timing of some of the major milestones in the history of life. The prokaryotes were the first life forms to become established, and this level of organisation has apparently been successful ever since. Only after photosynthetic prokaryotes (the cyanobacteria – page 349) appeared was oxygen gas added to the atmosphere. The quantity of atmospheric oxygen has been increasing ever since, and currently stands at almost 21%. Eukaryotic cells appeared much later, and only relatively recently did living things invade the land. Something of the subsequent succession of plants and animals is shown in Figure 21.2. Not shown there are the vast numbers of extinctions that have also occurred. In the long history of life there have been many losers, too.

Figure 21.2
The geological timescale.   **geological timescale and some biological events**

Era	Period	Epoch	mya	Climate (in area of Britain)	Animal life	Plant life
Cainozoic	Quaternary	Holocene	0.01	Postglacial	Historic time, dominance of humans	Flora of modern UK
		Pleistocene	2	Ice ages	Origin of humans	
	Tertiary	Pliocene Miocene Oligocene Eocene Palaeocene	65	Part of south-east England submerged; climate warm to subtropical	Development of most mammal groups, and of pollinating insects	Development of flowering plants
Mesozoic	Cretaceous		135	Climate cool; sea covers much of England (chalk deposited); fresh water covers south-east England	World-wide extinction of many large reptiles; extinction of ammonites; beaked birds appear; mammals all small	Flowering plants appear
	Jurassic		200	Climate warm and humid	Large dinosaurs dominate; mammals all small	Floating phytoplankton abundant
	Triassic		250	Climate hot, with alternating wet and dry periods	Adaptive radiation of reptiles; first mammals appear	Development of conifers and related plants
Palaeozoic	Permian		290	Desert conditions	Insects diversify on land and in fresh water	First conifers
	Carboniferous		355	Equatorial climate; coal measures laid down	Reptiles and insects appear; development of amphibians	Widespread 'coal forests' and swamps, with tree-like ferns
	Devonian		405	Climate warm to moderate sandstones laid down	Amphibians appear; development of bony fish	Development of fern-like plants
	Silurian		440	Climate warm to moderately warm	Invasion of land by arthropods	First vascular land plants
	Ordovician		500	Climate warm to moderately warm	First vertebrates (jawless fish)	Marine algae abundant
	Cambrian		580	Climate uncertain	Origin of many non-vertebrate phyla	Many algae
Precambrian	75% of Earth's history		700 1500 3000 4500	Origin of Earth	Origin of first animals Origin of eukaryotes Oldest fossils (prokaryotes)	First photosynthesis

the history of life on the 24 hour clock

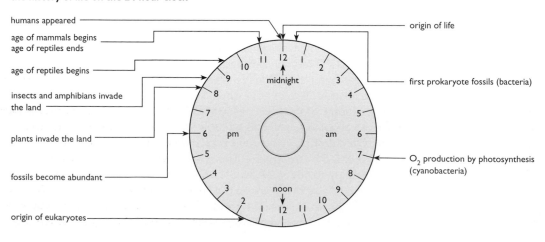

460

A mechanism for evolution

Charles Darwin (1809–1882) (Figure 21.3) was a careful observer and naturalist who made many discoveries in biology. After attempting to become a doctor (at Edinburgh University), and then a clergyman (at Cambridge University), he became the unpaid naturalist on an Admiralty-commissioned expedition to the southern hemisphere, on a ship called *HMS Beagle*. On this 5-year expedition around the world, and in his later investigations and reading, he developed the idea of **organic evolution by natural selection**.

Two years after his return from the *Beagle* expedition, Darwin moved to Down House, near Bromley, Kent. Here, in his family home and large garden, most of his experiments were conducted. He also worked on his Theory of Natural Selection. The idea of evolution did not start with Charles Darwin. Biologists and geologists discussed this issue before Darwin, and various hypotheses were proposed. Darwin's achievements were to state the evidence for evolution convincingly, and to show that the objections to the idea of evolution were answerable. He proposed a mechanism for evolution, called natural selection, which could be tested.

Darwin remained very anxious (always) about how the idea of evolution might be received, and he made no moves to publish it until the same idea was presented to him in a letter by another biologist and traveller, Alfred Russel Wallace. Only then (1859) was *On the Origin of Species by Natural Selection* completed and published. The arguments of the *Origin of Species* are summarised in Table 21.2.

After publication, Darwin avoided becoming involved in the 'heated' public debate his book caused. He left all that to his outspoken friend, Thomas Huxley. Today, the controversy has died down, and natural selection is widely accepted as the organising principle of modern biology.

Table 21.2
The arguments of the *Origin of Species*.

	presented as statements (S) and deductions (D):
S_1	organisms produce a far greater number of offspring than survive to be mature individuals
S_2	the number of individuals in species remain more or less constant
D_1	therefore many organisms die before they can reproduce
S_3	the individuals in a species are not all identical, but show variations in their characteristics
D_2	therefore some individuals are more successful than others in the competition for survival; so, the parents for the next generation will be selected from among those members of the species better adapted to the conditions of the environment
S_4	hereditary resemblances between parents and offspring are a fact
D_3	therefore subsequent generations will maintain and improve on the degree of adaptation of their parents, by gradual change

Figure 21.3
Charles Darwin 1809–1882. A statue in the University Museum, Oxford.

Neo-Darwinism

Charles Darwin, together with virtually everyone else working in science at that time, knew nothing of Mendel's discovery of the principles of modern genetics (page 450). Chromosomes had not been reported, and the existence of genes, alleles and DNA were unknown.

Instead, biologists then believed in '**blending inheritance**' to account for the similarities and differences between parents and offspring. According to this explanation, an offspring was a 'blend' or average of the characteristics of the parents. The outcome of the blending of the characteristics of parents in their offspring, if it happened, would be increasing uniformity. That is, genetic variation (which is essential for natural selection) would actually be reduced.

Today, modern genetics has shown us that blending generally does not occur, and that there are several ways by which genetic variations arise in gamete formation and fertilisation. **Neo-Darwinism** is a restatement of the ideas of evolution by natural selection in terms of modern genetics. Table 21.3 summarises the ideas of Neo-Darwinism.

Table 21.3 The ideas of Neo-Darwinism.	**Genetic variations arise via:** • **mutations** – including chromosome mutations and gene mutations (pages 115–16) • **random assortment** of paternal and maternal chromosomes in meiosis – this occurs in the process of gamete formation (page 105) • recombination of segments of maternal and paternal homologous chromosomes – during the crossing over that occurs in meiosis in gamete formation (page 106) • the random fusion of male and female gametes in sexual reproduction – this was understood in Darwin's time **Then, when genetic variation has arisen in organisms:** • it is expressed in their phenotypes • some phenotypes are better able to survive and reproduce in a particular environment • natural selection operates, determining the survivors and the genes that are perpetuated • in time, this process may lead to new varieties and new species

● Extension   So what is a species?

We begin in biology by defining the term 'species' as a group of individuals of common ancestry that closely resemble each other and that are normally capable of interbreeding to produce fertile offspring. Members of a species do not normally interbreed with members of other species. Organisms of the same species not only look very similar, but behave and respond in similar ways, and have bodies that function similarly (they are physiologically similar).

'Species' is a term we use confidently, but a clear-cut definition is more difficult to give. For example, species change with time as one species evolves from another. This is mostly a slow process, but it means there is a time when the differences between members of a species become significant enough to identify separate varieties or subspecies. Eventually these may become new species. When this happens is a matter of judgement.

● Population genetics

Population genetics is the study of genes in populations. Populations are important to our argument, because they are where evolution may occur.

A **population** is a group of individuals of a species, living close together, and able to interbreed. So a population of garden snails might occupy a small part of a garden, say around a compost heap (Figure 21.4). A population of thrushes might occupy some gardens and surrounding fields. In other words, the area occupied by a population depends on the size of the organism and on how mobile it is, for example, as well as on environmental factors (for example, food supply, predation, etc.). The boundaries of a population may be hard to define, too. Some populations are fully '**open**', with individuals moving in or out from nearby populations. Alternatively, some populations are more or less '**closed**' – that is, they are isolated communities, almost completely cut off from neighbours of the same species.

Populations and gene pools

In any population, the total of the alleles of the genes located in the reproductive cells of the individuals make up a **gene pool**. A sample of the alleles of the gene pool will contribute to form the **genomes** (gene sets of individuals) of the next generation, and so on, from generation to generation. When the gene pool of a population remains more or less unchanged, then we know that population is not evolving. However, if the gene pool of a population is changing (that is, the proportions of particular allele pairs are altered – we say 'disturbed' – in some way), then evolution may be going on. We can imagine, for example, that some alleles are increasing in frequency because of an advantage they confer to the individuals carrying them. With those alleles the organism is more successful, and may produce more offspring. If we can detect change in a gene pool we may detect evolution happening, possibly well before a new species is observed.

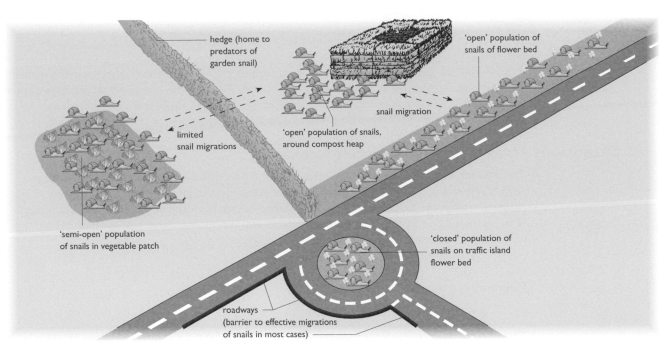

Figure 21.4
The concept of 'population'.

How can we detect change or constancy in gene pools?

The answer is, by a mathematical formula called the **Hardy–Weinberg formula** (Figure 21.5). This principle was discovered independently by two people, as they attempted to explain why dominant characteristics don't take over in populations, driving out the recessive form of that characteristic. (For example, at the time, people thought (wrongly) that human eye colour was controlled by a single gene, and that the allele for blue eyes was recessive to the allele for brown eyes. 'Why doesn't the population become brown-eyed?', was the issue.)

Figure 21.5
Deriving the Hardy–Weinberg formula.

Let the frequency of the dominant allele (**G**) be p, and the frequency of the recessive allele (**g**) be q.

(The frequency of alleles must add up to 1, so $p + q = 1$.)

This means in a cross, a proportion (p) of the gametes carry the **G** allele, and a proportion (q) of the gametes carry the **g** allele.

The offspring of each generation are given by the Punnett square diagram:

gamete frequency	**G** p	**g** q
G p	**GG** p^2	**Gg** pq
g q	**Gg** pq	**gg** q^2

So the progeny are respectively:
p^2 = frequency of **GG** homozygote
$2pq$ = frequency of **Gg** heterozygote
q^2 = frequency of **gg** homozygote

Hardy–Weinberg formula:

If the frequency of one allele (**G**) is p, and the frequency of the other allele (**g**) is q then the frequencies of the three possible genotypes:

GG, **Gg** and **gg**

are respectively: p^2, $2pq$ and q^2

The general formula to represent the frequency of dominant and recessive alleles is:

$p + q = 1$, where p = dominant alleles and q = recessive alleles

This equation was developed by Hardy and Weinberg to describe stable gene pools:

p^2	+	$2pq$	+	q^2	=	1
frequency of dominant homozygous individuals		frequency of heterozygous individuals		frequency of homozygous recessive individuals		total

The main problem of finding gene frequencies is that it is not possible to distinguish between homozygous dominant and heterozygotes based on their appearance or phenotype (pages 438 and 440).

However, using the above equation, it is possible to calculate gene frequency from the number of homozygous recessive individuals in the population. This is q^2. By taking the square root of this we can find q. The result tells us the frequency of the recessive allele, and this can then be substituted into the initial equation $p + q = 1$ to find the frequency of the dominant allele.

Extension   Using the Hardy–Weinberg formula

The absence of the skin pigment, melanin, is a condition called **albinism** (Figure 20.12, page 443), a genetically controlled characteristic. An albino has the genotype **pp** (homozygous recessive), whereas people with normal pigmentation are homozygous (**PP**) or heterozygous (**Pp**). In a large population only one person in 10 000 was albino. From the equation above, homozygous recessive (**pp**) $= q^2$. Thus:

$$q^2 = 0.0001, \text{ so } q = \sqrt{0.0001} = 0.01$$

So substituting into the initial equation $p + q = 1$

$$p + 0.01 = 1, \text{ therefore } p = 0.99$$

Thus the Hardy–Weinberg formula has allowed us to find the frequencies of alleles **P** and **p** in a population.

Incidentally, it has also shown that the frequency of 'carriers' of an allele for albinism in the population (**Pp**) is quite high (about 1 in 50 of the population) despite the fact that albinos make up only 1 in 10 000. In other words, very many more people carry around an allele for 'albinism' than those who know they may do so.

The Hardy–Weinberg principle and 'disturbing factors'

The **Hardy–Weinberg principle** predicts that the gene pool in a population does not change in succeeding generations. That is, genes and genotype frequencies normally remain constant in a breeding population *provided that*:

- the breeding population under investigation is a large one
- there is random mating, with individuals of any genotype all equally likely to mate with individuals of any other genotype (for example, no one genotype is being selectively predated)
- there is no introduction of new alleles into the population, either by mutations or by immigration of new breeding individuals.

But gene pools do change!

In some populations, the composition of the gene pool changes. This may be due to a range of factors, known as 'disturbing factors' in that they operate to alter the proportions of some alleles. Disturbing factors include:

1 **Selective predation** of members of the population with certain characteristics that are genetically controlled will lead to changing frequencies of certain alleles. For example, selective predation of snails with a particular shell coloration that makes them visible in (say) a woodland habitat, but is effective camouflage in a grassland habitat (Figure 21.6).
2 **Emigration/immigration**, snails with superior locomotory musculature, for example, or those better able to withstand moisture loss during journeys, are more likely to survive a migration than others.
3 **Mutation**, that is random, rare, spontaneous change in the genes, occurs in the gonads. This leads to the possibility of new characteristics in the offspring, for example, the ability to inactivate a pesticide molecule (page 392).
4 **Random genetic drift**, that is, a sudden hostile physical condition (for example, cold, flooding, drought) may sharply reduce a natural population to very few survivors. On the return of a favourable environment, numbers of the affected species may quickly return to

normal (for example, because of reduced competition for food sources). However, the new population has been built from a very small sample of the original population, with numerous 'first cousin' and backcross matings (causing fewer heterozygotes and more homozygotes) and with some alleles lost altogether.

5 **Founder effect**, in this, a barrier arises within a population, instantly isolating a small sample of the original population, which may carry an unrepresentative selection of the gene pool, yet be the basis of a new population. This is another form of genetic drift.

1 What factors may cause the composition of a gene pool to change?

Figure 21.6
Selective predation of snails.

The banded, coloured shells of the snail *Cepaea nemoralis* are common sights in woods, hedges and grasslands. The shells may be brown, pink or yellow and possess up to five dark bands. In woodland leaf litter the shells that are camouflaged are darker and more banded than those camouflaged among grasses.

woodland leaf litter

the **thrush** (*Turdus ericetorum*) selectively predates local populations of snails, using a stone as an 'anvil'

grass sward

How changing gene pools may lead to speciation

We have seen that species exist almost exclusively as local populations, even though the boundaries to these populations are often rather open and mostly ill defined. Individuals of local populations tend to resemble each other more closely than they do members of other populations. Local populations are very important in that they are potentially a starting point for speciation.

Figure 21.7
A case of geographic isolation by a human-imposed barrier. The by-pass at Newbury cuts through established habitats, separating local populations.

Speciation is the name given to the process by which one species may evolve into another. A first step to speciation may be when a local population (particularly a *small*, local population) becomes completely cut off in some way. Even then, many generations may elapse before the composition of the gene pool has changed sufficiently to allow us to call the new individuals a different species. Such changes in local gene pools may be detected at an early stage by application of the Hardy–Weinberg formula.

Speciation by isolation

In this, a population is occasionally suddenly divided by the appearance of a barrier into two populations isolated from each other. Before separation, individuals shared a common gene pool but, after isolation, 'disturbing processes' like natural selection, mutation and random genetic drift may occur independently in both populations, causing their features and characteristics to diverge.

Geographic isolation between populations occurs when natural (or human-imposed) barriers arise and sharply restrict movement of individuals (and their spores and gametes, in the case of plants) between the divided population (Figure 21.7). Geographic isolation is known as **allopatric** ('different countries') speciation.

Reproductive isolation mechanisms occasionally develop that are strong enough to prevent interbreeding between members of small, isolated populations that have diverged genetically, if only slightly, as a result of their isolation. Cases of reproductive isolation are likely to be less consistently effective than geographic isolation in bringing about complete isolation in the early stages. This is especially true if the isolation is based on slight physiological differences, as is the case in some mechanisms producing incompatibility in flowering plants (Figure 21.8).

Nevertheless, if members of a population become further isolated in this way, their gene pools may diverge more as a result. Reproductive isolation is also known as **sympatric** ('same country') speciation.

Figure 21.8
An example of reproductive isolation in flowering plant reproduction.

Incompatibility in flowering plants is the name given to physiological mechanisms that may make fertilisation impossible by preventing the growth of pollen tubes on the stigma or through the style.

Pollen that lodges on a stigma 'germinates' and attempts to send out a pollen tube that may eventually reach the embryo sac. Growth of pollen tubes that are opposed or unsupported by the stigma tissue fails.

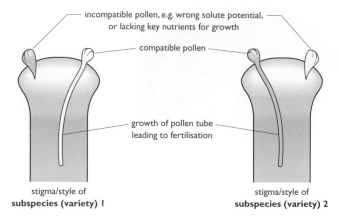

performance of pollen grains on different varieties of plant

incompatible pollen, e.g. wrong solute potential, or lacking key nutrients for growth

compatible pollen

growth of pollen tube leading to fertilisation

stigma/style of **subspecies (variety) 1**

stigma/style of **subspecies (variety) 2**

Speciation by polyploidy, a form of mutation

A mutation is a sudden change in the genetic information of an organism that may be heritable. It may arise by a change in structure, arrangement or quantity of the DNA of the chromosomes. These events occur randomly and spontaneously, and usually result in a marked difference in characteristics of an organism.

Chromosomal mutations involve a change in the structure or number of chromosomes. In plants, polyploidy is a rare occurrence, but one that more or less instantly creates a new species (provided the polyploidy survives the early period when its numbers are incredibly low).

The types of chromosome mutation that may lead to a new species generally involve an alteration in the number of whole sets of chromosomes, known as **euploidy**. An organism with more than two sets of chromosomes is called a **polyploid**. Polyploids are largely restricted to plants and (some) animals that reproduce asexually (the sex determination mechanism of vertebrates prevents polyploidy).

In polyploids, the additional set(s) of chromosomes may come from a member of the same species. Typically, this occurs if the spindle fails in meiosis (see Figure 5.5, page 104), causing diploid gametes to be formed. A well-known and economically very important example is the origin of the cultivated potato *Solanum tuberosum* ($2n = 48$), a polyploid of the smaller, wild *S. brevidens* ($2n = 24$).

Alternatively the additional set(s) of chromosomes may come from a different species. The additional set(s) are most likely not to be homologous, so pairing cannot occur early in meiosis, and the new individual is sterile. However, if the chromosome number is accidentally doubled by mitosis in the polyploid cell immediately the polyploid is formed, then pairing is possible. The origin of modern bread wheat is an example (Figure 21.9).

Natural selection and speciation

Natural selection operates on individuals, or rather on their phenotypes. Phenotypes are the product of a particular combination of alleles, interacting with the effects of the environment of the organism. Consequently, natural selection causes changes to gene pools. For example, individuals possessing a particular allele or combination of alleles may be more likely to survive, breed and pass on their alleles than are other, less-adapted individuals. This process is also

Figure 21.9
The origin of bread wheat by natural polyploidy.

- Three wild grasses, all diploid plants, each contributed one-third of the genome of our modern wheat.
- Two natural hybridisations were involved, and happened accidentally, 9000–7000 years ago.
- Each new species had heavier inflorescences of larger fruits that did not blow away (or break off) when harvested, but had to be threshed.

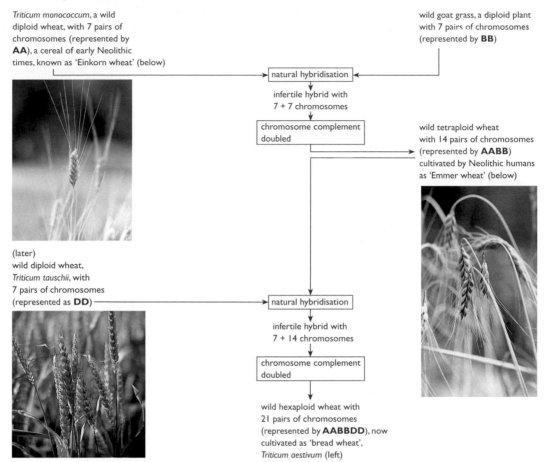

Triticum monococcum, a wild diploid wheat, with 7 pairs of chromosomes (represented by **AA**), a cereal of early Neolithic times, known as 'Einkorn wheat' (below)

wild goat grass, a diploid plant with 7 pairs of chromosomes (represented by **BB**)

natural hybridisation

infertile hybrid with 7 + 7 chromosomes

chromosome complement doubled

wild tetraploid wheat with 14 pairs of chromosomes (represented by **AABB**) cultivated by Neolithic humans as 'Emmer wheat' (below)

(later)
wild diploid wheat, *Triticum tauschii*, with 7 pairs of chromosomes (represented as **DD**)

natural hybridisation

infertile hybrid with 7 + 14 chromosomes

chromosome complement doubled

wild hexaploid wheat with 21 pairs of chromosomes (represented by **AABBDD**), now cultivated as 'bread wheat', *Triticum aestivum* (left)

referred to as **differential mortality**. However, natural selection does not require the death of the less fit, but rather that their genes are not perpetuated.

Natural selection operates to change the composition of gene pools, but the effect of this varies. We can recognise different types of selection.

Stabilising selection

Stabilising selection occurs where environmental conditions are stable and largely unchanging. Stabilising selection does not lead to evolution; rather it maintains the favourable characteristics that enable a species to be successful. Probably most populations undergo stabilising selections. It is a mechanism that maintains a favourable characteristic and the alleles responsible for them, and eliminates variants and abnormalities that are useless or harmful. The example in Figure 21.10 comes from human birth records on babies born between 1935 and 1946 in London. It shows there is an optimum birth weight for babies, and those with birth weights heavier or lighter are at a selective disadvantage.

Directional selection

Directional selection is associated with changing environmental conditions. In these situations the majority of an existing form of an organism may no longer be the best suited to the environment. Some unusual or abnormal forms of the population may have a selective advantage.

An example of directional selection is the development of resistance to an antibiotic by bacteria (page 468) (Figure 21.11). Certain bacteria cause disease, and patients with bacterial infections are frequently treated with an antibiotic to help them overcome the infection. Antibiotics are very widely used.

Figure 21.10
Birth weight and infant mortality, a case of stabilising selection.

The birth weight of humans is influenced by **environmental factors** (e.g. maternal nutrition, smoking habits, etc.) and by **inheritance** (about 50%).

When more babies than average die at very low and very high birth weights, this obviously affects the gene pool because it tends to eliminate genes for low and high birth weights.

This is an example of **stabilising selection** in that the values (weights) at the extremes of a continuous variation are at a selective disadvantage. This means that infants of these birth weights are more likely to die in infancy.

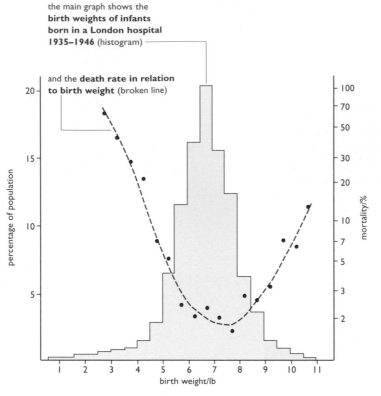

the main graph shows the **birth weights of infants born in a London hospital 1935–1946** (histogram)

and the **death rate in relation to birth weight** (broken line)

The data are an example of continuous variation. The 'middleness' or central tendency of this type of data is expressed in three ways:

1 **mode** (modal value) – the most frequent value in a set of values

2 **median** – the middle value of a set of values where these are arranged in ascending order

3 **mean** (average) – the sum of the individual values, divided by the number of values

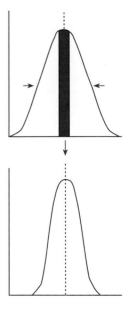

In a large population of a species of bacteria, some may carry a gene for resistance to the antibiotic in question. Sometimes such a gene arises by spontaneous mutation. Sometimes the gene is acquired in a form of sexual reproduction between bacteria of different populations.

A 'resistant' bacteria has no selective advantage in the absence of the antibiotic, and must compete for resources with non-resistant bacteria. But when the antibiotic is present most bacteria of the population are killed off. Resistant bacteria remain, however, and create the future population, all of which will then carry the gene for resistance to the antibiotic. The genome has been changed abruptly.

Figure 21.11
Directional selection. Development of antibiotic resistance in bacteria.

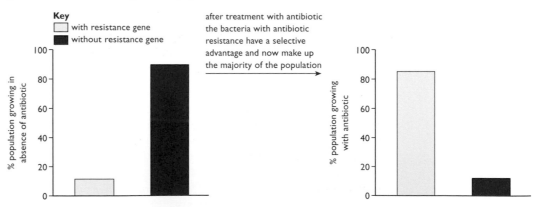

Key
- with resistance gene
- without resistance gene

after treatment with antibiotic the bacteria with antibiotic resistance have a selective advantage and now make up the majority of the population

Disruptive selection

Disruptive selection is associated with a fluctuating environment that favours two extremes of a variable characteristic. This rare form of selection occurs when a population is adapting to contrasting habitats, and is also associated with evolutionary change. The example of polymorphism in the peppered moth, *Biston betularia*, is illustrated in Figure 21.12.

Figure 21.12
The peppered moth *Biston betularia* and industrial melanism – a case of disruptive selection.

- As a result of the Industrial Revolution in Britain, in areas of heavy industry and in the surrounding countryside, the pollutant chimney gases (e.g. SO_2) and the particulate matter (e.g. soot) had killed off epiphytes (lichens, algae and moss growing on the surface of trees, etc.) and had blackened exposed surfaces.
- Black and dark-coloured species of moth (known as **melanic forms**) tended to increase in these areas, but their numbers were low in unpolluted countryside, where **pale forms** of moths were far more common.
- Organisms that exist in two forms are examples of **polymorphism**.
- In areas where pollution has stopped, surfaces have been cleaned up and epiphytes have returned, pale forms of the moths have become more frequent once again.

The moth *Biston betularia* is an example of this phenomenon, known as **industrial melanism**.

In different habitats, one or other form is effectively camouflaged, and is the dominant species. So, this is a case of **disruptive selection**. However, in the areas of the Industrial Revolution, during the hey-day of heavy industries, the fate of *Biston betularia* was a case of **directional selection** (i.e. exclusive selection of the melanic form).

Disruptive selection favours two extremes of the 'chosen characters' at the expense of intermediate forms.

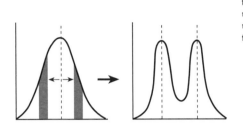

Biston betularia

pale form　　　　　　　　　　**melanic form**

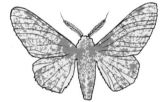

results of frequency studies in polluted and unpolluted habitats

mark–release–recapture experiments using laboratory-reared moths of both forms, in polluted and unpolluted habitats

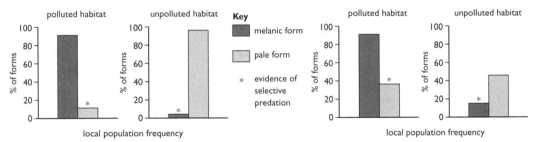

Key
- melanic form
- pale form
- * evidence of selective predation

Extension　Issues in macroevolution – a summary

Speciation, meaning the **origin of new species**, is the key process in organic evolution by natural selection, but if evolution is a fact of life then Neo-Darwinism should also account for the major steps in evolution (often called **macroevolution**). These steps include:

- the origin of life and the first cells
- the origin of the eukaryotic cell
- the origin of multicellular organisation
- the origin of vertebrates from non-vertebrates
- the rise of flowering plants
- the origin of viruses
- human evolution.

In many cases *we know little or nothing about how these changes came about*, and current ideas are mostly speculative. It is possible that some of these issues will remain largely a mystery. However, the evolution of humans is recent in geological terms and over time the fossil evidence of our early ancestors has accumulated. We are now able to speculate with some confidence on the likely steps in our own origins.

Artificial selection

Artificial selection is the process by which plants and animals used by humans in horticulture, agriculture, transport, companionship and leisure have been derived from wild organisms. Artificial selection involves identifying the largest, the best or the most useful of the offspring for an intended purpose, and using them as the next generation of parents. The continuous culling out of offspring deficient in the desired features, generation by generation is intentional manipulation of the gene pool. The genetic constitution of the population changes rapidly.

Darwin drew attention to the varieties of animals and plants that humans have bred artificially. Selection by humans can parallel the part played by natural selection in the production of new species. As part of his research for 'The origin', Darwin made a study of the artificial selection of pigeons (Figure 21.13). Breeders had produced varieties so different that, he argued, if they were found in the wild they would be classified as separate species. Humans have similarly bred dogs, but over a much longer period, since dogs were the first wild animals to be domesticated. Domestication of dogs from wolves (*Canis lupus*) began 13 000 years ago. Differences in size and other features of American, European and Asian wolves are reflected in the great diversity of breeds that have been developed.

Figure 21.13
Charles Darwin's observation of pigeon breeding.

From his breeding of pigeons, Darwin noted that there were more than a dozen varieties that, had they been presented to an ornithologist as wild birds, would have been classified as separate species.

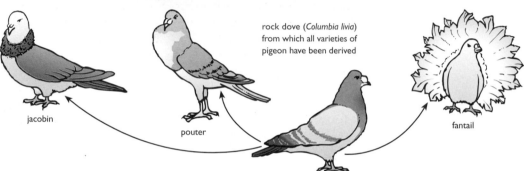

jacobin

pouter

rock dove (*Columbia livia*) from which all varieties of pigeon have been derived

fantail

Selective breeding in agriculture and horticulture

The breeding of domesticated animals and the cultivation of many plant crops, all from the 'wild' stock found in the vicinity, was begun when groups of *Homo sapiens* stopped their nomadic existence and became farmers in settled communities after the last Ice Age, about 10 000 years ago. At this stage, domestication of wild animals involved:

- the **identification** of a population of 'species' that was useful as a source of hides, or meat perhaps, and learning to distinguish them from related species; herd animals (for example, sheep and cattle) are naturally sociable, and lend themselves to this
- the selective killing (**culling**) of the *least* useful members of this herd for human purposes, in order to meet immediate needs for food and materials for living
- encouraging **breeding** among the docile, well-endowed members of the herd, and their protection against predators
- **selecting** from the offspring those individuals with the most useful features (in terms of the desired trait), and making these the future breeding stock
- **maintenance** of the breeding stock during unfavourable seasons
- ultimately, the **trading of individual animals** of the domesticated herd for other animals from neighbouring herdspeople's stocks, in order to introduce breeding stock with new features.

Many of the plant and animal species of modern farming were first produced at this time without any knowledge of heredity. Since these early beginnings, selective breeding of fruits, vegetables, flowers and livestock has continued more or less throughout human history. As a result, new organisms have been added to the list of previously wild species now cultivated, and many new varieties of cultivated organisms have been developed. There are no organisms cultivated and grown in agriculture and horticulture that have not been 'genetically modified' by humans.

The object of **modern animal breeding** is to improve the yields or quality of wool or hide, or milk production, or to increase meat quality (protein at the expense of fat, perhaps), or litter size, according to local needs and the animal species concerned. The animal breeder has a clear idea of the kind of animals wanted. The manager of a milking herd of cows keeps records of the quantity and quality of milk produced by individuals of the herd, for example. Those with better milk yields are used as mothers for the next generation. Animal breeding makes use of **artificial insemination** techniques, particularly in the breeding of cattle. In artificial insemination, semen is collected in an artificial vagina, and then diluted and stored in quantities suitable for individual insemination. Semen is held at low temperatures, which provides viable sperm samples over a prolonged period. A semen sample is injected into the uterus of a cow at oestrus (page 427). The farmer requests semen from a bull already renowned for offspring with qualities in either milk or meat productions, according to whether calves for beef rearing, or more cows for milk production, will get the best price in the market place.

The object of **modern plant breeding** is to improve crop yield by combining together superior genes. Plant breeding is carried out by crossing different varieties and then selecting offspring with particular features from which to breed further, such as:

- fast germination and/or growth
- limited stem growth and enhanced leaf growth
- rapid uptake and use of applied fertilisers
- resistance to disease and pests
- high yields and superior nutritive value of the product.

Inbreeding, outbreeding and hybrid vigour in selective breeding

Inbreeding occurs when the gametes of closely related organisms fuse. Inbreeding is common in plants that self-fertilise. In animals, inbreeding is achieved by sibling crosses. The genetic effect of inbreeding is to increase homozygosity, as the proportions of heterozygotes in the progeny decreases with each generation. With the loss of allele diversity comes the eventual loss of vigour and fertility.

2 What are the differences between natural selection and artificial selection?

Outbreeding occurs by crossing of unrelated varieties. This promotes heterozygosity, and the outcome may be referred to as **hybrid vigour**. New combinations of chromosomes produce differences and are often complementary in their effects.

SUMMARY

- **Evolution** is the development of living things in geological time.
- Evolution occurs by **natural selection** of chance variations. Variations arise by mutations of genes and chromosomes and by the reshuffling of genes that occurs in meiosis as a result of independent assortment, crossing over and the random nature of fertilisation.
- The total of all the genes in a breeding population is known as a **gene pool**. The frequency of an allele in a population is known as the **allele frequency**. Allele frequency does not change in a breeding population in succeeding generations in the absence of 'disturbing factors'.
- **Disturbing factors** that may alter the proportions of alleles are selective predation, emigration or immigration, mutation and random genetic drift arising from a dramatic reduction in the size of a population.
- New species may form when a small part of a population becomes **genetically isolated** from others by a geographical or reproductive barrier.
- An abrupt change in the structure or number of chromosomes (a **chromosomal mutation**) may cause an instant appearance of a new species.
- Natural selection may work to keep the characteristics of a species constant (**stabilising selection**), but if the environment changes then new forms may emerge (**directional** or **disruptive selection**).

continued

In addition to accounting for the evolution of new species, evolution should be able to explain the major steps (**macroevolution**) of eukaryotic cells from prokaryotic cells, the origin of multicellular organisms, the origin of vertebrates from non-vertebrates, the origin of flowering plants and the origin of living things from the non-living.
- **Artificial selection** is the process by which humans selectively breed the animals and plants used in agriculture, horticulture, transport and leisure from wild plants and animals.
- **Selective breeding** is carried out by careful selection of the parents in breeding crosses and the selection of progeny with the required features (and also by genetic engineering techniques, see Chapter 6).

Examination questions

I *Cepaea nemoralis* is a common British snail which is found in a variety of habitats. The shells of this species of snail vary in the pattern of dark bands found on the surface. The drawings show a banded snail and an unbanded snail.

banded snail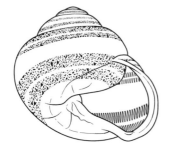

unbanded snail

Song thrushes feed on these snails. A bird finds a snail and takes it to a suitable stone known as an anvil. It hits the snail shell against the stone, breaks it open and eats the soft parts. The remains of the shell can be found on the ground near the thrush's anvil stone.

In one investigation, two areas of woodland floor were cleared of all snails and equal numbers of banded and unbanded snails were then introduced. Over the next two weeks the snail shells found around the anvil stones in one area were compared with the shells of living snails found in a control area where there were no thrushes. The results are shown in the table.

	Number of unbanded snails	Number of banded snails
snail shells found around anvil stones	153	264
shells of living snails found in control area	204	217

a Describe and explain the effect of predation by thrushes on the snails in this investigation. (2)

b The presence of bands on the shells of *C. nemoralis* is controlled by a single gene with two alleles. Explain how natural selection might account for different proportions of these alleles in different habitats. (2)

c In order to collect the sample of living snails in the control area, quadrats were placed at random in the area and all the snails found in the quadrat were collected. Explain why it was necessary to
i place the quadrats at random; (1)
ii ensure that every snail found within the quadrat was collected. (1)

d In a separate investigation, the population of *C. nemoralis* was estimated using the mark–release–recapture method.
i Giving a reason for your answer, describe where on the shell you would mark the snails. (1)
ii Explain why the results would be more accurate if there was only a short time between releasing the marked snails and catching the second sample. (1)

NEAB, A level, Paper 1/Sections A & B, June 1997

APPENDICES

Appendix 1: Background chemistry for biologists

Elements, atoms, molecules and compounds

Elements are the basic units of pure substances that make up our entire world. The Earth is composed of about 92 stable elements in varying quantities, including substances like carbon, hydrogen, calcium and sodium. The names of the elements are usually written down as a **chemical symbol** – a convenient shorthand for the full name. For example, the symbol for carbon is C, for hydrogen it is H, for calcium it is Ca, and for sodium it is Na (derived from its Latin name of *natrium*).

Most elements are divided into two groups – **metals** and **non-metals** – based on their appearances, states and properties (Table A.1). Living things are built from both metal and non-metallic elements, but it is non-metallic elements that make up the bulk. The range of elements that compose living things is quite different from the composition of the environment around them. The four most common elements of the Earth's crust are oxygen (O), silicon (Si), aluminium (Al) and iron (Fe), whereas the bulk of living things (about 99%) is formed from hydrogen, oxygen, carbon and nitrogen (N) (Table A.2).

Table A.1
Metallic and non-metallic elements.

Non-metallic elements e.g. hydrogen, oxygen, carbon, silicon	Metallic elements e.g. calcium, potassium, magnesium, iron
usually solids or gases (at room temperature)	usually solids (at room temperature)
solids appear dull	have a shiny appearance
a low density with low melting point	dense, with a high melting point
usually do not conduct electricity	conduct electricity

An **atom** is the smallest part of an element that can take part in a chemical change. The atoms of different elements are of different sizes, but all atoms are incredibly small. Because of the small size of atoms we cannot refer to their mass by a standard unit, like the gram, for example. Instead, we compare the mass of an atom relative to an agreed standard. For this purpose the reference atom is that of carbon. The carbon atom is given a **relative atomic mass*** of 12 ($A_r = 12$). By comparison, atoms of hydrogen ($A_r = 1$) are much lighter than carbon, but atoms of nitrogen ($A_r = 14$) are slightly heavier, and atoms of potassium ($A_r = 39$) substantially heavier. Table A.3 gives the relative atomic mass of the atoms of 13 common elements of living things.

*Note that the term **relative atomic mass** replaces the former term 'atomic weight'.

474

Table A.2
The relative abundance (%) of the elements of living things.

Element	Symbol	Organisms	Earth's crust
hydrogen	H	49.0	0.22
carbon	C	25.0	0.19
oxygen	O	25.0	47.0
nitrogen	N	0.27	<0.1
calcium	Ca	0.073	3.5
potassium	K	0.046	2.5
silicon	Si	0.033	28.0
magnesium	Mg	0.031	2.2
phosphorus	P	0.030	<0.1
sodium	Na	0.015	2.5
others		traces	13.7

Trace elements include iron (Fe), manganese (Mn), copper (Cu), cobalt (Co), and zinc (Zn)
Iron (Fe) makes up almost 5% of the Earth's crust

Table adapted from: E. J. Wood and W. R. Pickering (1982), *Introducing Biochemistry*, John Murray (page 7).

Figure A.1
The structure of a carbon atom.

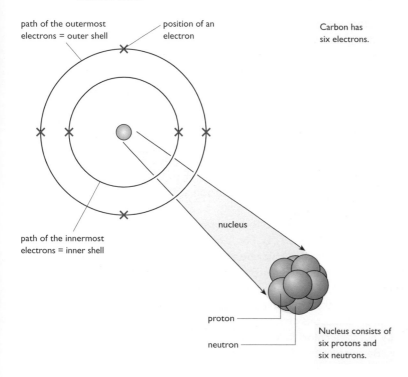

path of the outermost electrons = outer shell

position of an electron

Carbon has six electrons.

path of the innermost electrons = inner shell

nucleus

proton

neutron

Nucleus consists of six protons and six neutrons.

The **structure of an atom** is shown in Figure A.1. This is the carbon atom. You can see that this atom is made of three kinds of smaller particles.

At the centre of the atom is the nucleus. This consists of **protons** (positively charged particles) and, usually, **neutrons**, which are uncharged particles. (The single exception is the nucleus of the hydrogen atom which contains no neutron, only a single proton.) Protons and neutrons have virtually the same mass. (Note that the nucleus of an atom must not be compared or confused with the cell nucleus.)

Around the nucleus occur incredibly tiny particles called **electrons** (negatively charged particles), moving in orbits or 'shells'. Electrons have almost no mass at all.

The final point to note is that the whole atom is electrically neutral. This is because the number or protons (positively charged) in the nucleus is equal to the number of electrons (negatively charged) in the surrounding orbits.

Table A.3
The relative atomic mass (A_r) of the atoms of 13 elements of living things.

Element	Symbol	A_r	Element	Symbol	A_r
hydrogen	H	1	sodium	Na	23
oxygen	O	16	potassium	K	39
carbon	C	12	calcium	Ca	40
nitrogen	N	14	magnesium	Mg	24
phosphorus	P	31	iron	Fe	56
sulphur	S	32	copper	Cu	63.5
chlorine	Cl	35.5			

A **molecule** is the smallest part of most elements or compounds that can exist alone under normal conditions. For example, oxygen and nitrogen are not found as single atoms, but as pairs. Each atom naturally combines with another atom of the same type to form a molecule. So, molecular oxygen has the symbol O_2 and molecular nitrogen N_2, to indicate that there are two atoms in each case. Some molecules that form naturally contain more than one element, and so we call these compounds. A **compound** is a molecule which contains two or more elements chemically combined together. For example, carbon dioxide (CO_2) contains atoms of carbon and oxygen, molecules of water (H_2O) contain atoms of hydrogen and oxygen, and molecules of common salt, sodium chloride (NaCl), contain atoms of sodium and chlorine.

How atoms form molecules

Atoms naturally combine together (they 'bond') to form molecules in ways that have a stable arrangement of electrons in the outer shells of each atom. Atoms are most stable when their outer shell of electrons is complete. The electron shell closest to the nucleus can hold up to two electrons and then it is full. Similarly, the second shell can hold up to a maximum of eight electrons, the third shell can hold up to 18 electrons, and the fourth shell can hold up to 32 electrons. (There are further shells in the largest atoms, but they do not concern us here because the elements that make up living things have atoms that are among the smallest and lightest in the Earth's crust.)

How are these bonds formed that achieve complete outer shells? This may happen in two different ways. Atoms *either* may share electrons (called covalent bonding), *or* they may give and take electrons (called ionic bonding).

- In **covalent bonding**, electrons are shared between atoms. Covalent bonds are the strongest bonds occurring in biological molecules. This means that the greatest amount of energy has to be used to break them. So, covalent bonds provide great stability to biological molecules, many of which are very large and elongated. Bonding of this kind is common in non-metallic elements such as hydrogen, nitrogen, carbon and oxygen.

   When one pair of electrons is shared, as in the hydrogen molecule, a single covalent bond is formed, known as a **single bond**. If two pairs of electrons are shared, then a **double bond** is formed. Double bonds are quite common between two carbon atoms (Figure A.2), or between carbon and oxygen.

- In **ionic bonding**, atoms gain or lose electrons to form positive or negative ions that have a stable arrangement of outer electrons (Figure A.3). For example, sodium ions and chloride ions are much more stable than sodium atoms and chlorine atoms, because the sodium loses the single electron in the outer shell to form a complete shell, and the chlorine gains the electron to complete a third-level shell.

   Ionic bonding is the electrostatic attraction between oppositely charged particles. The electrostatic attraction acts in all directions around the ion so, for example, the positive sodium ion is surrounded by negative chloride ions, while each chloride ion attracts and is surrounded by sodium ions. Because of this, in solid sodium chloride the ionic bonds hold the ions together in a regular arrangement (known as a **crystal lattice**), as seen in crystals of salt. In solution, however, the presence of water molecules, surrounding the sodium and chloride ions (page 57), causes them to be separated and dispersed.

Figure A.2
Sharing of electrons in covalent bonds.

I In the hydrogen molecule a covalent bond is formed.

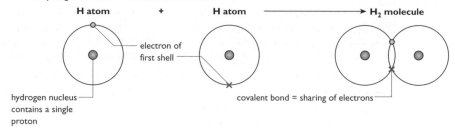

H atom + **H atom** ⟶ **H₂ molecule**

electron of first shell

hydrogen nucleus contains a single proton

covalent bond = sharing of electrons

2 In **methane,** four single bonds are formed with hydrogen atoms to make the outer shell of carbon up to eight electrons.

4H + **C** ⟶ **CH₄ (methane)**

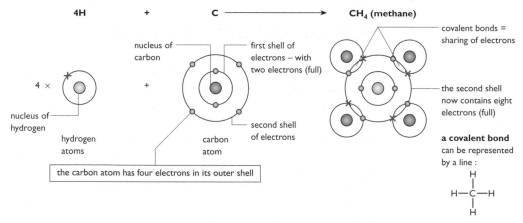

4 ×

nucleus of hydrogen

hydrogen atoms

nucleus of carbon

first shell of electrons – with two electrons (full)

second shell of electrons

carbon atom

the carbon atom has four electrons in its outer shell

covalent bonds = sharing of electrons

the second shell now contains eight electrons (full)

a covalent bond can be represented by a line :

```
    H
    |
H — C — H
    |
    H
```

3 In **ethene (C₂H₄),** the carbon atoms make up their outer electron shells to eight electrons by forming a double bond (with the other carbon atom) and two single bonds (with hydrogen atoms).

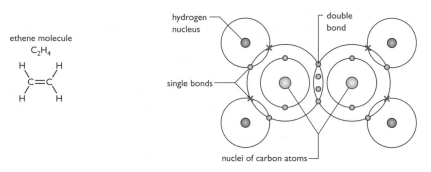

ethene molecule
C_2H_4

```
 H        H
  \      /
   C == C
  /      \
 H        H
```

hydrogen nucleus

single bonds

double bond

nuclei of carbon atoms

Figure A.3
Transfer of electrons in ionic bonds.

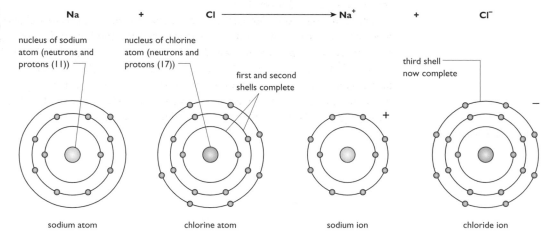

Na + **Cl** ⟶ **Na⁺** + **Cl⁻**

nucleus of sodium atom (neutrons and protons (11))

nucleus of chlorine atom (neutrons and protons (17))

first and second shells complete

third shell now complete

sodium atom

chlorine atom

sodium ion

chloride ion

a sodium atom donates an electron to a chlorine atom

Ions

Ions are the charged particles formed in ionic bonding. They are very stable because their outermost electron shell is complete. Positively charged ions are called **cations**, and negatively charged ions are called **anions**. Six ions are of particular biological importance, as these ions occur widely in living cells. Table A.4 details some of their specialised roles in functioning cells.

Table A.4
Some ions of importance in biological systems.

Positively charged ions (cations):	
Na$^+$ (sodium ion)	involved in the setting up of the action potential of a nerve fibre, and the flow of the action potential (impulse) (page 278)
K$^+$ (potassium ion)	involved in the setting up of the action potential of a nerve fibre, and the flow of the action potential (impulse) (page 278)
Ca^{2+} (calcium ion)	involved in the contraction of the muscle myofibrils by combining with blocking molecules, so that the myosin head of the cross bridge can attach to the myosin (page 310)
Negatively charged ions (anions):	
NO$_3^-$ (nitrate ion)	plants reduce nitrate to ammonia, and combine it with an organic acid, forming an amino acid. From this come all 20 amino acids that are used to manufacture proteins
PO$_4^{3-}$ (phosphate ion)	the phosphate ion is combined with ADP to form ATP; ATP is the primary energy currency of cells, involved in energy-requiring reactions and processes, like protein synthesis and muscle contraction
HCO$_3^-$ (hydrogencarbonate ion)	this is the form in which carbon dioxide is transported in the blood (plasma and red cells). It is formed when CO$_2$ reacts with water, catalysed by carbonic anhydrase enzyme

Why carbon is important to life

The importance of carbon lies in its unique collection of properties. These are so remarkable, in fact, that we can say that they make life possible:

Figure A.4
Covalent bonds and carbon 'skeletons'.

- **Carbon is a relatively small atom, and is able to form four strong, stable bonds.** The bonds that carbon atoms form are called covalent bonds. A great deal of energy has to be put into carbon molecules to break them.

covalent bonds are formed by sharing of electrons, one from the carbon atom and one from the neighbouring atom it reacts with:

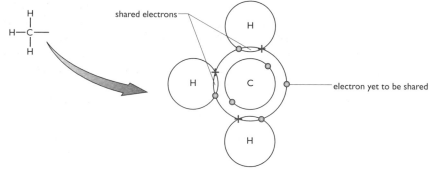

carbon atoms bond with other carbon atoms to form carbon 'skeletons':

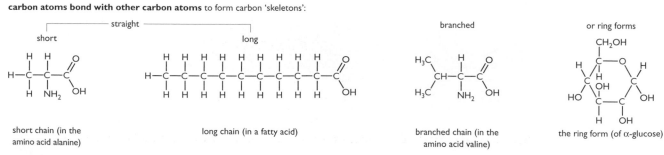

short chain (in the amino acid alanine)   long chain (in a fatty acid)   branched chain (in the amino acid valine)   the ring form (of α-glucose)

- **Carbon atoms are able to react with each other to form extended chains.** These 'carbon skeletons' may be straight chains, branched chains or rings (Figure A.4). So, a vast number of extremely stable carbon compounds exist – more than the combined total of known compounds of all the other elements, in fact. Biologists believe that this great wealth of carbon compounds has made possible the diversity of life as we know it.
- The **four covalent bonds of carbon atoms** point to the corners of a **regular tetrahedron** (a pyramid with a triangular base) (Figure A.5). This is because the four pairs of electrons repel each other, and so position themselves as far away from each other as is possible. If there are different groups attached to each of the four bonds around a carbon atom then there are two different ways of arranging the groups. This leads to forms of molecules that are 'mirror images' of each other. Carbon atoms with four different atoms or groups attached are said to be asymmetric. This is another cause of variety among organic molecules.

Figure A.5 The tetrahedral carbon atom.

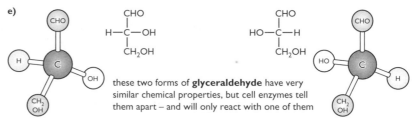

the carbon atom is at the centre of the tetrahedron, a three-dimensional structure, e.g. methane

'ball and spring' model

space-filling model

perspective formula

with different groups attached to each of the four bonds, there are *two* **ways of arranging them**, each a mirror image of the other

these two forms of **glyceraldehyde** have very similar chemical properties, but cell enzymes tell them apart – and will only react with one of them

- **Carbon atoms form covalent bonds with other atoms**, such as oxygen, hydrogen, nitrogen and sulphur, forming different groups of organic molecules with distinctive properties.
- **Carbon compounds**, although numbering 2–3 million in total, **fit into a relatively small number of 'families' of compounds**. The families are identified by a part of their molecule called the **functional group**; this gives them their characteristic chemical properties. Chemical families we often come across in biology include the alcohols, organic acids, ketones and aldehydes. The chemical structure of these functional groups is shown in Figure 2.3 (page 27). The remainder of the organic molecule, apart from the functional group, has little or no effect on the chemical properties of the functional group, and is referred to as the **R group**.
- **Carbon atoms can form more than one bond between them.** For example, carbon atoms may share two pairs of electrons to form a double bond (Figure A.6). Carbon compounds that contain double carbon–carbon bonds are known to chemists as '**unsaturated**', and carbon compounds not containing double bonds are **saturated** compounds.

  In fact carbon, nitrogen and oxygen all form double bonds. This is another way in which variety is introduced to the range of carbon compounds that make up cells.

Figure A.6 Carbon–carbon bonds, or double bonds.

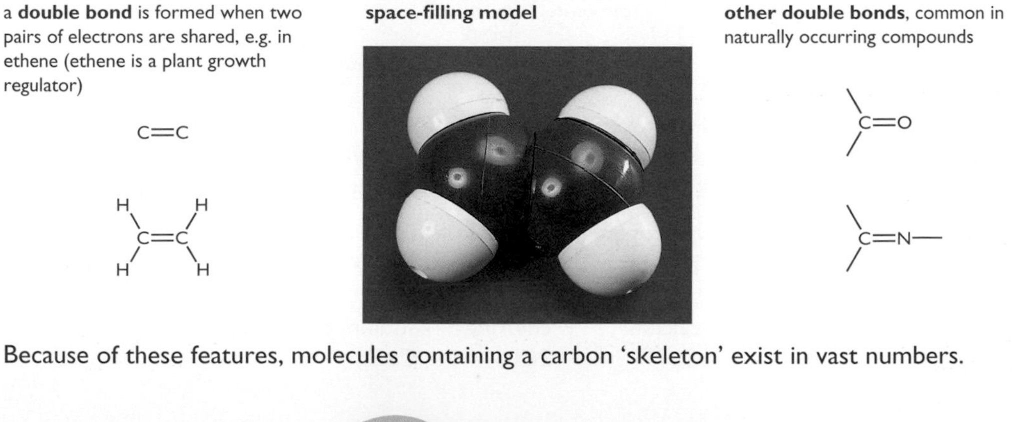

a **double bond** is formed when two pairs of electrons are shared, e.g. in ethene (ethene is a plant growth regulator)

space-filling model

other double bonds, common in naturally occurring compounds

Because of these features, molecules containing a carbon 'skeleton' exist in vast numbers.

Chemical equations

In a chemical reaction, the reacting molecules (**reactants**) are converted into new molecules (**products**). The change involved in the reaction is summarised in an equation. The process of constructing a chemical equation has three steps.

1 A **word equation** is written. Examples are:

hydrogen + oxygen → water

calcium + chlorine → calcium chloride

2 Below the word equation, the **formulae** for the substances involved are written using the symbols for the elements. Molecules must be shown containing the correct number of atoms. For this you need to know how many bonds an atom can form. This is known as the combining power or valency (Table A.5).

$$\begin{array}{lll}
\text{hydrogen} + \text{oxygen} & \rightarrow \text{water} \\
H_2 & O_2 & H_2O
\end{array}$$

$$\begin{array}{lll}
\text{calcium} + \text{chlorine} & \rightarrow \text{calcium chloride} \\
Ca & Cl & CaCl_2
\end{array}$$

The **valency** of an atom, ion or group of atoms is needed for writing chemical formulae. Valency is the number of electrons used by an atom in bonding:

• the number of electrons lost by a cation in formation
• the number of electrons gained by an anion in formation
• the number of electrons shared by a covalent atom in forming a bond.

Table A.5
Combining power or valencies.

Valencies of covalent atoms

1	2	3	4
H	O	N	C
	S	P	

Charges on some ions

−3	−2	−1	+1	+2	+3
Single element ions:		Cl^-	H^+	Ca^{2+}	
			Na^+	Mg^{2+}	
			K^+		
			Cu^+ (copper(I))	Cu^{2+} (copper(II))	
				Fe^{2+} (iron(II))	Fe^{3+} (iron(III))

Ions containing more than one element:

PO_4^{3-}	SO_4^{2-}	NO_3^-	NH_4^+
(phosphate)	(sulphate)	(nitrate)	(ammonium)
	CO_3^{2-}	OH^-	
	(carbonate)	(hydroxyl)	
		HCO_3^-	
		(hydrogencarbonate)	

3 The equation is then **balanced**, so that the number of atoms on either side of the equation are equal, since matter is neither created nor destroyed in chemical reactions.

$$\begin{array}{lll}
\text{hydrogen} + \text{oxygen} & \rightarrow \text{water} \\
2H_2 & O_2 & 2H_2O
\end{array}$$

$$\begin{array}{lll}
\text{calcium} + \text{chlorine} & \rightarrow \text{sodium chloride} \\
Ca & 2Cl & CaCl_2
\end{array}$$

Acids and bases

An **acid** is a compound that produces hydrogen ions in water (Table A.6). We are familiar with the sharp taste that acids such as lemon juice or vinegar give to the tongue. These are relatively weak acids – weak enough to use on foods. The stronger the acid the more dangerous and corrosive it is, and the more hydrogen ions it produces. An example of a **strong acid** is hydrochloric acid. In water, this acid dissociates completely. The word dissociate means 'separates into its constituent ions':

$$HCl \rightarrow H^+ + Cl^-$$

With organic acids such as citric acid (present in lemon juice) and ethanoic acid (of vinegar), which we recognise as **weak acids**, relatively few molecules are dissociated, and few hydrogen ions are present:

$$C_2H_5COOH \rightleftharpoons C_2H_5COO^- + H^+$$

A **base** is a substance that can accept a hydrogen ion and so neutralise an acid. From this reaction a salt and water only are formed. Many bases are insoluble in water. Those that are soluble in water are called **alkalis**. Examples of strong bases (that are also alkalis) are sodium hydroxide and potassium hydroxide. Strong alkalis, like strong acids, are completely dissociated in water:

$$NaOH \rightarrow Na^+ + OH^-$$

Some substances, called **indicators**, change colour when mixed with acid or alkalis. Examples of indicators are litmus and universal indicator, which turn red in acid (see Figure A.7).

Table A.6 Acids and bases in biological systems.

Strong acids:		
HCl hydrochloric acid	$H^+ + Cl^-$	produced in the gastric glands of the stomach
H_2SO_4 sulphuric acid	$2H^+ + SO_4^{2-}$	produced when sulphur trioxide (atmospheric pollutant) dissolves in rain water
HNO_3 nitric acid	$H^+ + NO_3^-$	produced when oxides of nitrogen (NO_x) – atmospheric pollutant – dissolves in rain water
Weak acids:		
CH_3COOH ethanoic acid	$H^+ + CH_3COO^-$	formed by bacterial action on ethanol
H_2CO_3 carbonic acid	$H^+ + HCO_3^-$	formed when carbon dioxide dissolves in water
Strong alkalis:		
NaOH sodium hydroxide	$Na^+ + OH^-$	commonly used laboratory alkali, very corrosive when concentrated
KOH potassium hydroxide	$K^+ + OH^-$	commonly used laboratory alkali, very corrosive when concentrated
Other bases:		
$CaCO_3$ calcium carbonate $MgCO_3$ magnesium carbonate		both these bases are found in soils, and tend to neutralise acid rain

pH and buffers

pH is a measure of acidity or alkalinity of a solution. Strictly, pH is a measure of the hydrogen ion concentration. The pH scale runs from 0 to 14. pH 7 is neutral; this is the pH of pure water, where the concentrations of hydrogen ions and hydroxyl ions are low and equal in number.

A solution of pH of less than 7 is an acidic solution; strong acids have a pH of 0–2. Solutions of pH of more than 7 are alkaline. Because the pH scale is logarithmic, a change in the scale of one unit (for example, from pH 4 to pH 5) represents a ten-fold change in the amount of hydrogen ions present. This means that pH values cannot be added up and an average (mean) value found.

pH is measured experimentally, using either an indicator solution or a pH meter. For example, universal pH indicator is a mixture of several different indicators, and changes colour with the pH, as shown in Figure A.7.

pH is very important in living organisms, largely because it affects the shape of enzymes, almost all of which are proteins (page 40). In the mammal's body there are mechanisms to maintain the pH at a constant level, at a value just slightly above pH 7.0. If the pH varies very much from this value this is quickly fatal. For plants that obtain essential mineral ions from the soil solution, the pH of the soil affects the availability of ions for absorption.

Figure A.7
The pH scale of universal pH indicator solution.

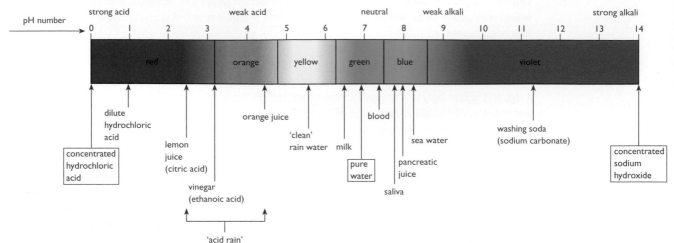

A **buffer solution** acts to resist pH change when diluted, or if a little acid or alkali is added. Many buffers used in laboratory experiments contain a weak acid (such as ethanoic acid) and its soluble salt (for example, sodium ethanoate). In this case, if acid is added, the excess hydrogen ions are immediately removed by being combined with ethanoate ions to form undissociated ethanoic acid. Alternatively, if alkali is added, the excess hydroxyl ions immediately combine with hydrogen ions, forming water. At the same time, more of the ethanoic acid dissociates, adding more hydrogen ions to the solution. The pH does not change in either case.

In the body of the mammal, the blood is very powerfully buffered by the presence of a mixture of phosphate ions, hydrogencarbonate ions and blood proteins (page 227). The blood is held between pH 7.35 and 7.45.

Isotopes

Atoms of certain elements exist in more than one form, and these are known as **isotopes** of the element. All the isotopes of an element have the same number of orbiting electrons and the same number of protons in their nuclei, so they have the same **chemical properties**. Consequently, they react identically. However, the isotopes of a particular element have different numbers of neutrons in the nucleus, and so they have different masses.

Isotopes are classified as stable or unstable. **Stable isotopes** persist in nature because they do not undergo radioactive decay. Oxygen-16 and oxygen-18 are stable isotopes. **Unstable isotopes** are radioactive. This means they break down steadily, often emitting α or β particles. This process is known as radioactive decay. The product of the decay process is a stable isotope. For example, carbon-14 (radioactive) decays to nitrogen-14 and emits β particles.

The radiation emitted by radioactive isotopes fogs photographic film placed near the radioactive source in the dark, a technique known as **autoradiography**. The presence of radioactive isotopes can alternatively be detected by instruments, such as a Geiger–Müller tube (**Geiger counter**). Non-radioactive isotopes are detected by their difference in mass, using a **mass spectrometer**. Examples of stable and radioactive isotopes, and the uses they may be put to in biology, are given in Table A.7.

Stable isotopes:	
oxygen-16 and oxygen-18	these isotopes have been used in experiments showing that oxygen given off in photosynthesis comes from the 'splitting' of water
potassium-40 and argon-40	these isotopes are used in the dating of volcanic lava deposits in the process of determining the approximate age of fossils, originally trapped in the cooling lava
Stable/radioactive (*) isotopes: carbon-12/carbon-14(*)	these isotopes have been used to investigate the 'fixation' of carbon from carbon dioxide into sugar, in photosynthesis
phosphorus-31/phosphorus-32(*) and sulphur-32/sulphur-35(*)	these isotopes have been used to show that DNA and not protein carries the genetic message

Table A.7 Some isotopes of importance in biology.

Oxidation and reduction

When the fuel methane (CH_4) is burnt in air, carbon dioxide and water are formed:

$$2CH_4 + 4O_2 \rightarrow 2CO_2 + 4H_2O$$

Some oxygen has been added to the carbon, so the carbon has been **oxidised**. At the same time, some of the oxygen has been **reduced** to water. Oxidation and reduction always occur together in this way. When one substance in a reaction is oxidised another is automatically reduced; that is, an oxidation/reduction reaction has occurred. The shorthand name for **red**uction–**ox**idation reactions is **redox reactions**.

In redox reactions in biology, hydrogen atoms are often involved. We have seen that a hydrogen atom is an electron and a proton. Gaining hydrogen atom(s) (a case of reduction) involves gaining one or more electrons. In fact, the best definition of oxidation is the loss of electrons, and reduction is the gain of electrons. Remembering this definition has given countless people problems. A mnemonic has been devised, namely:

OILRIG = **O**xidation **I**s **L**oss of electrons; **R**eduction **I**s **G**ain of electrons

Redox reactions mostly take place in biological systems because of the presence of a compound with a strong tendency to *take* electrons from another compound (an **oxidising agent**) or the presence of a compound with a strong tendency to *donate* electrons to another compound (a **reducing agent**). For example, in respiration (in which glucose is oxidised to CO_2 and H_2O – page 195), a common oxidising agent is a large molecule known as NAD, and the corresponding reducing agent is NADH. In photosynthesis (in which CO_2 is reduced to glucose – page 178), a common reducing agent is a large molecule known as NADPH, and the corresponding oxidising agent is NADP.

Another feature of oxidation and reduction is **energy change**. When reduction occurs energy is absorbed (an **endergonic reaction**, Figure 4.2, page 76). When oxidation occurs, energy is released (an **exergonic reaction**). An example of energy release in oxidation is the burning of a fuel in air. Here, energy is given out as heat. In fact, the amount of energy in a molecule depends on its degree of oxidation. An oxidised substance has less stored energy than a reduced substance; this is illustrated by the fuel molecule methane (CH_4), which has more stored chemical energy than carbon dioxide (CO_2).

Hydrolysis and condensation

When two molecules **join together** to form a larger molecule with the loss of a molecule of **water**, a **condensation reaction** has occurred. This happens when sugar molecules are condensed together to make disaccharides and polysaccharides. Other examples are when glycerol reacts with fatty acids to form triglycerols, or an organic acid reacts with an alcohol to form an ester:

$$R-COOH + HO-R \underset{\text{hydrolysis reaction}}{\overset{\text{condensation reaction}}{\rightleftharpoons}} R-COOR + H_2O$$

Hydrolysis is the reverse of condensation. It occurs when **water splits a molecule** into two or more smaller molecules.

Molarity and concentration

The **mole** is the scientific unit for the amount of substance. We use the mole in situations where we need **a unit that contains the same number of atoms (or molecules or ions)**, whatever the substance being referred to. All atoms are incredibly small, but atoms of different elements vary in mass. Some atoms are very heavy, others are lighter, but a mole of each will contain exactly the same number of atoms. So the mole is a particularly useful way of describing concentration, and when you use the mole, you count the atoms (or molecules or ions) by weighing them!

A mole (symbol mol) contains the **relative atomic mass (A_r) expressed in grams**. We have seen that the relative atomic mass of carbon-12 is taken as 12, and that hydrogen has a relative atomic mass of 1. Similarly oxygen has a relative atomic mass of 16. So, 1 mol of carbon has a mass of 12 g, 1 mol of hydrogen 1 g, and 1 mol of oxygen 16 g.

Actually, hydrogen and oxygen both exist as molecules, H_2 and O_2. Consequently 1 mol of hydrogen molecules has a mass of 2 g (H_2) and 1 mol of oxygen molecules has a mass of 32 g (O_2). Moles all contain the same number of units of substance.

The **concentration of a solution** can be expressed in moles, too. A **molar solution** contains 1 mol in a litre ($=dm^{-3}$). For example, the relative molecular mass of glucose ($C_6H_{12}O_6$) is 180 ($C = 12 \times 6$; $H = 1 \times 12$; $O = 16 \times 6$). So, we make a molar solution of glucose by taking the relative molecular mass in grams (180 g), and dissolving it in 1 litre of distilled water.

In the same way, the relative molecular mass of sodium chloride is 58.5 (relative atomic mass of sodium = 23, chlorine = 35.5 – see Table A.3). So a molar solution of sodium chloride contains 58.5 g NaCl per dm^3. However, unlike glucose, sodium chloride ionises ($NaCl \rightarrow Na^+ + Cl^-$). This means a molar solution of sodium chloride contains twice as many particles (ions) as does a molar solution of glucose (molecules). This brings us back to the definition – that is, a mole always contains the same number of units of substance, whether that substance exists as atoms, or molecules or ions.

Taking things further

1 A book that is focused on the needs of A level biology students is:
   Bernard Rockett and Raul Sutton (1996) *Chemistry for Biologists at Advanced Level*. John Murray.

2 The Biochemical Society produces a series of booklets (and other resources) to help understanding of biological chemistry of A level biology, including:
   E. J. Wood and A. Myers, *Essential Chemistry for Biochemistry*.
   Available from The Biochemical Society, 59 Portland Place, London W1N 3AJ.

Appendix 2: Investigations

Undertaking longer-term experiments and **investigations** develops your understanding of **scientific methods**. The stages involved in carrying out a successful investigation can be outlined as follows.

- **Formulating an hypothesis.** 'Hypothesis' is the name we give in science to a tentative explanation of an event or process that we have observed and are puzzling over. The key feature of any hypothesis is that it is a testable explanation. That is, we have to be able to design a series of observations or an experiment with a control (see page 489 for an explanation of controlled variables), which will enable us either to support or reject our hypothesis. So, the first step in planning an investigation is to formulate a testable hypothesis. You can practise formulating testable hypotheses for the topics for investigation listed below.
- **Planning.** The problem to be investigated is first defined, bearing in mind the time and resources available. It is easy to initially overestimate what can be achieved, and to set yourself too demanding a schedule. Using your knowledge and experience, and with the guidance of a teacher, or with a group of students, discuss your ideas in detail to ensure that the experimental procedure can be carried out safely and effectively. Consider too, the ethical implications of your approach, such as the involvement of living organisms and possible environmental consequences.
- **Implementing plans.** An important step is the design of a record sheet because this requires that you are clear about exactly what data you have to obtain and when.
- **Analysing evidence** and **drawing conclusions.** It is essential to present your results in a way that it is easy for others to understand what has been undertaken, and for any trends and patterns in the data to stand out. It is often necessary to apply statistical tests of significance to your numerical data (Appendix 3, page 488), so that you can quantify your results and draw valid conclusions.
- **Evaluating evidence** and the ways it is obtained. In the final part of your report assess the reliability and precision of your data and the conclusions that can be drawn from it. Evaluate your techniques in light of the outcomes of your investigation, recognising the limitations of your approach. Identify what changes you would make to your method, with hindsight.

Topics for investigation

You need to discuss the details with your teacher and ensure the appropriate resources are available.

Section I Working cells

I Cells, the building blocks

- The thermal deathpoint of cytoplasm, using beetroot tissue.
- The structure of different papers.

2 Biological molecules

- The presence of reducing and non-reducing sugars in ripening fruits.
- The distribution of the starch stores between the roots, stem and leaves of a plant species.

3 Traffic across cell membranes

- Plasmolysis in rhubarb epidermis and the effects of lipid solvents.
- Turgor in dandelion flower stalks.

4 Enzymes, in metabolism and for industry

- The effect of copper sulphate on the activity of an enzyme.
- Protease activity in pineapple fruit.
- The distribution of catalase activity in animal or plant tissues.
- Biological oxidation through enzymatic browning of an apple.

5 The nucleus: in division and in control

- The propagation of nuclei at different stages of mitosis, seen in root-tip squashes.

6 Gene technology

- Characteristics of cultivated vegetable plants (e.g. *Brassica oleracea*) and of the wild types from which they were originally bred.

Section II Resources for living

7 Feeding by digestion

- The vitamin C content of different fruits or vegetables, and the effects of storage or cooking.
- The percentage of a student's required energy intake that comes from convenience snacks eaten between meals.

8 Plant nutrition

- The wavelength of light and rate of photosynthesis in *Elodea*, using an Audus photometer.
- Sizes of leaves in exposed and shaded areas for a particular plant species.
- Factors affecting growth of *Lemna*.
- Effect of mineral deficiencies on seedling growth.

9 Respiration

- The effects of temperature on the rate of fermentation by yeast.
- Investigations in exercise physiology by measuring human blood pressures and pulse rates.

10 Gaseous exchange

- Distribution of stomata on different leaf surfaces.
- The effects of exercise on breathing rate.

11 Internal transport

- Investigation of the effect of ethanol and caffeine on the heart rate of *Daphnia pulex*.
- Factors affecting transpiration.

Section III Coordination and control

12 The internal environment

- Water loss by woodlice.
- Investigation of antiperspirant action on skin function, using filter paper as model skin.
- Human body clock and behaviour.

13 Control and communication

- Is fruit ripening triggered by volatile growth regulators?
- Hormone rooting powders and root growth on cuttings.
- Sensitivity of the skin to touch.
- Judgement of distances.

14 Support and movement

- Reaction times, and speed of responses.
- Detecting nocturnal animals by tracks and footprints.

15   Health and disease

- Milk deterioration under different environmental conditions.
- Smokers' and non-smokers' responses to data on health risks.
- Commercial antiseptics and growth of bacteria.

Section IV Organism and environment

16   Biodiversity

- The effects of cultivation or pesticide treatments on the earthworm population of soils.
- The minibeast communities of different cultivation regimes, using carpet squares to sample.
- The succession of coprophilous fungi on a fresh 'cowpat'.

17   Ecology: the interdependence of organisms

- Rate of water flow and species diversity in streams.
- Eutrophication and the growth of *Lemna*.
- Effects of coppicing on the ground flora and fauna of woodlands.
- Water loss and recovery of dehydrated seaweeds, such as *Ascophyllum* or other brown seaweeds.
- Mark–release–recapture technique of population measurements, using taxis, trolleys or buses.

18   Humans and the environment

- The biodegradability of various packaging/wrapping materials.
- The effects of sulphur dioxide on the germination of seedlings.
- Studying atmospheric dust (trapped on exposed microscope slides coated with petroleum jelly).

Section V Life goes on

19   Reproduction

- Growing pollen grains.
- The efficiency of fruit and seed dispersal mechanisms.

20   Inheritance

- The inheritance of flowering pigments in *Antirrhinum*.
- Observing genetic principles in cats.

21   Evolution

- Visual selection by birds, using coloured 'pastry' prey.
- Evidence for natural selection in snail shells left in woodland and downlands by bird predators.

All practical work requires **risk assessment**.

Further information on ways, means and methods in project work, and on risk assessment can be found in:

C. J. Clegg with D. G. Mackean, P. H. Openshaw and R. C. Reynolds (1996) *Advanced Biology Study Guide*, John Murray.

Appendix 3: Handling data

Types of data

In practicals and investigations, observations are recorded as **data**. There are different forms of data (singular **datum**), but they are all potentially useful. No one type of data that is relevant to your enquiry is superior to another, providing they have been accurately taken and recorded. We define the types of data we collect as:

- **Qualitative (or descriptive) observations**, for example in behaviour studies, such as the feeding mechanism of honey bees visiting flowers, or nesting behaviour of a species of bird. Qualitative data may be recorded in written observations or notes, or by photography, or in drawings.
- **Quantitative (or numerical) observations**, for example the size (length, breadth or area) of organs, such as the leaves of a plant in shaded and exposed positions, or the pH values of soil samples in different positions.

Note that quantitative data may be **discrete** or **continuous**. Examples of discrete data are the number of eggs laid in a nest, or the number of petals formed in a species of flower. In other words, discrete data are whole numbers – no nest ever contains 2.5 eggs! Examples of continuous data might be the heights or weights of the individuals of a population, or the time taken for seeds to germinate after different treatments. This data can be any value within some broad limit. The difference between discrete and continuous data is also illustrated in Figure 20.2 (page 437). Note that in genetics discrete data is also known as **discontinuous**.

Extension Handling very large and very small numbers

In science 'powers of ten' are used to avoid writing long strings of zeros when recording numbers. For example, the age of the Earth, about 4 500 000 000 years, is written as 4.5×10^9 years. Similarly, a cyanobacterium, a photosynthetic bacterium, may be about 0.000 003 6 metres in diameter, which is written simply as 3.6×10^{-6} m.

This way of recording numbers is called scientific or **standard notation**. It is used to avoid the errors that are easily made in writing down a large number of 0s.

When we need to multiply numbers we can do so by adding powers,

$$(1.5 \times 10^4) \times (2.0 \times 10^3) = (1.5 \times 2.0) \times (10^4 \times 10^3) = 3.0 \times 10^7$$

Similarly, to divide, the powers are subtracted,

$$(2.0 \times 10^6) \div (0.5 \times 10^4) = \frac{2.0 \times 10^6}{0.5 \times 10^4} = 4.0 \times 10^2$$

Several of the '**powers of ten**' have prefixes which are frequently used in biology, and are represented by agreed symbols. For example:

$\times 10^3$	kilo- or k
$\times 10^6$	mega- or M
$\times 10^9$	giga- or G
$\times 10^{-3}$	milli- or m
$\times 10^{-6}$	micro- or μ
$\times 10^{-9}$	nano- or n

Collecting and recording data

Recording the data

When you plan an investigation or experiment, think carefully about the data you expect to collect. This allows you to prepare a record sheet with spaces for the information (both qualitative and quantitative). Design a table for the numerical data. This table should indicate how often you must record the data as well as exactly what will be recorded.

Variables

In an investigation or experiment the specific conditions are called **variables**. Most of the variables are deliberately kept the same, but others vary. In fact there are really three types of variable. We can demonstrate them by referring to an example experiment, such as the investigation of the rate of an enzyme-catalysed reaction, shown in Figure 4.9, page 83.

The variables that are always kept the same in this investigation of the rate of reaction of catalase are the conditions, such as temperature, the volumes and concentrations of the reagents, and perhaps the pH (the amount and type of buffer, if used, for example). Variables that are kept constant are called the **controlled variables**. Meanwhile, in Figure 4.9 you can see that the rate of reaction is measured at 30-second intervals. The times that readings are taken are the variable that is manipulated by the experimenter, and this is called the **independent variable**. Note that it has been recorded in the table as a list, before the experiment was started. In the experiment, the amount of gas (oxygen) that has collected at 30-second intervals is the variable accurately measured by the experimenter. It is called the **dependent variable**. This is recorded in the second column of the table.

As a matter of interest, it would be equally possible for the experimenter to have recorded the time taken for (say) 20 cm^3 of oxygen to collect. In this case, what is now the independent variable, and what is the dependent variable?

Errors, and the need for 'replicates'

Errors and mistakes may occur in experiments and investigations, just as in any other human activity. You cannot have complete confidence about the reliability of every individual observation you make. For example, an incorrect amount of reagent may accidentally be measured out and the mistake not noticed, a stop watch may be misread, or a reading from an instrument may be inaccurately taken. You need confidence that your results are accurate.

Consequently, you need to repeat readings at each time interval. If the second reading is significantly different, you would expect to repeat that reading as a check. Repetitions are called **replicates**. In a class or large group experiment these replicate readings can be the results of the class, pooled together. The more replicate readings you can take, the more confidence you can have.

Displaying data

Firstly, you must select from the data what is important. For example, it may be appropriate to round up numbers to fewer figures, in order to avoid giving data to a greater level of accuracy than the measurements warrant. Then, display the important data, using a visual summary, making their importance clear. For example, this may involve using one or more of the following:

1 **Graphs** show relationships or trends between two variables. It is conventional to plot the dependent variable (variable being accurately measured) on the vertical y-axis, and the independent variable (the variable altered by the experimenter) on the horizontal x-axis. Both axes must be labelled and the units indicated. Points must be plotted with a sharp pencil using a cross or a circle. The points should be joined by a smooth curve only if you are confident that it indicates the likely points of intermediate readings. If you are not confident of this, connect points with a straight line. If more than one line is plotted, then the plot points and lines must be different and clearly labelled. If the two plots have different vertical axes, then the scale of the axes should be placed on either side of the graph.

2 **Bar charts** are used with discrete data to show relative proportions. There should be small gaps between the bars and the bars should be presented in order of magnitude.

3 **Histograms** are useful with continuous data, and the data can be arranged in classes. The bars touch, and the height and area of each bar must match the proportion of the data.

4 **Kite histograms** are used for displaying transect data. The horizontal length of the kite represents the range of the species over the transect, whereas the vertical height (amplitude) of the kite indicates the abundance of the animals or plants.

5 **Scatter graphs** show relationships between two variables, such as length and breadth of leaves. Where one of the variables is determined by the other it is customary to put the independent variable on the horizontal axis and the dependent variable on the vertical axis. From the scatter graph, the strength of the relationship (correlation) can be assessed.

6 **Pie charts** are best used for showing relative proportions.

Statistical checks on data

Statistical tests should be used when you are not sure about the numerical relationships your data indicate. The application of simple statistical tests is described in the references below. Many calculators are programmed to carry out statistical tests. Microcomputers will run spreadsheet programs with statistical tests programmed in. Dedicated statistical software is also available.

Normal distributions

Data obtained from biological experiments may show a 'normal distribution'. By this we mean that when the frequency of a particular class of measurements (such as the number of humans at any particular height – y-axis) is plotted against the classes of measurements (their different heights arranged in ascending order – x-axis), a symmetrical bell-shaped curve is obtained (Figure 20.2, page 437). With normal distributions, two issues may arise.

1 How clustered are the readings (that is, the 'middleness' of the data)? This can be expressed as:

- the **average** or **arithmetic mean**, calculated by dividing the sum of the individual values by the number of values obtained
- the **mode**, the most frequent value in a set of values
- the **median**, the middle value in a set of values arranged in ascending order.

2 How spread out are the readings (that is, the 'spreadoutness' of the data)? This can be expressed as the **standard deviation (SD)** of the mean. This is a measure of the variation from the mean of a set of values. A low SD indicates the observation (the values) differs very little from the mean.

Other common statistical tests

You can use standard deviations to calculate the significance of the difference between two means by the **t-test**.

You can test whether observed numerical results differ from the expected numerical result by means of a **chi-squared test** (page 451).

Details of these and other statistical procedures, together with guidance in selection and application are available in:

A. Cadogan and R. Sutton (1994) *Maths for Advanced Biology*, Thomas Nelson.
J. W. Garvin (1986) *Skills in Advanced Biology: Volume 1 Dealing with Data*, Stanley Thornes.
A. Edmondson and D. Druce (1996) *Advanced Biology: Statistics*, Oxford University Press.

Glossary

Entries are *aides-mémoire*, rather than formal definitions.

abiotic factor   non-biological factor (e.g. temperature), that is part of the environment of an organism

abscisic acid   plant growth substance tending to inhibit growth

absorption spectrum   range of a pigment's ability to absorb various wavelengths of light

acetylcholine   neurotransmitter, liberated at synapses in the CNS

'acid rain'   cocktail of chemical pollutants that may occur in the atmosphere

acrosome   organelle at the tip of sperm containing hydrolytic enzymes that digest the coating of the egg, enabling sperm to penetrate

action potential   rapid change in membrane potential of an excitable cell, e.g. a neurone

action spectrum   range of wavelengths of light within which a process like photosynthesis takes place

actin   a protein of muscle that forms the thin filaments in myofibrils

activation energy   energy a substrate molecule must have before it can undergo a chemical change

active site   region of enzyme molecule where substrate molecule binds

active transport   movement of substances across a membrane involving a carrier protein and energy from respiration

adaptation   the process by which an organism becomes fitted to its environment

adenine   purine organic base, found in the coenzymes ATP and NADP, and in nucleic acids (DNA and RNA) in which it pairs with thymine

adenosine diphosphate (ADP)   nucleotide, present in every living cell, made of adenosine and two phosphate groups linked in series, and important in energy transfer reactions of metabolism

adenosine triphosphate (ATP)   nucleotide, present in every living cell, formed in photosynthesis and respiration from ADP and P_i, and functioning in metabolism as a common intermediate between energy-requiring and energy-yielding reactions

adrenaline   hormone secreted by the adrenal medulla (and a neurotransmitter secreted by nerve endings of the sympathetic nervous system), having many effects, including speeding up of heart beat, and the breakdown of glycogen to glucose in muscle and liver

aerobic respiration   respiration requiring oxygen, involving oxidation of glucose to CO_2 and H_2O

agglutinogen   cell surface antigen, e.g. ABO antigens of human blood cells

aldose sugar   monosaccharide containing an aldehyde group (—CHO)

algal bloom   an exceptional growth of algae or cyanobacteria occurring in waters, e.g. as a result of excess nutrients present

alimentary canal   the gut; a tube running from mouth to anus in vertebrates, where complex food substances are digested and the products of digestion are selectively absorbed into the body

allele   an alternative form of a gene, occupying a specific locus on a chromosome

allosteric enzyme   enzyme susceptible to reversible binding of a small molecule to a part of the protein, inducing change to the shape of the active site of the enzyme

alpha cell (pancreas)   glucagon-secreting cells of the islets of Langerhans in the pancreas

alternation of generations   alternation of haploid and diploid stages in the life cycle

alveolus   air sac in the lung

amino acid   building block of proteins, of general formula $RCH(NH_2)COOH$

amnion   innermost of the embryonic membranes in reptiles, birds and mammals

amphoteric   molecule possessing both acidic and basic properties, as in amino acids

anabolism   building up of complex molecules from smaller ones, in cellular biochemistry

anaerobic respiration   respiration in the absence of oxygen, involving breakdown of glucose to lactic acid or ethanol

analogous structure   similar in structure but of different evolutionary origin

anaphase   phase in nuclear division when the chromatids (mitosis and meiosis II) and chromosomes (meiosis I) move to opposite poles of the spindle

androecium   collective name of stamens (male parts) of a flower

anion   negatively charged ion

annual plant   plant living for a year only

antagonism   effects of, for example, a hormone that counteracts the effects of another

anther   part of the stamen in flowers, consisting of pollen sacs enclosed in walls that eventually split open, releasing pollen

antibody   a protein produced by blood plasma cells derived from B lymphocytes when in the presence of a specific antigen; it binds with the antigen, aiding its destruction

antibiotic   organic compounds produced by microorganisms which selectively inhibit or kill other microorganisms

anticodon   three consecutive bases in tRNA, complementary to a codon on RNA

antidiuretic hormone (ADH)   hormone secreted by the pituitary gland that controls the permeability of the walls of the collecting ducts of the kidney

antigen   substance capable of binding specifically to an antibody

antipodal cell   group of three cells in the embryo sac

apoenzyme   protein part of an enzyme, after the removal of the prosthetic group

apoplast   collective name for the cell walls of a tissue or plant

aqueous humour   fluid between lens and cornea

archegonium   female sex organ of liverworts, mosses and ferns

arteriole   very small artery

artery   vessel that carries blood away from the heart

articulate   jointed

artificial classification   classifying organisms on the basis of few, self-evident features

artificial selection   selection in breeding exercises, carried out deliberately, by humans

asexual reproduction   reproduction not involving gametes or fertilisation

assimilation   uptake of nutrients into cells and tissues

asymmetric carbon atom has four different groupings attached, forming a molecule that can be built in two ways (optical isomerism)

atherosclerosis deposition of plaque (cholesterol derivative) on inner wall of blood vessels

atrio-ventricular node mass of tissue in the wall of the right atrium, functionally part of the pacemaker mechanism

atrio-ventricular valve tricuspid or bicuspid valve

atrium (plural atria) one of the two upper chambers of the mammalian four-chambered heart

autolysis self-digestion

autotrophic (organism) self-feeding, that is, able to make its own elaborated foods from simpler substances

autonomic the involuntary nervous system

auxin plant growth substance, indoleacetic acid

axon fibre carrying impulses away from the cell body of a neurone

bacillus rod-shaped bacterium

bacteriophage virus that parasitises bacteria

baroreceptor sensory receptor responding to stretch, found in the walls of blood vessels

basal body tiny cylindrical structure in the cytoplasm at the base of flagella and cilia, in eukaryotic cells

basal metabolism metabolic activity in an organism at rest

basement membrane the thin fibrous layer separating an epithelium from underlying tissues

beta cell (pancreas) insulin-secreting cells of the islets of Langerhans of the pancreas

bicuspid valve valve between atrium and ventricle on the left side of the mammalian heart

bile alkaline secretion of liver cells which collects in the gall bladder, and is discharged periodically into the duodenum

binary fission when a cell divides into two daughter cells, typically in reproduction of prokaryotes

binomial system system of double names for organisms, in Latin, the generic preceding the specific name

bioassay use of living organisms or tissues for assay purposes

biological pest control control of pests and weeds by other organisms

biomass total weight (or volume, or energy equivalent) of living organisms in a given area, e.g. a quadrat

biome a major life-zone over an area of the Earth, characterised by the dominant plant life present

biosphere inhabited part of the Earth

biotechnology industrial and commercial applications of biology, particularly of microorganisms, enzymology and genetic engineering

biotic factor influence of living things on the environment of other living things

biuret test test for the presence of proteins (peptides), based on the reaction of the peptide linkage

bivalent (chromosomes) pair of duplicated chromosomes, held together by chiasmata during meiosis

blastocyst hollow ball of cells, formed from the morula at the stage of implantation

blastomere cells formed by early divisions of a fertilised animal egg cell

blastula hollow ball of cells, formed early in embryogenesis in many animals, containing a blastocoel (fluid-filled cavity)

blind spot region of the retina where the optic nerve leaves

body mass index (BMI) (body mass (kg)/height (m)^2)

bolus chewed food, formed into a ball with saliva

bone marrow tissue special connective tissue filling the cavity of certain bones

boreal forest northern coniferous forests (example of a biome)

bovine somatotrophin (BST) hormone produced by the pituitary, controlling milk production

bract modified leaf, often scale-like, usually having a protective role

brain coordinating centre of the nervous system

breed (animal) animal equivalent of a plant variety

bronchiole small terminal branch of a bronchus

bronchus tube connecting the trachea with the lungs

Brunner's gland gland in the wall of the duodenum that discharges into the lumen

brush border tiny, finger-like projections (microvilli) on the surface of epithelial cells of the ileum

buccal cavity part of the alimentary canal between the mouth and pharynx

budding common method of asexual reproduction

buffer solution which minimises change in pH when acid or alkali are added

bundle of His bundles of long muscle fibres that transmit myogenic excitation throughout the ventricle walls

bundle sheath layer(s) of parenchyma cells surrounding a vascular bundle

C$_3$ pathway the 'dark reaction' in photosynthesis, producing as its first product, a three-carbon compound, glycerate 3-phosphate

C$_4$ plants plants with an additional CO$_2$ fixation pathway that augments the supply of this raw material of photosynthesis at the chloroplast

caecum 'blind' pouch of the gut

Calvin cycle cycle of reactions in the stroma of the chloroplast by which some of the product of the 'dark reaction' is reformed as the acceptor molecule for CO$_2$ (ribulose bisphosphate)

calyx collective name for the sepals of flowers

canaliculus (plural canaliculi) tiny channel in the liver lobules, containing bile

capillary water bulk of soil water held around particles of soil, available to plants

cardiac cycle stages of the heartbeat, by which the atria and then the ventricle walls alternately contract (systole), followed by relaxation (diastole)

carotenoids fat-soluble pigments coloured red–yellow to brown; accessory pigments in photosynthesis

carpel female reproductive structure of the flower, containing one or more ovules

carrier protein one of the types of protein in plasma membranes, responsible for active transport across the membranes

cartilage firm but plastic skeletal material, e.g. hyaline cartilage over bones at joints

casparian strip band of cells with impervious walls, found in the endodermis of plant roots

catabolism breaking down of complex molecules in the biochemistry of cells

catalyst substance that alters the rate of a chemical reaction, but remains unchanged at the end

cell sap fluid in the vacuoles of plant cells

cellulase enzyme capable of hydrolysing cellulose, the major ingredient of most plant walls

cellulose unbranched polymer of 2000–3000 glucose residues, combined by α-1,4 glycosidic bonds

central dogma the idea that transfer of genetic information from DNA of the chromosome to RNA to protein (amino acid sequence) is irreversible

centriole one of two organelles that make up the centrosome; found in animal cells, outside the nuclear membrane, and involved in nuclear division

centromere constriction of the chromosome, the region that becomes attached to the spindle fibres in division

centrosome organelle situated near the nucleus in animal cells, involved in the formation of the spindle prior to nuclear division

cephalisation development of a head at the anterior of an animal

cerebellum part of hindbrain, concerned with muscle tone/posture/movement

cerebral cortex superficial layer of grey matter on extension of forebrain, much enlarged in humans and apes

cerebral hemispheres (cerebrum) the bulk of the human brain, formed during development by the outgrowth of part of the forebrain; consisting of densely-packed neurones and myelinated nerve fibres

chemoreceptor sense organ receiving chemical stimuli

chemosynthesis use of chemical energy from oxidation of inorganic compounds to synthesise organic compounds, typically from CO_2 and H_2O

chiasma (plural chiasmata) site of crossing over (exchange) of segments of DNA between homologous chromosomes

chitin chemically related to cellulose; a polymer built from glucosamine

chlorophyll main photosynthetic pigment of green plants; occurs in the granal membranes (thylakoid membranes) of the chloroplasts

chloroplast organelle that is the site of photosynthesis and contains chlorophyll in grana

cholesterol a lipid of animal plasma membranes; a precursor of the steroid hormones; in humans it is formed in the liver and transported in the blood as lipoprotein

chordae tendineae tendons anchored to heart valves

chordate animal having tubular dorsal nerve cord, a dorsal supporting rod (notochord), a postanal tail, gill slits in the throat (visceral clefts), and a closed blood circulation in which blood flows down the body in a dorsal artery and returns in a ventral vein

choroid layer of blood vessels lying below the retina

chromatid one of two copies of a chromosome after it has replicated

chromatin a nuclear protein material in the nucleus of eukaryotic cells at interphase; forms into chromosomes during mitosis and meiosis

chromosome visible in appropriately stained cells at nuclear division, each chromosome consists of a long thread of DNA packaged with protein; chromosomes replicate prior to division, into chromatids; contents of nucleus appears as granular chromatin between divisions

chyme the partly digested food leaving the stomach

ciliary body contains a ring of muscle; regulates the shape of the lens in the vertebrate eye

cilium (plural cilia) motile, hair-like outgrowth from the surface of certain eukaryotic cells

citric acid cycle see Krebs cycle

climax community mature (stable) stage of a succession of communities

clone group of genetically identical individuals (or cells)

cnidoblast stinging cells of cnidarians (coelenterates) such as *Hydra*

coccus spherical bacterial cell

codon three consecutive bases in DNA (or RNA) which specify an amino acid

coelom fluid-filled body cavity within the mesoderm of many non-vertebrate and all vertebrate groups

coenzyme non-protein part of some enzymes, can become attached to different enzymes

coleoptile protective sheath around germinating plumule of grasses

collenchyma flexible supporting tissue of plants; walls thickened with cellulose

colon part of the gut, preceding the rectum

colostrum first milk secreted by the mother, after birth of young

commensalism mutually beneficial association between two organisms of different species

community populations of organisms living together in a habitat

companion cell component of phloem tissue, cells lying beside sieve tubes

compensation point point where respiration and photosynthesis are balanced

condensation reaction formation of larger molecules involving the removal of water from smaller component molecules

cone (retinal cell) light-sensitive cell in the retina, responsible for colour vision

conjugate protein protein combined with a non-protein part

connective tissue tissues that support and bind other tissues together

conservation applying the principles of ecology to manage the environment

contractile vacuole small vesicle in the cytoplasm of many freshwater protozoa that expels excess water

cork cambium cells below bark layer that cut off cork cells to the exterior

cornea transparent covering at the front of the eye

corolla collective name for the petals of a flower

corpus luteum glandular mass that develops from an ovarian follicle in mammals, after the ovum is discharged

cotyledon first leaf (leaves) of a seed plant, found in the embryo

covalent bond bond between atoms in which electrons are shared

cranial nerves nerves arising from the brain

cristae folds in the inner membrane of mitochondria

crossing over exchange of genetic material between homologous chromosomes during meiosis

crypts of Lieberkühn glands at base of the villi in the gut

cuticle layer of waxy material on outer wall of epidermis

cyanobacterium photosynthetic prokaryote

cytokinesis division of cytoplasm after nucleus has divided into two

cytokinin plant growth regulator, derived from organic base adenine; involved in the breaking of dormancy and in facilitating development

cytology study of cell structure

cytoplasm living part of the cell bound by the plasma membrane, excluding the nucleus

cytosine a pyrimidine organic base found in DNA and RNA, in which it pairs with guanine

cytosol what remains of cytoplasm when the organelles have been removed

data recorded product of observations and measurements

  qualitative observations not involving measurements

  quantitative precise observations involving measurements

deamination removal of NH_2 from an amino acid, e.g. as a prelude to formation of urea

deciduous loss at the end of the growing season, e.g. of leaves from broadleaved trees

decomposer organisms (typically microorganisms) that feed on dead plant and animal material; causing matter to be recycled by other living things

degenerate code triplet code contains more 'words' (codons) than there are amino acids to be coded, so most amino acids are coded by more than one codon

denaturation irreversible changes to the structure of a protein

dendrite   a fine fibrous process on a neurone, that receives impulses from other neurones

dendron   a fibre carrying impulses towards the cell body of a neurone

dentine   hard, bone-like material, making up the interior of the vertebrate tooth

depolarisation (of axon)   temporary and local reversal of the resting potential difference of the membrane, that occurs when an impulse is transmitted along the axon

desertification   conversion of marginal, cultivated land into desert, caused either by climate change or by over-grazing or inferior cultivation

detrital chain   food chain based on dead plant matter

detritivore   organism that feeds on detritus (dead organic matter)

dialysis   separation of large and small molecules in solution by the inability of the former to pass through a selectively permeable membrane

diaphragm   sheet of tissue, largely muscle, separating thorax from abdomen in mammals

diastema   gap in the jaw between two types of teeth, common in many herbivores

diastole   relaxation phase in the cardiac cycle

dichotomous key   key in which a group of organisms is progressively divided into equal-sized groups of smaller size

dicotyledon   class of angiosperm having an embryo with two cotyledons (seed leaves)

dihybrid cross   cross in which the inheritance of two pairs of contrasting characters (controlled by genes on separate chromosomes) is observed

diploblastic   body of two layers, e.g. ectoderm and endoderm of cnidaria (coelenterates)

diploid condition   organisms whose cells have nuclei containing two sets of chromosomes

disaccharide   sugar that is a condensation product of two monosaccharides, e.g. maltose

disulphide bond   S—S bond between two S-containing amino acids (residues) in a polypeptide/protein chain

diuresis   increased secretion of urine

division of labour   carrying out of specialised functions by different types of cell in a multicellular organism

DNA   form of nucleic acid found in the nucleus; consists of two complementary chains of deoxyribonucleotide subunits, and containing the bases adenine, thymine, guanine and cytosine

dormancy   resting condition with reduced metabolic activity which may be imposed on seeds, for example, or may arise from internal factors (innate)

double bond   covalent bond involving the sharing of two pairs of electrons (rather than one)

double circulation   the blood passes twice through the heart (pulmonary circulation then systemic circulation) in any one complete circuit of the body

double fertilisation   feature of flowering plants in which two male nuclei enter the embryo sac; one fuses with the egg cell and another fuses with the endosperm nucleus

duodenum   first part of the intestine after the stomach

ecosystem   natural unit of living (biotic) components and non-living (abiotic) components, e.g. temperate deciduous forest

ectoderm   outer layer of an embryo of vertebrates, e.g. layer giving rise to epidermis and nervous system

edaphic factor   factors influenced by the soil

effector   organ or cell that responds to a stimulus by doing something, e.g. a muscle contracting, a gland secreting, etc.

egestion   disposal of waste from the body, e.g. defecation

egg cell   alternative name for an ovum

electron microscope (EM)   microscope in which beam of electrons replaces light, and the powers of magnification and resolution are correspondingly much greater

electron transport system   carriers that transfer electrons along a redox chain, permitting ATP synthesis in the process

electroporation   technique for infiltrating DNA into a cell, through short-lived holes in the plasma membrane

embolism   blood clot blocking a blood vessel

embryo   earliest stages in development of a new animal or plant, from a fertilised ovum, entirely dependent on nutrients supplied by the parent

embryo sac   occurs in the ovule of flowering plants; contains the egg cell and endosperm nucleus

emulsify   to break fats and oils into very tiny droplets

enamel   hard material of calcium and magnesium salts, which forms a cap over the dentine of teeth

endemic species   restricted to a particular region

endergonic reaction   metabolic reaction requiring energy input

endocrine gland   hormone-producing gland that releases secretions directly into the body fluids

endocytosis   uptake of fluid/tiny particles into vacuoles in the cytoplasm; carried out at the plasma membrane

endoderm   inner layer, e.g. in vertebrate embryo, giving rise to the gut

endodermis   layer of cells surrounding the pericycle, around the stele in plant roots

endogenous rhythm   rhythm originating within an organism, that persists despite external changes

endoplasmic reticulum   system of branching membranes in the cytoplasm of eukaryotic cells; exists as rough ER (with ribosomes), or as smooth ER (without ribosomes)

endoskeleton   internal skeleton system

endosperm   stored food reserves within the seed of flowering plants

endothelium   single layer of cells lining blood vessels and other fluid-filled cavities

endothermic   generation of body heat metabolically

enteron   gut

enzyme   mainly proteins (a few are RNA) that function as biological catalysts

epidermis   outer layer(s) of cells

epigeal germination   germination in which cotyledons are carried above the ground

epiglottis   flap of cartilage that closes off the trachea when food is swallowed

epiphyte   plant living on the surface of other plants

epithelium   sheet of cells bound strongly together, covering internal/external surfaces of multicellular organisms

erythrocyte   red blood cell

ester   organic chemical formed by condensation reaction between an organic acid and an alcohol

etiolation   condition of plants when grown in the dark

eukaryotic (cell)   cell with a 'good' nucleus, e.g. animal, plant, fungi and protoctista cells

exergonic reaction   metabolic reaction releasing energy

exocrine gland   gland whose secretion is released via a duct

exocytosis   secretion of liquids and suspensions of very fine particles across the membrane of eukaryotic cells

exoskeleton   skeleton secreted external to the epidermis of the body

exothermic   chemical reaction that releases energy as heat (an endothermic reaction requires heat energy)

expiration   emitting air during breathing

extensor muscle   muscle that extends or straightens a limb

F$_1$ generation   first filial generation, that is, arises by crossing parents (P), and then selfed or crossed via sibling crosses to produce the F$_2$ generation

facilitated diffusion   diffusion across a membrane, facilitated by molecules in the membrane (without the expenditure of metabolic energy)

facultative   having the capacity to do something, if necessary or if the opportunity arises, e.g. be anaerobic, or be a parasite

fermentation   anaerobic breakdown of glucose, with end products ethanol and CO_2 or lactic acid

fertilisation   fusion of male and female gametes to form a zygote

fetus   mammalian embryo when it reaches the stage at which it becomes recognisable

field layer   layer of herbaceous plants in a forest or wood

filter feeding   feeding on tiny organisms, which are strained from the surrounding medium

fimbria (singular fimbrium)   thin, short filament protruding from some bacteria; involved in attachment

fission (of a cell)   division of a unicellular organism into two (or more) parts

flaccid   state of a tissue with insufficient water, as in wilting leaves

flagellum (plural flagella)   long thin structure, occurring singly or in groups on some cells and tissues, used to propel unicellular organisms, and to move liquids past anchored cells; flagella of prokaryotes and eukaryotes are of different internal structure

flexor muscle   muscle that, on contraction, bends a limb (or part of a limb)

flower   develops from the tip of a shoot, with parts (e.g. sepals, petals) that are modified leaves, surrounding the male (stamens) and female (carpels) reproductive organs

fluid feeder   feeding holozoically by taking in of fluids or very soft tissues

fluid mosaic model   the accepted view of the structure of the plasma membrane; a phospholipid bilayer with proteins embedded but free to move about

food chain   sequence of organisms within a habitat in which each is the food of the next, starting with a primary producer, which is photosynthetic

food web   interconnected food chains

founder effect   genetic differences that develop between the original breeding population and a small isolated interbreeding group of these organisms

fovea   point on the retina of greatest acuity of vision

free energy   part of the potential chemical energy in molecules that is available to do useful work when molecules are broken

freeze-etching   shadowing of a surface of freeze-dried tissue/cells after the organelles have been exposed, for examination of structure under the electron microscope

frequency   commonness of an occurrence

fruit   forms from the ovary after fertilisation, as the ovules develop into seeds

functional group   chemically active part of a member of a series of organic molecules

fungi (singular fungus)   heterotrophic, non-motile, largely multicellular eukaryotic organisms with 'plant' body and a mycelium of hyphae with cell walls of chitin; constitute a separate Kingdom

furanose   five-sided structure found in some monosaccharides

gall bladder   sac beside the liver that stores bile

gamete   sex cell, e.g. ovum, sperm

gametophyte   haploid, gamete-forming phase in plant life cycles showing alternation of generations

ganglion   part of a nervous system, consisting of cell bodies

gaseous exchange   exchange of respiratory gases (O_2, CO_2) between cells/organism and the environment

gastric   relating to the stomach

gene   basic unit of inheritance by which inherited characteristics are transferred from parents to offspring, consisting of a length of DNA on a chromosome

gene pool   all the genes (and their alleles) present in a breeding population

gene probe   artificially prepared sequence of DNA made radioactive with ^{14}C, coding for a particular amino acid residue sequence

gene therapy   various mechanisms by which corrected copies of genes are introduced into a patient with a genetic disease

generative layer   layer of cells that divide, cutting off cells for a particular role

generator potential   localised depolarisation of a membrane of a sensory cell

genetic code   order of bases in DNA (of a chromosome) that determines the sequence of amino acids in a protein

genetic counselling   genetic advice given to potential parents on the risks of having children with an inherited disease

genetic engineering   change to the genetic constitution of individuals or populations by artificial selection

genome   genetic complement (genes) of an organism or of an individual cell

genotype   genetic constitution of an organism

genus   group of similar and closely related species

geotropism   tropic response (tropism) by plants to gravity

germination   resumption of growth by an embryonic plant in seed or fruit, at the expense of stored food

gestation   time between fertilisation and birth in a viviparous animal

gill   organ for gaseous exchange found in many species of aquatic animals

gland   cells or tissues adapted for secretion

glial cell   see neuroglial cell

global warming   hypothesis that the world climate is warming due to rising levels of atmospheric CO_2, a 'greenhouse' gas

glomerulus   network of capillaries which are surrounded by the renal capsule

glottis   opening from the trachea in the throat

glycocalyx   long carbohydrate molecules attached to membrane proteins and membrane lipids

glycogen   much-branched polymer of glucose; the storage carbohydrate of many animals

glycogenesis   synthesis of glycogen from glucose (the reverse is glycogenolysis)

glycolysis   first stage of tissue respiration in which glucose is broken down to pyruvic acid, without the use of oxygen

glycoprotein   membrane protein with a glycocalyx attached

glycosidic bond   type of chemical linkage between monosaccharide residues in polysaccharides

goblet cell   mucus-secreting cell of an epithelium

Golgi apparatus   stack of flattened membranes in the cytoplasm; the site of synthesis of biochemicals

gonad   organ in which gametes are formed

gonadotrophic hormone   follicle-stimulating hormone (FSH) and luteinising hormone (LH), secreted by the anterior pituitary, that stimulate gonad function

GLOSSARY

granum (plural grana) stacked disks of membranes found within the chloroplast, containing the photosynthetic pigments, and the site of the light step of photosynthesis

grey matter regions of the brain and spinal cord consisting largely of nerve cell bodies

growth more or less irreversible increase in size and amount of dry matter, classified as limited (as in an annual plant) or unlimited (as in a colony of sponge)

guanine a purine organic base found in DNA and RNA, in which it pairs with cytosine

gut alimentary canal

gynoecium female reproductive organs of a flower

habitat locality or surroundings in which an organism lives

habituation adjustments by which contact with the same stimulus produces a diminished effect

haemocoel blood-filled cavity bathing the body organs

haemodialysis artificial kidney function, carried out by a dialysis machine

haemoglobin a conjugated protein, found in red cells, effective at carrying oxygen from regions of high partial pressure (e.g. lungs) to regions of low partial pressure of oxygen (e.g. respiring tissues)

hallucinogen a drug, such as cannabis, capable of causing hallucinations

halophyte a plant adapted to survive at abnormally high salt levels, e.g. sea shore or salt marsh plant

haploid (cell) cell having one set of chromosomes, the basic set

Haversian canal arrangement of bone cells and canaliculi in compact (hard) bone

heliotropism plant growth movement in response to the stimulus of light

hepatic associated with the liver

herb layer layer of herbaceous plants (mainly perennials) growing in woodland

herbaceous non-woody

herbicide pesticide toxic to plants

herbivore animal that feeds (holozoically) exclusively on plants

hermaphrodite organism with both male and female reproductive systems

heterogamous fusion of unlike gametes

heteromorphic alternation having different forms at different times, e.g. haploid and diploid generations that are morphologically different

heterothallic cells (or mycelia), e.g. of fungi, that may undergo sexual reproduction with members of a different physiological strain

heterotroph organism incapable of synthesising its own elaborated nutrients

heterozygous a diploid organism that has inherited different alleles from each parent

hexose a monosaccharide containing six carbon atoms, e.g. glucose, fructose

hibernation passing the unfavourable season in a resting state of sleep

histology study of the structure of tissues

histone basic protein (rich in amino acids arginine and lysine) that forms the scaffolding of chromosomes

holdfast attachment organ of many algae, particularly the larger seaweeds

holozoic ingesting complex food material and digesting it

homeostasis maintenance of a constant internal environment

homeotherm organism that maintains a constant body temperature

homologous pair chromosomes in a diploid cell which contain the same sequence of genes, but are derived from different parents

homologous structures structures which are similar due to common ancestry

homozygous a diploid organism that has inherited the same alleles (for any particular gene) from both parents

hormone substance formed by an endocrine gland and transported in the blood all over the body, but having a specific physiological response in one type of organ or tissue

host organism in or on which a parasite spends all or part of its life cycle

humus complex organic matter; the end-product of the breakdown of the remains of plants and animals, which colours the soil

hybrid individual produced from a cross between two genetically unlike parents

hybridoma artificially produced hybrid cell culture, used to produce monoclonal antibodies

hydrocarbon chain linear arrangement of carbon atoms combined together and with hydrogen atoms, forming a hydrophobic 'tail' to many large organic molecules

hydrogen bond weak bond caused by electrostatic attraction between a positively charged part of one molecule and a negatively charged part of another

hydrolysis reaction in which hydrogen and hydroxyl ions from water are added to a large molecule, causing it to split into smaller molecules

hydrophilic 'water loving'

hydrophobic 'water hating'

hydrophyte an aquatic plant

hydrosere plant succession that originated from open water

hydrostatic pressure mechanical pressure exerted on or by liquid (e.g. water), known as pressure potential

hyperglycaemia excess glucose in the blood

hypertonic solution one with a less negative water potential than that of the cell solution

hypha the tubular filament 'plant' body of a fungus; in certain species it is divided by cross walls into either multicellular or unicellular compartments

hypocotyl part of the stem below the point of attachment of the cotyledons in an embryonic plant

hypogeal germination germination in which the cotyledons remain below ground

hypoglycaemia very low levels of blood glucose

hypothalamus part of the floor of the rear of the forebrain; a control centre for the autonomic nervous system, and source of 'releasing factors' for pituitary hormones

hypothesis tentative (and testable) explanation of an observed phenomenon or event

hypotonic solution one with a more negative water potential than that of the cell solution

ileum part of the gut where digestion is completed and absorption occurs; the second part of the small intestine

immunisation (e.g. inoculation/vaccination) the injection of a specific antigen, derived from a pathogen, to confer immunity against a disease

immunity resistance to the onset of a disease after infection by the causative agent

immunoglobin proteins synthesised by the B lymphocytes of the immune system

immunology study of the immune system

immunosuppressant   a substance causing temporary suppression of the immune response

implantation   embedding of the blastocyst (developed from the fertilised ovum) in the uterus wall

impulse   see action potential

imprinting   processes occurring soon after birth, causing young birds to follow their mother

in situ   in the original place (in the body/organism)

in vitro   biological process occurring in cell extracts (literally 'in glass')

in vivo   biological process occurring in a living organism (literally 'in life')

inbreeding   when gametes of closely related individuals fuse, leading to progeny that is homozygous for some or many alleles

incubation period   period between infection by a causative agent and the appearance of the symptoms of a disease

industrial melanism   increasing proportions of a darkened (melanistic) form of an organism, in place of light-coloured forms, associated with industrial pollution by soot

infectious disease   disease capable of being transmitted from one organism to another

inflorescence   groups of flowers arranged on a stem

inhibitor (enzyme)   substance which slows or blocks enzyme action, e.g. competitive inhibitor binding to the active site, and a non-competitive inhibitor binding to another part of the enzyme

inhibitory synapse   synapse at which arrival of an impulse blocks forward transmission of impulses in the postsynaptic membrane

innate behaviour   behaviour that does not need to be learnt

inner cell mass   thickening of the inner wall of the mammalian blastocyst; composed of cells that become the embryo

innervation   nerve supply

inspiration   air taken in during breathing

inspiratory capacity   amount of air that can be drawn into the lungs

integument   wall or coat to the ovule

intelligence   ability to learn by reasoning and to solve problems not yet experienced

interferon   proteins formed by vertebrate cells in response to viral infections

intermediate   metabolite formed as components of a metabolic pathway

internode   stem between two nodes

interphase   period between nuclear divisions when the nucleus controls and directs the activity of the cell

interspecific competition   competition between organisms of different species

interstitial fluid   body fluid between the cells

intestine   the gut

intracellular enzymes   enzymes operating inside the cell

intraspecific competition   competition between organisms of the same species

intrinsic factor   a factor originating and operating within

intron   a non-coding nucleotide sequence of the DNA of chromosomes; present in eukaryotic chromosomes

invagination   intucking of a surface or wall

ion   charged particle formed by transfer of electron(s) from one atom to another

ionic bonding   when atoms give or take electrons to form ions

iris   circular disc of tissue in front of the lens, containing circular and radial muscles

irreversible inhibition   inhibitors that bind tightly and permanently to an enzyme, destroying its catalytic properties

islets of Langerhans   groups of endocrine cells scattered throughout the pancreas

isogamy   union of male and female gametes of the same size

isomer   chemical compounds of the same chemical formula but different structural formulae

isotonic   being of the same osmotic concentration, and therefore of the same water potential

isotope   different forms of an element, chemically identical but with slightly different physical properties; based on differences in atomic mass (due to different number of neutrons in the nucleus)

joule   SI unit of energy

keratin   a fibrous protein, found in horn, hair, nails, and in the upper layer of skin

ketose   a monosaccharide containing a ketone functional group ($C=O$)

kinesis   random movements maintained by motile organisms until more favourable conditions are reached

kinetic energy   energy in movement

Kingdom   largest and most inclusive group in taxonomy

Krebs cycle   part of tissue respiration, the tricarboxylic acid (TCA) cycle

lactation   secretion of milk in mammary glands

larva   an independent, juvenile stage in the life cycle, distinctly different from the adult form into which it changes by metamorphosis

leaching   washing out of soluble ions and nutrients by water drainage through soil

learned behaviour   when the behaviour of an animal is constantly modified as a result of experiences

lenticel   pore in the bark of a tree that permits gaseous exchange

leucocyte   white blood cell

leucoplast   colourless plastid

lichen   permanent, mutualistic associations between certain fungi and algae, forming organisms found encrusting walls, tree trunks and rocks

ligament   strong fibrous cord or capsule of slightly elastic fibres connecting moveable bones

light-dependent step   step in photosynthesis occurring in grana of chloroplasts, in which water is split and ATP and $NADPH_2$ are regenerated

light-independent step   part of photosynthesis, occurring in the stroma of the chloroplasts, and using the products of the light-dependent step to reduce CO_2 to carbohydrate

lignin   complex chemical impregnating the walls of xylem vessels, fibres and tracheids, imparting great strength

lipid   diverse group of organic chemicals essential to living things, insoluble in water but soluble in organic solvents (e.g. ether, alcohol), such as lipid of the plasma membrane

lipoprotein   a complex of lipid and protein of various types which are classified according to density (VLDL = very low density lipoprotein, LDL = low density lipoprotein, HDL = high density lipoprotein)

liver lobule   polygonal block of liver cells; a functional unit within the liver structure

loop of Henle   loop of mammalian kidney tubule, passing from cortex to medulla and back; important in the process of concentration of urine

lumen   internal space of a tube (e.g. gut, artery, etc.) or sac-shaped structure

lymph   fluid derived from the plasma of blood, bathing all tissues spaces, draining back into the lymphatic system

lymph node   tiny gland in the lymphatic system; part of the body's defence against disease

lymphatic system   network of fine capillaries throughout the body of vertebrates, draining lymph and returning it to the blood circulation

lymphocyte   type of white blood cell

lysis   breakdown, typically of cells

lysosome   membrane-bound vesicles, common in the cytoplasm, containing digestive enzymes

macromolecule   very large organic molecule (r.m.m. = 10 000+), e.g. protein, nucleic acid or polysaccharide

macronutrient   ion required in relatively large amounts by organisms

Malpighian body   glomerulus and renal capsule of mammalian nephron

mandible   the lower jaw of vertebrates; in arthropods paired, biting mouthparts

mastication   chewing of food to small pieces

matrix   ground substance of connective tissue, and the innermost part of a mitochondrion

mechanoreceptors   a sensory receptor sensitive to mechanical stimuli

meiosis   nuclear division with daughter cells containing half the number of chromosomes of the parent cell

melanic   pigmented

menopause   cessation of ovulation and menstruation in women

menstrual cycle   monthly cycle of ovulation and menstruation in human females

meristem   plant tissue capable of giving rise to new cells and tissues

mesentery   connective tissue holding body organs (e.g. gut) in position

mesoderm   layer of embryonic cells in gastrula, giving rise to muscle, blood, etc.

mesoglea   non-cellular layer between outer and inner body wall layers in cnidaria (coelenterates)

mesophyll   parenchyma containing chloroplasts

mesosome   invagination of the plasma membrane of a bacterium

metabolic pathway   sequence of enzyme-catalysed biochemical reactions in cells and tissues

metabolic water   water released within the body by oxidation, typically of dietary lipids

metabolism   integrated network of all the biochemical reactions of life

metabolite   chemical substance involved in metabolism

metamorphosis   change in form and structure of the body between larva and adult forms, e.g. as in many insects

metaphase   stage in nuclear division (mitosis and meiosis) in which chromosomes become arranged at the equator of the spindle

microfilament   a protein microfibre in cytoplasm, part of the 'cytoskeleton'

microhabitat   environment immediately surrounding an organism, particularly applied to tiny organisms

micronutrient   ion required in relatively small amounts by organisms

micropyle   small hole in the seed coat; site of passage of pollen tube into an ovule, prior to fertilisation

microtubule   hollow protein tube in cytoplasm; a component of eukaryotic cilia and flagella, and of the spindle

microvilli   tiny infoldings of the plasma membrane, making up a 'brush border'

middle lamella   layer of pectins between the walls of adjacent plant cells

mitochondrion   organelle in eukaryotic cells; site of Krebs cycle and the electron-transport pathway

mitosis   nuclear division in which the daughter nuclei have the same number of chromosomes as the parent cell

mitral valve (bicuspid valve)   left atrio-ventricular valve

mode   the most frequently occurring value in a distribution

monoclonal antibody   antibody produced by a single clone of B lymphocytes, consisting of a population of identical antibody molecules

monocotyledon   class of angiosperms having an embryo with a single cotyledon

monocyte   large phagocytic white blood cell

monohybrid cross   a cross (breeding experiment) involving one pair of contrasting characters exhibited by homozygous parents

monosaccharide   simple carbohydrate (all are reducing sugars)

morphology   form and structure of an organism

motile   capable of moving about

motor area   areas of the brain where muscular activity is coordinated

motor end plate   the point of termination of an axon in a voluntary muscle fibre

motor neurone   nerve cell that carries impulses away from the central nervous system to an effector (e.g. muscle, gland)

moult   periodic shedding of outer layers, e.g. of an exoskeleton of an insect larva

mRNA   single-strand ribonucleic acid that is formed by the process of transcription of the genetic code in the nucleus, and then moves to ribosomes in the cytoplasm

mucilage   mixture of various polysaccharides that become slippery when wet

mucosa   inner lining of the gut

mucus   water solution of glycoprotein with protective/lubrication functions

muscle spindle   sensory receptor in muscle, responding to 'stretch' stimuli

muscularis mucosa   smooth muscle fibres of gut wall

mutagen   agent that causes mutation

mutant   organism with altered genetic material (abruptly altered by a mutation)

mutation   change in the amount or the chemical structure (i.e. base sequence) of DNA of a chromosome

mutualism   a case of symbiosis in which both organisms benefit from the association

mycelium   mass or network of hyphae

mycology   study of fungi

mycorrhiza   a mutualistic association between plant roots and fungi, with the mycelium restricted to the exterior of the root and its cells (ectotrophic), or involving a closer association between hyphae and root cell contents (endotrophic)

myelin sheath   insulating sheath of axons of nerve fibres, formed by the wrapping around of the cell bodies of Schwann cells

myelinated nerve fibre   nerve fibre 'insulated' by a lipid sheath formed from membranes of Schwann cells (glial cells)

myofibril   contractile protein filament from which muscle is composed

myogenic   originating in heart muscle cells themselves generating the basic heartbeat

myosin   a protein that forms thick filaments in myofibrils, which forms cross-bridges with actin filaments after reacting with ATP

nasties/nastic movement plant growth movement in which the direction of the response is not determined by the direction of the stimulus

natural classification organism classified with as many common features as possible, and therefore likely to reflect evolutionary relationships

natural selection selection by which evolutionary change is brought about, according to Darwin's Theory

nectary group of cells secreting nectar (dilute sugar solution) in a flower

nematocyst stinging cell of cnidarians (coelenterates), e.g. *Hydra*

Neolithic Revolution period of human development involving the establishment of settled agriculture, and including the breeding and cultivation of crop plants and herd animals

nephron functional unit of a vertebrate kidney

nerve bundle of many nerve fibres (axons), connecting the central nervous system with parts of the body

nerve cord present in non-vertebrates; a bundle of nerve fibres and/or nerve ganglia running along the length of the body

nervous system (NS) organised system of neurones which generate and conduct impulses

autonomic NS the involuntary nervous system

central NS (CNS) present in vertebrates; the brain and spinal cord

parasympathetic NS part of the involuntary nervous system; antagonistic in effects to those of the sympathetic nervous system

peripheral NS present in vertebrates; neurones that convey sensory information to the CNS, and neurones that convey impulses to muscles and glands (effector organs)

sympathetic NS part of the involuntary nervous system, antagonistic in effects to those of the parasympathetic nervous system

neuroglia cells (glial cells) cells other than neurones that make up the nervous system

neurone nerve cell

neurotransmitter substance chemical released at the presynaptic membrane of an axon, on arrival of an 'impulse', which transmits the 'impulse' across the synapse

neutrophil type of white blood cell

niche both the habitat an organism occupies and the mode of nutrition employed

node points on a plant stem where leaves arise

node of Ranvier junction in the myelin sheaths around a myelinated nerve fibre

noradrenaline neurotransmitter substance in the sympathetic nervous system

notochord slim rod of cells along the dorsal midline in the embryo of chordates, which appears to be the 'organiser' for the neural tube, and which is later replaced by the spinal cord

nucellus present in the ovule; tissue that persists around the embryo sac

nuclear division first step in the division of a cell, when the contents of the nucleus are subdivided by mitosis or meiosis

nuclear membrane double membrane surrounding the eukaryotic nucleus

nuclear pore organised gaps in the nuclear membrane; exit points for mRNA

nucleic acid polynucleotide chain of one of two types: deoxyribonucleic acid (DNA) or ribonucleic acid (RNA)

nucleus largest organelle of eukaryotic cells; controls and directs the activity of the cell

nucleolus compact region of nucleus where RNA is synthesised

nucleoside organic base (adenine, guanine, cytosine, thymine) combined with a pentose sugar (ribose or deoxyribose)

nucleotide phosphate ester of a nucleoside, i.e. an organic base combined with pentose sugar and phosphate (P_i)

nutrients substances required as food or in nutrition

nutrition process by which an organism acquires the matter and energy it requires from its environment

obesity condition of being seriously overweight (BMI of 30+)

obligate anaerobe restricted to living in the absence of air (oxygen)

obligate parasite restricted to living as a parasite

oestrous cycle reproductive cycle in female mammal in the absence of pregnancy

oestrus period of fertility (immediately after ovulation) during the oestrous cycle

olfactory relating to the sense of smell

omnivore animal that eats both plant and animal food

oncogene cancer-initiating gene

oocyte female sex cell in the process of a meiotic division to become an ovum

oogamy union of unlike gametes, e.g. large ovum and tiny sperm

opsonin type of antibody that attacks bacteria and viruses, facilitating their ingestion by phagocytic cells

optical isomer organic compound containing an asymmetric carbon atom, and therefore existing in two forms that rotate the plane of polarised light in opposite directions

Order a group of related families

organ part of an organism, consisting of a collection of tissues having a definite form and structure and performing one or more specialised functions

organelle unit of cell substructure

organic compounds of carbon (except CO_2 and carbonates)

organism a living thing

ornithine cycle cycle of biochemical reactions by which urea is formed

osmoreceptor sense cells/organ stimulated by changes in water potential

osmoregulation regulation of the water potential of body fluids by the regulation of water and/or salt content

osmosis diffusion of free water molecules from a region where they are more concentrated to a region where they are less concentrated

osteocyte cell that secretes the ground substance (matrix) of bone

ovarian cycle monthly changes that occur to ovarian follicles, leading to ovulation and the formation of a corpus luteum

ovarian follicle spherical structure found in the mammalian ovary; contains a developing ovum with liquid surrounded by numerous follicle cells, from which a secondary oocyte is released at ovulation

ovary female reproductive organ where the female gametes are formed

ovule present in the flowering plant flower; the structure in an ovary which, after fertilisation, grows into the seed

ovulation shedding of ova from the ovary

ovum (plural ova) female gamete

oxygen dissociation curve graph of % saturation (with oxygen) of haemoglobin against concentration of available oxygen

oxyntic cells cells in the gastric glands which secrete hydrochloric acid

pacemaker   origin of the myogenic heartbeat, known as the sino-atrial node

Pacinian corpuscle   sensory receptor in joints

pancreas   exocrine gland discharging pancreatic juice into the duodenum, combined with endocrine glands (islets of Langerhans)

parasite   organism that lives on or in another organism (its host) for most of its life cycle and derives its nutrients from the host

parenchyma   living cells forming the greater part of cortex and pith in primary plant growth

pathogen   disease-causing microorganism

pectins   chemically complex, gelatinous polysaccharides, built from sugar–acid residues, important in plant wall chemistry and wall function

pentadactyl   having four limbs terminating in five digits

pentose   five-carbon monosaccharide sugar

peptide   chain of up to 20 amino acid residues, joined by peptide linkages

peptide linkage   covalent bonding of the α amino group of one amino acid to the carboxyl group of another (with the loss of a molecule of water)

perception   mental interpretation of data from sense organs (i.e. occurring in the brain)

perianth   collective name for the sepals and petals of flowers

pericardium   tough membrane surrounding and containing the heart

pericycle   ring of cells around the central stele in roots

peristalsis   wave of muscular contractions passing down the gut wall

pesticide   chemical used to kill 'pests'

petal   modified leaves, often brightly coloured, collectively forming the corolla of flowers

petiole   leaf stalk

phagocytic cell   cell that ingests bacteria, etc., e.g. certain leucocytes, *Amoeba*

pharynx   anterior part of the alimentary canal, immediately following the mouth

phenotype   appearances (structural, biochemical, etc.) of an organism

pheromone   volatile chemical signals ('hormones') released into the air

phloem   tissue that conducts elaborated food in plant stems

phosphate (P_i)   phosphate ions, as involved in metabolism

phospholipid   formed from a triacylglycerol in which one of the fatty acid groups is replaced by an ionised phosphate group

photomorphogenesis   effects of light on plant growth

photoperiodism   day-length control of flowering in plants

photophosphorylation   formation of ATP, using light energy (in the light step, in the grana)

photosynthesis   production of sugar from CO_2 and H_2O; occurs in chloroplasts, using light energy, and producing O_2 as a waste product

phototropism   tropic response of plants to light

phylogenetic classification   classification based upon evolutionary relationships (rather than on appearances)

Phylum   organisms constructed on a similar general plan, usually thought to be evolutionarily related

physiology   study of the functioning of organisms

phytoplankton   photosynthetic plankton, including unicellular algae and cyanobacteria

pinocytosis   uptake of a droplet of liquid into a cell, involving invagination of the plasma membrane

pith   central region of an herbaceous plant stem, typically occupied by large parenchyma cells

pituitary gland   the 'master' endocrine gland, attached to the underside of the brain

placenta   maternal and fetal tissue in the wall of the uterus; site of all exchanges of metabolites and waste products between fetal and maternal blood systems

plankton   very small, aquatic (marine or freshwater) plants and animals, many of them unicellular, that live at or near the water's surface

plant growth substance   substances produced by plants in relatively small amounts, that interact to control growth and development

plaque   food debris, saliva and bacteria that builds up at sites on the teeth

plasma   liquid part of blood

plasma membrane   membrane (plasmalemma) of lipid and protein that forms the surface of cells (constructed as a 'fluid mosaic membrane')

plasmid   small circular DNA that is independent of the chromosome in bacteria (R plasmids contain genes for resistance to antibiotics)

plasmodesmata   cytoplasmic connection between plant cells, passing through the walls at simple pits

plasmolysis   withdrawal of water from a plant cell by osmosis (incipient plasmolysis is established when about 50% of cells show some shrinkage of cytoplasm away from the walls)

plastid   organelle containing pigments, e.g. chloroplast

platelets   tiny cell fragments that lack a nucleus; found in the blood and involved in the blood-clotting mechanism

pleural membrane   lines lungs and thorax cavity and contains the pleural fluid

plumule   embryonic stem in a seed

polar body   smaller product of the first and second meiotic division of human oocytes, the chief product being the ovum

polarise   setting up of an electrical potential difference across a membrane

polarised light   light in which rays vibrate in one plane only

pollen   microspore produced in anthers (and male cones), containing male gamete(s)

pollen tube   grows out of a pollen grain attached to a stigma, and down through the style tissue to the embryo sac

polymer   large organic molecules made up of repeating subunits (monomers)

polynucleotide   long, unbranched chain of nucleotides, as found in DNA and RNA

polypeptide   chain of amino acid residues linked by peptide linkages

polyploidy   having more than two sets of chromosomes per cell

polysaccharide   very high molecular mass carbohydrate, formed by condensation of vast numbers of monosaccharide units, with the removal of water

polysome   aggregation of ribosomes along a mRNA strand

population   individuals of one species in a habitat

portal vein   vein beginning and ending in a capillary network (rather than at the heart)

postsynaptic neurone   neurone 'downstream' of a synapse

potential difference   separation of electrical charge within or across a structure, e.g. a membrane

potential energy   stored energy

predator   organism that catches and kills other animals to eat

pressure potential   hydrostatic pressure, perhaps generated osmotically

presynaptic membrane   membrane of the tip of an axon at the point of the synapse

presynaptic neurone   neurone 'up-stream' of a synapse

prey–predator relationship   interrelationship of population sizes due to predation of one species (the predator) upon another (the prey)

proboscis   projection from the head, used for feeding

procambial strand   meristematic tissue from which the vascular bundles develop

producer   an autotrophic organism

productivity   amount of biomass fixed by primary producers (photosynthetically)

proglottid   segment of an adult tapeworm

prokaryote   tiny unicellular organism without a true nucleus (has a ring of RNA or DNA as a chromosome), e.g. bacteria and cyanobacteria

prophase   first stage in nuclear division, mitotic or meiotic

proprioceptor   internal sensory receptor

prosthetic group   non-protein substances, bound to a protein as part of an enzyme, often forming part of the active site, and able to bind to other proteins

protein   long sequence of amino acid residues combined together (primary structure), which take up a particular shape (secondary and tertiary structure)

Protoctista   Kingdom of the eukaryotes consisting of single-celled organisms and the multicellular organisms related to them (e.g. protozoa and algae)

protoplast   living contents of a plant cell, contained by the cell wall

protozoan   single-celled animal, belonging to the sub-Kingdom Protozoa, of the phylum Protoctista

pseudopodium   temporary extension of the body of an amoeboid cell, by which movement or feeding may occur

pulmonary circulation   circulation to the lungs, in vertebrates this is a double circulation

pulmonary ventilation rate   breathing rate

pulse   wave of increased pressure in the arterial circulation, generated by the heartbeat

pump (membrane)   proteins in plasma membranes that use energy directly to carry substances across (primary pump), or work indirectly from metabolic energy (secondary pump)

pupil   central aperture in the eye through which light enters

pure breeding   homozygous for the specified gene(s)

Purkyne tissue   fibres of the bundle of His that conduct impulses between atria and ventricles of the heart

pyloric sphincter   circular muscle at the opening of stomach to duodenum

pyranose   monosaccharide in the form of a six-membered ring

pyruvic acid   three-carbon organic acid, $CH_3COCOOH$; product of glycolysis

quadrat   sampling area enclosed within a frame

radical   short-lived, intermediate product of a reaction, formed when a covalent bond breaks, with one of the two bonding electrons going to each atom

radicle   developing root of the embryonic plant

radioactive dating   using the proportions of different isotopes in fossilised biological material in order to estimate when the original organism was alive

reaction centre   protein–pigment complexes in the grana of chloroplasts; sites of the photochemical reactions of photosynthesis

receptacle   swollen tip of a flowering stem, where the flower parts are attached

receptor   a sense organ

recessive allele   allele not reflected in the phenotype

reciprocal cross   crosses between the same pair of genotypes, in which the sources of the gametes (male versus female) is reversed

recombinant   chromosome (or cell, or organism) in which the genetic information has been rearranged

recombinant DNA   DNA which has been artificially changed, involving joining together genes from different sources, typically from different species

recycling (of nutrients)   process by which the materials from dead organisms are broken down and made available for reuse in the biosphere

Red Data Book   internationally produced record of actions for endangered species

redox reaction   reaction in which reduction and oxidation happen simultaneously

reducing sugar   monosaccharide sugar with either an aldehyde (—CHO) or ketone (—CO) group; able to reduce Cu^{2+} ions to Cu^+ ions, causing a brick-red precipitate of copper(I) oxide to be formed

reductive division   meiosis, in which the chromosome number of a diploid cell is halved

reflex action   response automatically elicited by a stimulus

reflex arc   functional unit in the nervous system, consisting of sensory receptor, sensory neurone (possibly relay neurones), motor neurone and effector (e.g. muscle or gland)

refractory period   period after excitation of a neurone, when a repetition of the stimulus fails to induce the same response; divided into periods known as absolute and relative

relative atomic mass   ratio of the mass of an atom of an element to the mass of a carbon atom

renal capsule   cup-shaped closed end of a nephron, which, with the glomerulus, constitutes a Malpighian body

renewable energy   energy that comes from exploiting wave power, wind power, tidal power, solar energy, hydroelectric power or 'biological sources', such as biomass

replication   duplication of DNA by making a copy of an existing molecule

semi-conservative   each strand of an existing DNA double helix acts as the template for the synthesis of a new strand

replicative division   mitosis

reproduction   formation of a new individual by sexual or asexual means

residual volume   volume of air remaining in the lungs, after maximum expiration

respiration   cellular process by which sugars and other substances are broken down to release chemical energy for other cellular processes

respiratory centre   region of the medulla concerned with the involuntary control of breathing

respiratory pigment   substances such as haemoglobin, which associate with oxygen

respiratory quotient   ratio of the volume of CO_2 produced to O_2 used in respiration

respiratory surface   surface adapted for gaseous exchange

respirometer   apparatus for the measurement of respiratory gaseous exchange

resting potential   potential difference across the membrane of a neurone when not being stimulated

restriction enzymes   enzymes, also known as endonucleases, that cut lengths of nucleic acid at specific sequences of bases

retina   light-sensitive layer at the back of the eye

retrovirus viruses that, on arrival in a host cell, have their own RNA copied into DNA, which then attaches to the host DNA for a period

ribonucleic acid (RNA) form of nucleic acid containing the pentose sugar ribose; found in nucleus and cytoplasm of eukaryotic cells (and commonly the only nucleic acid of prokaryotes), and containing the organic bases adenine, guanine, uracil and cytosine

ribosome non-membranous organelle; site of protein synthesis

ribulose bisphosphate five-carbon acceptor molecule for CO_2, involved in the dark step of photosynthesis

rod cell one of two types of light-sensitive cells in the retina, responsible for non-colour vision

root cap cap of protective tissue at the root tip

roughage indigestible matter (such as cellulose fibres) in the diet

Rubisco ribulose bisphosphate carboxylase, the enzyme that fixes CO_2 in photosynthesis

saliva secretion produced by salivary glands

saltatory conduction impulse conduction 'in jumps', between nodes of Ranvier

saprotroph organism that feeds on dead organic matter (i.e. saprotrophic nutrition)

sarcolemma membranous sheath around a muscle fibre

sarcomere unit of a skeletal (voluntary) muscle fibre, between two Z-discs

sarcoplasm cytoplasm around the myofibril of a muscle fibre

sarcoplasmic reticulum network of membranes around the myofibrils of a muscle fibre

saturated fat lipid with fully hydrogenated carbon backbone, i.e. no double bonds present

Schwann cell type of neuroglial (glial) cell which forms the sheath around nerve fibres

sclera opaque, fibrous coat of the eyeball

sclerenchyma plant tissue with thickened, lignified wall: the fibres (and sclereids)

scolex 'anchorage' unit at the anterior of a tapeworm, with suckers and hooks

secondary sexual characteristics sexual characteristics that develop under the influence of sex hormones (androgens and oestrogens)

secondary succession plant succession on soil already formed, from which the community has been abruptly removed

secretion material produced and released from glandular cells

sedentary animal living attached to the substratum

seed formed from a fertilised ovule; contains an embryonic plant and food store

segmentation body plan built upon a repeating series of similar segments, e.g. as in annelids

selection differential survivability or reproductive potential of different organisms of a breeding population

self-pollination transfer of pollen from the anther to the stigma of the same plant (normally the same flower)

selfing self-pollination or self-fertilisation

semi-lunar valve half-moon shaped valve, preventing backflow in a tube (e.g. a vein)

seminiferous tubule elongated tubes in the testes; the site of sperm production

sense organ organ of cells sensitive to external stimuli

sensory area area of the cerebral cortex of the brain receiving impulses from the sense organs of the body

sensory neurone nerve cell carrying impulses from a sense organ or receptor to the central nervous system

sensory receptor cell specialised to respond to stimulation by the production of an action potential (impulse)

sepal outermost parts of a flower, usually green, protective, and bract-like

seral stage/sere stages in a seral succession, the whole succession being known as a sere

sex chromosome chromosome which determines sex rather than other body (soma) characteristics

sexual reproduction reproduction involving the production and fusion of gametes

shrub layer low-level (below trees) woody perennials growing in a forest or wood; normally most numerous in 'clearings', e.g. where a full-grown tree has died

siblings offspring of the same parent

sieve tube a phloem element; accompanied by a companion cell, and having perforated end walls, known as sieve plates

silage animal winter feed, derived from grass; grass is cut and then preserved by fermentation, with the exclusion of air

simple sugar monosaccharide sugar, e.g. triose sugar (3C), pentose sugar (5C), or hexose sugar (6C)

sino-atrial node cells in the wall of the right atrium in which the myogenic heartbeat is initiated; also known as the 'pacemaker'

sinus cavity or space

sinusoid minute, blood-filled space

solar energy electromagnetic radiation derived from the fusion of hydrogen atoms of the Sun, reaching Earth from space

solute potential water potential of a solution; determined by the amount of dissolved substance

somatic cell (soma) body cell, i.e. not a cell producing gametes (sex cells)

specialisation adaptation for a particular mode of life or function

speciation evolution of a new species

species group of individuals of common ancestry that closely resemble each other and are normally capable of interbreeding to produce fertile offspring

sperm motile male gametes of animals

spermatocyte cell formed in seminiferous tubules of testes; develops into sperm

spermatophore sperm enclosed in a capsule ready for insertion into the female genital opening in many insect species

spindle cell structure formed from microtubules; guide the movements of chromosomes in mitosis and meiosis

spiracle hole in the side of an insect (thorax and abdomen) by which the tracheal respiratory system connects with the atmosphere

spiral vessel xylem vessel with spirally arranged lignin thickening in its lateral walls

spirometer apparatus for measurements of lung capacity and breathing rates

sporangiophore aerial hyphae in 'pin moulds' (e.g. *Mucor*) on which a sporangium forms

sporangium (plural sporangia) container of spores found in some fungi, in ferns and other plants

spore small, usually unicellular, reproductive structure from which a new organism arises

sporocyst larval stage of the liver fluke; formed in the secondary host (a snail)

sporophyll leaf of a fern, bearing sporangia

sporophyte diploid phase in the alternation of generations in plants

stamen male reproductive organ of the flower, consisting of filament and anther, containing pollen sacs where pollen is formed and released

statolith   large starch grains in cells near stem and root apex that may change positions when a plant is moved

steroid   organic molecule formed from a complex ring of carbon atoms, of which cholesterol is a typical example

stigma   part of the carpel receptive to pollen

stimulus   change detected by the body that leads to a response

stoma (plural stomata)   pore in the epidermis of plants, surrounded by two guard cells

stretch receptor   sensory receptor in muscles

stroma   membranous matrix of the chloroplast; site of the dark reaction in photosynthesis

style   present in a carpel, linking stigma to ovary

substrate   molecule that is the starting point for a biochemical reaction; forms a complex with a specific enzyme

subthreshold stimulus   stimulus not strong enough to trigger an action potential

succession   sequences of different communities developing in a given habitat over a period of time

sugars   of a general formula $C_x(H_2O)_y$, where x is approximately equal to y, and containing an aldehyde or a ketone group

   compound   composed of monosaccharide sugars condensed together

   simple   single monosaccharide sugar

summation   combined effect of many nerve impulses

   spatial   many impulses arriving from different axons

   temporal   many impulses arriving via a single axon

suspensory ligament   attaches lens to ciliary body in the vertebrate eye

symbiosis   literally 'living together'; covering parasitism, commensalism and mutualism

symplast   pathway (e.g. of water) through the living contents of plant cells

synapse   connection between two nerve cells; functionally a tiny gap, the synaptic cleft, traversed by transmitter substances

synaptic knob   terminal swelling of a presynaptic neurone

synergid cell   cells found within the embryo sac, beside the egg cell

synergism   acting together, producing a larger effect than when acting separately

synovial fluid   secreted by the synovial membrane at joints, having a lubricating role

systematics   study of the diversity of living things

systemic circulation   blood circulation to the body (not the pulmonary circulation)

systemic pesticide   pesticide that is absorbed and carried throughout the body

systole   contraction phase in the cardiac cycle

tapetum   nutritive tissue inside the anther, supplying developing pollen grains

target organ   organ on which a hormone acts (although it broadcasts to all organs)

taste bud   sense organ found chiefly on the upper surface of the tongue

taxis   response by a motile organism (or gamete), where the direction of the response is determined by the direction of the stimulus

taxon   a classificatory grouping

taxonomy   science of classification

telophase   phase in nuclear division, when the daughter nuclei form

template (DNA)   DNA of the chromosome, copied to make mRNA

tendon   fibrous connective tissue connecting a muscle to bone

tentacle   flexible structure found at anterior of some non-vertebrates, typically a sensory structure

terminal bud   bud at the apex of the stem

testa   seed coat

testis   male reproductive gland, producing sperms

testosterone   steroid hormone; the main sex hormone of male mammals

thermogenesis   generation of heat by metabolism

thermonasty   nastic movements in response to change in temperature

thorax   (in mammals) the upper part of the body separated from the abdomen; (in insects) the region between head and abdomen

threshold of stimulation   level of stimulation required to trigger an action potential (impulse)

thrombosis   blood clot formation, leading to blockage of a blood vessel

thylakoid   membrane system of chloroplast

thymine   a pyrimidine organic base found in DNA, in which it pairs with adenine

thyroid gland   endocrine gland found in the neck of vertebrates; site of production of thyroxine and other hormones influencing the rate of metabolism

tidal volume   volume of air normally exchanged in breathing

tight junction   point where plasma membranes of adjacent cells are sealed together

tissue   collection of cells of similar structure and function

tissue fluid   liquid bathing cells, formed from blood minus cells and plasma protein

tissue respiration   biochemical steps by which energy is released from sugars

tonoplast   membrane around the plant cell vacuole

toxic   poisonous

toxin   poison

toxoid   inactivated poison

trabecula   cross-barred sheets or strands of bone, making up the spongy bone structure

trachea   windpipe

tracheal system   system of tubes by which air is passed to tissues (in insect body)

tracheids   fibre-like water-conducting cells of some plants

tracheole   small air-conducting tube (insects)

transcription   when the DNA sequence of bases is converted into mRNA

transducer organelle   one in which energy is converted (transduced), e.g. chloroplast: light → chemical energy

transect   arbitrary line through a habitat, selected to sample the community

transfer cell   parenchyma cell surrounding phloem in a leaf, with ingrowths of cell wall

transfer RNA (tRNA)   short lengths of specific RNA that combine with specific amino acids prior to protein synthesis

translation   information of mRNA is decoded into protein (amino acid sequence)

translocation   transport of elaborated food via the phloem

transmitter substance   substance released into the synaptic cleft on arrival of an impulse at the presynaptic membrane, that conducts the 'signal' across the synapse

transpiration   loss of water vapour from the aerial parts of plants

triacylglycerol   ingredient of fats and oils

tricarboxylic acid cycle (TCA)   stage in tissue respiration in which pyruvate is broken down to carbon dioxide, and hydrogen is removed for subsequent oxidation

tricuspid valve   right atrio-ventricular valve

triose   three-carbon monosaccharide (trisaccharide)

tripeptide   peptide of three amino acid residues

triploblastic   body wall of three (embryonic) layers

trophic level   'level' in a food chain, determined by the method/type of nutrition

trophoblast   outer layer of cells of the early embryo stage, known as a morula (ball of cells)

tropism   growth response of plants in which the direction of growth is determined by the direction of the stimulus

true fruit   fruit formed from the wall of the ovary, containing fertilised ovules

tumour   abnormal proliferation of cells, either benign (if self-limiting) or malignant (if invasive)

tunica   body wall or outer covering

turgid   having high internal pressure

ultrafiltration   occurs through the tiny pores in the capillaries of the glomerulus

ultrastructure   fine structure of cells, determined by electron microscopy

unisexual   of one or other sex

unsaturated fat   lipid with double bond(s) in the hydrocarbon chain

uracil   a pyrimidine organic base found in RNA, in which it pairs with adenine

urea NH_2CONH_2, formed from amino groups 'deaminated' from excess amino acid

ureter   tube from kidney to bladder

urethra   tube from bladder to exterior

uric acid   insoluble purine, formed from the breakdown of nucleic acids and proteins

urine   excretory fluid produced by the kidneys, consisting largely of a dilute solution of urea

uterine cycle   '28-day' cycle of changes to the wall of the human uterus

uterus   organ in which the embryo develops in female mammals

vaccination   conferring immunity from a disease by injecting an antigen (of attenuated microorganisms or inactivated component), so that the body acquires antibodies prior to potential infections

vascular bundle   strands of xylem and phloem (often with fibres) separated by cambium; the site of water and elaborated food movements up and down the stem

vacuole   fluid-filled space in the cytoplasm, especially large and permanent in plant cells

vagus nerve   10th cranial nerve; supplies many internal organs, including the heart

valve (diatom)   part of the cell wall of a 'pill box' type of structure

variety   taxonomic group below the species level

vasa recta   capillary loop supplying the loop of Henle

vascular tissue   xylem and phloem of plants; blood vessels of animals

vasoconstriction   constriction of blood supply to capillaries (of skin)

vasodilation   dilation of blood supply to capillaries (of skin)

vector   organism that transmits a disease-causing organism, OR, a device for transferring genes during genetic engineering

vein   vessel that returns blood to the heart

ventral   underside

ventricle   chamber

venule   branch of a vein

vernalisation   exposure of seeds or buds to low temperature as a prerequisite for growth

vertebrate   animal with a vertebral column

vesicle   membrane-bound sac

vestibular apparatus   semi-circular canals of the inner ear, concerned with balance

vestibular canal   upper compartment of the cochlea

vestigial   small, imperfectly developed structure

virus   minute, intracellular parasite, composed of protein and nucleic acid

visceral cleft   gill slits

vital capacity   total possible change in lung volume

vitalism theory   idea that organic compounds are only produced in living cells

vitreous humour   clear jelly of inner eye

viviparity   producing live young

water potential   tendency of water molecules to move

water table   level of ground water in the Earth

wax   complex form of lipid

weathering   breakdown of rock

white matter   regions of the brain and spinal cord containing nerve fibres wrapped in their myelin sheaths

xeromorphic   modified to withstand drought

xerophyte   plant showing modifications to withstand drought

xerosere   succession of a plant starting from dry terrain

xylem   water-conducting vessels of plants

yolk   food stores of egg cells, rich in proteins and lipids

yolk sac   membranous sac with numerous blood vessels, developed by vertebrate embryos around the yolk (e.g. in birds and reptiles) or as a component of the placenta (in mammals)

zonation   naturally-occurring distribution of organisms in zones

zygote   product of the fusion of gametes

zymogenic cells   cells of gastric glands, secreting pepsinogen

Index

cellulase 162, 163
cellulose 4, 31, 352
  digestion 162–3, 199
cell wall 17–18, 31
cement layer (teeth) 153
census 376
central dogma of molecular biology 114
central nervous system 287, 288–90
centrifuge 12
  high speed, refrigerated 12
centriole 4
centromere 99, 101, 103
centrosome 3
cephalisation 356
cerebellum 290
cerebral cortex 290
cerebral hemispheres 288, 289, 290
cervix 423, 427
chaetae 315
channel protein 278
cheese 129
chemical equations 480
chemical symbols 474
chemosynthetic organisms 185
chiasma (plural chiasmata) 103
chi-squared test see statistical tests
chitin 31, 215, 314, 351
Chlorella 5
chlorofluorocarbons (CFCs) 398
chlorophyll 169, 174–5
chloroplasts 4, 16, 21, 169, 173, 178, 180
choice chamber 301–2
cholecystokinin 161
cholesterol 36
chordates 363
choroid 284
choroid plexus 289
chromatids 99, 100
chromatin 13, 98
chromatography 174
chromoplasts 16
chromosomes
  autosomal 444
  mutations 116
  number 19, 99, 106, 453
  sex 444
  structure and function 13, 19, 98–100,
    106–7
chyme 155, 156
ciliary body (eye) 284
ciliated epithelium 16
cilium (plural cilia) 16, 305
citric acid cycle see Krebs cycle
classification see taxonomy
cleavage 427

climate change 392, 397
climax community 383, 390
Clinistix™ 93
cloning 121, 123, 410
closed fermenter tank 330
Clostridium tetani 200, 201
cnidarians 358
cnidoblast 358
coccus (plural cocci) 349
  see also bacteria
codominance 447
codon 111
  see also genetic code
coelom 356
coenzymes 49, 80, 197
cofactors
  enzymes 59, 80
  see also enzymes; micronutrients
cohesion–tension theory of water
    movement 56, 244
coleoptiles 295–7
collagen 40, 44
collenchyma 316–17
colon 148
colostrum see lactation
colour blindness 444–5
colour vision 286
commensalism 162
common cold virus 327
community 365
companion cells 247
compensation point 176
competition 366, 379
competitive inhibitors 87
complementary alleles 446
complementary bases 109, 114
complement proteins 336
compound 476
compression stress 304
concentration of solutions 484
condensation reaction 28, 484
condenser (microscope) 7
conditioned reflex 152
cone cells (eye) 285–6
conifers 353, 354
  see also forests; trees
conjugated protein 80
conjunctiva 284
connective tissue see bone; cartilage;
    collagen
conservation 404–7
consumers 366
continuous culture (in biotechnology) 330
continuous and discontinuous variation
    436–7

contraception 433
contractile vacuole 68
control
  behaviour 287–8
  breathing 220
  flowering 420–1
  heart 234
  pollution 406
  reproduction 430–3
controlled variables 489
cornea 284
corolla 413
coronary arteries 323
coronary heart disease 323
corpus luteum 424, 432
cortex
  cerebral 290
  of stem 316
cotyledons 355
countercurrent mechanism 214, 266
covalent bonding 476, 477, 479
cranium 289, 306
creatine phosphate 313
cristae 13, 200
cross-fertilisation 412
crossing over 103, 105–6, 452, 453, 454
cross-pollination 415, 417, 439
crustaceans 361
crypts of Lieberkühn 156
crystal lattice 476
cuticle 172, 360
cyanobacteria 185, 349, 372
cyclic AMP 293
cycling and recycling of materials 370–3
cyclosis 172
cystic fibrosis 133–4
cytochrome oxidase 87
cytochromes 198
cytokinesis 100, 101
cytokinins 294, 300
cytoplasm 4
cytosine see nucleotides
cytosis 71
cytosol 11

Darwin, Charles 461, 470
data handling 488–90
daylength, and plants 421
DDT 393–4
deamination 145, 199, 261–2
decarboxylase 196
decarboxylation 196
decomposers see detritivores
decomposer food chain 366
deficiency diseases 146, 147